SOURCEBOOK ON ATOMIC ENERGY

by

SAMUEL GLASSTONE

Consultant to the United States Atomic Energy Commission

SECOND EDITION

D. VAN NOSTRAND COMPANY, INC.

PRINCETON, NEW JERSEY

TORONTO   LONDON

NEW YORK

D. VAN NOSTRAND COMPANY, INC.
120 Alexander St., Princeton, New Jersey (*Principal office*)
24 West 40 Street, New York 18, New York

D. VAN NOSTRAND COMPANY, LTD.
358, Kensington High Street, London, W.14, England

D. VAN NOSTRAND COMPANY (Canada), LTD.
25 Hollinger Road, Toronto 16, Canada

02636b50

PRINTED IN THE UNITED STATES OF AMERICA

Foreword to the Second Edition

THE Atomic Energy Commission, at the request of the American Textbook Publishers Institute, sponsored the first edition of the *Sourcebook on Atomic Energy* written by Dr. Samuel Glasstone and published in 1950. The world-wide acceptance of the book has fully justified the original expectations that it would provide a source of basic atomic energy information for readers with many different interests. About 50,000 copies of the English language edition have been sold and the book also has been translated into several foreign languages. Its use in schools, colleges and universities has made it a significant contribution to education in atomic science.

The fund of knowledge in the field of nuclear energy has increased rapidly since 1950. Therefore, in keeping with the Commission's policy to distribute information as broadly as possible, Dr. Glasstone was requested to prepare this revised edition.

As in the case of the first edition, the staff of the Commission has assisted in the provision of material for inclusion in the book, but its presentation and scientific evaluation are wholly the work of its distinguished author, Dr. Glasstone.

Lewis L. Strauss

CHAIRMAN, UNITED STATES ATOMIC ENERGY COMMISSION

Acknowledgment

I WISH to thank all those whose names were mentioned in the first edition of this book for help given me in connection with the original manuscript. In particular, I would like to record my very great appreciation of the efforts of the late Dr. Alberto F. Thompson, whose foresight and persistence made the work possible.

In preparing the revised edition, the suggestions and comments of many colleagues and correspondents have been very useful. Special thanks are due to Drs. O. R. Frisch, A. V. Grosse, L. Szilard and H. C. Urey, for interesting historical side lights; to Drs. R. K. Wakerling and H. Bradner, University of California Radiation Laboratory, for the provision of illustrations; to Mr. Bernard M. Fry, Assistant Director for Technical Information Service, A.E.C., and his staff, especially Dr. A. Frank Owings and Mr. Paul S. Feinstein, for their cooperation and encouragement, and Mr. Carl B. Holmes, for assistance with the art work; and to Dr. Norris E. Bradbury, Director, and other members of the Los Alamos Scientific Laboratory for placing the excellent facilities of the Laboratory at my disposal.

Finally, I wish to express my indebtedness to my wife for her continued help in innumerable ways.

Los Alamos, N. M.
January 1958.

SAMUEL GLASSTONE

Contents

Foundations of the Atomic Theory

Chapter I

THE ATOMIC CONCEPT

EARLY HISTORY OF THE ATOM

1.1. The broad concept of the atomic structure of matter can be traced back some 2500 years to the scholars of ancient Greece, and even to the Hindu philosophers of a still earlier age. In the fifth century B.C., Leucippus and his pupil Democritus, as founders of the Greek school of atomists, taught that all material things were made up ultimately of small, indivisible units which Democritus called *atoma* (atoms).* Although these teachings were supported by Epicurus, whose ideas were elaborated at length by Lucretius in his famous Latin poem, *De Rerum Natura* (Concerning the Nature of Things), during the early part of the first century B.C., the considerations made little headway, largely because of the objections of the influential Greek philosopher Aristotle (384 to 322 B.C.). Thus, atomistic concepts lay dormant for several hundred years, until they were revived in the active period of learning which followed the Renaissance in Europe. During the sixteenth and seventeenth centuries after Christ, philosophers and scientists, such as Galileo Galilei in Italy, René Descartes in France, and Francis Bacon, Robert Boyle and Isaac Newton in England favored the view that matter was not continuous in nature but was made up of ultimate particles or atoms.

DALTON AND THE ATOMIC THEORY

1.2. It was not until the nineteenth century, however, that the work of the chemist transformed the atom from a somewhat vague philosophical idea to a material reality, while the discoveries of the physicist laid the foundation for the development during recent years of a remarkable body of detailed knowledge concerning its internal structure.

1.3. Credit for originating the modern atomic theory is usually given to the English schoolteacher John Dalton, who became interested in the subject as a result of his investigations of the solubilities of gases in water and other liquids. The part he played in the development of the theory, although of the greatest importance, is frequently misunderstood. In writing of

---

* The term *atom,* derived from two Greek words, *a* (not), *temnein* (to cut), implies something that is not divisible.

1

Dalton's contribution, the German physical chemist W. Nernst stated that "by one effort of modern science, [it] arose like a phoenix from the ashes of the old Greek philosophy." That this is a misconception can be proved by a quotation from Dalton's *New System of Chemical Philosophy*, published in 1808, in which he discussed in detail his ideas concerning the atom as the unit of chemical structure.

1.4. In considering the existence of a substance such as water in gaseous (steam), liquid and solid (ice) states, Dalton said: "the observations have tacitly led to the conclusion which seems universally adopted, that all bodies of sensible magnitude . . . are constituted of a vast number of extremely small particles, or atoms of matter bound together by a force of attraction." The phrase "which seems universally adopted" is significant, for it implies that the atomic concept of matter was already widely accepted. It has been suggested that Dalton was indebted to Newton, whose works he probably studied, for in his notes of a lecture delivered at the Royal Institution, London, in January 1810, he remarked: "Newton had demonstrated clearly . . . that an elastic fluid [i.e., a gas] is constituted of small particles or atoms of matter."

1.5. There is no doubt, also, that the contemporary Irish chemists, Bryan Higgins (1737-1820) and his nephew William Higgins (1769-1825), had expressed themselves very clearly on the subject of combination by atoms some years prior to Dalton. Why then is the latter regarded as the founder of the atomic theory? The answer lies in the fact that John Dalton made the theory quantitative. By showing how the weights of different atoms relative to one another could be determined, he

introduced a feeling of reality into a purely abstract idea. In a paper submitted to the Literary and Philosophical Society of Manchester, England, in October 1803, Dalton wrote: "An enquiry into the relative weights of the ultimate particles [atoms] of bodies is a subject, so far as I know, entirely new. I have lately been prosecuting this enquiry with remarkable success." Most of his weights were subsequently proved to be erroneous, but Dalton sowed the seed which grew, where others had previously merely turned over the soil.

1.6. In the Lowell Lectures on *Science in the Modern World,* delivered at Harvard University in 1925, the Anglo-American philosopher and mathematician A. N. Whitehead said: "In considering the history of thought, it is necessary to distinguish the real stream, determining a period, from the ineffectual thoughts casually entertained. In the eighteenth century every well educated man read Lucretius and entertained ideas about atoms. But John Dalton made them efficient in the stream of science; and in the function of efficiency atomicity was a new idea." The atomic theory of the classical thinkers was somewhat in the nature of a vague philosophical speculation, but the theory as enunciated by Dalton was much more specific. It provided an explanation or, at least, an interpretation of many chemical facts and, of greater consequence, it acted as a guide to further experimentation and investigation.

1.7. From the time of Dalton the atomic hypothesis has played an increasingly important role in science, first in chemistry and later in physics. It is true that a few scientists, some of them men of influence like the German physical chemist Wilhelm Ostwald, doubted the existence of atoms, but by the early years of the present century even these objectors were converted. Today the arguments in favor of the atomic structure of matter are so numerous and convincing that the concept is universally accepted as an established fact rather than a theory.*

THE CHEMICAL ELEMENTS

THE FOUR-ELEMENT THEORY

1.8. While the atomic concept was undergoing development, another important principle, also based on Greek philosophy, was being refined in the fire of successive generations of the human mind. In contemplating the make-up of the universe, Empedocles, in the fifth century B.C., entertained the idea that all matter was composed of four "elements," namely, fire, earth, air and water. It is probable that in this respect also, as with the atom, the ancient Hindu thinkers had anticipated the Greeks, but our present views stem more directly from the latter than from the former. Having the influential support of Aristotle and others, the four-element theory was widely accepted for more than two thousand years, in spite of a considerable degree of vagueness concerning its actual implications.

1.9. Some scholars undoubtedly regarded the elements as referring to material earth, air, fire and water, while others thought of them more in the nature of principles or representations of physical attributes. Aristotle, for example, envisaged all matter as consisting of one primordial substance which he called *hyle* (stuff or material) ;† and this could acquire varying amounts of the four qualities, or "principles," hot, cold, dry and moist. Thus air was hot and moist, water was cold and moist, fire was hot and dry, and earth was cold and dry. The difference between one material and another was regarded as due to variations in the primal qualities, but the fundamental matter was always the same.

1.10. It is apparently on this interpretation of the four-element theory that the ancient alchemists based their vain efforts to change common metals into gold. For hundreds of years all attempts to bring about transmutation met with complete failure, although at the present time, thanks to the accumulated knowledge concerning the behavior of atoms, the deliberate change of one element into another is a daily occurrence in many laboratories (Chapter X).

ELEMENTS AND COMPOUNDS

1.11. Although the Aristotelian theory was widely accepted, even as late as the seventeenth century, doubts began to develop concerning its ability to account for the nature of different forms of matter. Some of the strongest objections were expressed by the Irish-born Robert Boyle in a book entitled *The Sceptical Chymist,* published in London in 1661. In this book he gave his own interpretation of an element; thus, he wrote: "I mean by elements,

---

* A fact may be defined as something for the actual existence of which there is definite evidence. A theory or hypothesis, on the other hand, is a purely conceptual attempt to explain or interpret known facts. While facts are presumably established and unalterable, a theory may be altered or discarded if it proves to be inadequate.

† In later years, this was changed, possibly by Roger Bacon in the thirteenth century, to *protyle,* from *protos* and *hyle,* meaning the first or primal matter.

as those chymists that speak plainest do by their principles, certain primitive and simple, or perfectly unmingled bodies; which not being made of any other bodies, or of one another, are the ingredients of which . . . mixt bodies are immediately compounded, and into which they are ultimately resolved . . . I must not look upon any body as a true principle or element . . . which is not perfectly homogeneous, but is further resolvable into any number of distinct substances, how small soever."

1.12. It has been argued that the foregoing concept of an element was not original with Boyle, and some support for this contention may be found in his parenthetical remark, "as those chymists that speak plainest do [mean] by their principles," near the beginning of the quotation given above. Be that as it may, the fact remains that Boyle did express clearly the basic ideas from which developed the modern view concerning the nature of an element. However, more than a century was to elapse before these ideas had any real influence on scientific thought. It was only after the French chemist A. L. Lavoisier proved in 1774 that air was not a simple elementary substance, but a mixture of at least two different gases, now called nitrogen and oxygen, and after the work, in 1781, of Joseph Priestley and of Henry Cavendish, in England, established the fact that water was compounded of hydrogen and oxygen, that the four-element theory was finally abandoned. In its place, Lavoisier established, in 1789, the modern concept of an element, thus: "We apply the term elements . . . to bodies to express our idea of the last point which analysis is capable of reaching." An element was thus regarded as a substance containing, as far as was known, only one kind of matter, and which could not be split up in any known way into anything simpler.

1.13. On this basis, Lavoisier substituted for the four elements of the Greek philosophers a list of thirty-three elementary substances, of which more than twenty are still regarded as elements even to this day. By 1819, the Swedish chemist J. J. Berzelius had increased the number of elements to fifty, and at the present time ninety different elements are definitely known to exist on the earth, while several more have been obtained by other means, as will be explained in Chapter XVI. All material things contain at least one of these elements, and when two or more elements unite with one another, by the process referred to as chemical combination, the resulting product is known as a *compound*.

DEFINITION OF AN ELEMENT

1.14. Until the beginning of the present century a chemical element would have been defined simply as a form of matter which could not be split up into other forms of matter. Now, with the discovery of the phenomena of radioactivity, accompanied by the spontaneous change of one element into another (Chapter V), and the development of various means of bringing about transmutation and disintegration of numerous elements (Chapter IX), it is not easy to give such a precise definition. It will be seen, in succeeding chapters, that these processes, whether spontaneous or brought about by artificial means, are associated with very large amounts of energy. Chemical reactions, on the other hand, involve energy changes of a much lower order of magnitude. It is thus possible to describe an element as a form of matter which cannot be decomposed into (or be produced from) simpler forms of matter by means of chemical reactions, that is, by reactions associated with relatively small amounts of energy. In spite of the somewhat vague character of this definition,* there is never any doubt at the present time concerning the elementary or compound nature of a material. Numerous tests, now available, based on characteristic physical properties, such as the optical spectrum, mass spectrum and X-rays, permit elements to be distinguished and identified.

1.15. The atom may now be defined as the smallest possible or ultimate particle of an element, each element having its own characteristic atoms. As will be seen in Chapter IV, the atom itself has an internal structure and can be split up into subatomic particles. But these particles, most of which are electrical in nature, do not have the characteristic properties of the element. In the sense that the identity of the element is to be retained, the atom may therefore be regarded as indivisible.

SYMBOLS AND FORMULAS

1.16. In order to represent pictorially the building up of compounds from elements, Dalton introduced a set of symbols for the atoms. Thus, an atom of oxygen was indicated by a circle, one of hydrogen by a circle with a central dot, and a nitrogen atom was represented by a circle with a vertical line through it. This type of formulation was not only somewhat cumbersome when compounds were being considered, but the discovery of each new element presented the problem of inventing an appropriate symbol. The difficulty was overcome by Berzelius who devised the method which forms the basis for the symbolic representation of elements and compounds in use at the present day.

1.17. In his treatise *On the Theory of Chemical Proportions* (Paris, 1819), Berzelius proposed that "chemical symbols should be letters of the alphabet, in order to be easily drawn and printed without disfiguring the text," and that "the initial letter [or letters] of the Latin name of each element" should be used for this purpose. Consequently, oxygen (oxygenium) was symbolized by O, hydrogen (hydrogenium) by H, copper (cuprum) by Cu, gold (aurum) by Au, silver (argentum) by Ag, and so on.† The symbol, or *formula*, as it is generally called, of a compound is then obtained by combining the symbols for the appropriate elements, with subscripts to indicate the numbers of atoms present. Thus, the formula for water, which involves a chemical union of two atoms of hydrogen with one of oxygen, is H_2O; sulfuric acid, containing two atoms of hydrogen, one of sulfur and four of oxygen, has the formula H_2SO_4, and so on.

THE DETERMINATION OF ATOMIC WEIGHTS

DALTON'S ATOMIC WEIGHT SYSTEM

1.18. As mentioned earlier, perhaps Dalton's most significant contribution to the atomic theory was his attempt

---

* An element may be defined more precisely as a form of matter all the atoms of which have the same nuclear charge (Chapter IV).

† Some symbols, e.g., O and H, were obtained from Latinized names of French or other origin. The complete list of modern symbols for the elements is given in § 1.37.

to determine the relative masses or weights* of atoms. The actual atoms are, of course, much too small to be weighed directly, and so it is convenient to express their weights relative to that of a specified atom. For this purpose Dalton chose the atom of hydrogen, the lightest atom known to him and, as it happens, the lightest of all the elements. Hence, to the hydrogen atom was ascribed a weight of unity, and the weights of other atoms were then recorded in terms of that of the hydrogen atom.

1.19. The actual procedures for obtaining the relative atomic weights were then based on certain postulates concerning the nature of atoms and their mode of combination. The following quotations from Dalton's *New System of Chemical Philosophy*, mentioned earlier, give the arguments in his own words.

"Whether the ultimate particles of a body, such as water, are all alike, that is of the same figure [i.e., size and shape], weight, etc., is a question of some importance. From what is known, we have no reason to apprehend a diversity in these particulars: if it does exist in water, it must equally exist in the elements constituting water, namely, hydrogen and oxygen. Now it is scarcely possible to conceive how the aggregates of dissimilar particles should be so uniformly the same. . . . Therefore we may conclude that the ultimate particles of all homogeneous bodies are perfectly alike in weight, figure, etc. In other words, every [ultimate] particle of water is like every other particle of water; every [ultimate] particle of hydrogen is like every other particle of hydrogen, etc. . . .

"Chemical analysis and synthesis go no further than to the separation of particles from one another, and to their reunion. No new creation or destruction of matter is within the reach of chemical agency. . . . All the changes we can produce consist in separating particles that are in a state of cohesion or combination, and joining those that are previously at a distance. . . .

"If there are two bodies, A and B, which are disposed to combine, the following is the order in which combinations may take place, beginning with the most simple: namely, 1 atom of A + 1 atom of B [= AB] . . . , 1 atom of A + 2 atoms of B [= AB_2] . . . , 2 atoms of A + 1 atom of B [= A_2B], etc."

1.20. Stated briefly, Dalton's conclusions were threefold: that the ultimate particles of a given pure substance, whether element or compound, are alike in size, shape and weight; that chemical reaction does not cause any change in the nature of atoms but results merely in their rearrangement; and, that combination between atoms takes place in the ratio of the simplest numbers, preferably AB, then AB_2, and so on. If, as Dalton supposed, the atoms of a given element are all alike and are unchanged by chemical action, then the relative weight of the atom, as determined from the analysis of a compound, should have a definite and constant value. While the actual determination of relative atomic weights made use of the third of the postulates stated above, the results could have no significance without the first two.

1.21. The procedure used by Dalton may be illustrated by reference to his estimate of the atomic weight of oxy-

* Although mass and weight are treated here as synonymous, it is, strictly speaking, necessary to make a distinction. Mass is a measure of the quantity of matter in a body, while weight is the force exerted by the body, under the influence of gravity. It has become the practice to speak of "atomic weights" although "atomic masses" would perhaps be more accurate.

gen. At the time only one compound of oxygen with hydrogen—water—was known, and so Dalton, in accordance with the principles he enunciated, assumed it to have the simplest possible composition, namely, the combination of one atom of hydrogen with one of oxygen, i.e., HO. Upon analysis he found that water consisted of one part by weight of hydrogen and seven—later shown to be eight—parts by weight of oxygen. It followed, therefore, that if the weight of hydrogen is taken as unity, the relative atomic weight of oxygen should be seven—actually eight. That is to say, the weight of a single atom of oxygen, according to Dalton, was seven—actually eight—times that of a single hydrogen atom. Similarly, by assuming the formula of ammonia to be NH, the atomic weight of nitrogen appeared to be five—more accurately 4.7—relative to that of hydrogen.

Combining or Equivalent Weights

1.22. Apart from the errors in Dalton's experimental work, several of his atomic weights, such as those of oxygen and nitrogen given above, were incorrect. The reason for the discrepancies lay in the fact that the postulated simple formulas of the type AB, such as, HO for water and NH for ammonia, were erroneous; water is now known to be properly represented by H_2O and ammonia by NH_3. What Dalton determined was, in general, the *combining weight* or *equivalent weight* of an element, that is, the weight of the element which combines with or replaces—that is, is equivalent to—one part by weight of hydrogen.*

1.23. If the formula of the com-pound under consideration is actually HX, as is the case, for example, when X is the element chlorine, then the atomic and combining weights are identical. In other instances, however, the atomic weight is a simple multiple of the equivalent weight. It can be readily seen that this multiple must be the same as the number of atoms of hydrogen which unite with, or replace, one atom of the given element. Thus, since the formula of water is H_2O, and two atoms of hydrogen combine with one of oxygen, the atomic weight of oxygen is exactly twice the equivalent weight. If, therefore, Dalton had used the correct formula for water, he would have arrived at an atomic weight of twice seven, i.e., 14, relative to hydrogen, which is in fair agreement with the more accurate value of 16. Similarly, if he had known that ammonia was NH_3, the atomic weight of nitrogen would have been given as three times five, i.e., 15, not very different from the accepted atomic weight of approximately 14.

The Atomic Weight Scale

1.24. It is evident from the figures just cited that Dalton's experimental work was not too reliable. One of the factors responsible was his choice of hydrogen as the basis of comparison for atomic weights. In the first place, relatively few elements form compounds with hydrogen, and these are not easy to analyze; in the second place, on account of the lightness of hydrogen, a small error in weighing leads to a large over-all discrepancy. Since most elements combine with oxygen, the atom of which is about sixteen times as heavy as that of hydrogen, Berzelius used oxygen as the

---

* The modern definition of combining (or equivalent) weight of an element uses **8.000** parts by weight of oxygen, rather than 1 part of hydrogen, as the basis of comparison (§ 1.24).

standard, assigning to it an arbitrary combining weight of 100. Later there was a return to the Daltonian system and the weight of the atom of oxygen was then found to be very close to 16, in comparison with unity for hydrogen. Because of its practical value, as indicated above, chemists therefore agreed to take the atomic weight of oxygen, as it occurs in the air, to be exactly 16.0000, and its equivalent weight to be 8.0000; this is still the basis of modern chemical atomic and equivalent weights.* The atomic weight of hydrogen on this scale is now known to be 1.0080, rather than exactly unity.

ATOMIC AND EQUIVALENT WEIGHTS

1.25. In Dalton's time the principles of quantitative chemical analysis were not well understood, and the precision balance had not been developed, so that combining weights of a high or-

der of accuracy could not have been expected. With improvements in the techniques and methods of analytical chemistry during the first half of the nineteenth century, there became available increasingly exact values of the combining or equivalent weights of many elements, for which J. J. Berzelius, in Sweden, and J. S. Stas, in Belgium, were largely responsible. Before these could be converted into atomic weights there still existed the problem of finding for each element the integer by which the equivalent weight was to be multiplied. In this connection, Berzelius obtained guidance from the *law of isomorphism*† proposed by his German pupil E. Mitscherlich in 1819, as well as from the *law of the constant heat capacity* of atoms‡ discovered in the same year by the French scientists P. L. Dulong and A. T. Petit.

ATOMS AND MOLECULES

EARLY DEVELOPMENTS

1.26. A fundamental postulate, which would have been of inestimable value in the early attempts at determining atomic weights, had been proposed independently by the Italian physicist Amadeo Avogadro in 1811, and some three years later by A. M. Ampère, for whom the unit of electric current is named. Unfortunately, the concepts involved were not too clearly

expressed nor too well understood until 1858, when Stanislao Cannizzaro, in his *Sketch of a Course of Chemical Philosophy* as given in the University of Genoa, clarified and explained the significance of the ideas of his fellow countryman, Avogadro, published more than forty years earlier.

1.27. In order to appreciate the circumstances at that time, it is necessary to consider the distinction between

* The reasons for the qualifications "as it occurs in air," applied to oxygen, and "chemical," applied to atomic weight, will be given in § 8.61.
† According to this law, isomorphous substances, i.e., substances which form crystals of similar shape, having similar chemical properties can usually be represented by analogous formulas, e.g., Cu_2S and Ag_2S, Fe_2O_3 and Al_2O_3. The *valence* of an element, i.e., the ratio of the atomic weight to the equivalent weight, can be derived from the formula of an appropriate compound.
‡ The product of the atomic weight and the specific heat has approximately the same value for most solid elements. The specific heat can be readily measured, and hence a rough atomic weight can be estimated. The accurate value can then be obtained from the combining weight.

atom and *molecule*.* In the early years of the nineteenth century no very clear differentiation was made. Dalton, for example, occasionally used the term molecule as synonymous with his ultimate particle or atom. Further, he did not discriminate between the particles of an element and those of a compound; he referred to both types as "atoms." Avogadro, on the other hand, went to the other extreme; he did not use the term atom, but applied the general name of "molecule" to various particles. However, a careful reading of Avogadro's writings shows that he distinguished between three different types of molecules, although the distinction is implicit rather than explicit. There is little doubt that the situation was clear in Avogadro's mind, but it is not so certain that his views were expressed plainly enough to be grasped by his contemporaries. In the succeeding decades, efforts were made to define the terms "atom" and "molecule," particularly by the French scientists A. M. Gaudin (1833), A. M. Ampère (1835), A. Laurent (1846) and C. L. Gerhardt (1856). It was Cannizzaro's logical development of the consequences of the distinction between these quantities that resulted in the opening of a new era in the determination of atomic weights.

1.28. A molecule may be defined as the smallest particle of any substance —element or compound—as it normally exists. A molecule of a compound always contains atoms of two or more elements; thus, a molecule of water is represented by H_2O, because it consists of two atoms of hydrogen and one of oxygen. Since an atom of an element is indivisible, it is not pos-

sible for a molecule to contain less than one atom of any element. Hence, for the present purpose, an atom may be regarded as the smallest portion of an element that can be found in a molecule of any of its compounds. Alternatively, an atom is described as the smallest particle of an element that can enter into chemical combination. It is no longer permissible to speak of an "atom of a compound," or of a "compound atom," as Dalton did; the ultimate particle of a compound is the molecule. If such a molecule were further subdivided it would break up into the atoms of its constituent elements, and hence would cease to be a compound.

ATOMS AND MOLECULES OF ELEMENTS

1.29. One further point remains to be clarified, namely, the distinction between the atom and molecule of an element. The atom is the smallest *conceivable* particle of an element, as well as the smallest portion that can take part in chemical combination. However, it is not necessarily the smallest unit that can normally *exist* as such; it is the latter which is the molecule of the element.† Consider, for example, the element oxygen, the gas which constitutes about one fifth of the air. The atom would be represented by the symbol O, but the molecule, as present in the atmosphere, is made up of a combination of two such atoms and hence is O_2. It is true that by the use of high temperatures or by means of an electrical discharge some of the molecules could be split up into two atoms, but as soon as normal conditions were restored the atoms would

---

* From the diminutive of the Latin word *moles* (mass); hence, molecule means a small mass.

† Avogadro referred to the atoms of elements as "molécules élémentaires," and the molecules of elements he called "molécules constituantes." Molecules of compounds he termed "molécules intégrantes."

reunite in pairs to form molecules. Single atoms of oxygen tend to combine chemically with other atoms; if two atoms of oxygen interact with one another the result is an oxygen molecule, but if one atom of oxygen unites with two atoms of hydrogen the result is a molecule of water.

1.30. Under ordinary conditions of temperature and pressure, most elements, at least those which are gases, such as oxygen, hydrogen, nitrogen and chlorine, form diatomic molecules, that is to say, the molecule contains two atoms. There are, however, some important elements, often referred to as the "inert gases of the atmosphere," for which the atom and the molecule are identical. The element helium, for example, as it occurs in the atmosphere and in certain natural gases, consists of single atoms and these may equally correctly be described as molecules. Thus, helium is said to be a monatomic gas. The atoms of helium, and of its related gases neon, argon, etc., are so inert that they will neither unite with one another nor with the atoms of other elements.

AVOGADRO'S LAW

1.31. Bearing in mind the correct significance of the term molecule, the law of Avogadro states that under the same conditions of temperature and pressure equal volumes of different *gases* contain equal numbers of molecules.* The density of a gas is defined as the weight of a given volume, say 1 liter, and hence is equal to the weight of the molecules contained in that volume. But, since for different gases, this definite volume always includes the same number of molecules, it fol-

lows that the density of a gas is directly proportional to the weight of its individual molecules. In the words of Avogadro: "Setting out from this hypothesis [as stated above], it is apparent that we have the means of determining very easily the relative masses of the molecules of substances obtainable in the gaseous state . . . for the ratios of the masses of the molecules are then the same as those of the densities of the different gases at equal temperature and pressure."

DETERMINATION OF MOLECULAR WEIGHTS

1.32. By the comparison of densities it is thus possible to determine the weight of one molecular species with reference to that of another, and hence, for practical purposes, it is desirable to choose a uniform basis of reference for expressing molecular weights. That proposed by Cannizzaro, and now universally adopted, is to use the same standard as is employed for atomic weights. The molecular weight is then recorded as the weight of a given molecule relative to the weight of the oxygen atom taken as 16.0000. Defined in this manner, the molecular weight is equal to the sum of the conventional atomic weights (§ 1.37) of its constituent elements, due allowance being made for the number of atoms of each present in the molecule.

1.33. There are good reasons for believing that the oxygen molecule consists of two atoms, and so the molecular weight of ordinary oxygen is taken as 32.0000. Hence the molecular weight of any substance is the weight of a molecule of that substance compared with the assumed weight of 32.0000 for

---

* Dalton had previously (1808) considered this possibility but had rejected it, perhaps because of the confusion between atoms and molecules. He wrote: "I had a confused idea . . . that a given volume of oxygenous gas contains just as many particles as the same volume of hydrogenous. . . . But . . . I became convinced that the different gases have not their particles of the same size [i.e., do not occupy equal volumes]."

an oxygen molecule. It can be readily seen, therefore, that in view of Avogadro's law, it is possible to write for any *gaseous* substance, element or compound, at the same temperature and pressure, the relationship

16, i.e., 18, as is actually found from gas density measurements. This type of argument has been used to determine the atomic weights of several elements.

$$\frac{\text{Molecular weight of substance}}{\text{Molecular weight of oxygen}} = \frac{\text{Density of substance}}{\text{Density of oxygen}}$$

or,

$$\text{Molecular weight} = \frac{\text{Density of substance}}{\text{Density of oxygen}} \times 32.0000,$$

so that a determination of gaseous density is sufficient to yield the molecular weight of the substance. It may be remarked that the use of ordinary densities does not give results of a high order of accuracy; but by applying certain corrections it is possible to obtain molecular weights with a considerable degree of precision.*

Molecular Weights and Atomic Weights

1.34. It now remains to be seen how the development of a reliable method of determining molecular weights provided a solution for the atomic weight problem. If Dalton had known the molecular weight of water to be 18, with reference to hydrogen as unity, it would have been obvious that its formula could not be HO, as he thought; as stated above, this formula implied an atomic weight of 8 for oxygen, and hence a molecular weight of $1 + 8$, i.e., 9, for water. By taking the formula of water to be H_2O, and making use of the experimental fact that one part by weight of hydrogen is united with eight parts of oxygen, it is readily seen that the atomic weight of oxygen should be 16. In this event, the molecular weight of water would be $2 +$

1.35. Since the atom is the smallest portion of an element that can be present in a molecule, the atomic weight must be the smallest weight of the element that can be found in a molecular weight of any of its compounds. This contention formed the basis of the procedure introduced by Cannizzaro for the evaluation of atomic weights. Volatile compounds of a given element were prepared and their molecular weights derived from gas-density measurements. The various substances were then analyzed so as to find the weight of the element present in the molecular weight of each compound. The smallest of the weights found in this manner or, more correctly, the highest common divisor of these weights, is the atomic weight of the element.

1.36. Other uses have been made of molecular weights in connection with the derivation of the atomic weights of the elements, but sufficient has been stated here to indicate that the proper application of Avogadro's law helped to remove one of the outstanding difficulties that faced the chemists of the early 1800s. In the latter part of the same century methods were developed for determining molecular weights without resort to gas densities, so

---

* These corrections are necessary because Avogadro's law is strictly applicable to "perfect" or "ideal" gases, whereas actual gases do not behave ideally at ordinary temperatures and pressures.

that nonvolatile solid compounds could be utilized in atomic weight studies. Further, greatly improved procedures, based on the use of chlorides and bromides, in place of oxides, have been employed for obtaining accurate combining (or equivalent) weights. As a result, chemical atomic weights of nearly all the elements, as they occur on the earth, have been ascertained with a considerable degree of accuracy. In addition, very precise determina-

ATOMIC WEIGHTS

Element	Symbol	Atomic Number	Atomic Weight	Element	Symbol	Atomic Number	Atomic Weight
Aluminum	Al	13	26.98	Neodymium	Nd	60	144.27
Antimony	Sb	51	121.76	Neon	Ne	10	20.183
Argon*	Ar	18	39.944	Nickel	Ni	28	58.71
Arsenic	As	33	74.91	Niobium†	Nb	41	92.91
Barium	Ba	56	137.36	Nitrogen	N	7	14.008
Beryllium	Be	4	9.013	Osmium	Os	76	190.2
Bismuth	Bi	83	209.00	Oxygen	O	8	16.0000
Boron	B	5	10.82	Palladium	Pd	46	106.4
Bromine	Br	35	79.916	Phosphorus	P	15	30.975
Cadmium	Cd	48	112.41	Platinum	Pt	78	195.09
Calcium	Ca	20	40.08	Potassium	K	19	39.100
Carbon	C	6	12.011	Praseodymium	Pr	59	140.92
Cerium	Ce	58	140.13	Protactinium	Pa	91	231
Cesium	Cs	55	132.91	Radium	Ra	88	226.05
Chlorine	Cl	17	35.457	Radon	Rn	86	222
Chromium	Cr	24	52.01	Rhenium	Re	75	186.22
Cobalt	Co	27	58.94	Rhodium	Rh	45	102.91
Copper	Cu	29	63.54	Rubidium	Rb	37	85.48
Dysprosium	Dy	66	162.51	Ruthenium	Ru	44	101.1
Erbium	Er	68	162.27	Samarium	Sm	62	150.35
Europium	Eu	63	152.0	Scandium	Sc	21	44.96
Fluorine	F	9	19.00	Selenium	Se	34	78.96
Gadolinium	Gd	64	157.26	Silicon	Si	14	28.09
Gallium	Ga	31	69.72	Silver	Ag	47	107.880
Germanium	Ge	32	72.60	Sodium	Na	11	22.991
Gold	Au	79	197.0	Strontium	Sr	38	87.63
Hafnium	Hf	72	178.50	Sulfur	S	16	32.066
Helium	He	2	4.003	Tantalum	Ta	73	180.95
Holmium	Ho	67	164.94	Tellurium	Te	52	127.61
Hydrogen	H	1	1.0080	Terbium	Tb	65	158.93
Indium	In	49	114.82	Thallium	Tl	81	204.39
Iodine	I	53	126.91	Thorium	Th	90	232.05
Iridium	Ir	77	192.2	Thulium	Tm	69	168.94
Iron	Fe	26	55.85	Tin	Sn	50	118.70
Krypton	Kr	36	83.8	Titanium	Ti	22	47.90
Lanthanum	La	57	138.92	Tungsten	W	74	183.86
Lead	Pb	82	207.21	Uranium	U	92	238.07
Lithium	Li	3	6.940	Vanadium	V	23	50.95
Lutetium	Lu	71	174.99	Xenon	Xe	54	131.3
Magnesium	Mg	12	24.32	Ytterbium	Yb	70	173.04
Manganese	Mn	25	54.94	Yttrium	Y	39	88.92
Mercury	Hg	80	200.61	Zinc	Zn	30	65.38
Molybdenum	Mo	42	95.95	Zirconium	Zr	40	91.22

* In 1957, the Commission on Inorganic Nomenclature of the International Union of Pure and Applied Chemistry recommended that the symbol Ar be used for argon, although A had previously been employed in English-speaking countries.

† Alternative name, Columbium (Cb)

tions of atomic weights have been made by means of the mass spectrograph (Chapter VIII).

1.37. The accompanying table gives what are believed to be the best values of the atomic weights of eighty six elements, arranged in alphabetical order of their names. The recognized symbols for the various elements are also given.* It should be borne in mind that although the data are considered to be reliable, some of the results may be based on experimental determinations containing unsuspected errors. Consequently, revised lists of atomic weights, which frequently contain minor corrections, are issued from time to time, as new and more accurate experiments are performed.

PROUT'S HYPOTHESIS

1.38. In 1816, when few atomic weights were yet known, and those only approximately, the English physician William Prout thought it possible that all atomic weights were integral, i.e., whole numbers without fractions. All atomic weights, he considered, might thus be multiples of that of hydrogen. Prout then went on to say: "If the view we have ventured to advance be correct, we may consider the *protyle* of the ancients to be realized in hydrogen." †

1.39. One of the consequences of the announcement of Prout's hypothesis of the integral nature of atomic weights was the stimulus it gave to accurate determinations of these quantities. When definite fractional atomic weights, such as those of chlorine (35.46) and copper (63.54), were obtained, the hypothesis fell into disfavor, but in due course it came to be realized that there was some basis for the idea. If the appended table is examined, it will be seen that nearly half the elements have atomic weights which are within about 0.1 of a whole number. As R. J. Strutt (later Lord Rayleigh, 4th Baron) said in 1901: "The atomic weights tend to approximate to whole numbers far more closely than can reasonably be accounted for by any accidental coincidence . . . the chance of any such coincidence being the explanation is not more than 1 in 1000." After the subject of isotopes has been considered in Chapter VIII, it will be seen that both integral and fractional atomic weights have an explanation, and that Prout's hypothesis, in a modified form, has real significance. Even the suggestion that hydrogen is the primal matter or protyle, of which other elements are built up, is not completely invalid.

THE PERIODIC SYSTEM

CLASSIFICATION OF THE ELEMENTS

1.40. As far back as 1829, J. W. Döbereiner had called attention to a simple relationship among the atomic weights of elements having similar properties. The matter attracted the interest of other scientists, but their ac-

tivities were handicapped by the uncertainties concerning actual atomic weight values. After the publication of Cannizzaro's historic paper in 1858, reliable atomic weights became available and attempts to correlate them with the physical and chemical properties of the

* The significance of the "atomic number" will be explained in §§ 1.44, 4.23.
† Prout referred to this as "an opinion . . . not altogether new," apparently because his eminent contemporary Humphry Davy and others thought they had proved, by experiments now known to be faulty, that hydrogen might actually be present in many elements.

elements were increasingly successful. In France, for example, B. de Chancourtois, in 1862, had arranged the elements, in order of increasing atomic weight, in the form of a spiral or screw. He then found that elements with analogous properties occupied related positions on the spiral. Quite independently, the English chemist J. A. R. Newlands made a similar discovery in 1865, which he published as the "law of octaves." Newlands stated that if the elements are placed in a sequence, according to their atomic weights, they fall into groups such that the eighth element has properties similar to the first, the ninth to the second, the tenth to the third, and so on, somewhat like a series of octaves in music. Although the scheme had some merit, Newlands carried the octave rule too far. This fact, combined with his use of incorrect atomic weights in some instances and his failure to realize that elements might exist which had not yet been identified, resulted in some highly improbable associations. Thus, iron found itself classified with sulfur, and gold with iodine, associations which no chemist could accept.

The Periodic Law

1.41. In 1869, the Russian scientist D. I. Mendelyeev* published a short note *On the Relationships of the Properties of the Elements to their Atomic Weights,* which he subsequently elaborated, in 1871, in the form of a lengthy paper on *The Periodic Regularities of the Chemical Elements.* Although Lothar Meyer in Germany had indicated in 1864, and again in 1869, that certain properties of the elements were a periodic function of their atomic weights, it is the Russian chemist who is regarded as the effective originator of the *periodic law,* and of the method of classifying the elements based on this law. It was already apparent, Mendelyeev said, "during the period 1860-1870 . . . that relations between atomic weights of analogous elements were governed by some general and simple law. . . . When I arranged the elements according to the magnitude of their atomic weights, beginning with the smallest, it became evident that there exists a kind of periodicity in their properties. I designate by the name periodic law the mutual relations between the properties of the elements and their atomic weights; these relations are applicable to all the elements and have the nature of a periodic function."

1.42. The success of Mendelyeev's arrangement of the elements lay in his emphasis on the repetition of physical and chemical properties at definite intervals. Where the periodic properties appeared to break down, he boldly proclaimed that, in some instances, the accepted atomic weights were grossly in error, while in others allowance must be made for elements as yet undiscovered. It is in the latter connection that the periodic law achieved its most striking successes. By considering the properties of known elements surrounding the gaps left for apparently missing elements, Mendelyeev predicted the behavior of the latter in great detail. In three cases, in particular, the discovery of the actual elements, gallium in 1875, scandium in 1879 and germanium in 1886, provided a brilliant vindication of these predictions. It was, in fact, not until 1875, when the French chemist L. de Boisbaudran identified, in zinc blende from the Pyrenees, a hitherto unknown element, which he called gallium, that

---

* The Russian name has been transliterated in many different ways; the one given here is taken from Webster's *New International Dictionary,* Second Edition, 1941.

The Periodic Table of the Elements

Groups

	IA	IIA	IIIA	IVA	VA	VIA	VIIA	VIII			IB	IIB	IIIB	IVB	VB	VIB	VIIB	0
Period 1	1 H																	2 He
Period 2	3 Li	4 Be											5 B	6 C	7 N	8 O	9 F	10 Ne
Period 3	11 Na	12 Mg											13 Al	14 Si	15 P	16 S	17 Cl	18 Ar
Period 4	19 K	20 Ca	21 Sc	22 Ti	23 V	24 Cr	25 Mn	26 Fe	27 Co	28 Ni	29 Cu	30 Zn	31 Ga	32 Ge	33 As	34 Se	35 Br	36 Kr
Period 5	37 Rb	38 Sr	39 Y	40 Zr	41 Nb	42 Mo	43 (Tc)	44 Ru	45 Rh	46 Pd	47 Ag	48 Cd	49 In	50 Sn	51 Sb	52 Te	53 I	54 Xe
Period 6	55 Cs	56 Ba	57–71 Lanthanides	72 Hf	73 Ta	74 W	75 Re	76 Os	77 Ir	78 Pt	79 Au	80 Hg	81 Tl	82 Pb	83 Bi	84 Po	85 At	86 Rn
Period 7	87 Fr	88 Ra	89– Actinides															

Lanthanide Series	57 La	58 Ce	59 Pr	60 Nd	61 (Pm)	62 Sm	63 Eu	64 Gd	65 Tb	66 Dy	67 Ho	68 Er	69 Tm	70 Yb	71 Lu

Actinide Series	89 Ac	90 Th	91 Pa	92 U	93 (Np)	94 (Pu)	95 (Am)	96 (Cm)	97 (Bk)	98 (Cf)	99 (Es)	100 (Fm)	101 (Md)	102 (No)

the periodic law began to attract general interest.*

1.43. Although some of Mendelyeev's prognostications were subsequently found to be incorrect, and certain features of his original periodic classification have had to be amended, the fundamental principles of his law remain unchallenged. It is now accepted as one of the cardinal truths of nature, and a close connection has been established between the positions of the elements in the periodic arrangement and the internal structure of their atoms.

1.44. A modern form of the periodic table, which includes all the known elements arranged, with some minor exceptions,† in the order of increasing atomic weights, is appended. The twelve elements whose symbols are in parentheses appear to be too unstable to exist in nature to any appreciable extent; they have, however, been produced in recent years by the disintegration and transmutation of other elements. The ordinal number of each element in the series, referred to as the *atomic number* (§ 4.23), is given in each case.

1.45. The table is seen to consist of a number of horizontal lines, called *periods*, containing 2, 8, 8, 18, 18, 32 and 16 (incomplete) elements, respectively.‡ In each period there is definite and characteristic gradation of chemical and physical properties, from one element to the next. In some places the gradation is quite marked, e.g., Al, Si, P, S, Cl, Ar; but at other points, e.g., Cr, Mn, Fe, Co, Ni, Cu,

Zn, it is relatively small. These facts have been explained in terms of the structures of the atoms of the respective elements.

1.46. The vertical columns into which the table is divided are called *groups;* most of these groups consist of A and B subgroups, viz., IA, IB, IIA, IIB, etc. Similarities of a minor character exist between the members of an A subgroup on the one hand, and those of the corresponding B subgroup on the other hand. In each subgroup the elements have analogous properties, although there is a steady but gradual variation with increasing atomic weight. It is this repetition of physical and chemical characteristics, occurring at regular intervals, that represents the periodicity to which Mendelyeev, and others, called attention.

1.47. The presence of Group 0, consisting of the "inert gases," is of particular interest. None of the elements of this group had been identified, at least on the earth, until 1895; hence, the early groups in the periodic table were numbered from I to VIII. When the inert gases of the atmosphere were discovered it was soon seen that they formed a group between VIIB and IA, but, in order to avoid a complete renumbering, the symbol 0 (zero) was assigned to the new group. This symbol is especially appropriate because of the highly inert nature of the elements concerned.

LANTHANIDE AND ACTINIDE SERIES

1.48. There are numerous other important features of the periodic table,

---

* An account of Mendelyeev's work, believed to be the first in English, was published in the London *Chemical News* in December, 1875; his 1871 paper was translated in this journal in 1879-80.

† These are the pairs argon and potassium, cobalt and nickel, and tellurium and iodine for which the atomic weight differences are small.

‡ It was the occurrence of the second and third periods of eight elements, of which seven were known at the time, that led Newlands to propose his "law of octaves." Since the subsequent periods are considerably longer it is obvious that the "law" must then break down.

but the discussion given here will be restricted to one of particular interest. In Group IIIA, Period 6, there appears, in place of a single element, a series of fifteen elements with atomic (ordinal) numbers from 57 to 71, inclusive, the details of which are recorded below the main table. These elements, called the *lanthanide series*, after the name of its first member (lanthanum), are more familiarly known as the *rare-earth series*. They have properties which are so closely related that their separation from one another has been a challenging chemical problem.

1.49. In view of the existence of the lanthanide series, there has been much speculation concerning the possibility of the occurrence of an analogous *actinide series*, beginning with the element actinium, atomic number 89. In the periodic tables to be found in books and papers published before 1945, and even later, the four elements of this possible series, whose properties were generally known at the time, namely, actinium, thorium, protactinium and uranium, are placed in Groups IIIA, IVA, VA and VIA. In other words, prior to 1945, most chemists would have doubted the existence of an actinide series; the feeling was that Period 7 would behave more like Period 5 than like Period 6. However, information obtained since 1939 has thrown an entirely new light on the situation (see Chapter XVI). A detailed study of the chemical properties of the new "artificial" elements neptunium (Np, 93), plutonium (Pu, 94), americium (Am, 95), curium (Cm, 96), berkelium (Bk, 97), californium (Cf, 98), einsteinium (Es, 99), fermium (Fm, 100), mendelevium (Md, 101) and nobelium (No, 102), and a reinvestigation of those of uranium (92), has shown clearly that these elements have properties which would make them members of a series similar to the lanthanide series.

THE SIZES AND WEIGHTS OF ATOMS

ATOMIC WEIGHTS AND THE REALITY OF ATOMS

1.50. So far, the atomic concept has been presented here purely as a working theory, without any definite proof that atoms actually exist. By assuming that compounds are composed of molecules, which are themselves built up from atoms of various elements, it has been possible to ascribe so-called atomic weights to these elements. The fact that the arrangement of the elements in order of increasing atomic weight brings out a striking periodicity of characteristic properties, suggests that these weights do have significance.

The results thus provide some support for the theory that all matter is constructed ultimately of atoms. However, if information could be obtained from various sources concerning the sizes and actual weights, as distinct from the relative weights, of atoms, a general agreement among the results might serve as a more convincing argument for the atomic theory.

MOLECULAR SIZE: EARLY ESTIMATES

1.51. The first reasonably accurate estimate of molecular size was published by the English physicist Thomas

Young, in an essay on *Cohesion*, written in 1816 for the Supplement of the *Encyclopaedia Britannica*. In this article, he said: "Within certain limits of accuracy, we may obtain something like a conjectural estimate of the mutual distance of the particles of vapours, and even of the actual magnitude of the elementary atoms of liquids, as supposed to be nearly in contact with each other; for if the distance, at which the force of cohesion begins, is constant at the same temperature, and if the particles of steam are condensed when they approach within this distance, it follows that at 60° of F. the distance of particles of pure aqueous vapour is about the 250 millionth of an inch." From this result and a comparison of the densities of liquid and vapor, Young concluded that the diameter of a water molecule was about a billionth, i.e., 10^{-9}, of an inch. Considering the approximate nature of the calculation and the very small magnitudes involved, this result is remarkably good, being only about ten times smaller than the value now accepted.

1.52. Thomas Young's estimate of molecular size was based on intelligent guessing, but further developments in physical theory were necessary before substantial progress could be made. One of these was related to the behavior of gases. The fact that gases exert a pressure or "spring," as Robert Boyle called it, had been explained by the *kinetic theory*. According to this theory the molecules of a gas are assumed to be constantly in motion, frequently striking one another and the walls of the containing vessel, and so continually changing their directions. Making use of this relatively simple concept, mathematicians and physicists, notably R. Clausius in Germany and J. C. Maxwell in England, in the period between 1850 and 1860, were able to derive a number of equations relating certain measurable properties of a gas to the characteristics of the individual molecules. One of these equations showed how the *viscosity*, or resistance to flow, of a gas depended on the size of the molecules and the number present in unit volume. However, since neither of the latter quantities was known, the relationship to the viscosity, which could be determined experimentally, appeared to have no practical value, since no solution can be obtained for a single equation with two unknown quantities.

1.53. The dilemma was solved in a simple, if approximate, manner by the German scientist J. Loschmidt in 1865. He pointed out that if molecules could be regarded as spherical in shape, and if, further, it was supposed that in the liquid state these molecular spheres were packed as closely as possible, another equation could be readily derived relating these same two quantities to the density of the liquid. Hence, if there are known the viscosity of a particular gas and the density of the liquid which is formed when the gas is compressed and cooled, the two equations permit the size of the given molecule and the number present in a unit volume to be calculated.

1.54. Applying this procedure to nitrogen, oxygen and carbon dioxide, Loschmidt found these molecules to be slightly more than one ten-millionth of a centimeter i.e., 10^{-7}cm., in diameter, a value now known to be too large by a factor of about five, but, nevertheless, of the correct order of magnitude. In addition, the calculations showed that in each case there were present, under ordinary conditions of temperature and pressure, about two billion billion, i.e., 2×10^{18}, individual molecules in one cubic centimeter (1 cc.), a figure which is some fourteen times too small.* The weight of 1 cc. of oxygen gas, for example, is known, and consequently the weight of a single oxygen molecule could be calculated. The weight of an atom would then be one-half of this quantity. In spite of their approximate nature, partly due to the use of inaccurate viscosity data and partly because of the assumption that a liquid consists of close-packed spheres, Loschmidt's results are important, for they represent the first attempt, based on sound theoretical principles, to estimate the properties of single molecules.

1.55. In 1870, the eminent Scottish physicist and inventor, William Thomson, later Lord Kelvin, reviewed a number of methods for determining molecular size, and concluded that they all led to values of the same order, namely, about 10^{-8} cm. for the diameter of a molecule. In a lecture delivered at the Royal Institution, London, in 1881 he tried to convey some idea of the extreme smallness of atoms and molecules as follows: "To form some conception [of molecular size] . . . imagine a globe of water as large as a [spherical] football . . . , say 16 centimetres in diameter, to be magnified up to the size of the earth, each constituent molecule being magnified in the same proportion. The magnified structure would be more coarse-grained than a heap of small shot but probably less coarse-grained than a heap of footballs."

The Avogadro Number

1.56. Before proceeding to a discussion of more recent work dealing with molecular properties, reference must be made to an incidental matter. By Avogadro's law, the number of individual molecules in a given volume of (ideal) gas is independent of the chemical nature of the gas. For purposes of record any convenient volume may be chosen, but there is a particular volume that has special significance. If the molecular weight of any substance is expressed in grams, the resulting quantity is known as a *gram molecular weight*, a *gram molecule* or, more briefly, as a *mole* of the substance. Thus, 2.016 grams of hydrogen, 32.000 grams of oxygen and 28.020 grams of nitrogen, each represent one mole of the respective substances. Experiments with a large number of gases have shown, in accordance with Avogadro's law, that, after correcting for departure from ideal behavior (§ 1.33, footnote), one mole of any gas always has a volume of 22.414 liters at a temperature of 0°C and a pressure of 1 atmosphere. This is known as the gaseous *molar volume* at standard temperature and pressure, and the number of individual molecules present in this volume, which is the same for all gases, is called the *Avogadro number* or *Avogadro's constant*.

1.57. Since the molar volume contains one mole, the Avogadro number is the number of individual molecules in one gram molecule.† Hence, if the molecular weight of any substance, element or compound, is divided by the Avogadro number, the result is the weight expressed in grams of a single molecule of that substance. Similarly, the weight in grams of a single atom of any element is obtained upon dividing

* According to Avogadro's law, the number of molecules in 1 cc. of gas should be the same, at a given temperature and pressure, for *all* gases. Within the limits of their accuracy, Loschmidt's results confirmed the law.

† One mole of a substance must contain the same number of individual molecules irrespective of its state, solid, liquid or gaseous. Consequently, the Avogadro constant gives the number of molecules in one mole of any substance.

its atomic weight by the Avogadro constant.

1.58. One of the most notable studies relating to molecules was undertaken in France by J. Perrin, beginning about 1908. Some eighty years earlier, the English botanist Robert Brown had noticed that when microscopic pollen grains were suspended in water, they exhibited continual and haphazard motion in all directions. In fact, their behavior was, on a large scale, exactly what would have been expected from molecules if they behaved in accordance with the kinetic theory (§ 1.52). The phenomenon, which has been observed with small suspended particles of many kinds, is called the *Brownian movement*, the motion being attributed to the continuous bombardment of the particles by the molecules of the medium in which they are suspended. Thus, the movement of the particles, as seen in the microscope, represents in a sense a highly magnified picture of the motion of the invisible molecules which surround them. Perrin made a series of measurements on various types of suspended particles, and by assuming that they behaved just like molecules obeying the equations derived from the kinetic theory of gases, he was able to calculate the Avogadro number.

1.59. In other experiments on the motion of suspended particles, Perrin made use of an equation, first derived by A. Einstein in 1905. By combining this with other equations, further relationships were obtained which permitted independent estimates to be made of the number of molecules contained in a given volume of gas. The striking fact that emerged from this work was that the value of the Avogadro number was always the same—about 6×10^{23}—within the limits of experimental error, irrespective of the type of measurement upon which it was based. Further, the value was in excellent agreement with that derived from more refined calculations, of the type first made by Loschmidt, utilizing the properties of gases. The fact that observations of such entirely different types gave virtually identical results was of the greatest significance. Apart from yielding information concerning the Avogadro number, the work of Perrin has been regarded as providing some of the most convincing evidence for the real existence of molecules.

1.60. Several other procedures for evaluating the Avogadro constant, ranging in scope from radioactivity to the blue color of the sky, have been developed. Two of these give results of special accuracy; the first is based on measurement of the charge carried by an electron (§ 2.41), and the second involves X-ray studies with crystals. The value of the Avogadro number thus obtained is 6.025×10^{23}, and this is the number of individual molecules in a gram molecular weight, i.e., in a mole, of any substance.

ATOMS IN GAS, SOLID AND LIQUID

1.61. Under ordinary atmospheric conditions, 1 cc. of a gas, irrespective of its nature, contains about 2.7×10^{19} molecules. Gaseous molecules are usually made up of from 1 to 10, or perhaps more, atoms and so the volume of gas specified includes, on an average, a total of something like 10^{20} atoms. In certain atomic studies, some of which will be referred to later in this book, it is necessary to produce what is known as a "high vacuum," by pumping as much as possible of the gas from the containing vessels. However, even in the best vacuum normally attainable, with the pressure reduced to one billionth (10^{-9}) of an atmosphere, or less, 1 cc. of gas, at normal temperature, still contains more than ten billion, i.e., more than 10^{10} molecules.

1.62. Liquids and solids, being more highly condensed than gases, contain even more atoms and molecules per unit volume. As distinct from the behavior of gases, the number of molecules now depends on the nature of the substance. It is determined, essentially, by the ratio of the density of the solid or liquid to that of the same material in the form of gas or vapor. But, as a rough approximation, it may be stated that a solid or liquid contains about one thousand times as many atoms as an equal volume of gas at normal pressure. Consequently, under ordinary conditions, there are something like 10^{23} atoms in 1 cc. of liquid or solid material.

1.63. The number of molecules in a specified weight of any material, gaseous, liquid or solid, can be calculated in the following manner. The weight in grams is first divided by the molecular weight, to give the number of moles present. Upon multiplication of this result by the Avogadro number, i.e., 6.02×10^{23}, which is the number of molecules in 1 mole, there is obtained the total number of individual molecules in the material. If the latter is an element, division of the weight by the atomic weight and multiplication by the Avogadro number gives, correspondingly, the number of atoms present.

WEIGHTS AND SIZES OF
ATOMS AND MOLECULES

1.64. As already stated, the weight in grams of a single atom or molecule can be determined by dividing the respective atomic or molecular weight by the Avogadro number. Thus, the weight of the lightest atom, hydrogen, is found to be 1.67×10^{-24} gram, while that of the heaviest, naturally occurring element, uranium, is 3.95×10^{-22} gram.* Special balances, designed for weighing small quantities (§ 16.16), can detect a weight as small as 10^{-8} gram. Such a minute speck of matter, say of uranium, would be invisible to the naked eye, but it would, nevertheless, contain more than 10^{13} atoms.

1.65. Now that the Avogadro constant, and hence the number of molecules in 1 cc. of gas, may be regarded as known, use may be made of the kinetic theory equations, referred to earlier, to derive molecular diameters from such measurements as the viscosity, diffusion or heat conductivity of gases. Since the number of atoms in the molecule is usually known, an estimate may be made of the diameters of some of the lighter atoms. In this way, the diameter of a hydrogen atom, the smallest atom of all, is found to be 1.35×10^{-8} cm., that of helium 2.2×10^{-8} cm., and of nitrogen and oxygen about 1.8×10^{-8} cm.† Thus, the lighter atoms, and molecules containing a relatively few atoms, have diameters of the order of 10^{-8} cm. For atoms, at least, which may be regarded as spherical in shape, this also represents the order of magnitude of their radii.

1.66. An approximate estimate of molecular and atomic radii can be made by utilizing Loschmidt's assumption that a liquid or, better, a solid

---

* The word "heaviest" as used here refers to the relative weights of the atoms. The conventional "heaviness," of the solid, for example, which is really the density, or weight of a specified volume, depends on the weight of the atoms and also on the way they are packed together in the solid. Heavy atoms loosely packed might give a solid of lower density than lighter atoms very tightly packed.

† These figures are probably all about 0.3×10^{-8} cm. larger than the true atomic diameters because the kinetic theory equations give *collision diameters,* the closest distance to which two molecules can approach each other.

may be treated as an arrangement of closely-packed spherical molecules (or atoms). The molecular weight of water, for example, is 18, and hence 18 grams of water, which occupy about 18 cc. in the liquid state, contain 6×10^{23}, the Avogadro number, of molecules. If the water molecules were cubic in shape, so that they packed together without any free space, the volume of a single molecule would be 18 divided by 6×10^{23}, i.e., 3×10^{-23} cc. Assuming a spherical shape, the volume would be somewhat less, say about 2×10^{-23} cc. The volume of a sphere of radius r is $4\pi r^3/3$, where π has its usual value of 3.14; consequently, it can be readily calculated that, if the water molecule were spherical, its radius would be about 1.7×10^{-8} cm. It can be seen that this simple method gives results of the correct order of magnitude, and provides an approximate indication of molecular and atomic dimensions.

1.67. Individual atoms thus are so small that they cannot be detected, even in the most powerful electron microscopes, which give a magnification of about 100,000. It is possible that some large naturally occurring molecules, particularly those which are protein-like in character, can be rendered visible in this manner, but each of these complex molecules consists of thousands of atoms. The smallest speck of matter which might be expected to be visible in a good, optical microscope would contain something like a billion (10^9) atoms!

1.68. In recent years three methods, in particular, have been used to deter-mine the sizes of atoms and molecules. For solids the diffraction of X-rays (§ 2.93) has been employed, and for gases application has been made of the diffraction of electrons (§ 3.42), and also of the so-called "band" spectra of molecules. For purposes of reference, and as a matter of general interest, the approximate atomic radii of a number of the more familiar elements are quoted here. For convenience, the results are expressed in Angstrom units, where 1 Angstrom, represented by the symbol A, is equal to 10^{-8} cm.*

APPROXIMATE ATOMIC RADII

Element	Atomic Radius	Element	Atomic Radius
Hydrogen	0.53 A	Aluminum	1.45 A
Oxygen	0.74	Magnesium	1.6
Carbon	0.77	Lead	1.75
Arsenic	1.2	Sodium	1.9
Tin	1.4	Potassium	2.35

1.69. It is a remarkable achievement that, in spite of their almost infinitesimal smallness, atoms have been weighed and measured. The results have been obtained indirectly, it is true, but they are believed to be just as certain as if each individual atom had been handled. Still more wonderful is the fact that methods have been found for prying into the very interior of the atom and of studying its detailed structure. Although a great deal still remains to be discovered in this field, striking progress has already been made. Much of the information has stemmed from studies on the passage of electricity through gases at low pressures, a subject which will be considered in the next chapter.

* This unit, named for the Swedish spectroscopist A. J. Ångström, was originally introduced to express the wave lengths of light in the spectra of atoms (see § 3.16).

Fundamental Particles   *Chapter II*

THE NATURE OF ELECTRICITY

POSITIVE AND NEGATIVE ELECTRICITY

2.1. As with so many modern ideas, the origin of the study of electricity may be traced to the Greeks. The philosophers of ancient Greece were inclined to be thinkers rather than experimenters, but they did observe, as far back as 600 B.C., that when a piece of amber is rubbed, for example, with fur or cloth, it acquires the property of attracting to itself light particles, such as feathers and wool. This phenomenon was studied by William Gilbert, personal physician to Queen Elizabeth, in the latter half of the sixteenth century, and for it he proposed the name *electricity*, after the Greek word *elektron*, meaning amber. Gilbert also noticed that other substances besides amber, such as glass and some gems, become electrified when rubbed, so that they are then able to attract light particles.

2.2. Little progress was made for over a hundred years until 1733 when C. F. DuFay in France found that although sealing wax rubbed with cat's fur and a glass rod rubbed with silk both became electrified, there is a difference in the electrification they acquire. Thus, an electrified body which is attracted by the sealing wax is strongly repelled by the glass, and vice versa. The two kinds of electricity were called *vitreous* (glass) and *resinous* (sealing wax). But it was the remarkable American philosopher and statesman Benjamin Franklin, who, in 1747, proposed the terms *positive* and *negative* electricity, which are still in general use. In the middle of the eighteenth century electrification was considered to be due to a "fluid," and Franklin thought that when glass was rubbed with the dry hand, some of the electric fluid passed from the hand to the glass. The latter thus having an excess, or "plus," of electric fluid was said to be electrified positively, while the hand, having a deficit, or "minus," of the fluid was regarded as having a negative charge.

2.3. Franklin was apparently unaware of DuFay's classification of vitreous and resinous electricities, but others soon realized that the former was equivalent to Franklin's positive and the latter to his negative electricity. Thus, while glass becomes positively charged, sealing wax acquires a negative charge when rubbed. The observations made by DuFay relating to the attraction and repulsion of charged bodies are readily explained if it is supposed that unlike charges attract, whereas like charges repel one another. The positively charged glass attracts the negatively charged sealing wax, but repels another positively charged glass rod.

2.4. Actually, Franklin had no valid grounds, as he seemed later to realize, for believing that glass acquires an excess of electricity when rubbed. Consequently, his use of the terms positive and negative were really arbitrary. Nevertheless, they are used today in the same sense as when they were introduced about two hundred years ago. Any electrified body which repels, or is repelled by, electrified glass, or attracts, or is attracted by, electrified sealing wax is said to be positively electrified or to carry a positive electric charge. Similarly, an electrified body is regarded as having a negative charge when it attracts electrified glass and repels electrified sealing wax. It will be seen in § 2.53 that it would have simplified many things if Franklin had concluded, as he might well have done, that glass became negatively electrified when rubbed. Unfortunately, he did not do so, and the study of electricity has become so thoroughly imbued with these particular associations of positive and negative charges that it would now be virtually impossible to make any change, no matter how convenient such a change might prove to be.

STATIC AND DYNAMIC ELECTRICITY

2.5. The electrical phenomena studied by Gilbert, DuFay, Franklin and others have become known as frictional or *static* electricity—because of its mode of production—to distinguish it from the so-called *dynamic* electricity, discovered at the end of the eighteenth century. In 1780, the anatomist Luigi Galvani, in Italy, had noticed that when one of the nerves of a freshly killed frog was

touched with a metal scalpel while an electric spark was being produced on a nearby frictional machine, the muscles of the frog twitched. Later, while investigating the phenomenon, which he attributed to "animal electricity," he found that similar effects could be produced by making contact between two pieces of metal, one of which was placed touching a muscle, and the other a nerve of the frog.

2.6. The "animal" nature of the electricity was doubted by a contemporary Italian physicist Alessandro Volta, who suggested that the essential factor in the production of the effects observed was the presence of two metals. He proved the point in 1796 by showing that electricity could be generated by means of pieces of two different metals, such as zinc and silver, separated by wet pasteboard or leather. A system of this type subsequently became known as a galvanic or voltaic cell, in honor of Galvani and Volta, respectively.

POTENTIAL AND CURRENT

2.7. The kind of electricity produced by a cell—called galvanic or voltaic electricity—appeared at first to be different from the frictional electricity which resulted from rubbing a nonmetallic substance. The former had the property of flowing along a metal wire, whereas the latter appeared to be confined to a particular body, so that the terms dynamic and static were employed, as stated above. However, after various experimenters, during the early years of the nineteenth century, had shown that identical effects could be produced by both static and dynamic electricity, the famous English scientist Michael Faraday, in 1833, explained the apparent difference.

2.8. In 1776, Henry Cavendish had

suggested that two electrical factors, namely, "quantity" and "intensity," must be distinguished. For the purpose of analogy, electricity may be compared with the flow of water in a waterfall. The intensity of electricity, referred to as the *potential* or *voltage*, since it is usually measured in *volt* units, is equivalent to the height of the fall; while the quantity of electricity, sometimes called the *charge*, is similar to the amount of water in the fall. One waterfall may be very high but contain the merest trickle of water, whereas another may consist of a large volume of water falling through a relatively small height. So it is with electricity. Faraday showed that in static electricity the potential or voltage is high, but the charge or quantity is small; in dynamic electricity, however, the situation is reversed, comparatively speaking, the voltage being smaller while the quantity is larger. The energy available at the bottom of a waterfall is determined by the product of the height of the fall and the quantity of water falling. A similar rule applies to electricity: the electrical energy is calculated by multiplying together the potential and the charge.

2.9. When two bodies, one of which is charged positively and the other negatively, are connected together, by a metal rod or wire for example, a flow of electricity, referred to as an *electric current*, will be produced. Even if the connecting wire is not used, and the potentials of the charged bodies—one positive and one negative—are high enough, so that there is a large *potential difference* between them, electricity will flow from one body to another in the form of an electrical discharge, such as a spark or a series of sparks. Lightning is a discharge of this type.

2.10. Since the quantity of electricity on a body charged statically, e.g., by friction, is small, the current strength, i.e., the rate at which the charge flows, usually measured in amperes, will be small. If higher currents are required, at a sacrifice of potential, a form of voltaic or galvanic cell is employed. By combining a large number of such cells in series, it is possible to step up the potential, to something of the order of a thousand volts or more, while maintaining a moderate current strength. A similar result may be achieved by using a dynamo, which is a machine for converting mechanical into electrical energy (§ 3.2).

2.11. By convention, the positive direction of flow of electric current is taken to be from the positively charged body to the one carrying the negative charge. The terms positive and negative as used here correspond exactly to their definitions by Franklin. However, it is no longer necessary to use the primitive tests of attraction and repulsion of charged bodies. When an electric current passes through a wire, disturbances occur in its neighborhood which influence a magnet in a definite manner,* depending on the direction of flow. Similarly, chemical effects observed when electricity passes through a solution are characteristic of the current direction. Thus, magnetic or chemical (electrolytic) tests readily serve to indicate the direction of current flow. Every source of electric current, whether it be a single cell, a group of cells or a dynamo, consists of two poles, plates or electrodes, as they are variously termed. A positive sign is allocated to

---

* It is frequently stated that a *magnetic field* exists in the vicinity of a wire carrying an electric current. The term *field* refers, in general, to a region or space throughout which a particular kind of force, e.g., magnetic, electric, gravitational, etc., is being exerted.

one and a negative sign to the other, so that the direction of current flow is from positive to negative.

ALTERNATING CURRENT

2.12. Hitherto it has been tacitly assumed that the flow of electricity is unidirectional; this is known as *direct current* or DC. However, several devices in common use, such as a dynamo (without a commutator), an induction coil and a vacuum-tube oscillator, produce *alternating current* or AC, i.e., a current whose direction is continually reversed at definite intervals. Each pole thus becomes alternately positive and negative, and has no specific sign. With a dynamo the frequency of the alternations depends on the rate of rotation of the armature, and is usually moderately low, for example, sixty cycles per second for ordinary house current in the United States. By means of properly designed vacuum-tube oscillators, alternating current of various frequencies, from relatively low to very high, e.g., radio and radar, can be obtained.

2.13. The advantage of alternating current is that its voltage, or potential difference, can be greatly increased, or decreased, very simply by means of the instrument known as a transformer. As will be seen in Chapter IX, such high voltage currents, of relatively high frequency, have important uses in atomic studies. It is true that in the transformer the current strength is diminished proportionately as the voltage is increased, but this is usually of no significance. By means of a rectifier, alternating current can be converted into direct current. Various types of rectifying devices are available, as, for example, mechanical, vacuum-tube, copper-copper oxide and selenium rectifiers. In order to obtain direct current at high potentials, the common procedure is to produce alternating current in a convenient manner, step up its potential by means of a transformer, and then rectify.

PASSAGE OF ELECTRICITY THROUGH GASES

ELECTRICAL DISCHARGE AT LOW PRESSURES

2.14. In 1705, F. Hauksbee, in England, found that there was an emission of light when amber was electrified by rubbing in a closed vessel, in which the pressure of the air had been reduced by a pump. At ordinary atmospheric pressure the light was not observed. A related effect was noted by William Watson in 1752; he found that a discharge of static electricity would pass much more readily through a gas at low pressure than at atmospheric pressure. The passage of the discharge was accompanied by a luminosity in the containing vessel. Although it is pos-sible, by means of sufficiently high potential, which may be either alternating or unidirectional, to pass a discharge in the form of a spark through a gas at atmospheric pressure, it is apparently much easier to do so if the gas pressure is decreased. The voltage adequate to produce the discharge at reduced pressures, although still high, is considerably lower than the sparking potential at atmospheric pressure. Further, the low-pressure discharge is less violent than a spark, and is associated with various luminous phenomena. The familiar neon signs widely used in advertising provide an excellent illustration of the effect of electrical discharge in a gas at reduced pressure.

2.15. The reason why electricity will travel more readily through a gas at low pressure is, briefly, somewhat as follows. The passage of electricity from one point to another requires the presence of electrically charged particles, frequently atoms or molecules, to which the general name of *ions** is given. Under the influence of a potential difference the ions move, those carrying a positive charge traveling in the direction of current flow, according to the convention described earlier, while negatively charged ions move in the opposite direction. If not obstructed the ions would move with a steadily increasing speed, acquiring increased energy, the maximum attained being dependent on the magnitude of the potential difference. Air normally contains a few ions, and if a potential is applied to two metal plates (or electrodes) in air, the ions are accelerated in one direction or the other according to their signs.

2.16. In their motion through the gas, at least two things may happen: first, the ions may collide with gas molecules and be robbed of their energy, or second, suitable encounters may result in the formation of more ions, a phenomenon known as *ionization by collision*. If the pressure of the air is in the region of atmospheric, the former effect will predominate, with the result that very few ions will be available for carrying the electricity. As the pressure is diminished, the latter effect becomes more important so that the number of ions produced by collisions gradually becomes larger than, and eventually greatly exceeds, the number losing their energy. Hence the electric discharge passes with increasing ease. At sufficiently low pressures the ionization decreases, because of the smaller number of collisions, and the discharge does not occur so readily.

CATHODE RAYS

2.17. By taking advantage of the fairly constant potentials that could be secured by means of the then recently invented voltaic battery, M. Faraday (1838) made the first systematic studies of electric discharges through gases under diminished pressure. Although he observed a number of interesting phenomena, he was limited by the fact that the suction pumps available at the time for reducing the gas pressure were not too efficient. A great step forward was made, about 1854, when H. Geissler, a German glass-blower of exceptional skill, not only developed an improved vacuum suction pump, but succeeded in sealing into glass tubes wires attached to metal electrodes. The evacuated Geissler tubes which he made were particularly suitable for the study of the passage of electricity through gases at low pressure, and with them J. Plücker, in Germany, made numerous experiments between the years 1858 and 1862. Among other things, he observed that the tube in the vicinity of the *cathode,* i.e., the electrode attached to the negative side of the source of potential,† emitted a green glow or

---

* From the Greek word meaning traveler, because they travel from one point to another when a difference of potential is applied.

† The other electrode, i.e., the one joined to the positive side of the potential source, is called the *anode.* The words anode and cathode, derived from the Greek prefixes *ana* (up) and *cata* (down), were first used by Faraday (1834), at the suggestion of the Cambridge philosopher W. Whewell. The term *ion,* mentioned earlier, for the carriers of electricity, originated in the same manner.

luminescence.* The position of the glow could be changed by bringing a magnet up to the tube.

2.18. The studies of electrical discharge through gases were continued in Germany by Plücker's pupil, W. Hittorf (1869), and by E. Goldstein (1876). From their observations they concluded that the luminescent glow on the tube was caused by "rays" originating at the cathode, which Goldstein consequently called *cathode rays*. The rays could be deflected by a magnet and were able to cast a shadow of an obstacle placed in their path, showing that they traveled in straight lines.

2.19. Between the years 1879 and 1885 the English scientist William Crookes, who designed improved vacuum discharge tubes, made a very comprehensive series of investigations of the electrical discharge. From these he concluded that the cathode rays actually consisted of a stream of negatively charged particles, which were expelled from the cathode—the negative electrode—with extremely high velocities. This view of the nature of cathode rays supported a suggestion made in 1872 by C. F. Varley, but it was opposed by many European physicists, including such eminent men as E. Wiedemann (1880), H. Hertz (1883) the discoverer of radio waves, and P. Lenard (1894). The latter group thought the cathode rays were an electromagnetic wave motion or vibration, analogous to light waves but of shorter wave length.† If the rays are really a stream of charged particles then they should be deflected by passage through an electric field, as well as by a magnetic field, but

Goldstein, in spite of several trials, had failed to observe any such effect. However, the deflection of cathode rays in the field of a magnet was an accepted fact, and this could not be explained if the rays were similar to light waves.

THE NATURE OF CATHODE RAYS

2.20. In an apparently decisive experiment, performed by J. Perrin in France in 1895, the cathode rays were allowed to fall on a device known as a Faraday cylinder, connected to an electrometer by means of which the sign and magnitude of electric charge could be determined. It was found that a negative charge collected in the cylinder, and so it was argued that the rays were made up of negative particles. Objection was taken to this conclusion on the grounds that negatively charged particles might well be ejected from the cathode, but there was no proof that they are identical with the cathode rays.

2.21. The required proof was provided in 1897 by J. J. Thomson, the famous English physicist, whose work has had a profound effect, both direct and indirect, on the study of atomic structure. In the first place, he repeated Perrin's experiment and confirmed that charged particles are emitted by the cathode. But, in addition, he showed that when the cathode rays are deflected by a magnetic field, as indicated by the change in position of the luminescence they produce, the negatively charged particles are correspondingly deflected. Further, Thomson succeeded, where Goldstein and

---

* The phenomenon has often been described as "fluorescence" or "phosphorescence," but these words have specific meanings which do not apply here (see § 2.98, footnotes). Consequently, the general term *luminescence* will be used. It refers to any emission of light due to factors other than a high temperature.

† An explanation of the nature of light and related electromagnetic radiations is given in Chapter III.

others had failed, in deflecting the path of the cathode rays by means of an electric field. Previous failures had been due to excessive ionization of the gas still present in the discharge tube, thus offsetting the effect of the electric field. By working at very low pressures Thomson minimized the influence of this ionization and then he was able to observe the anticipated deflection.

2.22. Now that it had been established that the cathode rays are actually a stream of particles carrying negative electrical charges, there still remained the question of the identity of these particles. As a result of his numerous experiments, Crookes had become convinced that the particles did not consist of ordinary matter; that is to say, they were neither solid,

liquid nor gaseous. At the end of a lecture delivered before the Royal Society of London in 1879 he said: "The phenomena in these exhausted tubes reveal to physical science a new world —a world where matter may exist in a fourth state." In a confession of ignorance, Crookes referred to this as the "ultragaseous" state. Subsequent events were to prove that there was, in fact, no such state of matter, but it was nevertheless true that the study of electrical discharges in gases at low pressures was bringing to light a "new world" of science. The elucidation of the real nature and significance of the negatively charged, cathode-ray particles was the result of a number of converging studies; some of the more important of these will now be considered.

THE ELECTRON

ELECTROLYSIS: THE FARADAY

2.23. In the early years of the nineteenth century, following the invention of the voltaic cell as a means of producing an electric current, it was found that the passage of such current through aqueous solutions of acids, alkalies and salts was accompanied by chemical changes which were manifested by the appearance of specific products at the two electrodes. The process of decomposition, either of the water or of the substance dissolved in it, as the result of the passage of an electric current, was given the general name of *electrolysis*. For example, the electrolysis of a dilute solution of an acid, with platinum or other inert electrodes, almost invariably results in the liberation of hydrogen gas at the electrode (cathode) attached to the negative pole of the cell (or battery)

and of oxygen at the electrode (anode) joined to the positive pole. Similarly, when an appropriate salt solution, for example, a solution of a zinc, copper, iron or mercury salt, is electrolyzed, the corresponding metal can be observed to separate at the cathode.

2.24. Some of the most fundamental investigations in the field of electrolysis were made by M. Faraday (1831-1834), and as a result of this work he discovered that a given quantity of electricity always sets free at the electrodes chemically equivalent weights (§ 1.22) of different substances. In other words, it always requires the same quantity of electricity to liberate one equivalent weight of any substance, irrespective of its nature. Careful experiments have shown that to set free exactly 1 gram equivalent, i.e., the equivalent weight in grams, of any substance at an electrode it is necessary to pass 96,500 coulombs* of electricity; this quantity is called a *faraday.*

THE ATOMIC NATURE OF ELECTRICITY: THE ELEMENTARY CHARGE

2.25. In considering the significance of his results, Faraday wrote: ". . . if we adopt the atomic theory or phraseology, then the atoms of bodies which are equivalent to each other in their ordinary chemical action, have equal quantities of electricity naturally associated with them." In these words he implied the existence of a unit or atom of electricity, but apparently Faraday was not too sure of his ground for he was very cautious about committing himself to this point of view. Similarly, the eminent English scholar J. Clerk Maxwell, writing in 1873 in his great *Treatise on Electricity and Magnetism,* thought that, in view of Faraday's results, it might be convenient to speak of a "molecular charge" of electricity. But, he went on to say, "it is extremely improbable that when we come to understand the true nature of electrolysis we shall retain . . . the theory of molecular charges." This was one of the few respects in which time proved Maxwell to be wrong.

2.26. It was left to the Irish physicist, G. Johnstone Stoney who, during the years 1873 and 1874, was a member of the British Association Committee on the Selection and Nomenclature of Dynamical and Electrical Units, to take the final plunge. At the Belfast meeting of the Association in 1874, he read a paper *On the Physical Units of Nature,* which was not published until 1881. In it he stated: "Nature presents us in the phenomenon of electrolysis with a single definite quantity of electricity which is independent of the particular bodies acted upon. For each chemical bond which is ruptured within an electrolyte, a certain quantity of electricity traverses the electrolyte, which is the same in all cases. . . . If we make this our unit of electricity we shall probably have made a very important step in our study of molecular phenomena."

2.27. On the basis of this argument, the quantity of electricity, referred to above as the faraday, which is associated with 1 gram equivalent of any substance, should bear the same relationship to the postulated unit of electricity as the atomic weight does to the weight of a single atom. In other words, the value of the unit quantity of electricity should be obtained upon dividing the faraday by the Avogadro number (§ 1.56). In 1868 Stoney, following Loschmidt, had made an estimate of the latter number from kinetic-theory equations, as already described, and in his 1874 paper he used this result together with the best available datum for the faraday to derive a value of 3×10^{-11} electrostatic units (e.s.u.) for the unit of electrical charge.†

2.28. The concept of an "atomic" unit of electricity received powerful support from the eminent German physicist H. von Helmholtz. In the Faraday Lecture of the Chemical Society of London, in 1881, he said:

---

* The coulomb is a convenient unit of quantity of electricity or electric charge. It corresponds to 1 ampere of current flowing for 1 second. The electrostatic unit of charge, based on the centimeter-gram-second system of measurement, is frequently used in physical studies, as will be seen below. One coulomb is equivalent to 3.00×10^9 electrostatic units (e.s.u.), so that the faraday is $96500 \times 3.00 \times 10^9$, i.e., 2.89×10^{14} e.s.u.

† Using modern data, i.e., 2.89×10^{14} e.s.u. for the faraday and 6.02×10^{23} for the Avogadro number, the unit is found to be 4.80×10^{-10} e.s.u., as accepted at present.

"Now the most startling result of Faraday's Law [that a given quantity of electricity always sets free chemically equivalent weights] is perhaps this: if we accept the hypothesis that the elementary substances are composed of atoms, we cannot avoid concluding that electricity also, positive as well as negative, is divided into definite elementary portions which behave like atoms of electricity." Similarly, at the British Association meeting in 1885, Oliver Lodge stated: "This quantity, the charge of one monad atom, constitutes the smallest known particle of electricity, and is a real natural unit."

2.29. By the early 1890s the ideas expressed above had become widely accepted, and Stoney, in 1891, proposed the name *electron* for the elementary unit of electric charge. Thus, Faraday's experiments on electrolysis, by logical development, led to the view that in solution every electrically charged atom, or perhaps group of atoms, i.e., every ion, is associated with a definite whole number—one, two, three or more—of electronic charges. The number of unit charges associated with each ion is equal to its valence, i.e., the ionic (atomic or molecular) weight divided by its equivalent weight.

GASEOUS IONS AND THE ELEMENTARY CHARGE

2.30. Since the foregoing conclusions were reached from studies of solutions, the estimated magnitude of the unit electronic charge, namely, about 10^{-10} e.s.u., could be regarded as applying only to the electrical carriers (ions) in solution. In the years 1890 to 1892, several attempts were made to determine the unit charge associated with other electrically charged bodies, notably by F. Richarz and H. Ebert, in

Germany, and by A. Chattock, in England. Although some of the methods used were based on theoretical considerations of doubtful validity, it is a remarkable fact that the values of the elementary (or unit) charge were almost invariably found to be in the vicinity of 10^{-10} e.s.u., so that Chattock (1891) was moved to say: "I cannot help thinking that . . . [the results obtained by a variety of methods] furnish strong grounds for supposing that electrified atoms in gases are associated with the same quantity of electricity as in electrolysis."

2.31. More definite confirmation of this point of view was obtained in England by J. S. Townsend in 1897. If a solution of acid or alkali is electrolyzed with a large current, the gases —hydrogen and oxygen—which are liberated, are ionized. When these electrically charged gases are bubbled through water they form a dense cloud, apparently as a result of the condensation of moisture on the gaseous ions (§ 6.67). The cloud thus consists of minute drops of water carrying electric charges. From the total weight of the water contained in the cloud, and the average weight of a drop, derived from the measured radius and the known density, it is possible to calculate the number of individual drops in the cloud. Townsend measured the total charge on the cloud by means of an electrometer, and knowing the number of drops present, it was a simple matter to determine the average charge associated with each drop. If the assumption is made that a gaseous ion upon which the moisture condenses carries a single elementary electric charge, this result is the magnitude of the unit (electronic) charge. The value found in this manner was 3×10^{-10}, later corrected to 5×10^{-10}, e.s.u., in satisfactory agreement with the unit charge borne by ions in solution. Similar results were obtained in the year 1898 by J. J. Thomson in his studies of the electric charge carried by gaseous ions produced by X-rays in their passage through air and hydrogen (§ 2.89).

DETERMINATION OF THE
ELECTRONIC CHARGE

2.32. By the turn of the century there was no longer any doubt about the existence of a definite unit of electric charge, namely, the electronic charge. Scientific interest then became centered upon methods for the determination of a really accurate value of this charge. In 1903, J. J. Thomson had used the rays emitted by radium (§ 2.111) to ionize the air, and had then measured the average charge per ion, but this work did no more than supply further confirmation of views already established. However, in the same year, a technical advance was made in Thomson's laboratory in England by H. A. Wilson, later of the Rice Institute, Houston, Texas, and this proved to be the basis for some of the most important subsequent investigations. He showed that it was possible to avoid the inaccurate and difficult determination of the total charge on the cloud of water droplets condensed upon ions, as used by previous workers, by studying the rate of fall of the cloud under gravity and also under the influence of an electric field.

2.33. Further improvements were made in 1909 by F. Ehrenhaft in Austria, and by R. A. Millikan in the United States; instead of making observations on a cloud as a whole, and so obtaining a gross average, Ehrenhaft studied individual suspended particles of gold, silver, platinum and phosphorus, whereas Millikan worked with single water droplets. Later (1911) Millikan used oil, instead of water, to form the droplets, and thus eliminated errors due to evaporation, and consequent change in weight of the drops, during the course of an experiment.

2.34. In outline, Millikan's apparatus consisted of two horizontal metal plates about 22 cm. diameter and 1.6 cm. apart, as indicated by A and B in Fig. 2.1. The plates were supported in

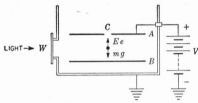

FIG. 2.1. Diagrammatic representation of apparatus used by Millikan to determine electronic charge.

a closed vessel containing air at low pressure, and were connected to the poles of a high-voltage (10,000 volts) battery, V. In the upper plate there were a number of small holes, as indicated at C. By means of an atomizer a fine spray of a nonvolatile oil was introduced into the vessel; as a result of friction in the atomizer, the droplets of oil so obtained were electrically charged. From time to time, one of these droplets would pass through the hole C, and then it could be observed by means of a telescope (not shown in figure). By using the illumination of a powerful beam of light, entering the window W (at left), the droplet appeared as a bright star on a dark background.

2.35. With the battery V disconnected, the droplet fell slowly under the influence of gravity, and the rate of fall was measured. This rate, or velocity, represented by v_1, is dependent on the mass m of the droplet, and is given by the equation

$$v_1 = kmg, \qquad (2.1)$$

where g is the gravitational constant (981 cm. per sec. per sec.), and k is a proportionality constant which is related to the viscosity of the air and the size of the oil droplet. The high-voltage battery was then switched on, thus producing an electric field, the direction being such as to make the charged droplet move *upward*, against the force of gravity. If E is the strength of the electric field, i.e., the voltage of the battery divided by the distance between the plates, then the upward force acting on the droplet is Ee_n, where e_n is the charge carried by the droplet. Since this is opposed by the gravitational force mg, the net upward force is $Ee_n - mg$; the upward velocity v_2 of the oil droplet, which is measured, is then represented by

$$v_2 = k(Ee_n - mg), \qquad (2.2)$$

the proportionality constant k having the same significance as in equation (2.1). If one of these two equations is divided by the other, the constant k cancels out, and the result is

$$\frac{v_1}{v_2} = \frac{mg}{Ee_n - mg} \qquad (2.3)$$

or

$$e_n = \frac{mg}{Ev_1}(v_1 + v_2). \qquad (2.4)$$

2.36. Since the quantities v_1, v_2, E and g are available, it should be possible to calculate the charge e_n carried by the oil drop, provided its mass m were known. In order to determine the latter, Millikan, like several of his predecessors, employed an equation, derived by the English mathematician G. G. Stokes, applicable to small spherical drops falling under the influence of gravity. According to Stokes, the velocity v_1, with which the droplet falls in air under the influence of gravity alone, is related to the coefficient of viscosity,

i.e., resistance to flow, η (Greek, *eta*), of the air and the radius r of the drop by

$$v_1 = \frac{2gr^2d}{9\eta}, \qquad (2.5)$$

where d is the density of the oil of which the drops are made. Since v_1 has been determined, as described above, and g, η and d may be regarded as known, the radius r of the drop can be obtained from equation (2.5).

2.37. If the oil drop is spherical, as assumed, the mass m is related to the radius r by

$$m = 4\pi r^3 d/3, \qquad (2.6)$$

the quantity π having its usual significance. The value of r has just been derived, and the density d of the oil is known; hence the mass m of the drop can be calculated. Upon inserting this result into equation (2.4), together with the measured velocities v_1 and v_2, the magnitude of the charge e_n carried by the oil droplet can now be determined.

2.38. By exposing the air in the vessel in Fig. 2.1 to the action of X-rays, Millikan caused gaseous ions to form, and occasionally an oil drop would attach itself to one of these ions with a consequent change in the value of e_n, the charge of the droplet. The new upward velocity v_2 of the oil drop in the electric field was measured, and e_n recalculated, v_1 and m remaining unchanged. Sometimes the droplet acquired a positive charge and sometimes a negative charge, but the experimental method was the same, except that the high-voltage battery connection had to be reversed.

2.39. As a result of a large number of measurements, Millikan found that the charge e_n was always an integral, i.e., a whole number, multiple of a definite elementary charge, which was presumably the electronic charge. After applying numerous corrections to the foregoing equations, Millikan concluded, in 1917, that the most reliable value of the unit charge was 4.774×10^{-10} e.s.u. For several years, this value was widely accepted, but in 1928 the work of E. Bäcklin, in Sweden, and of J. A. Bearden, in the United States, began to throw some doubt upon its accuracy.

2.40. By the middle of the second decade of the present century, the faraday (§ 2.24) had been determined with great care both in the United States and in England, and hence its value was known with some certainty. An accurate determination of the Avogadro number would then have permitted the evaluation of the electronic charge, utilizing the principle first employed by Stoney (§ 2.27). If the wave lengths of X-rays were available, then the Avogadro number, and consequently the electronic charge, could be obtained from diffraction studies in crystals (§ 2.93). In 1926, A. H. Compton and R. L. Doan, in the United States, showed how X-ray wave lengths could be measured by means of a ruled line grating (§ 3.10), and it was as a result of experiments of this kind that Bäcklin and Bearden found the electronic charge to be slightly higher than Millikan's value, namely, 4.80×10^{-10} e.s.u. Other investigators, using a generally similar procedure, subsequently confirmed this result.

2.41. Although the difference between 4.77×10^{-10} and 4.80×10^{-10} may not appear large, it is much greater than the known experimental errors in the respective methods. Many scientists were concerned with this discrepancy, and in 1932 E. Shiba, of Japan, suggested that the value for the viscosity of the air used by Millikan, in equation (2.5), might have been in error. Actually, Millikan had adopted what he thought was the most reliable published datum, but, as events turned out, this proved to be incorrect. Upon recalculating the results of his experiments, making use of more recent viscosity determinations, Millikan found the elementary electronic charge to be in good agreement with that given by the X-ray method. At the present time, from various studies, using both oil drop and X-ray diffraction procedures, the unit electronic charge is confidently known to be very close to 4.803×10^{-10} e.s.u.* This value applies to both positive and negative unit charges.

SPECIFIC CHARGE OF CATHODE RAY PARTICLES

2.42. It is opportune, at this point, to revert to a consideration of the cathode rays which, in 1897, J. J. Thomson showed to consist of a stream of negatively charged particles originating from, or in the vicinity of, the negative electrode, i.e., the cathode, of an evacuated discharge tube (§ 2.21). Even before this time, while the controversy as to the nature of the cathode rays was still in progress, experiments and calculations had been made on the properties of the rays, in the event that they should prove to consist of charged particles. If a stream of such particles moves initially in a straight line, and a magnetic field is applied in a direction at right angles to the direction of motion, the particles will be forced by the

---

* In the period 1914 to 1916 a controversy raged between F. Ehrenhaft, on the one hand, and R. A. Millikan, on the other hand, as to the elementary nature of the electron. The former contended that he had proved the existence of a "sub-electron," having a charge smaller than the accepted value. The latter, however, refused to accept the evidence, and there is little doubt that his stand was justified.

field to follow a circular path (Fig. 2.2).
If e is the magnitude of the charge
carried by each particle and v is the
velocity with which it moves, the mag-

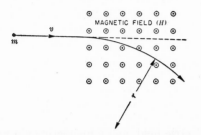

Fig. 2.2. Path of charged particle moving
in a magnetic field at right angles to direction of motion.

netic force acting on a particle is Hev,
where H is the magnetic field strength.
This force is exactly balanced by the
centrifugal force mv^2/r of the particle
of mass m moving, under the influence
of the field, in a circular path of radius
r. Hence, equating the two expressions,

$$Hev = \frac{mv^2}{r} \qquad (2.7)$$

so that

$$\frac{e}{m} = \frac{v}{Hr}. \qquad (2.8)$$

The strength H of the magnetic field
may be regarded as known, and so if
the velocity of the charged particles
and the radius of curvature of the circular path they follow could be measured, the value of e/m, i.e., the ratio of
their charge to mass, sometimes called
the *specific charge*, could be determined
by means of equation (2.8).

2.43. The foregoing considerations
apply to any charged particles irrespective of charge and mass, and they were
applied by A. Schuster in England, in
1890, to cathode rays. He measured
the radius of the circular path in a
magnetic field without difficulty, but
his estimate of the velocity of the particles was highly approximate. As a
result his value of e/m was incorrect,
and he drew the erroneous conclusion
that the cathode-ray particles were
negatively charged, gaseous atoms,
probably nitrogen ions. In the early
part of 1897, both E. Wiechert and W.
Kaufmann, in Germany, reported results of measurements on the path of
cathode rays in a magnetic field. Their
determinations of the velocity of the
particles—about one-tenth of the speed
of light, i.e., 3×10^9 cm. per sec.—
proved to be fairly accurate and their
values of e/m, expressing the charge
e in e.s.u. and the mass m in grams,
were approximately 10^{17} e.s.u. per
gram.* Kaufmann found the value of
e/m for the cathode-ray particles was
the same irrespective of the nature of
the gas present in the discharge tube,
or of the conditions of the discharge.
By comparing his results with the e/m
calculated for a hydrogen ion in solution, approximately 3×10^{14} e.s.u.
per gram,† Wiechert concluded that
the particles had a mass of something
between a one-thousandth and a four-
thousandth part of the mass of a hydrogen atom (or ion). However, it was
left to J. J. Thomson to appreciate the
importance of similar results, which he
obtained independently, and to interpret their significance.

* Since e/m determinations generally involve studies in a magnetic field, it is the custom
to express them in *electromagnetic units* (e.m.u.) per gram, rather than in electrostatic units.
The latter are used here to avoid the confusion resulting from the employment of different
systems. The e.s.u. are converted into e.m.u. upon dividing by 3×10^{10}.

† This result is obtained upon dividing the unit (electronic) charge carried by a hydrogen
ion in solution, i.e., 4.8×10^{-10} e.s.u., by the mass of a hydrogen atom (or ion) 1.6×10^{-24}
gram (§ 1.64).

THOMSON'S EXPERIMENTS

2.44. Because of the part they played in the study of atomic structure, Thomson's experiments, although not of the greatest accuracy, have become classical. In order to determine the velocity of the cathode-ray particles, required in connection with equation (2.8), he made use of an idea which, curiously enough, had been indicated in 1883 by H. Hertz, one of the opponents of the view that the cathode rays consist of charged particles. A moving charged particle can be deflected from its initial path by the application of either an electric or a magnetic field. As seen in § 2.35, the force acting on a particle of charge e in an electric field of strength E is Ee, whereas in a magnetic field of strength H, the force, as stated above, is Hev, where v is the speed of the particle. If the electric and magnetic fields are arranged so that their effects on a moving charged particle exactly compensate each other, and the particle is not deflected from its path, it follows that

$$Hev = Ee, \qquad (2.9)$$

and hence

$$v = \frac{E}{H}. \qquad (2.10)$$

It should thus be possible to determine the speed of motion v of electrically charged particles from the strengths of the compensating electric and magnetic fields. Introduction of this result into equation (2.8) will permit e/m

to be obtained from the radius of curvature of the path in the magnetic field alone.

2.45. The experimental procedure used by Thomson may be explained by means of Fig. 2.3. The rays were emitted from the cathode C, in an evacuated tube, passed through a hole in the anode A, and a narrow beam was picked out by the slit S. By connecting the plates PP, within the tube, to a source of high voltage, the cathode rays were subjected to the action of an electric field, and a magnetic field was applied by means of a magnet M outside the tube. The deflection of the beam was studied by observing the luminous spot produced by the rays when striking the wall of the tube at the extreme right, a scale F permitting actual measurement. After noting the position of the undeflected beam, i.e., with neither electric nor magnetic fields operating, the magnetic field H only was applied, and from the deflection the radius of curvature r of the circular path could be calculated. Then the electric field was put on and its magnitude E was adjusted so as to bring the luminous spot back to its original position. Thus the information required to determine v by equation (2.10), and hence e/m by equation (2.8), was available.

2.46. In agreement with previous workers, Thomson found that the cathode-ray particles moved with the enormous speed of 3×10^9 cm. per sec., and that e/m was about 2×10^{17}

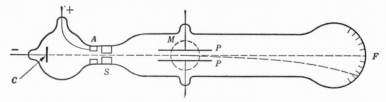

FIG. 2.3. Thomson's method for studying charged particles by deflection in electric and magnetic fields.

e.s.u. per gram. Further, he noted that the results were the same for different cathode materials, namely, aluminum, iron and platinum, and also for different gases, air, hydrogen and carbon dioxide, present in the discharge tube. Hence, Thomson concluded that the "carriers of the electric charge in the cathode rays are the same whatever the gas through which the discharge passes." He went on to say: "The explanation which seems to me to account in the most simple and straightforward manner for the facts is founded on the view of the constitution of the chemical elements which has been favorably entertained by many chemists: this view is that the atoms of the different chemical elements are different aggregations of . . . [ultimate particles] of the same kind. . . . If, in the very intense field in the neighbourhood of the cathode, the molecules of the gas are . . . split up, not into ordinary chemical atoms, but into these primordial atoms which we shall for brevity call *corpuscles;* and if these corpuscles are charged with electricity and projected from the cathode by the electric field, they would behave exactly like the cathode rays. This would evidently give a value of m/e [or e/m] which is independent of the nature of the gas . . . for the carriers are the same whatever the gas may be. . . . Thus we have in the cathode rays matter in a new state, a state in which the subdivision of matter is carried very much further than in the ordinary gaseous state; a state in which all matter—that is, matter derived from different sources such as hydrogen, oxygen and carbon—is one and the same kind; this matter being the substance from which all the chemical elements are built up." Thus, the negatively charged, cathode-ray corpuscles were believed by Thomson to be the ultimate particles of which all matter was constituted.

2.47. As seen above, the e/m value found for the corpuscles was roughly a thousand times greater than for the hydrogen ion in solution; for this difference there were two possible explanations. Either the charges e were approximately the same, so that the cathode-ray particles would be something like a thousand times lighter than a hydrogen atom, or the masses m might be of the same order, in which case the corpuscles would carry a much larger charge than the elementary electronic charge. As indicated earlier (§ 2.43), Wiechert apparently favored the former view. Thomson, on the other hand, was at first inclined to the latter alternative, but further experimental work caused him to change his mind.

THE ELECTRON AS A PARTICLE

2.48. In 1899, Thomson set out to resolve the doubt concerning the significance of the e/m values of the corpuscles by determining directly their charge, as well as the charge-to-mass ratio. Unfortunately, this could not be done with the cathode-ray particles, and so he turned to another source. It was well known toward the end of the nineteenth century that ultraviolet light falling on certain metals, particularly zinc, was associated with the emission of negatively charged particles, a phenomenon known as the *photoelectric effect.* Thomson determined the e/m ratio for these particles, by means of electric and magnetic fields, and found it to be virtually the same as for the cathode-ray corpuscles. Charged particles produced by an incandescent filament, i.e., by the *thermionic effect,* also had a similar e/m value. Utilizing the cloud method, described in § 2.31, Thomson measured the charge on the photoelectric particles; this turned out to be not essentially different from the unit electronic charge. In view of the constancy of e/m for the negatively charged particles produced in different ways, it was reasonable to conclude that the particles were identical.

2.49. In the words of Thomson: "The experiments just described, taken in conjunction with previous ones . . . on cathode rays, show that in gases at low pressures negative electrification, *though it may be produced by very different means,** is made up of units each having a charge of electricity of a definite size; the magnitude of this negative charge is . . . equal to the positive charge carried by the hydrogen atom [ion] in the electrolysis of solutions."

2.50. Since their charge is equal to that carried by a hydrogen ion, it is clear that the mass of the negative particles, irrespective of their origin, must be about a thousandth part of that of a hydrogen atom. As Thomson pointed out, these are the lightest particles hitherto recognized as capable of a separate existence. The fact that the same particles are produced in different ways—by electric discharge and by photoelectric and thermionic effects—lends support to the view that they are ultimate constituents of all matter.

2.51. Because the charge on the particles present in the cathode rays, and associated with the thermionic and photoelectric effects, was identical with the elementary electronic charge, the name *electron*, originally intended by Stoney (§ 2.29) for the magnitude of the charge, soon became associated with the actual particles themselves. Possibly in the interest of strict accuracy, Thomson adhered to the term corpuscle for about twenty years, but

ultimately he gave it up in favor of electron. At the present time, the electrically charged particles, carrying a *negative* charge of 4.803×10^{-10} e.s.u., and having a mass slightly more than a two-thousandth part of that of a hydrogen atom, are called electrons. They are undoubtedly fundamental constituents of all material atoms.

2.52. As matter is normally electrically neutral, that is to say, it is not electrically charged, it follows that there must be something in the atom which carries a positive charge to balance the negative charge of the electrons. This subject will be considered more fully in Chapter IV. In the meantime, it may be stated that the positive charge is an integral part of the atom, but the electrons can be made to pass from one atom to another. A negatively charged body is thus one which contains more electrons than in the normal, or neutral, state; a positively charged body is one with fewer electrons than in the neutral state. Thus, when glass is rubbed with silk, electrons pass from the glass to the silk so that the former acquires a positive electric charge and the latter a negative charge. A positive ion is an atom or group of atoms which has been deprived of one or more of its electrons, whereas a negative ion is an atom or group which has acquired additional electrons.

2.53. A flow of electric current is invariably accompanied by a flow of electrons from one pole to another. Since the electron carries a negative charge the direction of flow is opposite that of the conventional flow of the positive electric current. This apparently anomalous situation is the result of Franklin's somewhat arbitrary choice of electrified glass as positive rather than negative (§ 2.4). If he had

---

* The present writer has italicized this phrase because of its importance.

made the opposite choice, the conventional charge of the electron would have been described as positive, instead of negative. The direction of flow of the positive current would then have been the same as that of the electrons.

SPECIFIC CHARGE OF THE ELECTRON

2.54. During the present century numerous determinations of the specific charge, i.e., of the charge-to-mass ratio, of electrons have been made. Some of these depend on a study of their behavior in various types of electric and magnetic fields, while others are based on spectroscopic measurements. It will be shown later (§ 4.42) that the characteristic light emitted, or absorbed, by an atom, known as its *spectrum*, is determined by the electrons. Consequently, relationships have been developed among the properties of the electron and the frequencies, or wave lengths, of spectral lines.

2.55. Further, as the Dutch physicist P. Zeeman showed in 1896, certain of these spectral lines are split up into component lines when the substance emitting the spectrum is placed in a very intense magnetic field. The frequency difference between the components is related to the field strength and also to the specific charge e/m of the electron. From his earliest measurements of the splitting of spectral lines in a magnetic field, Zeeman calculated the specific charge of the electron to be about 3×10^{17} e.s.u. per gram, in striking agreement with the value obtained in the same year by Thomson, and others, from cathode-ray studies. The frequencies of spectral lines can now be measured with great precision, so that e/m can be obtained

with a high order of accuracy. The general conclusion, from experiments of various kinds is that the best value for the specific charge of an electron is 5.273×10^{17} e.s.u. per gram.

MASS AND SIZE OF THE ELECTRON

2.56. Since both the actual charge e and the specific charge e/m of the electron are now known, it is obviously a simple matter to calculate the mass m of a single electron. All that is necessary is to divide e, which is 4.803×10^{-10} e.s.u., by e/m, i.e., 5.273×10^{17} e.s.u. per gram, and the result is 9.108×10^{-28} gram for the mass of an electron. Upon comparing this with the mass of a hydrogen atom, i.e., 1.673×10^{-24} gram, it is seen that it would require 1837 electrons to have the same mass as an atom of hydrogen. On the usual chemical atomic weight scale, with atmospheric oxygen being assigned a value of 16.000, the weight of an electron is 0.000548, as is found either upon multiplying the actual electron mass by the Avogadro number or by dividing the atomic weight of hydrogen by 1837. The electron is thus considerably lighter than the atom of even the lightest element.

2.57. Attention should be called here to the fact, which will be understood later (see Chapter III), that the apparent mass of an electron depends on the speed with which it is moving. The mass value recorded here is applicable when the electron is either at rest or moving at a relatively low speed, say, less than about one tenth of the velocity of light.* It is consequently referred to as the *rest mass* of the electron.

2.58. After the discovery of the electron and the realization of its extremely small mass, the possibility was

---

* The velocity of light is close to 3×10^{10} cm. per sec. (§ 3.14), so that one tenth of the velocity of light is about 3×10^9 cm., or 18,600 miles, per sec. This is actually a very high speed, but it may be regarded as relatively slow compared with the speed of light.

considered that this might be due entirely to its electric charge. In the scientific sense, a body is said to have mass or *inertia* when energy (work) must be supplied to set it in motion. In other words, if energy is required to start a body moving, it must, by the definition, possess mass, in its most general sense. A moving electric charge, no matter what its nature, produces a magnetic field in its vicinity, and since establishment of such a field requires energy, it follows that energy is needed to set the charge in motion. Consequently, the charge must be associated with mass or, at least, with something that behaves like, and therefore cannot be distinguished from, mass. Such mass is said to be electromagnetic. Since the electron carries an electric charge, and does, in fact, produce a magnetic field when in motion, it must have, at least, electromagnetic mass. If the assumption is now made that the mass of the electron derived above is entirely electromagnetic, it is possible to calculate the radius of an electron.

2.59. Several years before he had become interested in cathode rays, J. J. Thomson in 1881 had derived an equation, from theoretical principles, relating the electromagnetic mass m of a spherical charged particle of radius r, to its charge e expressed in *electromagnetic* units (see § 2.43, footnote), thus,

$$r = \frac{2e^2}{3m}. \qquad (2.11)$$

This equation is strictly applicable only when the charged particle is moving relatively slowly, and hence the rest mass of the electron may be used. Taking e as $4.80 \times 10^{-10}/3 \times 10^{10}$ e.m.u. and m as 9.1×10^{-28} gram, the radius of the electron is found from equation (2.11) to be 2×10^{-13} cm. This figure may be taken as an indication of the size of an electron, on the basis of two assumptions: first, that its charge is uniformly distributed over a spherical surface, and second, that its rest mass is purely electromagnetic in nature, that is to say, assuming the apparent mass of the electron to be due entirely to its charge.* If it should transpire that part of the mass is due to other causes, the radius would be somewhat greater than 2×10^{-13} cm. The result cannot be regarded as very exact, in any event, because it is doubtful whether the theory used in the derivation of equation (2.11) is applicable to a particle as small as an electron. However, in so far as an electron can be regarded as having a definite radius (see § 3.45), it is probably safe to say it is about 2×10^{-13} cm.

2.60. As indicated in § 1.65, the radii of most atoms are in the vicinity of 2×10^{-8} cm., and consequently the radius of the electron is about 10^{-5}, i.e., one hundred-thousandth, of the radius of an average atom. In the bowl of water magnified to the size of the earth, referred to in § 1.55, an electron would be so small that it would be barely visible in a good optical microscope!

* Although J. J. Thomson was responsible for the definite proof of the existence of the electron, and also for the derivation of the equation for electromagnetic mass, Lord Rayleigh, in *The Life of Sir J. J. Thomson*, Cambridge University Press, 1942, says that he did not at first favor the idea that the mass of the electron was entirely electromagnetic in origin, but it became accepted because of its advocacy by Oliver Lodge and others.

THE PROTON, ANTIPROTON AND POSITRON

Positive Rays and the Proton

2.61. After the discovery of the negatively charged electron, it was natural that search should be made for a corresponding particle carrying a positive charge. In 1886, E. Goldstein, in Germany, had used a perforated metal disc as a cathode in a discharge tube, and observed luminous rays emerging in straight lines from the holes on the side away from the anode (Fig. 2.4). These

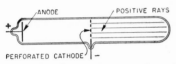

Fig. 2.4. Positive rays emerging from holes in the cathode on the side away from the anode.

rays were originally called *canal rays*, since they passed through holes, or channels, in the cathode.* By collecting the rays in a Faraday cylinder, J. Perrin (1895) showed that they were associated with a positive charge, and this was confirmed by W. Wien in 1898 by studying their deflection in electric and magnetic fields. Consequently, J. J. Thomson later (1907) proposed the more appropriate name *positive rays*, and this has been universally adopted.

2.62. In the course of his work, Wien had determined the charge-to-mass ratio (e/m) of the particles present in the positive rays, and found that the values were very much smaller than that for electrons, and often less than for the hydrogen ion in solution. Assuming, as is very probable, that the charge carried by the positive particles is a small integral number of elementary charges, the only conclusion to be drawn is that the particles in the positive rays are much heavier than electrons, being actual atoms or molecules which have become electrically charged. With a discharge tube containing air, Wien found the masses of the particles indicated that they consisted of oxygen or nitrogen molecules. Subsequent work proved that, in general, the masses of the positively charged particles were determined by the gas present in the discharge tube.

2.63. Apart from the sign of the electric charge, the positive rays thus differ in two respects, at least, from cathode rays. In the first place, the particles in the positive rays consist of actual atoms or molecules, whereas in the cathode rays they are very much smaller and lighter even than hydrogen; and, in the second place, the cathode-ray particles are independent of the nature of the gas in the discharge tube or of the cathode material, but in the case of the positive rays the particles are usually charged atoms or molecules related to the gas in the tube.

2.64. In spite of a very thorough search, no positively charged particle similar to the electron was found in the discharge tube. The lightest particle so observed, which the New Zealand-born physicist Ernest Rutherford, in 1914, described as the "long sought positive electron," had the same mass as the hydrogen atom and carried one unit (positive) charge, equal in magnitude, but of opposite sign, to the charge carried by an electron. In other words, it is a singly charged, positive hydrogen ion, H^+. This presumably

---

* Goldstein called the rays *Kanalstrahlen,* which should perhaps have been translated as "channel rays" rather than "canal rays."

consists of a hydrogen atom from which one electron has been removed, apparently as a result of a collision in the discharge tube, leaving it with an equivalent positive charge.* By 1920, a number of circumstances, to which reference will be made in Chapter VIII, had arisen, indicating that the positively charged hydrogen atom just described represented an important unit in the structure of other atoms. The name *proton* was consequently assigned to it.† Since the weight of the hydrogen atom is 1837 times that of the electron, it follows that the weight of a proton, which is a hydrogen atom minus one electron, is 1836 times as great as that of an electron.

THE POSITIVE ELECTRON OR POSITRON

2.65. In spite of the absence of experimental evidence for the existence of a positive electron, i.e., a particle similar in mass to the electron but carrying a positive charge, the English mathematical physicist P. A. M. Dirac had, in 1930, presented some theoretical arguments indicating that such a particle was possible. Dirac's discussion was of a highly abstruse character, but it may be summarized, somewhat superficially, as follows. Ordi-

nary negatively charged electrons must be able to exist in two different types of energy states, called positive and negative. These terms have no relationship to the electric charge, but refer to energy values relative to a certain zero state. If one of the possible negative energy states is not occupied by an electron, there is a vacancy—sometimes referred to as a Dirac "hole," although it is not a hole in the ordinary three-dimensional sense —which should behave like a positively charged electron with positive energy.

2.66. At first Dirac thought that this represented a proton, since no positive electron had been observed, but it was soon seen that such could not be the case. In the first place, the mass of the proton is much greater than that of the electron, whereas the theory required the positive particle to have the same mass as the negative electron. In the second place, since Dirac's hypothetical positive electron is really a vacant "hole," it can readily be filled by an ordinary negative electron. In other words, the positive electron should have a very short life, because a negative electron, of which there are many always available, should quickly combine with it. The

---

* It may be remarked that this is in accord with the ideas expressed by Benjamin Franklin referred to in § 2.2.

† From the Greek *protos* (first). Various reports concerning the origin of the term proton are to be found in the scientific literature. The following is a quotation from a footnote by E. Rutherford to a paper by O. Masson, written in 1920: "The question of a suitable name for this unit [i.e., the positively charged hydrogen atom] was discussed at an informal meeting of a number of members of Section A [Physics] of the British Association at Cardiff this year. . . . The name 'proton' met with general approval, particularly as it suggests the . . . term 'protyle' given by Prout in his well-known hypothesis [§ 1.38] that all atoms are built up of hydrogen. . . . The need of a special name for the . . . unit of mass 1 was drawn attention to at the Sectional Meeting, and the writer [Rutherford] then suggested the name 'proton.'" It should be noted that Rutherford does not claim to have made the *original* suggestion, but only to have put it forward at the formal meeting of Section A. Lodge referring to the matter says: "At the Cardiff Meeting of the British Association, Sir Ernest Rutherford suggested, or tentatively approved the suggestion, that the name 'proton' should be applied to this hydrogen . . . unit of positive charge." There is thus some doubt concerning the identity of the individual who suggested the name in this particular connection. Actually, the term proton is to be found in the scientific literature as far back as 1908, and possibly earlier, being used in a general sense to refer to the fundamental unit, analogous to protyle, from which all elements are built up.

two charges will then neutralize and annihilate one another, leaving nothing but energy (§ 3.84). Actually, the proton is quite stable, and so it cannot satisfy the requirements of the particle which would be the equivalent of the Dirac "hole."

2.67. Proof of the existence of the long-sought positive electron was finally obtained by C. D. Anderson, at the California Institute of Technology, in 1932. In order to study the so-called

2.68. When the cloud chamber was operated, numerous tracks were observed due to charged particles resulting from the impact on matter of the very highly energetic cosmic rays. A lead plate of 6 mm. thickness was placed across the chamber with the object of depriving the particles of some of their energy, and, as Anderson stated in his Sigma Xi Lectures in 1939, "the degree of the curvature in the magnetic field shows a difference,

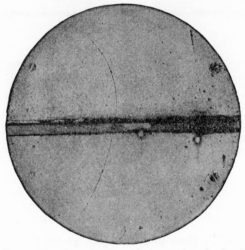

Fig. 2.5. Cosmic-ray photograph obtained by Anderson which led to the discovery of the positron.

cosmic rays (see Chapter XVIII), which appear to come from outer space, Anderson, in conjunction with R. A. Millikan (§ 2.33), had constructed an apparatus, known as a cloud chamber (§ 6.68), which was placed in a very strong magnetic field. In the cloud chamber the path of an electrically charged particle can be rendered visible, and actually photographed. The intensity of the track provides information concerning the mass of the particle, and the direction in which it is bent in the magnetic field indicates whether the charge is positive or negative.

depending on the amount of energy lost in the plate. Measurements made on the track of a particle before and after it has passed through a plate, together with observations of the density of the track itself, give definite information about the mass of the particle and the magnitude of the electric charge it carries."

2.69. One of the numerous photographs obtained in this manner, with the lead plate seen cutting across the center, is shown in Fig. 2.5; it is a photograph of historical significance, for its interpretation by Anderson led to the discovery of the positive electron. Since the curvature of the track is less below the plate than above, the energy of the particle is greater below the plate. Hence the particle must have been moving upward. Knowing the direction of the magnetic field, and the direction of motion of the particle, the curvature of the track to the left immediately showed that the particle must be positively charged. The den-

rays. Some of these photographs were of the type shown in Fig. 2.6, the two parts of which represent the same event taken from two different angles. The tracks of the charged particles are seen to fall into two groups, one being deflected to the left and the other to the right by the magnetic field. The outer group in each of the photographs consists of negative electrons while the

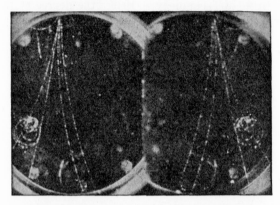

FIG. 2.6. Groups of tracks produced by positrons and electrons (positron-electron pairs) in magnetic field. (From "Introduction to Atomic Physics" by Semat, Rinehart and Company.)

sity of the track was less than would be expected for a proton, but its length was greater. "The photographs," Anderson said, "of these positively charged particles could be understood only if the particles were assumed to have a mass approximately equal to that of the ordinary electron of negative electric charge, and thus the first evidence for the existence of positive electrons . . . was obtained."

2.70. After the foregoing interpretation had been made of the photograph in Fig. 2.5, other cloud-chamber photographs were examined in the light of the new discovery, and further proof was obtained that positive electrons were produced by the action of cosmic

inner group is made up of positive electrons. The variation within each group is due to differences in the energies of the various electrons.

2.71. Anderson suggested the name *positron* for the positive electron, and this immediately came into general use. He also proposed the analogous term *negatron* for the negative electron, but the proposal did not apparently meet with approval, for it has not made much headway in the literature.* At the present time, the word electron, without qualification, is invariably taken to imply the negatively charged particle. A system consisting of a positive and a negative electron is called a *positron-electron*

* The Cosmic Ray Commission of the International Union of Physics, at its meeting in October 1947, favored the use of the terms *positon* and *negaton*.

pair; the tracks produced by several such pairs are seen in Fig. 2.6.

FORMATION AND DESTRUCTION
OF POSITRONS

2.72. Shortly after the publication of Anderson's discovery, P. M. S. Blackett and G. P. S. Occhialini, in England, announced in 1933 that they had obtained cloud-chamber photographs which showed pairs of tracks of the type depicted in Fig. 2.6. In reporting the results they said: ". . . it is necessary to come to the same remarkable conclusion that has already been drawn by Anderson from similar photographs. The only possible . . . [explanation] . . . of both the range and ionization is that these tracks are due to positively charged particles with a mass comparable with that of an electron. . . . Altogether we have found 14 tracks . . . which must almost certainly be attributed to such positive electron."

2.73. Before proceeding to consider other positron studies, reference may be made to measurements of its specific charge, i.e., of its charge-to-mass ratio, which should, of course, be the same as for an electron. The first such determination was made by J. Thibaud in Belgium in 1934, using an arrangement of crossed magnetic and electric fields (§ 2.44); he reported that e/m for the positron did not differ by more than 15 per cent from that of the electron. Later, A. H. Spees and C. T. Zahn, in the United States, compared the behavior in electric and magnetic fields of positrons and electrons which were emitted simultaneously from an artificially radioactive form of the element copper (§ 10.100). It was found that the specific charges of the positive and negative particles do not differ by more than 2 per cent.

2.74. Upon consideration of the origin of the positrons formed by cosmic rays, Blackett and Occhialini, making use of Dirac's theoretical treatment, thought it most likely that, as a result of interaction with matter, part of the energy of the rays was converted into positron-electron pairs. The minimum energy necessary to bring about the conversion could be calculated, and this was found to be well within the range of the cosmic rays, and even of some of the radiations (gamma rays) emitted by certain radioactive substances (§ 2.110). Hence such radiations might be expected to give positron-electron pairs upon interaction with matter.

2.75. Three groups of scientists, working independently in England, France and Germany, had reported that when the element beryllium is bombarded with alpha particles (§ 2.105) from the radioactive element polonium (§ 5.6), and the resulting radiations are allowed to impinge upon metallic lead, positron-electron pairs are produced. One of these groups, namely, Irène Joliot-Curie—daughter of Marie and Pierre Curie (§ 5.2)—and her husband F. Joliot, had suggested the possibility that the effect was really due to high-energy gamma rays emitted from beryllium under the action of the alpha-particles. This view was supported by the work of Anderson, reported in 1933, that gamma rays of high energy emitted by the radioactive element known as thorium C″ are, like cosmic rays, able to produce positron-electron pairs. These results were soon confirmed by other experimenters, and calculations of the various energies involved provided strong support for the theory of the origin of the positron-electron pairs (§ 3.84).

2.76. Since positrons were rare enough to elude discovery for many years, it is apparent that they are not a universal constituent of matter, as are electrons. When a positron is produced, either by the interaction with matter of rays of high energy or, as will be seen in § 10.82, by certain artificial radioactive elements, it soon disappears as the result of combination with an electron. As there are large numbers of the latter always available, a positron does not exist for any appreciable time. The average life of a positron varies with its environment, but it is usually of the order of a billionth part (10^{-9}) of a second. In view of its evanescent nature, it is not surprising that the positron remained undiscovered for so long. Actually, after it had been identified, several scientists, looking through their files, found cloud-chamber photographs, due to cosmic rays, which indicated the presence of positrons. There were probably extenuating circumstances to account for the failure to recognize them; nevertheless, Anderson must be commended, not only for his acute observation, but also for his courageous interpretation which solved a long-standing problem.

2.77. It may well be asked at this point: What happens when a positron and an electron unite? It appears that the positive and negative charges neutralize each other and the particles are annihilated leaving only energy in the form of radiation, often called *annihilation radiation*, similar to gamma rays (§ 2.110).* The energy to be expected for this radiation can be calculated, and it is a striking fact that exactly such radiation was observed by J. Thibaud and by F. Joliot, in 1933, when a stream of positrons was allowed to impinge on a metal surface. The same radiations were also de-

tected in other cases where positrons were presumably annihilated by combining with electrons.

2.78. Before the identification of the positron, several physicists had found that the absorption of high-energy gamma rays by matter was appreciably greater than calculated from a well-established equation, which gave excellent agreement with experiment for rays of lower energy. At the same time a secondary radiation, whose origin could not be explained, was detected in the United States by Chinese physicist C. Y. Chao in 1930, and in England by L. H. Gray and G. T. P. Tarrant in 1932. The interpretation of these results was provided by Blackett and Occhialini. The additional absorption of gamma rays was due to the conversion of their energy into positron-electron pairs, while the secondary radiation had just the right energy to be expected for the annihilation of the positrons as a result of combination with the omnipresent electrons.

2.79. It has thus been clearly established that energy, in the form of gamma rays or cosmic rays, can be converted into particle pairs, under suitable conditions, and, conversely, the pairs can combine to produce energy in the form of annihilation radiation. These results, as will be seen in Chapter III, have an important bearing on the general principle of the relationship between matter and energy, a principle upon which the realization of atomic energy is based.

THE ANTIPROTON

2.80. In the theory of Dirac which predicted the existence of the positron (§ 2.65) there is nothing that restricts it to electrons. In other words, the theory should be of wider applicabil-

---

* In some cases a temporary combination of electron and positron, called *positronium*, is formed before annihilation occurs (§ 3.86).

ity, both in its original and in its more recent forms, so that for every fundamental particle there should be a related "anti" (or opposite) particle. Corresponding to the ordinary proton, therefore, there is to be expected a negative proton, or *antiproton.* This particle should have the same mass (and other characteristic properties) as the proton but should differ from it in the respect that the antiproton carries a unit negative charge.

2.81. Just as positron-electron pairs are formed by the interaction with matter of rays (or particles) having sufficient energy, so it should be possible to produce proton-antiproton pairs in a similar manner. However, because the mass of the proton is nearly two thousand times as great as that of an electron, the energy needed to materialize a proton-antiproton pair would be greater in the same proportion. Until 1955, the required energy was available only in cosmic rays, and many tracks produced by these rays in cloud chambers and in photographic plates (Chapter VI) were carefully scrutinized for evidence of the antiproton. As a result, a number of claims were made to the identification of events that might be attributed to this particle. Some of these claims may well have been justified, but due to the highly complex character of cosmic ray phenomena, as well as to the inability of studying them under suitable conditions, it was impossible to accept the conclusions with any degree of confidence.

2.82. When the instrument known as the Bevatron (§ 9.100) went into operation at full power, at the Radiation Laboratory in Berkeley, California, there became available, for the first time, a controllable source of particles having energies large enough to create proton-antiproton pairs.

Even if antiprotons were produced, however, there still remained the formidable problem of identifying them unequivocally in the presence of many other particles formed at the same time. In a report made in October 1955, O. Chamberlain, E. Segrè, C. E. Wiegand and T. Ypsilantis described the procedure they used to obtain definite proof of the existence of the antiproton.

2.83. Briefly, the method was somewhat as follows. A stream of high-energy protons from the Bevatron was allowed to impinge on a copper block. The particles issuing from the target were passed through a magnetic field, so that those, including antiprotons, having negative charges were separated from the others. Then, making use of a complex and ingenious timing system, which registered only particles traveling a distance of 40 feet in the extremely small but precisely controlled time interval of 51 billionths (51×10^{-9}) of a second, signals were recorded that could be caused only by antiprotons. None of the other negatively charged particles present could have had the exact speed (nearly 80 per cent of the speed of light, i.e., 148,-000 miles per second) to traverse the given distance in the specified time.

2.84. Further confirmation of the production of antiprotons was obtained in two ways. These were both based on the anticipation that the encounter of an antiproton with an ordinary proton would lead to their mutual annihilation with the consequent liberation of a large amount of energy. As indicated earlier (§ 2.64), all atoms contain protons, so that the annihilation of antiprotons should occur in any material. In one of the confirmatory tests, a piece of glass was placed in the stream of particles containing antiprotons. The annihilation energy then caused the release in the glass of electrically charged particles which moved fast enough to cause the emission of light in the form of what is called Čerenkov radiation

capture by a silver or bromine atom in the photographic emulsion—was accompanied by the emission of several particles (Fig. 2.7).* The tracks of the particles appear in the form of a

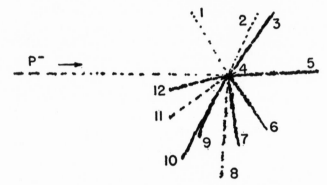

FIG. 2.7. Star produced in photographic emulsion due to capture of an antiproton whose track is indicated by P⁻. (University of California Radiation Laboratory.)

(§ 6.56). This light had properties that were in harmony with an antiproton annihilation process as the original energy source.

2.85. More definite proof of the proton-antiproton annihilation was secured by exposing photographic plates to the negatively charged particle stream. Some of the resulting plates were sent to Rome, Italy, for study by scientists working with E. Amaldi, and others were examined by a group in Berkeley, California. The annihilation of an antiproton—presumably after

"star" with several prongs (§ 18.51). Measurements made on these prongs showed that the total energy release was greater than was to be expected from the mass of the antiproton alone, so that another particle, either a proton or neutron (see § 2.120), must have been annihilated simultaneously. It may be mentioned that the antiproton, unlike the proton, is not a constituent of normal matter, since coexistence of the two particles is obviously not possible.

X-RAYS

THE DISCOVERY AND NATURE OF X-RAYS

2.86. While experimenting with the luminescence produced by cathode rays, the German physicist, W. C.

Röntgen made a discovery, toward the end of 1895, which has had a notable effect, both direct and indirect, on atomic science. It was stated earlier (§ 2.17) that the rays cause the glass

---

*Tracks 3, 5, 6, 7, 9, 10 and 12 are produced by protons ejected from the interacting atom (nucleus); tracks 1 and 2 are due to pi-mesons and 8 and 11 to K-mesons (see Chapter XVIII). Track 4 is produced by the atom (nucleus) remaining after the emission of these particles.

walls of the discharge tube to luminesce, but even more intense luminescense is produced in various chemical compounds, particularly barium platinocyanide, zinc blende (zinc sulfide) and willemite (zinc silicate). In the course of his work, Röntgen had enclosed a discharge tube in a box made of thin, black cardboard, placed in a darkened room. Near the tube there happened to be a sheet of paper coated on one side with barium platinocyanide, and Röntgen noticed that, when the tube enclosed in the box was operating, the paper exhibited a brilliant luminescence. He proved that whatever was responsible for this phenomenon originated in the vacuum tube, and he concluded that it was some form of penetrating rays, to which he gave the name of X-rays.*

2.87. Röntgen found that, in addition to producing luminescence, the rays caused darkening or fogging of photographic plates, even when wrapped in paper or enclosed in a box. Consequently, these substances, which are opaque to ordinary light, are transparent to the X-rays. This fact led Röntgen to take X-ray photographs of normally opaque bodies, such as the hand, thus revealing their internal structure due to the varying degrees of transparency of the different portions, e.g., bone and flesh, to the rays.

2.88. To Röntgen goes credit for a discovery that might well have been made at any time during the two preceding decades. William Crookes and F. Jervis Smith, in England, and, no doubt, others elsewhere, had found that photographic plates, although still in their unopened boxes, became fogged when kept in a room in which a discharge tube was in action. The phenomenon was usually attributed to some spurious external circumstances, and was not investigated. In addition, in 1890, A. W. Goodspeed, in Philadelphia, actually produced shadow photographs, which were really due to X-rays, but which he attributed to cathode rays. The Hungarian physicist P. Lenard obtained similar photographic results in 1894, using the so-called "Lenard rays" obtained by passing cathode rays through an aluminum window in a discharge tube.

2.89. In the early months of 1896, the investigation of the properties of X-rays attracted considerable attention in various parts of the world. Almost simultaneously, and independently, scientists in England, France and Italy found that, when X-rays were passed through air or other gas, the gas acquired the ability to conduct electricity. In other words, X-rays have the property of producing ions, i.e., electrically charged atoms or molecules (§ 2.15), in gases. There is little doubt that the experiments which resulted in this discovery were prompted by the photoelectric effect, well known at the time, whereby ultraviolet rays produce ionization in the air in the vicinity of a metal, such as zinc (§ 2.48). However, irrespective of its origin, it was a discovery destined to have a profound influence on atomic science.

2.90. For several years after their discovery there was no clear understanding of the nature of X-rays, and several different theories were proposed to account for their origin and behavior. It was not until 1912 that definite evidence, to be described in § 2.94, was obtained that the rays

---

* Röntgen said: ". . . X-rays, as I will call the rays, for the sake of brevity," but it is believed that he chose the letter X because it is frequently used in algebra to represent an unknown quantity. The rays are frequently referred to as *Röntgen rays*.

were an electromagnetic radiation analogous to light but of shorter wave length.

CHARACTERISTIC X-RAYS

2.91. In Röntgen's experiments the X-rays were produced by the cathode rays striking the walls of the discharge tube. Better results may be obtained by allowing the cathode rays to fall on a piece of metal, called an *anticathode*, placed in their path; the X-rays are then emitted from the anticathode. In general, any stream of fast-moving, i.e., high-energy, electrons—no matter how they are formed —will produce X-rays when they are slowed down upon striking a suitable material (§ 4.75).

2.92. As a rule, the wave lengths of the radiations emitted from an anticathode cover a considerable range, but if they are allowed to fall on a given material, most of the rays are absorbed leaving only X-rays with wave lengths characteristic of the elements present in the material; this appears to have been recognized by C. G. Barkla, in England, in 1911. These *characteristic X-rays*, as they are now called, can be produced in other ways, e.g., by permitting cathode rays of high velocity to impinge directly on a target (anticathode) made of, or containing, the particular element. The rays fall into several groups (or series) distinguished by the letters *K, L, M, N*, etc., in order of decreasing *hardness,* i.e., of decreasing ability to penetrate matter. As the atomic weight of the element increases, the rays of the *K* series, then the *L* series, become increasingly difficult to produce, cathode rays (electrons) of higher and higher energies being necessary. The importance of the characteristic X-rays in connection with atomic structure will be described in § 4.24.

THE DIFFRACTION OF X-RAYS

2.93. From various early experiments, of a somewhat crude nature, it appeared that X-rays might have a wave length of about 10^{-8} cm. If this were so, then, argued the German physicist M. von Laue, a crystal should exhibit the phenomenon of *diffraction* or interference of X-rays. Theoretical calculations, based on the wave theory of light, have shown that when light passes through a diffraction grating, consisting of a number of small gaps with a spacing of the same order as the wave length of light, rays proceeding in certain directions will either enhance or annul one another (§ 3.10). In this way a *diffraction pattern* can be produced.

2.94. In a crystal, the centers of atoms or molecules are in the vicinity of 10^{-8} cm. apart, and hence a crystal should act as a diffraction grating for X-rays, thus yielding a definite pattern depending on the nature of the crystal and the wave length of the rays. At the suggestion of von Laue, his associates W. Friedrich and P. Knipping made the experiment, in 1912, of pass-

FIG. 2.8. Laue type diffraction pattern produced by X-rays in passing through a crystal of sodium chloride.

ing a beam of X-rays through a slice of zinc blende (zinc sulfide) crystal; a diffraction pattern of the expected type was formed on a photographic plate upon which the rays fell (cf. Fig. 2.8). Thus, X-rays were proved to be of the same nature as light, but with a shorter wave length. Incidentally, the use of a crystal as a diffraction grating has provided a valuable method for determining the actual wave lengths of the rays, on the one hand, or for studying interatomic distances within the crystal, on the other hand.

2.95. A simple treatment of the diffraction of X-rays accompanying reflection at the surface of a crystal was developed by the English physicist W. L. Bragg in 1912. Suppose a train of waves, which may be X-rays, strikes a crystal, consisting of a regular arrangement of atoms, ions or molecules. The crystal then functions as a series of parallel reflecting planes, as indicated in Fig. 2.9. If the glancing

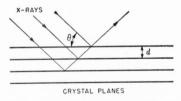

X-RAYS

CRYSTAL PLANES

FIG. 2.9. Reflection of X-rays by crystal planes to illustrate derivation of the Bragg equation.

angle θ is such that it bears a proper relationship to the distance d between the reflecting planes and to the wave length λ (§ 3.13) of the incident waves, the reflections from the various planes will be exceptionally intense. The reflections are then said to be in phase. But, if the angle θ does not satisfy the conditions for the various reflections to be in phase, they will interfere with one another and the resultant beam will have a greatly diminished intens-

ity. As the angle of incidence is changed, therefore, there will be observed a series of reflections exhibiting alternating maxima and minima of intensity. This is the manner in which diffraction due to reflection manifests itself.

2.96. The condition for obtaining reflection maxima for X-rays, as derived by Bragg and usually known as the *Bragg equation,* may be written in the form

$$n\lambda = 2d \sin \theta, \qquad (2.12)$$

where λ is the wave length of the X-rays, d is the distance between successive reflecting planes of atoms, ions or molecules, θ is the glancing angle and n is an integer, namely, 1, 2, 3, and so on. Consequently, if the angle θ is such that $\sin \theta$ satisfies the relationship derived from equation (2.12), that is,

$$\sin \theta = \frac{n\lambda}{2d}, \qquad (2.13)$$

where n may be 1, 2, 3, etc., then a reflection maximum will occur. If the diffraction effect is to be observed, the glancing angle θ must not be too small, and hence $\sin \theta$ must be appreciable. It can be readily seen from equation (2.13) that, for this to be the case, the wave length λ of the diffracted rays and the distance d between the reflecting planes must be of the same order of magnitude, in agreement with the statement made above.

2.97. In this and other ways it has been established that X-rays have wave lengths of the order of 10^{-8} cm. The actual values for characteristic X-rays have been determined with a considerable degree of accuracy for many elements. The results are so precise that they can even be used for purposes of identification.

RADIOACTIVITY

Discovery of Radioactivity

2.98. Shortly after Röntgen's announcement of his discovery of X-rays, the French physicist Henri Antoine Becquerel became interested in the subject as the result of a lecture given at the Academy of Sciences in Paris by H. Poincaré. In answer to a question, the latter stated that the X-rays appeared to originate in the luminescent spot produced where the cathode rays impinge on the discharge tube. Becquerel's father, Edmond Becquerel, also a physicist, had made a particular study of a type of luminescence known as fluorescence,* exhibited by various subtances, particularly upon exposure to sunlight. Henri Becquerel happened to have in his possession a pure specimen of the double-salt, potassium uranyl sulfate, which his father had used in his work on fluorescence. In an attempt to discover some connection between X-rays and the luminescence exhibited by this uranium salt,† Henri Becquerel wrapped a photographic plate in black paper, placed a thin crystal of the salt upon the paper, and then exposed the whole to sunlight. When the photographic plate was developed, it was found to be darkened, indicating that the uranium salt emitted radiations which could penetrate paper. Becquerel showed that those rays could, in fact, pass through thin sheets of aluminum and copper and still cause blackening of the photographic plate. At the time, he was of the opinion that the uranium salt had emitted the rays as a result of exposure to light, but, taking advantage of an unexpected circumstance, as mentioned below, he made a discovery which turned out to be of a revolutionary nature.

2.99. Describing his work, in the early part of 1896, Becquerel said, referring to his experiments with the uranium salt placed over the photographic plate wrapped in paper: "Some had been prepared on Wednesday, February 26th and Thursday, February 27th, but as on these days the sun shone only intermittently, I kept the experiments that had been prepared and returned the plates to the darkness of a drawer . . . leaving the crystals of the uranium salt in place. The sun not showing itself again the following days, I developed the photographic plates on March 1st, expecting to find very faint images. On the contrary, the silhouettes appeared with great intensity. . . . A hypothesis which occurs . . . to the mind will be to suppose that these radiations [emitted by the uranium salt] . . . are similar to invisible rays emitted by phosphorescent [fluorescent?] substances, except that the time of persistence is infinitely greater than that of the visible radiations emitted by such bodies." Thus, Becquerel showed that the uranium salt emitted rays, even without being exposed to sunlight, and that these rays persisted for a long time. In this manner was discovered the remarkable phenomenon to which Marie

---

* The term *fluorescence* is generally used to describe the emission of light of a particular wave length as a result of exposure of a material to light of another—usually shorter—wave length, the emitted light ceasing immediately the exciting light is cut off.

† H. Becquerel described this as "phosphorescence," a term which now generally refers to luminescence that continues for some time after the exciting light is cut off; however, the uranium salt is probably fluorescent rather than phosphorescent.

Curie, in 1898, gave the appropriate name of *radioactivity* (§ 5.5).*

2.100. After Becquerel found that the radiations from uranium were similar to X-rays in the respect that they could penetrate materials opaque to ordinary light, and also affect a photographic plate, he was naturally interested to see if the radiations, like X-rays, were able to produce ionization in air. For this purpose he used a *gold-leaf electroscope* which, in its simplest form, consists of a short, vertical metal rod with a metal sphere or plate at its upper end; to its lower end are attached two small rectangular sheets of gold leaf, hanging vertically. The rod is usually supported, with suitable insulation, in a box which serves to protect the delicate gold leaves from air currents. If an electric charge is applied to the sphere or plate, it is transferred through the metal to the gold leaves; since these both now carry charges of the same sign, they immediately repel each other, forming an inverted V (Fig. 2.10). If the air in

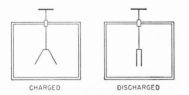

CHARGED   DISCHARGED

Fig. 2.10. Use of simple gold-leaf electroscope to detect ionizing radiations.

the vicinity is ionized in some manner, it becomes an electrical conductor and thus permits the charge on the leaves

to leak away. In other words, the electroscope becomes discharged. The repulsion then ceases and the leaves return to their original vertical positions. Becquerel observed that a uranium salt brought near a charged electroscope caused the latter to discharge. Thus, the rays from uranium had the property of ionizing the air in their vicinity.

2.101. The subject of radioactivity will be discussed in some detail in later chapters and for the present purpose, which is a brief consideration of the nature of the emitted radiations, it is sufficient to state that Becquerel's discovery was soon followed by the identification of other active elements, namely, thorium, polonium, radium and actinium, in which the French scientists Marie and Pierre Curie played an important part (Chapter V). At the present time, a considerable number of radioactive species are known; some occur in nature, others are produced by various transmutation and disintegration processes (Chapter X).

RADIOACTIVE RADIATIONS: ALPHA AND BETA RAYS

2.102. It was observed almost simultaneously in 1899 by Becquerel in France, by S. Meyer and E. von Schweidler and by F. Giesel in Germany, that the radiations from radioactive substances could be deflected in a magnetic field in the same direction as are cathode rays. It appeared there-

---

* The claim is sometimes made that the English physicist, S. P. Thompson, discovered radioactivity almost simultaneously and independently of Becquerel. In 1896 Thompson observed that, when a photographic plate was covered with a thin sheet of metal, upon which was placed a uranium salt, and exposed to sunlight, the plate was affected. He called the phenomenon "hyperphosphorescence." The essential point about radioactivity is that, as Becquerel found, sunlight is unnecessary, and Thompson did not realize this. It may be mentioned that as long ago as 1867, N. de St. Victor, of France, reported that if a sheet of paper impregnated with uranium nitrate was exposed to light, it was able to affect a photographic plate in the dark, so as to cause exceptionally rapid reduction of the silver salt in the plate.

fore that part, at least, of the radiations consisted of negatively charged particles. At about the same time, E. Rutherford (see § 2.64) was in England studying the extent to which passage through thin sheets of aluminum was able to reduce the ionizing power of the active radiations. From his results he concluded that the radiations emitted by a uranium compound were of two different types: the first, which Rutherford called *alpha* (*α*) *rays*, were unable to penetrate more than about 0.002 cm. of aluminum, while the second, the *beta* (*β*) *rays*, required a much thicker sheet of aluminum to absorb them completely. The penetrating power of the beta rays was found to be very roughly one hundred times that of the alpha rays.

2.103. The suggestion that there were two different kinds of rays was also made by Pierre Curie in 1900, when he found that part of the radiation from radioactive substances could be deflected in a magnetic field, whereas the other part appeared not to be deflected. Marie Curie showed that the undeflected rays had a much smaller penetrating power than the rays which were deflected in a magnetic field. The former were evidently identical with Rutherford's alpha rays and the latter with his beta rays. In addition to being deflected in a magnetic field, F. E. Dorn demonstrated in 1900 that beta rays are also deflected by an electric field.

2.104. By collecting the rays in a Faraday cylinder (§ 2.20), Marie and Pierre Curie in 1900 confirmed the fact, indicated by the deflections, that the beta rays were associated with a negative charge. It consequently appeared probable to Becquerel that the beta rays might be related to cathode rays; thus, in his own words: "The experiments which I have made during the past several months on the radiations from radium have shown that the properties of the part of this radiation which is deviable in a magnetic field have a great analogy with those of cathode rays." To demonstrate the complete identity of the beta and cathode rays, Becquerel (1900) determined both the speed and the charge-to-mass ratio i.e., the specific charge, of the particles which presumably constituted the beta rays, by studying their deflection in electric and magnetic fields (§ 2.42 *et seq.*). In this way, he found the velocity to be about 1.6×10^{10} cm. per sec., which is just more than half the speed of light, while the specific charge was approximately 3×10^{17} e.s.u. per gram. These results, as Becquerel said, "are entirely of the order of magnitude which have been found for cathode rays." Later work has established, with complete certainty, that beta rays do, in fact, like cathode rays, consist of negatively charged electrons. A beta particle is thus identical with an electron.

THE ALPHA PARTICLE

2.105. As stated above, early experiments indicated that the alpha rays could not be deflected in a magnetic field, and hence appeared to be uncharged. Nevertheless, some scientists, particularly R. J. Strutt (later Lord Rayleigh, 4th Baron) and W. Crookes, in England, noting the strong ionizing power of the radiations, thought they might consist of positively charged particles of relatively large mass. This view received confirmation from Rutherford when, in 1903, he succeeded in deflecting the alpha rays by using a powerful magnetic field; the direction of the deflection was opposite to that of an electron stream in the same field. It was apparent, therefore, that the alpha rays actually consist of positively charged particles.

2.106. Preliminary measurements of the specific charge (e/m) of alpha particles were made independently by Rutherford and by T. Des Coudres in 1903, by observing their deflections in magnetic and electric fields. The value so obtained was about 2×10^{14} e.s.u. per gram, as compared with 5.3×10^{17} e.s.u. per gram for an electron. The former figure is of the same order of magnitude as for the atomic and molecular particles in positive rays (§ 2.62), and so Rutherford concluded that "the alpha rays . . . are thus very similar to the Kanalstrahlen [i.e., positive rays] . . . which have been shown . . . to be positively charged bodies moving with high velocity." Shortly afterward, he said: "I have been . . . led by a mass of indirect evidence to the view that the alpha rays are in reality charged bodies of mass of the order of that of the hydrogen atom."

2.107. In 1906, Rutherford reported the results of more accurate measurements of e/m by deflecting the alpha particles, from several different radioactive sources, in both magnetic and electric fields.* The value found, 1.5×10^{14} e.s.u. per gram, was about one half the value for a proton, i.e., for a hydrogen atom with a single electric charge (§ 2.64). Two reasonable interpretations of this result were possible: first, the alpha particle might be a hydrogen molecule, having twice the mass of a hydrogen atom, but still carrying a single charge; and second,

it might be a helium atom, with a mass four times that of a hydrogen atom, carrying two elementary charges. In either case, the e/m value would be approximately half that for a proton. Since both radium and actinium salts had been found to liberate helium†, and this gas was known to be frequently associated with radioactive minerals, Rutherford favored the second possibility. He thought it probable, therefore, that alpha particles were helium atoms carrying two unit positive charges; in other words, they were doubly charged helium ions or helium atoms each of which had lost two electrons.

2.108. Partial confirmation of this view was obtained by E. Rutherford and H. Geiger in 1908, when they determined, by means of an electrometer, the total charge carried by the alpha particles emitted by a given radioactive source. Then the number of particles was counted, by methods to be described in Chapter VI, so that the charge on each alpha particle could be calculated. A somewhat similar procedure was used by the German physicist E. Regener in 1909, and both sets of experiments led to essentially the same result. The charge on an alpha particle was found to be about 9.6×10^{-10} e.s.u., which is twice the value of the elementary electronic charge (§ 2.41). The alpha particle must thus carry two unit charges, and since its specific charge (e/m) is half that of a proton, its mass must inevitably be four times as great. The only reasonable particle of this mass is an atom of

---

* The experiments were made in Montreal, Canada, but the paper in which they were described was written in Berkeley, Calif., where Rutherford gave a course of lectures on radioactivity at the University of California, in the summer of 1906. It is of interest to record, too, that part of the work was done with the assistance of O. Hahn, who was, more than thirty years later, to play an important part in connection with the discovery of nuclear fission which made possible the utilization of atomic energy (§ 13.7).

† W. Ramsay and F. Soddy found in 1903 that helium gas was continuously liberated from a sample of radium bromide.

helium, so that the alpha particle should be represented by the symbol He^{++}.

2.109. In 1909, E. Rutherford and T. Royds provided a final, and unequivocal, proof of the relationship between alpha particles and helium. A radioactive material, emitting alpha particles, was placed in a thin-walled, glass tube surrounded by a wider tube which had been evacuated. The alpha particles penetrated from the inner into the outer tube, through the thin glass walls. After several days, an electric discharge was passed through the outer tube, and it showed the unmistakable spectrum of helium gas. This could only have come from the alpha particles, and so it must be regarded as definitely established that these particles are doubly-charged helium ions, i.e., helium atoms carrying two unit positive charges. By picking up two electrons, an alpha particle eventually becomes an ordinary (neutral) helium atom.

GAMMA RAYS

2.110. A third type of radiation, which could not be deflected in a magnetic field, but which nevertheless had considerable penetrating power and a marked effect on a photographic plate, was discovered by P. Villard in France in 1900. These radiations are now called *gamma* (γ) *rays*.* As with cathode rays, the nature of the gamma rays was at first the subject of controversy. F. Paschen and W. H. Bragg thought they were high-speed particles, whereas C. G. Barkla and E. Rutherford favored the view that they were of a wave nature similar to X-rays. Definite proof of the correctness of the latter view was obtained by E. Rutherford and A. N. da C. Andrade in 1914 when they succeeded in causing the diffraction of the gamma rays by means of a suitable crystal (§ 2.93). Direct measurement of the wave lengths of the rays in this manner gave values corresponding to those for very short X-rays. The gamma rays, like X-rays and light rays, are thus a form of electromagnetic radiation (§ 3.23).

COMPARISON OF RADIATIONS

2.111. In reviewing the properties of the three types of radioactive rays, it may be said that the alpha rays have a very weak penetrating power, being completely absorbed by a few sheets of paper. These rays, however, are able to produce marked ionization of gases through which they pass, partly because of their relatively large mass and high velocity. The beta rays are much more penetrating than the alpha rays, some millimeters of aluminum being required to absorb them, but their ionizing power is appreciably less. Finally, the gamma rays are highly penetrating; several centimeters of lead may sometimes fail to cut them off completely, although they produce relatively little ionization in their path through air.

2.112. All three types of radiation can affect a photographic plate in the dark. It is of interest to recall that the initial discovery of radioactivity by Becquerel was due to the photographic action of the radiations from uranium. The differing electrical properties of the radiations are summarized in the form of a diagram (Fig. 2.11) which Marie Curie included in her doctorate *Thesis*, published in 1903. It is sup-

---

* It has been stated that Villard gave this name to the rays, but such does not appear to be the case. The term gamma rays came into general use in 1903, although it is not certain who originated it. The present writer is of the opinion that it was Rutherford, but there is a possibility that Becquerel was responsible.

posed that a radioactive material is placed in a narrow but deep cavity in a block of lead, so that, in the absence of electric and magnetic fields, the rays would emerge as a narrow vertical beam. However, if a strong magnetic field were applied in a direction perpendicular to and out of the plane of

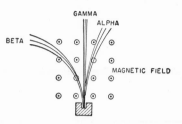

Fig. 2.11. Marie Curie's representation of alpha, beta and gamma rays in a magnetic field.

the paper, the alpha particles, being positively charged and relatively heavy, would be slightly deflected to the right, the beta particles, since they are negatively charged and light, would be deviated to a greater extent to the left, while the gamma rays, carrying no electric charge, would not be deflected at all.

2.113. Most naturally occurring radioactive elements radiate either alpha or beta particles, although in a few exceptional instances both are emitted.* In some cases, gamma rays accompany the alpha or beta particles. The essential nature of the rays is the same, irrespective of their origin; the alpha particles are always doubly-charged helium atoms, the beta particles are electrons, and the gamma rays are electromagnetic waves. However, the specific properties of the radiations, such as the velocities of the alpha and beta particles, their penetrabilities and power of ionizing gases, and the wave lengths of the gamma rays, vary with the particular radioactive element from which they originate.

2.114. The foregoing description of the radiations has referred in particular to those obtained from naturally occurring radioactive elements. In recent years a much larger number of active elements have been obtained in what might be called an artificial manner (Chapter XII). Some of these "artificially" radioactive elements, especially those of high atomic weight, emit alpha particles, while others expel either electrons or positrons (§ 2.71), together with gamma rays in many cases.

THE NEUTRON AND ANTINEUTRON

Prediction of the Neutron

2.115. In the year 1920 there appeared, from three widely separated sources, the suggestion that an entirely new and hitherto undiscovered particle, might be an important unit in the structure of atoms. The particle of which the possible existence was considered by W. D. Harkins in the United States, by Orme Masson in Australia, and by E. Rutherford in England, was believed to result from the neutralization of the electric charge of a proton by an electron, leaving a neutral, i.e., uncharged, particle, having a mass of unity, on the ordinary atomic weight scale.† In his Bakerian Lecture to the Royal Society in 1920,

---

* The emission of both alpha and beta particles by uranium salts, as observed by the early experimenters, was due to the presence of other active elements in addition to uranium (see Chapter V).

† In a letter dated February 28, 1921, to his former collaborator B. B. Boltwood of Yale University (see § 5.44), Rutherford wrote, concerning the particle of unit mass and zero charge: "Actually . . . most of the ideas . . . have been common property in this country [i.e., England] and especially to myself for the last five years."

Rutherford said: "Under some conditions . . . it may be possible for an electron to combine much more closely with the hydrogen nucleus [i.e., a proton], forming a kind of neutral doublet. Such an atom would have novel properties. Its external field would be practically zero . . . and consequently it should be able to move freely through matter. Its presence would probably be difficult to detect." This hypothetical particle, to which was given the name *neutron*,[*] was destined to play a totally unexpected role, not only in the history of atomic science but also in the fate of nations.

2.116. Since the neutron was regarded as a close combination of a proton, i.e., a gaseous hydrogen ion, and an electron, numerous unsuccessful attempts were made in Rutherford's laboratory, and probably elsewhere, to detect the formation of neutrons by the passage of an electric discharge through hydrogen. Rutherford also reported that he and his assistant, James Chadwick, who finally identified the neutron some years later (§ 2.118), had attempted to obtain neutrons by bombarding aluminum with fast alpha particles from a radioactive source; these efforts, too, met with failure, although, as later events proved, the experiments were actually on the right lines. In September 1924, Chadwick wrote to Rutherford, who was then on a visit to the United States: "I think we shall have to make a real search for the neutron. I believe I have a scheme which may just work but I must consult Aston first." But, if the scheme was tried, it was evidently not successful.

DISCOVERY OF THE NEUTRON

2.117. The actual discovery of the neutron came as an unexpected culmination of a series of events. In 1930, W. Bothe and H. Becker reported from Germany that if certain light elements, notably beryllium and to a lesser extent boron and lithium, were exposed to alpha rays from the natural radioactive element polonium, a very highly penetrating radiation was obtained. It was thought that this might be a form of gamma ray of high energy.[†] While repeating these experiments in 1932, I. Joliot-Curie and F. Joliot (§ 2.75) found that when a sheet of a hydrogen-containing material, particularly paraffin, was interposed in the path of the new radiation, protons were ejected with a considerable velocity. The Joliots thought they had discovered a "new mode of interaction of radiation with matter" whereby electromagnetic waves were able to impart large amounts of kinetic energy, i.e., energy of motion, and momentum to light atoms. The results were, however, not in accord with the requirement of the accepted laws of mechanics, and so there arose a dilemma: either the usual mechanical laws did not hold in this instance, or the so-called radiation was not of an electromagnetic nature analogous to gamma rays.

2.118. The situation was resolved by James Chadwick, in England, in 1932. Referring to the observations of Bothe and Becker, of the Joliots and also of H. C. Webster, made at about the same time, he said: "The experimental results are very difficult to explain on the hypothesis that the beryllium radi-

---

[*] The word neutron was apparently first employed in this connection by W. D. Harkins in 1921; thus, "neutron . . . a term representing one negative electron and one hydrogen nucleus [i.e., a proton]."

[†] It is very probable that gamma rays, arising from the Coulomb excitation of the nuclei of beryllium, etc., by the alpha particles, were actually present (§ 10.41).

ation was a quantum [i.e., electromagnetic] radiation, but followed immediately if it were supposed that the radiation consisted of particles of mass nearly equal to that of the proton and with no net charge." In other words, by supposing that the apparent new radiation was really a stream of neutrons, which have a particle nature but no charge, the observed facts could be interpreted without the necessity of discarding the laws of mechanics. It is easy to understand how a fast-moving particle like a neutron can impart kinetic energy and momentum to a hydrogen or other light atom. By attributing to the new particle a mass of approximately unity, on the atomic weight scale, i.e., about the same as that of the hydrogen atom (or the proton), Chadwick showed that the results of the earlier experimenters could be completely explained.*

2.119. Since the neutron carries no electric charge, it produces no appreciable ionization in its path and hence gives no visible track in a cloud chamber (§§ 2.67, 6.68). This is one explanation of why it proved difficult to detect. On the other hand, the absence of charge accounts for its very high penetrating power for reasons which will become apparent after the nature of the interior of the atom has been discussed (Chapter IV).

2.120. In the years since 1932, Chadwick's identification of the neutron has been amply verified in laboratories the world over. A number of different ways of producing neutrons have been discovered, and it is now known that these particles are fundamental units of atomic structure. In view of its great importance, the neutron merits a much more detailed treatment, and this will be given in Chapter XI.

THE ANTINEUTRON

2.121. From the occurrence of the antiparticles corresponding to the electron and the proton, namely, the positron and the negative proton (or antiproton), respectively, it is to be expected that an antineutron should also exist. However, the antineutron, like the positron and the antiproton, would not be a constituent of ordinary matter. The discovery of the antineutron, which had to await the availability of a fair source, at least, of antiprotons, was announced in September, 1956, by B. Cork, Y. Lamberton, O. Piccioni and W. Wenzel. It was stated in § 2.84 that, when a proton and an antiproton meet, mutual annihilation can, and generally does, take place. However, if the two particles come fairly close to one another but not close enough for annihilation to occur, it is possible for an electrical charge to be transferred from the positive proton to the negative antiproton, or vice versa. As a result, both particles would become electrically neutral, the proton being converted into a neutron and the antiproton into an antineutron; thus,

proton + antiproton → neutron + antineutron.

2.122. Proof that this process, leading to the formation of the antineutron, did indeed occur was obtained by allowing antiprotons, obtained from the Berkeley Bevatron as described above (§ 2.82), to impinge on liquid hydrogen. About three out of every

---

* F. Joliot is reported to have stated—after Chadwick's explanation of their observations—that if he and his wife (I. Joliot-Curie) had read Rutherford's 1920 Bakerian Lecture, in which the possible existence of a neutral particle of unit mass had been considered (§ 2.115), they would probably have identified the neutron themselves.

thousand antiprotons interacted with the protons in the hydrogen to form antineutrons. The latter were identified by the energy produced in the mutual annihilation of a neutron and an antineutron. The release of energy was accompanied by a flash of light (or scintillation) in a detector. Although flashes were caused in other ways, the recording system was designed to respond only to those associated with the correct amount of energy to be expected from neutron-antineutron annihilation.

2.123. The electron and its antiparticle, the positron, differ only in the respect that they have electrical charges of opposite sign, and the same is true of the proton and the antiproton. But since a neutron has no electrical charge, it is pertinent to inquire: What is the difference between a neutron and an antineutron? An answer to this question cannot yet be given with absolute certainty, but it is very probable that the following interpretation is correct. It will be seen later (§ 12.75) that the neutron, although it is electrically neutral, has the properties of a small magnet associated with a spinning negative charge. It is generally believed that the antineutron, on the other hand, will behave like a magnet due to a rotating positive charge. In other words, when spinning in the same direction, the neutron and the antineutron will act like magnets with their poles reversed, so that they will produce opposing magnetic fields.

MESONS

PIONS AND MUONS

2.124. In an attempt to account for the remarkable forces which hold together the interior (or nucleus) of an atom, the Japanese physicist H. Yukawa, in 1935, postulated the existence of a charged particle having a mass about 200 times that of an electron. This hypothetical particle would thus be intermediate in mass between an electron (or positron) and a proton.* At the time there was apparently no experimental evidence for such a particle, but during the years 1936 and 1937, C. D. Anderson and S. H. Neddermeyer, and J. C. Street and E. C. Stevenson, in the United States, demonstrated the presence in cosmic rays of charged particles, both positive and negative, having roughly the mass required by the Yukawa particle. This subject will be treated more fully in Chapter XVIII, but it may be stated here that further investigation fully confirmed the existence of this particle of intermediate mass, now called a *meson*.†

2.125. During the ten years following the discovery of the meson, its properties were studied in some detail and, as a result, a serious problem arose: interaction of mesons with atoms was very much less frequent than was expected from the Yukawa theory. In order to overcome this difficulty, the suggestion was made in 1947, independently by S. Sakata and T. Inoue in Japan and by H. A. Bethe and R. E. Marshak in the United States, that there were, in fact, two kinds of mesons which differed in mass, among other things. It appeared that a meson heavier than the one known at the time would possess the

---

* It will be recalled, from § 2.64, that the mass of the proton is 1836 times as great as that of an electron.

† From the Greek prefix *meso*, meaning intermediate (§ 18.69).

properties required to account for the atomic (nuclear) forces. Within a few hundred-millionths of a second, however, this meson, in the free state, would be expected to change into the lighter form.

2.126. A few weeks after the publication of these views, C. F. Powell and G. P. S. Occhialini and their collaborators, in England, obtained evidence for the existence of these two kinds of mesons. The heavier type, now known to have a mass 273 times that of the electron (or positron), is called a *pi* (*π*)-*meson*, or *pion;* the lighter, which is 207 times as heavy as an electron, is referred to as a *mu* (*μ*)-*meson*, or *muon*. Both positive and negative electrically charged pions and muons have been found in cosmic rays and have also been produced in the laboratory (§ 18.66 *et seq.*). Unless it is captured by an atom, as free negative pions frequently are, a charged pi-meson changes spontaneously into a mu-meson of the same sign, as predicted, accompanied by the liberation of energy. Then, in a little more than two millionths of a second, the muon decays into an electron or positron, depending upon the sign of its electrical charge. The sequence of events may thus be represented by

plates, and so neutral pi-mesons can be detected only by the electromagnetic radiations, similar to X-rays and gamma rays, which accompany their decay. Because of the complexity of cosmic ray phenomena, the presence of such radiations in nature could not be established with certainty. However, there is definite proof that neutral pions have been produced in the laboratory by means of simulated cosmic rays (§ 18.74). The mass of the neutral pi-meson is 264 times the electron mass, the difference between this value and that of the charged pi-meson (273 electron masses) being attributed to the electrical charge (§ 2.58). There are theoretical arguments for the non-existence of a neutral mu-meson, but if it does exist, it would be extremely difficult to detect.

K-MESONS

2.128. Since 1947, there have been identified, both in cosmic ray phenomena and in the laboratory, a number (about ten) of unstable particles considerably heavier than pi- and mu-mesons. They are, nevertheless, mesons because their masses lie roughly midway between those of the electron and proton. These particles, which have been given the general

pi-meson → mu-meson → electron or positron.
(+ energy)   (+ energy)

It will be seen from the arguments in Chapter III that the energy liberated in each stage corresponds to the difference in mass of the respective particles.

2.127. Neutral pions, having no electrical charge, are undoubtedly formed in cosmic rays, but they would be virtually impossible to observe in these circumstances. Unlike charged particles, they leave no tracks either in cloud chambers or in photographic

name of *K-mesons*, all appear to have the same mass, 966 times the electron mass, within the accuracy of the measurements. Some have a positive electrical charge, and there are corresponding ones with negative charges; in addition, there are probably two that are neutral. The charged *K*-mesons seem to have about the same average life, namely, about a hundred-millionth (10^{-8}) of a second. But these mesons are distinguished from each other by their modes of decay. In most instances the products are two or three pions, but in some cases a mu-meson or an electron is formed directly in the decay of a K-meson.

2.129. The foregoing brief description of mesons has been included in this chapter because of the possibly fundamental character of these particles. Further mention of mesons will be made from time to time, especially in connection with the problem of internal atomic (nuclear) forces, in Chapter XII. But there are many aspects of the production and properties of mesons which cannot be discussed until other topics have been considered. Consequently, a fuller treatment of these and other aptly-called "strange" particles will be deferred until Chapter XVIII.

Energy and Radiation Chapter III

THE NATURE OF ENERGY

3.1. Although the study of energy* is one of the most important aspects of physical science, it is difficult to supply a precise definition in simple language. Broadly, it may be stated that energy is work, or anything that can be converted into work. But this statement, obviously, has no meaning without an explanation of the significance of work, and for the present purpose it is sufficient to say that work is done whenever there is a movement of a body or particle against a resisting force. In general, therefore, energy has the capacity of causing the motion of a body in spite of the operation of a force resisting the motion. The expenditure of energy in this manner may result in its conversion into heat, as, for example, when two bodies are moved relative to one another against the force of friction.

3.2. Energy can take many forms, several of which are easily converted into each other, and all of which can be used, at least in principle, to perform some kind of work. This work is not necessarily obtained in a useful form, but the definition is satisfied in the respect that there is motion against a force. Coal or oil, together with oxygen from the air, contains energy

which appears as heat when the fuel is burned in a boiler. The heat energy may then be used to raise the temperature of water to produce steam, the molecules of the latter, possessing more energy than the molecules of cold water. Then the energy of the steam can be converted into mechanical energy, as in a steam engine, which may be used to drive a ship or a train against the resisting force of friction due to the water or to the rails and air, as the case may be. Alternatively, the mechanical energy can be changed into electrical energy in a dynamo, and back again into mechanical energy in an electric motor.

3.3. Atomic energy is a form of energy that is not essentially different from the forms described above. When an oil, which is a hydrocarbon or compound of hydrogen and carbon, burns in the oxygen of the air, there is a liberation of energy due to a chemical reaction resulting in the formation of water and carbon dioxide. In other words, energy is produced as a consequence of a rearrangement of the atoms of hydrogen, carbon and oxygen taking part in the reaction. Atomic energy, on the other hand, results from rearrangements within the interior of the atom itself. Once the release of the

---

* From the Greek, *en* (in) and *ergon* (work).

atomic energy is achieved in a suitable manner, it might, in principle if not in practice, be used for performing work.

3.4. Whenever a large amount of energy is liberated within a very short interval of time, the result is an explosion. The operation of an internal combustion engine, e.g., of an automobile, depends on the explosions occurring in the cylinder when a spark is passed through a mixture of gasoline (hydrocarbon) vapor and atmospheric oxygen. However, if gasoline is burned in the open air, the release of energy takes place more slowly and there is no explosion. The heat of the flame could be used to produce steam and this could be made to run a steam engine. In a general way, the same is true of atomic energy. The very sudden release of a tremendous amount of energy, in the so-called atomic bomb, leads to a powerful and devastating explosion. But it is possible to liberate the energy gradually so that it may be employed to do useful work. The way in which this application of atomic energy can be achieved will be considered in Chapter XIV.

3.5. Every form of energy can be regarded as *kinetic energy*, or *potential energy*, or both. The kinetic energy of a body or particle is energy of motion, while potential energy is that of position, relative to other bodies, or condition. Potential energy can usually be readily converted into kinetic energy. For example, the water at rest behind a dam has potential energy but if it overflows, its potential energy is converted into kinetic energy of motion. Ordinary fuels and certain atoms possess potential energy which can be changed into kinetic energy by suitable means. The kinetic energy of a body is determined by its mass m and its velocity of motion v, the actual value being $\frac{1}{2}mv^2$. When the temperature of a substance is raised, by supplying heat, the molecules move more rapidly, and hence their kinetic energy increases.

THE NATURE OF RADIATION

RADIANT ENERGY

3.6. Radiant energy, or *radiation*, is of great importance in various atomic studies, and hence the subject merits fairly detailed consideration. It is the form in which energy can be transferred from one point to another through space. Two very familiar, but apparently different, kinds of radiation are light and radio waves. The sun's energy, which incidentally is a type of atomic energy (§ 14.100), is conveyed to the earth largely in the form of light, or visible radiation as it is sometimes called. When it reaches the earth's surface, the energy of the sun- light is either absorbed by green plants and stored as chemical (potential) energy, mainly in carbohydrates such as sugars and starches, or it is converted into heat which warms the atmosphere (kinetic energy). In a somewhat related manner, small amounts of energy are transferred from a radio transmitter to a distant receiver in the form of radiation. This radiation, however, is not visible, that is to say, it does not affect the eye in the same manner as does light. Other forms of invisible radiations are ultraviolet light, X-rays and gamma rays.*

3.7. Since all kinds of radiation are

---

*Alpha and beta rays are also sometimes referred to as "radiations"; they are, however, not radiations in the sense of radiant energy or electromagnetic radiation considered here.

fundamentally the same, it will be convenient to discuss first what is perhaps the most familiar form, namely, light. The concept that light consists of particles projected from luminous bodies into the eye of the observer was proposed by the philosophical school of Pythagoras, around 500 B.C. This idea was revived in the latter part of the seventeenth century by the English mathematician Isaac Newton. He considered the best way to explain the fact that light travels in straight lines and casts sharp shadows was to suppose it to be made up of small particles or corpuscles. An alternative theory, that light is a form of undulation or wave motion, was proposed in a vague form by Robert Hooke in England, and its consequences were worked out in some detail, about 1680, by Christian Huygens, the noted Dutch authority on optics. But Newton was opposed to the wave theory because it seemed to him that it could explain neither the formation of sharp shadows nor certain other optical effects known at the time.

THE WAVE THEORY OF LIGHT

3.8. For over a hundred years the corpuscular structure of light was widely accepted, but, in the early 1800s, Thomas Young, in England, and Augustin Jean Fresnel, in France, revived the wave theory and showed how Newton's objections could be overcome. The sharpness of shadows, for example, could be accounted for by the extreme smallness of the light waves, so that the ability to turn corners, normally possessed by waves, was undetectable in the ordinary way. Nevertheless, careful study of the behavior of light as it passes by the sharp edge of an opaque body or through a very narrow slit, shows that it is actually bent and spread out from its linear path, as is to be expected for a wave motion. This is an aspect of the phenomenon known as *diffraction* of light (cf. § 2.93).

3.9. The facts of optical *interference* also appear to require the existence of light waves to provide an adequate explanation. If homogeneous light from a given source passes through a number of narrow slits very close together, and the emergent rays are allowed to fall on a screen, the result will not be an equal number of thin strips of light, as might have been expected, but a series of light and dark bands. This is referred to as an interference pattern, or *diffraction pattern*.

3.10. The explanation based on the wave theory is that the light is diffracted, that is to say, it is bent out of its path, and spread out somewhat, in passing through the small slits. If, at a certain point in the screen, two rays of light coming from the slits are in phase, i.e., if the crests of one set of waves coincide exactly with the crests in the other set, the two rays will reinforce one another giving a strip of increased brightness. At an adjacent point, however, the two rays will be out of phase, the crests in one ray coinciding with the troughs in the other; the two rays will thus tend to annul or interfere with one another, so that

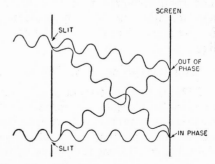

FIG. 3.1. Diagrammatic representation of a diffraction grating with light waves passing through slits.

there is a strip of virtual darkness (Fig. 3.1). The same general behavior should occur at a series of points, thus giving rise to a pattern of successive light and dark bands, as actually observed. While a satisfactory interpretation of interference effects is possible in terms of the wave concept, the corpuscular theory fails to offer any reasonable alternative. It should be noted that, in order to obtain satisfactory interference effects, the slits should be narrow and their distance apart must be of the same order as the wave length of light, i.e., about 5×10^{-5} cm. (§ 3.16). An arrangement of this kind for producing a diffraction pattern is known as a *diffraction grating*, because its structure is similar to that of a grating, but on a very small scale.

3.11. By the middle of the nineteenth century, moderately accurate measurements of the velocity (or speed) with which light travels from one point to another had been made, chiefly by A. H. L. Fizeau and by J. B. L. Foucault in France. This work provided a crucial test of the two rival theories concerning the nature of light. According to the wave concept, the speed should be greater in air than in a more dense medium like water, but the Newtonian corpuscular theory required the reverse to be the case. The results showed that the former was actually true, thereby providing further support for the wave theory of light.

THE NATURE OF WAVE MOTION

3.12. At this point an attempt must be made to consider the character of wave motion in general, and of the particular type that is involved in light. If a small stone is dropped verti-

cally in the center of a pool of water, a series of ripples or waves will be seen to move outward in concentric circles. However, a cork floating on the surface of the water will not move out with the waves, but will merely bob up and down as each wave crest and trough, respectively, passes it by. It is clear, therefore, that although the water acts as a medium in which the waves can move away from the center of disturbance, the water itself does not travel in the direction of propagation of the waves, but only at right angles to it. A wave motion of this kind is said to be *transverse*, since the direction of motion of the medium is transverse to, or across, that in which the waves are being propagated (Fig. 3.2). Various studies show that light

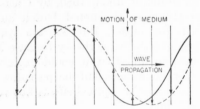

FIG. 3.2. Transverse wave motion: the motion of the medium is at right angles to the direction of propagation of the wave.

has the character of such a transverse wave motion, although there is no actual up and down movement of the medium, e.g., air or water, through which the light travels.*

3.13. A wave motion consists of a series of crests and troughs, as seen in Fig. 3.3; the distance between any two successive crests, or successive troughs, is known as the *wave length*, and is usually represented by the Greek letter *lambda*, λ. In general, λ is the linear distance from any position on one

---

* It may be remarked that sound is also propagated as waves, but these are *longitudinal* in nature, since the medium, e.g., the air, moves to and fro parallel to the direction in which the wave is traveling.

wave to the corresponding position on the next wave. Suppose the wave motion is propagated with a velocity c expressed, for example, in centimeters per second, and suppose further, that

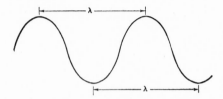

Fig. 3.3. Wave motion and wave length.

the wave length λ is also given in centimeters. The number of waves passing a certain point in the medium in the course of one second will then be equal to c/λ. This quantity is called the *frequency* of the wave motion and is represented by the symbol ν (Greek, *nu*), so that it is possible to write the important equation

$$\nu = \frac{c}{\lambda} \quad \text{or} \quad \lambda = \frac{c}{\nu}, \qquad (3.1)$$

giving the relationship among the wave length λ, the frequency ν, and c, the speed (or velocity) of propagation of any wave motion, including light.*

THE SPEED OF LIGHT

3.14. As implied earlier, the speed of light, as with other wave motion, depends on the medium through which it passes. The value usually recorded for light is that for empty space, i.e., for a perfect vacuum. Actually, measurements are made in air and a small correction is applied. In view of the tremendously high velocity with which light is propagated, about 186,000 miles per second, the measurement of the speed of light is difficult. Nevertheless, several highly accurate procedures have been developed for the purpose, so that the value is now known with a considerable degree of precision. This is indeed fortunate as the speed of light in empty space is one of the fundamental constants of nature. For scientific work it is usual to state the speed in centimeters per second, and this is 2.99779×10^{10} cm. per sec. However, for most purposes it is sufficient to round the value off to 3.00×10^{10} cm. per sec., which will be used throughout this book.†

3.15. In the foregoing discussion the term "light" has been used in a general sense without specifying any particular color. The reason is that experiment has shown that all forms of light travel in empty space with exactly the same speed. In this connection, therefore, the color of the light is immaterial. What, then, is responsible for the different possible colors which light manifests? Variations of color are now known to be due to differences in the wave length of the light. Since the speed of propagation is always the same, it may equally well be stated that color differentiation is attributed to frequency differences.

COLOR AND WAVE LENGTH

3.16. As Newton first showed, white light is actually a mixture of all the visible colors, i.e., all the colors to which the normal eye is sensitive; they are essentially red, orange, yellow, green, blue, indigo and violet—the colors of the rainbow. Of this series, red has the longest and violet the

---

* A quantity, known as the wave number, which is equal to the reciprocal of the wave length, i.e., $1/\lambda$, is commonly used in spectroscopic work. The wave number is the number of waves in a centimeter length, and is equal to the frequency of the waves divided by the velocity of light.

† The factor 3×10^{10} referred to in the first footnote in § 2.43 for the conversion of electrostatic to electromagnetic units of charge is the velocity of light.

shortest wave length, the values being approximately 7.60×10^{-5} cm. and 3.85×10^{-5} cm., respectively. The wave lengths of the other colors occupy intermediate positions in the order given. Quite frequently, wave lengths of light are quoted in terms of the Angstrom unit (A), which, as stated in § 1.68, is equal to 10^{-8} cm.; the wave lengths of visible light fall within the range of 7600 to 3850 A.

3.17. It was seen in Chapter I that atomic diameters are usually around 2×10^{-8} cm., that is, about 2 A; consequently, the wave lengths of light waves, although quite short from the ordinary standpoint, are still two or three thousand times the diameter of an average atom. The smallest particle that can possibly be seen in an ordinary optical microscope must have dimensions of the same order as the wave length of the light used. It is evident therefore that an atom or molecule is too small to be seen in such a microscope. A cube consisting of two or three thousand atoms in each of three directions, and thus containing a total of several billion atoms, would be just visible.

3.18. It is well known that photographic plates or films are sensitive to light, but all colors do not affect them equally. Most ordinary film is hardly affected by red light, so that a ruby lamp is often used in the so-called "dark room." By adding certain chemical substances to the photographic emulsion, the film can be rendered sensitive to red light, and even to radiations of longer wave length which are invisible to the eye. These are the *infrared rays* emitted to a greater or lesser extent by most substances under normal conditions. A hot body emits more infrared radiation than does a cold one. It is the presence of these infrared rays, in conjunction with spe-

cially prepared film, that makes it possible to obtain photographs through fog or even in the dark. It is not intended to consider this subject further here, except to emphasize the fact that radiations exist which are completely invisible to the human eye. There is no essential difference between infrared rays and visible light, except that the former have wave lengths greater than 7600 A, the normal upper limit of visibility.

3.19. The lower limit of visibility is represented by violet light, with a wave length of about 3850 A. Nevertheless, the existence of radiations of shorter wave length can be readily proved; these are the ultraviolet rays present to some extent in summer sunlight, especially in the upper atmosphere, and also in many electric discharges such as arcs and sparks. Ordinary photographic film is extremely sensitive to ultraviolet radiation, although this radiation is quite invisible to the human eye. By means of special instruments the wave lengths of ultraviolet rays have been measured down to about 1000 A.

ELECTROMAGNETIC WAVES

3.20. At this point it may well be asked: If there are radiations having wave lengths both longer and shorter than visible light, may there not be rays that are still longer and shorter, respectively, than those in the infrared and ultraviolet regions? The answer to this question is that such radiations are known. They include the great range of radio waves, from radar to long-wave radio, at the one extreme, and gamma rays and X-rays, at the other extreme. These radiations are fundamentally the same; they all travel with the same speed—the speed of light—and differ only in the length of their waves, covering the enormous range from about 10^{-10} cm. for gamma rays to 10^8 cm. for the longest known radio waves.

3.21. In the early years of the nineteenth century, M. Faraday (see § 2.7), following up the earlier investigations of H. C. Oersted in Denmark and of A. M. Ampère in France, showed by means of his classical experiments on electromagnetic induction that electric and magnetic effects are intimately related. An electric charge in motion, i.e., an electric current, produces a magnetic field in its vicinity. Similarly, a changing magnetic field can produce an electric current in a suitable conductor. The electrical and magnetic effects, as Faraday showed, can be transmitted through space, without actual material contact being necessary.

3.22. In 1864, J. C. Maxwell (see § 2.25) applied mathematical methods to the foregoing ideas and came to a remarkable conclusion concerning the nature of light. He showed that certain electrical disturbances should be accompanied by the emission of electric waves. In other words, an electric field whose intensity varies periodically, as in wave motion, should be propagated outward from the point of origin of the disturbance. The behavior is somewhat analogous to that observed when a stone is dropped into a pool of water, as described in § 3.12. However, the so-called electric waves do not require a material medium, like water or air, for their propagation.

3.23. Because of the interrelationship of electric and magnetic effects, the varying electric field will be accompanied by a magnetic wave whose period or wave length is identical with that of the electric wave. The direction of the oscillations associated with the respective waves (see Fig. 3.2) are at right angles to one another and both

are perpendicular to the direction of propagation of the wave motion. The *electromagnetic wave,* as the combination is called, has thus the character of a transverse wave motion (§ 3.12). Making use of both theoretical considerations and experimental data, Maxwell found that the velocity of propagation of all electromagnetic waves, no matter what their origin or wave length, should be identical with the speed of light. He, therefore, inferred that light is itself an electromagnetic wave phenomenon.

3.24. Although no electromagnetic radiations, other than light, were known to Maxwell, he realized that such radiations, with wave lengths different from those of visible light, but traveling with the same speed, might be discovered. This expectation was confirmed by Heinrich Hertz in Germany in 1887, eight years after Maxwell's death. By means of an oscillatory electrical discharge, obtained with the aid of an induction coil, Hertz produced electromagnetic waves which were invisible but which, nevertheless, had many of the properties of light. Their speed of propagation through space was, as Maxwell had foretold, the same as the velocity of light, but their wave lengths were considerably greater, being measured in meters while those of visible light are very small fractions of a millimeter. The electromagnetic radiations discovered by Hertz were called Hertzian waves, but they are now more generally known as radio waves. At the present time waves of this type are produced by oscillating surges of electric current obtained by suitable circuits involving vacuum tubes. In this way, the radiations have a specific wave length, rather than the range of wave lengths given by an induction-coil oscillator.

3.25. After the brilliant vindication

of Maxwell's ideas by the discovery of Hertzian waves, the value of the electromagnetic theory of radiation was widely appreciated. As stated earlier, a whole range of such radiations is now known, from gamma rays to very long radio waves; the wave length and frequency regions occupied by the various kinds of radiation are indicated approximately in Fig. 3.4. It should be understood that there is actually no line of demarcation, but rather a gradual transition from one type to another. Thus, the longer (lower frequency) of the gamma rays are identical with the shorter (higher frequency) of the X-rays. Similarly, the shorter (higher frequency) radio waves are indistinguishable from the longer (lower frequency) infrared rays.

The Quantum Theory of Radiation

3.27. Maxwell's concept of the relationship between electromagnetic waves and radiation appeared to be in harmony with the wave theory of light as described in § 3.23. But this apparently satisfactory state of affairs was to receive a staggering and unexpected blow in the early years of the present century. A black surface is known to be more efficient than any other color in absorbing radiations, and the theoretical concept of an ideal *black body* has been developed to represent a perfect absorber and emitter of radiation. Although no such black body can be realized in practice, an adequate approximation is possible which can be

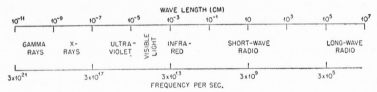

FIG. 3.4. Approximate wave length and frequency regions of various electromagnetic radiations.

3.26. In addition to having the same velocity as light, electromagnetic radiations have other properties in common. For example, they undergo reflection, and also exhibit diffraction and interference effects which are regarded as characteristic wave properties. As seen in Chapter II, the electromagnetic wave nature of X-rays and of gamma rays was not definitely established until it was shown that they could be made to undergo diffraction and yield definite interference patterns.

used for experimental studies. One type of measurement made with the black body was to determine the amounts of energy radiated at various wave lengths and at various temperatures. It was found that, at a given temperature, the energy emission is not the same for all wave lengths, but has a maximum value at a particular wave length which is inversely proportional to the absolute temperature (*Wien's law*).* Further, the total energy emitted per unit time by the black body varies as the fourth power

* The so-called absolute temperature of a body is obtained by adding 273.15° to the centigrade (Celsius) temperature.

of the absolute temperature (*Stefan-Boltzmann law*).

3.28. Attempts to account for the preceding facts relating to black body radiation were made by W. Wien in Germany in 1896, and by Lord Rayleigh (3rd Baron) in 1900, but the equation derived by the former was found to hold only at low temperatures or for short wave lengths, whereas that of the latter was applicable only at high temperatures or for long wave lengths. The dilemma was resolved in 1900, in a completely revolutionary manner, by the German physicist Max Planck. Both Wien and Rayleigh thought of the black body as consisting of a system of vibrators oscillating at a particular frequency corresponding to the frequency of the absorbed or emitted radiation. The radiation, which was regarded as wavelike in nature, was considered to be absorbed or emitted in a continuous manner.

3.29. While retaining the general concept of oscillators, Planck discarded the idea that energy can be continuously absorbed or emitted. He suggested that a body absorbs or emits energy in the form of radiation in integral multiples of a definite amount or quantum,* the magnitude of which depends on the vibrational frequency of the oscillator. In other words, the energy of a body is not continuously variable, but must consist of a specific whole number of quanta; the energy can be taken up or given out in such quanta only. A body can thus emit or absorb one, two, three, four, etc., quanta of energy, but no intermediate or fractional amounts. This statement forms the basis of the *quantum theory* of radiation, a theory which has found application in many areas of science.

3.30. According to Planck, the quantum E of energy for radiation of frequency ν † is given by the simple, but fundamental, expression

$$E = h\nu, \qquad (3.2)$$

where h is a universal constant, usually known as the *Planck constant*. The energy quantum for a particular radiation is thus directly proportional to its frequency. By equation (3.1), the frequency varies inversely as the wave length; hence, the magnitude of the energy quantum is inversely proportional to the wave length of the radiation. The quantum for gamma rays, for example, is consequently relatively large, whereas for radio waves it is very considerably smaller. The exact relationship between the energy quantum and the wave length λ of the radiation may be obtained by combining equations (3.1) and (3.2) to give

$$E = \frac{hc}{\lambda}, \qquad (3.3)$$

where c is the velocity of light.

3.31. Making use of equation (3.2), and the postulate that oscillators take up or give out energy in terms of whole numbers of quanta, Planck was able to derive an expression for the variation with the wave length of the energy radiated by a black body that

---

* Planck originally referred to these definite quantities of energy as "energy elements." The term "energy quantum" was introduced later, probably by A. Einstein in 1905 (see § 3.35).

† In his treatment, Planck defined ν as the frequency of the oscillator absorbing or emitting the radiation. Since the radiation has the same frequency as the oscillator, it is less confusing, and equally satisfactory for the present purpose, to take ν as the frequency of the radiation.

was in complete agreement with experiment at all reasonable temperatures and wave lengths. Further, for radiations of long wave length or for high temperatures, Planck's equation reduces to that of Lord Rayleigh, whereas for short wave length or for low temperatures it becomes identical with the one proposed by Wien. Thus, the quantum theory was shown to be superior to the previous attempts at treating the absorption and emission of radiation; this was to prove to be the first of its many achievements.

3.32. The magnitude of the Planck constant h, which is one of the fundamental constants of nature whose significance is not yet completely understood, has been determined in several ways. If the measurements are expressed in terms of the centimeter-gram-second, or c.g.s., system, where distance is measured in centimeters, mass in grams and time in seconds, the energy unit is the erg.* The experimental value of h is then 6.62×10^{-27} erg sec., with the frequency ν in vibrations per sec., or the wave length λ in cm. Thus, by equation (3.2),

$$E \text{ (ergs)} = 6.62 \times 10^{-27}\, \nu \text{ per sec., (3.4)}$$

and by equation (3.3), taking c, the velocity of light, as 3.00×10^{10} cm. per sec.,

$$E \text{ (ergs)} = \frac{6.62 \times 10^{-27} \times 3.00 \times 10^{10}}{\lambda \text{ (cm.)}}$$

$$= \frac{1.99 \times 10^{-16}}{\lambda \text{ (cm.)}}. \qquad (3.5)$$

For a gamma ray, for example, with a wave length of 10^{-10} cm., the quantum is 1.99×10^{-6} erg.

3.33. In atomic studies it has become the practice to express energies in *electron volt* units, abbreviated to ev, rather than in ergs. The electron volt is the energy acquired by any charged particle carrying a unit (electronic) charge when it falls through a potential of 1 volt; it is equivalent to 1.603×10^{-12} erg, but for present purposes it is sufficiently accurate to abbreviate this figure to 1.60×10^{-12} erg. For convenience, two other energy units are used; one, equal to a thousand electron volts, called the kilo-electron volt, is represented by kev, and the other, which is a million electron volts, is abbreviated to Mev. These are 1.60×10^{-9} and 1.60×10^{-6} erg, respectively. Hence, equation (3.5) may be written as

$$E \text{ (Mev)} = \frac{1.99 \times 10^{-16}}{1.60 \times 10^{-6}\, \lambda \text{ (cm.)}}$$

$$= \frac{1.24 \times 10^{-10}}{\lambda \text{ (cm.)}}, \qquad (3.6)$$

which is a general expression relating the energy quantum (in Mev) to the wave length (in cm.) of the corresponding radiation. Thus, for a gamma ray having a wave length of 10^{-10} cm., as in the example given above, the quantum would be 1.24 Mev. It will be seen in due course that gamma-ray energy quanta are very frequently in the vicinity of a million electron volts, so that the Mev is a convenient unit for stating these (and related) energies.

THE PHOTON

3.34. It should be made clear that Planck's theory referred to the taking up (absorption) or giving out (emission) of radiation. It was only these particular processes which were considered to take place in terms of an

---

* An erg is the work done when a force of 1 dyne acts through a distance of 1 cm. The dyne is the force which acting on a mass of 1 gram gives it an acceleration of 1 cm. per sec. per sec.

integral number of energy quanta. The propagation of the radiation through space was still regarded as a wave motion, as described earlier. However, this point of view began to encounter some difficulties. It was mentioned in § 2.89 that X-rays are able to cause ionization of a gas through which they pass; in other words, the X-rays eject electrons from the atoms or molecules of the gas. But the number of ions formed is not large, considering the energy of the radiation. If the X-rays are waves spreading in all directions, it might be anticipated that electrons would be removed from all molecules or atoms over which the rays passed, instead of from a select few. This discrepancy was difficult to explain. Further, in 1902, P. Lenard (see § 2.88) had found, when studying the emission of electrons from metals by the photoelectric effect (§ 2.48), that the energy of the electrons is independent of the intensity of the radiation employed to produce them. An attempt to explain these observations was made by J. J. Thomson by means of a modified form of the wave theory, but this proved to be not too satisfactory.

3.35. A solution of the problem was found in 1905 by Albert Einstein (see § 3.65), whose development of the theory of relativity was later to provide the basic atomic energy equation (§ 3.72). He suggested that not merely was radiation absorbed and emitted in whole numbers of energy quanta, as Planck had proposed, but also that it was actually propagated through space in definite quanta or *photons*,* moving with the speed of light. This surprising view, which apparently discarded the wave theory of light in favor of something very much akin to a particle concept, supplied a complete interpretation of the known photoelectric phenomena. The equations derived by Einstein proved to be correct in all details, so that the idea of radiation being transmitted through space in the form of individual photons—not unlike the Newtonian corpuscles—received such strong support that its validity could not be doubted.

3.36. One of the most significant arguments for the photon (or particle) nature of radiation is provided by the discovery of what is known as the *Compton effect*, made by the American physicist A. H. Compton in 1923. He found that when X-rays fall on carbon, or other material of low atomic weight, the scattered radiation contains some rays of longer wave length than the incident X-rays. Since the scattering is actually produced by the electrons present in the carbon atoms, it appears that interaction between X-rays and electrons results in an increase in the wave length of the former. By assuming the X-rays to consist of particles of energy $h\nu$, where ν is the frequency of the incident rays, and supposing that the encounter between one of these particles and an electron is just like a collision between two rigid spheres, Compton deduced equations which account perfectly both for the increase in wave length of the scattered X-rays, and for the

---

* From the Greek *photos,* meaning light. The term photon, which came into general use around 1928, was introduced by A. H. Compton (see § 3.36), following its earlier employment in a somewhat different, but related, connection by the noted American physical chemist, G. N. Lewis.

Although the photon is frequently regarded as synonymous with the energy quantum, it is, strictly, the quantity or quantum of *radiation* associated with a single quantum of *energy*. It might, in fact, be described as an "atom" or "particle" of radiation. By equation (3.2) a photon of radiation of frequency ν carries an amount (or quantum) $h\nu$ of energy.

simultaneous recoil of the struck electron (Fig. 3.5).

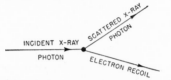

INCIDENT X-RAY
PHOTON
SCATTERED X-RAY PHOTON
ELECTRON RECOIL

FIG. 3.5. The Compton effect accompanying the interaction of an X-ray photon with an electron.

3.37. Ionization by X-rays apparently requires a direct encounter between an X-ray photon and an electron present in the atom or molecule to be ionized. Since such encounters are not too common, it is possible to understand why the extent of ionization produced by X-rays is less than would be expected from a wave motion spreading in all directions.

WAVES AND PARTICLES

WAVE-PARTICLE DUALITY

3.38. The situation now reached appears to be contradictory: having first established, fairly convincingly, that radiations consist of electromagnetic waves, it has now been shown, equally convincingly, that radiations are emitted, transmitted through space, and absorbed as energy particles! However, a more careful examination of the state of affairs will show that there is a possible way out of the apparent paradox. The diffraction and interference properties of radiation necessitate a wave structure, but photoelectric phenomena and the Compton effect imply that radiation consists of particles rather than waves. In other words, radiation may be regarded as having a dual wave-particle nature; some of the properties of radiation may be wave properties, while others are particle properties.

3.39. This dualism of the wave and particle functions of radiation led Louis de Broglie of France to suggest, in 1923, that a similar dualism might exist for material particles and electrons. His proposal was, essentially, that the wave-particle dualism represented something that is perhaps fundamental to the nature of the universe. By means of Planck's quantum theory equation and the mass-energy relationship of Einstein, to be considered shortly (§ 3.72), de Broglie showed that a particle of mass m moving with a velocity v should be associated with waves of length λ, given by

$$\lambda = \frac{h}{mv}, \qquad (3.7)$$

where h is the Planck constant. Similarly, radiation of wave length λ, will be equivalent to a particle of mass $h/\lambda v$, moving with speed v, where in this case v is the velocity of light.

3.40. Without going into details, it can be seen from equation (3.7) that the wave length is inversely related to the product of the mass and velocity of the particle; this product, i.e., mv, is known as the *momentum* of the particle. Actual calculations show that, unless the mass m is very small, such as would be the case for an electron or for the lightest known atoms, namely, hydrogen and helium, the wave length of the *matter waves*, as they are often called, are so short that there are no means at present available for their detection. Nevertheless, there is little doubt that something with a wavelike character is always associated with a moving particle, although it is different from the electromagnetic waves of light and other radiations.

3.41. It was mentioned in § 2.94

that crystals can act as diffraction gratings and can produce interference effects with X-rays, since the spacing of atoms and molecules in crystals are of the same order as the wave lengths of these rays. Soon after the publication of de Broglie's work, the suggestion was made in 1925 by W. Elsasser, in Germany, that evidence for the wave nature of electrons might be obtained in an analogous manner. From the known mass of the electron (§ 2.56), it was calculated that, with a moderately high velocity, such as could be obtained by passage through a potential of about 100 to 1000 volts, the de Broglie waves should have a wave length of the order of 10^{-8} cm. If this were the case, then crystals should be capable of producing diffraction effects with electrons.

THE DIFFRACTION OF ELECTRONS AND ATOMS

3.42. The first definite proof that electrons can be diffracted and consequently exhibit wave, as well as the familiar particle, properties was obtained in the Bell Telephone Laboratories in New York by C. J. Davisson and L. H. Germer in 1927. By studying the reflection and scattering, by a nickel crystal, of a beam of electrons, given a specific velocity by passage through a known potential difference, it was found that the electrons behaved like waves rather than like particles. Using electrons which had been accelerated by a potential of 54 volts, the experimental results were found to be equivalent to those expected from radiation of wave length 1.65 A. This was in remarkably good agreement with the value of 1.67 A calculated by means of the de Broglie equation (3.7).

3.43. Further evidence for the existence of electron waves was obtained independently in 1927, by the English physicist G. P. Thomson, son of J. J. Thomson. He passed a stream of fast moving electrons through a very thin sheet of metal, and then allowed the resulting beam to fall on a photographic plate. Upon development, the plate showed a diffraction pattern consisting of a series of concentric circles, just as might have been produced by X-rays, indicating that the electrons were manifesting wave properties. It is of special interest to mention that the diffraction pattern could be distorted by means of a magnet, showing it was actually produced by electrons and not by extraneous radiations, such as X-rays, which might have been present. Since 1927, the wave properties of electrons have become almost commonplace in scientific laboratories. The electron microscope, for example, which is used for the examination of particles much too small to be visible in the best optical instruments, depends on the behavior of electrons as waves, although diffraction is not involved.

3.44. Diffraction effects have been observed with streams of hydrogen and helium atoms—actually ions, i.e., protons and alpha particles, were used since they could be speeded up by means of an electric field—and even with neutrons. It is thus apparent that these particles which are two thousand, and more, times as heavy as the electron, also have wave properties. There is little doubt that, if suitable detecting means could be devised, even heavier atoms and molecules would be found to exhibit the diffraction effects characteristic of wave motion. At the present time, there does not appear to be any way in which this might be accomplished.

3.45. In view of the wave-particle duality of matter, it may be wondered if there is any point in making a distinction between a wave and a particle. In a sense, such a distinction is meaningless, since everything has wave character or particle character depending on the circumstances. Nevertheless, it is still the general practice to refer to an electron, a neutron, an atom or a molecule as a particle, whereas light, gamma rays and X-rays are regarded as waves. This is done because the familiar properties of the former group correspond to those associated with particles, but the members of the latter group commonly behave as waves. A more satisfactory approach would be to differentiate between particle properties and wave properties, rather than between particle and wave. Electrons, atoms and so on, usually exhibit particle properties, whereas light, gamma rays and similar radiations normally manifest wave properties. But, if suitable conditions are established, the electrons and atoms will behave like waves, whereas the radiations can act like particles.

The Uncertainty Principle

3.46. It was realized by W. Heisenberg, who was later in charge of Germany's unsuccessful effort to develop an atomic bomb, that the wave-particle duality of matter was merely one aspect of a general law of nature. On the basis of highly involved theoretical considerations, Heisenberg, in 1927, enunciated the *uncertainty principle* which represents a generalization of the greatest significance. For the present purpose, this principle may be stated in the following simplified form: The simultaneous exact determination of position and momentum, or of any property related to momentum, such

as velocity or energy, is impossible. That this is the case may be illustrated by reference to the electron. Its position might be found, in principle, by illuminating it with radiations of very short wave length, e.g., gamma rays, and then observing it in a suitable (imaginary) supermicroscope. However, in this process of determining the position of the electron its momentum will change, because of the recoil resulting from the Compton effect, i.e., from the interaction of the electron with a gamma-ray photon. Consequently, although the position of the electron might be obtained very exactly, the momentum could not possibly be estimated with any degree of accuracy.

3.47. At first sight, it seems that this difficulty might be overcome by making use of the wave character of the electron and measuring its wave length, by means of an appropriate diffraction grating; the momentum could then be calculated exactly by means of the de Broglie equation (3.7). But this device would be of no avail. Since the electron wave undergoes diffraction, in the determination of the momentum, its direction of motion is changed and the position of the electron is no longer defined. No matter what method is employed, the final result is inescapable: if the position of a particle can be determined exactly, then its momentum is indefinite, but if the momentum is obtained with considerable precision, the position will be uncertain. In every case, there will be an inevitable interaction of the particle under observation with the measuring system, so that if either the position or the momentum is determined accurately, the other will be indefinite. It is important to emphasize that these circumstances are not due to experimental errors, but to a fundamental characteristic of nature.

3.47. It can be seen from the foregoing discussion that when investigating the precise position of an electron, it is treated as a particle, but if its momentum is required, then use is made of the wave properties. Similar considerations apply to all particles and also to radiation. This means that for certain purposes a system may be treated as a particle, and for other purposes as a wave motion, but it cannot be considered as having both particle and wave characters simultaneously. Thus the wave and particle properties of matter and radiation are to be regarded as complementary and not contradictory.

Wave Mechanics

3.49. In order to determine the future behavior of a moving particle by means of Newtonian or classical mechanics, it is necessary to know both its position and momentum at any particular instant. According to the uncertainty principle, however, these two quantities cannot be precisely known at the same instant, and so the behavior of the particle cannot be predicted. This statement would appear to be contrary to experience, since calculations relating to the motion of both terrestrial and celestial bodies have proved remarkably accurate. The explanation is that for bodies of appreciable mass, the uncertainty in the determination of either the posi-

tion or the momentum is so very small, both relatively and absolutely, that it is less than the normal experimental error of observation.* The use of classical mechanics in such cases gives results which are, at least, as accurate as the actual measurements.

3.50. When dealing with very small particles, such as electrons and other constituents of atoms, however, the situation is very different. The uncertainties are here so relatively large that classical mechanics is virtually useless. For the treatment of such minute particles a new procedure, known as *quantum mechanics* or *wave mechanics,* in which the apparent certainties of classical mechanics are replaced by probabilities, was introduced by the Austrian-born physicist E. Schrödinger in 1926 and developed by himself and by others.† It is difficult to ascribe an exact physical significance to the mathematical treatment, but it may be thought of somewhat along the following lines. The position of an electron, or other particle, of definite momentum or energy cannot be known exactly, because of the operation of the uncertainty principle, and it is possible to state only the statistical probability that the particle will be found at any given point. Since it has been established that particles can exhibit what appear to be wave-like properties, the new mechanics postulates that this probability can be expressed by means of a relationship which is similar to that used for describing wave motion in general.

---

* According to the uncertainty principle the product of the uncertainties in the determination of the position and momentum is approximately equal to the Planck constant h, i.e., 6.62×10^{-27} erg sec. (or gram cm.^{2}/sec.). For a body of appreciable mass this uncertainty effect is negligible, but for an electron, with a mass of 10^{-27} gram, or even for a light atom, such is evidently not the case.

† Wave mechanics should really be used for all systems, large or small. But, for bodies larger than a single molecule, the results are essentially identical with those derived from classical mechanics, so that the latter, which is considerably simpler, is invariably employed.

The situation, as far as it can be given a physical interpretation, is that the statistical probability of finding a particle in a particular place can be represented by an equation of the same form as that which describes the propagation of waves.

3.51. It should be admitted quite frankly that at the present time the mathematical applications of wave mechanics have outrun their interpretation in terms of understandable realities. There is little doubt, in view of their remarkable success in various atomic studies, that the equations of wave mechanics are substantially correct, but their underlying significance is by no means obvious. Some scientists are content with the mathematics alone, for they consider that its exact physical meaning is beyond human comprehension at present. Louis de Broglie, for example, said: "Recent theoretical views suggest that a mechanistic view of nature cannot be pushed beyond a certain point, and that the fundamental laws can only be expressed in abstract terms, defying all attempts at an intelligible description." Even among those who attempt an interpretation in material terms, there is no complete agreement. At any rate, the point of view expressed in the preceding paragraph, which is based on that of Max Born (1926), even if not absolutely true, does provide a fairly simple, convenient, and probably not too misleading way of considering the postulates and results of wave mechanics. Some of these results as applied to atomic properties will be considered in later chapters.

SIGNIFICANCE OF WAVE PROPERTIES

3.52. Although it is admitted that particles are associated with wavelike properties, the nature of the so-called matter waves of de Broglie still presents a problem. It is known that they are not electromagnetic waves, like X-rays or gamma rays, although they may have similar wave lengths, but what they are is not evident. If the interpretation of wave mechanics given above is accepted, a possible solution of this problem may be found, for the matter waves would not represent an actual wave propagation. A stream of moving particles behaves like a train of waves merely because the statistical probability of finding a particle at any point in its path is represented by a wave equation. Why such an equation, rather than some other form, should give the distribution of the particles in space is still a mystery. There is little doubt that this view, like many other scientific theories, will have to undergo modification in the future, but for the present it may be accepted, at least as a working hypothesis.

3.53. Similar considerations may conceivably apply to radiations. Although these are still referred to as electromagnetic waves, for they are undoubtedly associated with electric and magnetic fields which obey a wave equation, there is not necessarily any wave motion. It may perhaps be permissible to consider radiation as consisting of photons whose statistical distribution is represented by an equation of the form applicable to the propagation of waves.

RELATIVITY AND THE MASS-ENERGY EQUATION

The Ether and the Velocity of Light

3.54. When physicists in the early years of the nineteenth century were developing the wave theory of light, they considered the waves to have reality and so it was felt there should be a medium which carried them. Just as ripples on the surface of a pool are transmitted by the water, and sound requires air or other material, so it seemed that a medium was necessary for the propagation of light waves. It was postulated, therefore, that there existed an all-pervading luminiferous (or light-bearing) *ether*, a view which, incidentally, is no longer accepted, at least not in its original sense. Since light reaches the earth from distant stars in outer space, the ether was presumed to extend indefinitely, so that it was regarded as virtually identical with space itself. When Maxwell showed that light was associated with a varying electromagnetic field (§ 3.23), the belief in the hypothetical ether was strengthened. In addition to carrying radiation, it provided the medium for the propagation of electromagnetic disturbances. No one could say exactly what the ether was, and there was no real proof of its existence; nevertheless, the view was widely accepted that the ether had real significance.

3.55. Various astronomical measurements had led to the conclusion that the ether, if it exists, is stationary, and that bodies such as the earth, sun and stars move through it without producing any disturbance. If this were the case, then it should be possible to determine the absolute speed with which the earth is moving through space by observations on the velocity of light.

Suppose the earth travels through the stationary ether at an absolute speed of v, say in miles per hour. Consider a fixed source on the earth from which light is emitted; let c be the speed of light through the ether. If the direction of propagation of light happens to coincide with that in which the earth is moving, the velocity of the light relative to the ether will be $c + v$. If, however, the light travels in the direction exactly opposite to that of the earth, its relative velocity will be $c - v$. The situation is similar to that of a man swimming with a speed c in a river flowing at the rate v; if the swimmer travels in the direction in which the river is flowing, his speed relative to a point on the river bank will be $c + v$. But if he travels in the opposite direction, his speed will be $c - v$.

3.56. The time taken for the light to travel a definite distance l in the direction of the earth's motion is then $l/(c + v)$, while the same distance in the opposite direction will require the time $l/(c - v)$. Hence, if light were to travel a certain distance l in the direction in which the earth is moving, then be reflected back and travel the same distance in the opposite direction, the time required would be given by

Time for travel parallel to earth's motion

$$= \frac{l}{c + v} + \frac{l}{c - v} = \frac{2cl}{c^2 - v^2}.$$

3.57. Suppose now that the light coming from the source on the earth is propagated in the ether in a direction perpendicular to the earth's motion. The speed will be unaffected by the movement of the earth, and the light will travel to and be reflected from a certain point with the velocity c, its absolute speed through the ether. However, because of the supposed motion of the earth through the ether, the distance over which the light has to travel will be increased. This case is exactly analogous to a man swimming in a direction perpendicular to that of the river's flow. His actual path will be as represented by the broken line in Fig. 3.6, rather than by the full line, as

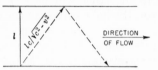

Fig. 3.6. Path of swimmer crossing stream at right angles to direction of flow.

would have been the case if the river had been stationary. It is a simple matter of geometry to show that the path is now $lc/\sqrt{c^2 - v^2}$, instead of l. Hence the time taken for the light to travel, at the speed c, in each direction is $l/\sqrt{c^2 - v^2}$, so that

Time for travel perpendicular to earth's motion

$$= \frac{l}{\sqrt{c^2 - v^2}} + \frac{l}{\sqrt{c^2 - v^2}} = \frac{2l}{\sqrt{c^2 - v^2}}.$$

The ratio of the times for propagation of light parallel and perpendicular to the earth's motion is then obtained by dividing the two expressions; thus,

Ratio of times

$$= \frac{2cl}{c^2 - v^2} \cdot \frac{\sqrt{c^2 - v^2}}{2l}$$

$$= \frac{c}{\sqrt{c^2 - v^2}} = \frac{1}{\sqrt{1 - v^2/c^2}}. \qquad (3.8)$$

3.58. The speed c at which light travels is known, namely, 186,266 miles (or 2.99779×10^{10} cm.) per sec.; hence, if the ratio of the times required for the light to travel in the two paths at right angles could be measured, the value of v, the rate at which the earth moves through the ether, could be readily calculated from equation (3.8).

The Michelson-Morley Experiment

3.59. If a means could be devised for dividing a beam of light from a given source into two rays propagated at right angles to one another, making them travel the same distance to a mirror where each is reflected back, and comparing the times of arrival of the two rays, the problem of determining the earth's speed through the ether would, presumably, be solved. The first reliable measurements of this kind were made in Potsdam, Germany, by the noted American physicist A. A. Michelson in 1881. The results were so unexpected that the work was repeated by Michelson, in Cleveland, Ohio, in conjunction with E. W. Morley. In 1887, a report of the historic *Michelson-Morley experiment* was published: it was found that there was no significant difference between the rates at which the light traveled in the two directions at right angles to each other. Various orientations of the beams were tried, but the results were always the same; the speed of light was independent of its direction of propagation.*

3.60. The Michelson-Morley experiment thus showed that the ratio of the times of travel of light in equation (3.8) is virtually unity, and this presumably meant that v, the rate at

---

* Actually, a difference, about a quarter of that expected for a stationary ether, was observed, but it was disregarded. However, as a result of numerous observations made by Morley with D. C. Miller (1902-1905) and by Miller alone (1921-1932), the latter concluded that this difference has real significance. Nevertheless, other experimenters consider that the discrepancy is due, mainly if not entirely, to experimental error.

which the earth moves through the ether, is zero. In other words, it appeared that the earth does not travel through a stationary ether, but carries the ether along with it. This surprising conclusion represented a complete contradiction of the long-accepted view that the earth, and other bodies, moved through the ether without disturbing it, and consequently it created a sensation in the world of science.

3.61. In seeking for a way out of the dilemma, the Irish scientist G. F. Fitzgerald (1893), while retaining the stationary ether hypothesis, suggested that a body traveling in a direction parallel to the earth's motion actually undergoes a contraction. This contraction would not normally be observed because the measuring instrument would contract correspondingly, and the distance would appear to be unchanged. Thus, it was supposed that in the Michelson-Morley experiment the apparatus changed its dimensions in such a way as to compensate exactly for the expected difference in the velocity of light in the two directions at right angles. The ratio of the velocities would thus appear to be unity. According to Fitzgerald, the contraction in the direction of the earth's motion would be represented by the factor $\sqrt{1 - v^2/c^2}$, which is, of course, identical with the denominator of equation (3.8).

VELOCITY AND MASS
OF THE ELECTRON

3.62. It was indicated in § 2.57 that the mass of an electron varies with its speed. The first evidence of such a variation was obtained by W. Kaufmann, who had made some of the very earliest measurements of the specific

charge of an electron (§ 2.43). In 1900, he described a method for determining e/m for high-velocity beta particles from a radioactive source, making use of deflections in electric and magnetic fields. The experimental arrangement was such that differences in the velocities of the beta-ray electrons could be detected at the same time, and it appeared that the e/m value decreased slightly as the velocity increased. This conclusion was apparently confirmed by A. H. Bucherer in 1908,[*] and by E. Hupka in 1910; the former used beta rays, and the latter highly accelerated cathode rays, as the source of electrons. Provided the speed of the electrons is less than about one tenth of the velocity of light, the specific charge e/m is essentially constant, but as the speed increases, the values of e/m exhibit a definite decrease. If, as is very probable, the actual charge e of the electron is independent of its velocity, it must be concluded that the mass of an electron increases as its speed is increased.

3.63. In the course of his studies in mathematical physics, the great Dutch scientist H. A. Lorentz had derived an expression relating the mass of an electron to its speed. His arguments may be stated in the following elementary form. A moving electron is assumed to contract in the direction of its motion by the Fitzgerald factor $\sqrt{1 - v^2/c^2}$, so that if r_0 is its radius when at rest, the value will be $r_0\sqrt{1 - v^2/c^2}$ when the electron is moving with a speed v. If the mass of a spherical electron is assumed to be electromagnetic in nature, then by equation (2.11) the mass should be inversely proportional to the radius. Representing the rest mass of the electron, i.e., the mass for very small velocities, by m_0, and its mass when moving with the speed v by the

---

[*] More recent work has shown that Bucherer's experimental procedure was not capable of giving the degree of accuracy which he claimed for his results.

letter m, it consequently follows that

$$\frac{m}{m_0} = \frac{r_0}{r_0 \left(\sqrt{1 - v^2/c^2}\right)} = \frac{1}{\sqrt{1 - v^2/c^2}}$$

or,

$$m = \frac{m_0}{\sqrt{1 - v^2/c^2}}. \qquad (3.9)$$

3.64. Since the factor $\sqrt{1 - v^2/c^2}$ is always less than unity, it is seen that the mass m of the electron when moving with a speed v should be greater than the rest mass m_0. If v is about one tenth of the velocity of light, i.e., v/c is 0.1, then $\sqrt{1 - v^2/c^2}$ is 0.995, and the actual mass m is $1.005\ m_0$, differing from the rest mass by only 0.5 per cent. But, if v is 99 per cent of the speed of light, so that v/c is 0.99, then the actual mass will be 7.10 times the rest mass. As the speed of the electron approaches that of light the ratio m/m_0 should increase very rapidly, as shown in Fig. 3.7. The experimental determination

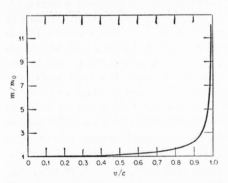

FIG. 3.7. Increase of mass, relative to its rest mass, of a moving particle with increasing velocity.

of e/m, for electrons moving at various speeds up to about eight tenths of the velocity of light, are in excellent agreement with equation (3.9), so that this may be taken as giving a satisfactory representation of the effect of motion on the mass of an electron.

THE THEORY OF RELATIVITY

3.65. The Lorentz equation for the influence of speed on electron mass is undoubtedly of the correct form, but the arguments upon which it was based have proved inadequate. However, in 1905, using his theory of relativity, the German-born Albert Einstein, at the time an examiner in the Swiss Patent Office, derived an expression identical with equation (3.9), but applicable to all moving particles, and not merely to electrons. The important point is that for all bodies, whether they carry an electric charge or not, and regardless of whether their mass is electromagnetic in origin or not, the mass should increase with increasing velocity. The reason why such an increase of mass is not usually observed will be clear from Fig. 3.7; it will not be detectable until the speed approaches that of light, for it is only then that m/m_0 becomes appreciably greater than unity. Such high speeds are, of course, unusual. They can be obtained with beta particles from radioactive sources, and with specially accelerated electrons and other charged particles (Chapter IX); in these cases, there is no doubt that the mass does increase with the speed.

3.66. In attempting to explain the Michelson-Morley experiment, Einstein first discarded the ether concept as unnecessary; he then made two assumptions: first, that determination of absolute motion is impossible, and, second, that the velocity of light always has a constant value, irrespective of the motion of the source or of the observer. These two postulates formed the basis of the *special theory of relativity*, which Einstein used to obtain results that have had a profound effect on many branches of science. It is not possible here to do more than touch very superficially on such aspects of the theory as are applicable to the problem of atomic energy.

3.67. Suppose a signal lamp flashes a beam of light of velocity c down a railroad track, along which a train is traveling at a speed v; according to the laws of classical mechanics, to an observer on the train, the speed of light relative to himself should be $c + v$ if he is moving toward the signal, or $c - v$ if he is traveling away from it. But the theory of relativity, based on the results of the Michelson-Morley experiment, states that the observer on the train will always find the velocity of light to have the constant value c, relative to himself, no matter in what direction he is moving. The explanation is that, although the observer does not realize it, his instruments for measuring both distance and time, which are necessary for determining velocity, are undergoing change as the train moves in one direction or the other. As a result of these changes the observer will always find the velocity of light to have the same value regardless of the direction of his motion. Another observer who remains stationary with respect to the signal lamp would, in theory, be able to detect the changes in the measuring instruments on the moving train, with respect to his own stationary instruments.

3.68. In order to satisfy the requirements of the theory of relativity, measurements of length and time made with respect to a moving body have to be converted, by the use of certain mathematical transformations, to give the corresponding values with respect to a stationary body. Thus, length and time are relative, and not absolute, quantities, the values depending on the motion of the body with respect to which they are measured.

3.69. These relativity corrections involve the term $\sqrt{1 - v^2/c^2}$, encoun-

tered in the preceding paragraphs, which does not differ appreciably from unity until the velocity v of the moving body is as high as about one tenth of the speed of light. Hence, for speeds which are small relative to the velocity of light, e.g., up to about 18,000 miles per second, but nevertheless, extremely high by ordinary standards, the corrections are quite negligible. Under normal conditions, therefore, it would not be possible to detect the expected changes in the instruments for determining length and time; classical mechanics is then adequate for treating moving bodies. From what has been stated here and in § 3.49, it is evident that Newton's laws of motion represent what are called limiting laws. Although they are entirely adequate for the limiting cases of relatively large bodies, i.e., larger than a molecule, moving with moderate speeds compared with that of light, they break down when applied to particles of small dimensions, traveling with very high speeds. It is these latter conditions which exist within the atom; consequently, in atomic studies new laws based on wave mechanics and relativity must replace the classical laws of motion.

The Mass-Energy Relationship

3.70. In the further development of his theory, Einstein was able to show that similar considerations apply to mass as to length and time. The transformation factor required to convert the mass of a moving body to the rest mass was found to be identical with that derived by Lorentz for the electron, so that equation (3.9) given above holds for any system. It is often referred to as the *relativistic mass equation*, the mass m being called the *relativistic mass*, to distinguish it from m_0, the rest mass, for low velocities.

3.71. Writing equation (3.9) in the equivalent form

$$m = m_0 (1 - v^2/c^2)^{-1/2}, \quad (3.10)$$

and expanding the right hand member by means of the well-known binomial theorem of algebra, all terms beyond the first being neglected since they are usually very small, the result is

$$m = m_0 + \frac{\frac{1}{2} m_0 v^2}{c^2} \quad (3.11)$$

The quantity $\frac{1}{2} m_0 v^2$ is approximately the kinetic energy of the body due to its motion with a speed v (§ 3.5); representing this by E_k, equation (3.11) may be written as

$$m = m_0 + \frac{E_k}{c^2}$$

or

$$m - m_0 = \frac{E_k}{c^2},$$

where, as usual, c is the velocity of light. The quantity $m - m_0$, the difference between the mass of the moving body and its rest mass, may be represented by Δm, so that

$$\Delta m = \frac{E_k}{c^2}. \quad (3.12)$$

The increase in mass Δm of a body as a result of its motion is thus directly related to the kinetic energy E_k. Hence, it would appear from the theory of relativity that there is a definite mass equivalent of energy, at least of kinetic energy.[*]

3.72. By the use of more detailed calculations, Einstein proved, as he put it, that "the mass of a body is a measure of its energy content" and that when the energy of a body is changed by an amount E—no matter what form the energy takes—the mass of the body will change in the same sense by E/c^2. Consequently, it is possible to write the general relationship

$$E = mc^2, \quad (3.13)$$

where the mass m is the equivalent of the energy E. This result, often referred to as the Einstein *mass-energy equation*, is fundamental to the whole subject of atomic energy. It shows that there is an exact equivalence between energy and mass, and it points to the possibility of releasing large amounts of energy by the "destruction" or, more exactly, by the conversion, of mass.

THE CONSERVATION OF MASS AND ENERGY

3.73. In the early years of the present century, there were two scientific laws which would have been universally regarded as completely inviolate. They were the laws of the conservation of mass and of the conservation of energy, which stated that matter, determined as mass, and energy can neither be created nor destroyed. From the time of the Greek philosopher Anaxagoras, about 450 B.C., through that of Francis Bacon, who in his *Novum Organum*, published in 1620, wrote: ". . . the absolute quantity or sum

---

[*] The derivation of equation (3.12) given here is simple but very approximate. A more exact procedure, using calculus, is the following. A force F acting on a body moving through a distance dx increases the kinetic energy by Fdx, which may be represented by dE. By Newton's second law, force is equal to the rate of change of momentum, so that $F = d(mv)/dt$, and consequently $dE = Fdx = d(mv)dx/dt$. Since dx/dt represents the velocity of the moving body, it may be replaced by v; consequently $dE = vd(mv)$, or $dE = v^2dm + mvdv$. Differentiation of the relativistic mass equation (3.9), in the form $m^2 (c^2 - v^2) = m_0^2 c^2$, gives $(c^2 - v^2)dm - mvdv = 0$, since m_0 and c are constant. Comparison with the preceding equation for dE shows that $dm = dE/c^2$, which is similar to, but more exact than, equation (3.12).

total of matter remains unchanged without increase or diminution," and of A. L. Lavoisier in the latter part of the eighteenth century, up to recent years, the indestructibility of matter (or mass) had been regarded as axiomatic. In fact all the quantitative aspects of chemistry involved the tacit assumption that there was no net change of mass in a chemical reaction. The extremely accurate and painstaking experiments of H. Landolt (1909) in Germany and of J. J. Manley (1912) in England showed that if there was such a gain or loss of mass, it could not exceed about one part in a hundred million, this being the limit of accuracy of the balances used for weighing.

3.74. The nature of heat and its relationship to energy was only vaguely understood until the end of the eighteenth century when, in 1798, the American-born Benjamin Thompson, Count Rumford of the Holy Roman Empire, and Minister of War in Bavaria, published a paper entitled *An Enquiry Concerning the Source of Heat which is Excited by Friction*. From studies made in the boring of brass cannon, he showed there is a direct connection between the heat generated and the mechanical work done. From the subsequent investigations of the English scientist Humphry Davy (1812), of the German physician J. R. Mayer (1842), of the Danish philosopher L. A. Colding (1843) and of the English brewer turned scientist J. P. Joule (1843-1878), the exact equivalence between work and energy was definitely established.

3.75. The fundamental implication of these studies was realized by the eminent German physicist H. von Helmholtz, who in 1847 enunciated the concept of the conservation of energy. The essence of this principle is that although one form of energy may be converted into another form, it can neither be created nor destroyed. In other words, whenever there is a production of energy of any kind, such as work, heat or electrical energy, an exactly equivalent amount of another kind must have been used up. Support for this law was provided not only by failure of the innumerable attempts to achieve perpetual motion, i.e., the continuous production of mechanical energy without the use of a corresponding quantity of some other form of energy, but, more significantly, by its undoubted success in thermodynamics and engineering.

3.76. It would appear from the foregoing review that Einstein's concept of the equivalence of mass and energy is entirely contrary to the laws of conservation of mass and energy. If a fast-moving body is slowed down, its mass should decrease, according to the mass-energy relationship; if its motion is accelerated the mass should increase. Similarly, if the mass of a system could be changed in any way, as is in fact possible for many processes taking place within the interior of atoms, there should be a corresponding liberation or absorption of energy. Although these conclusions appear to be contrary to the simple conservation laws, the results can be reconciled by a somewhat broader interpretation of the conservation principle. A useful way of looking at the situation is to regard mass and energy as different manifestations—as they probably are—of some fundamental property of matter. Then, in any process or change, it is always the combined mass and energy that is conserved. Energy can be "converted" into mass and mass into energy, but the total, based on equation (3.13) to express the equivalence of mass and energy, always remains unchanged.

3.77. In view of the postulated equivalence of mass and energy, it may well be asked: Why had changes in mass not been detected, especially in chemical reactions in which large amounts of energy are liberated as heat? This question can be readily answered by means of a quotation from the *Principles of Science,* by the English philosopher W. S. Jevons, published as long ago as 1879. "Physicists [and chemists] often assume quantities to be equal provided they fall within the limits of probable error of the process employed. . . . We cannot prove the indestructibility of matter; for were an exceedingly minute fraction of existing matter to vanish in any experiment . . . we should never detect the loss." In other words, a change in mass could not be detected if it were less than the experimental error, as it is indeed in chemical reactions even where measurements have been made with the greatest possible precision.

3.78. It can now be understood why the classical laws of conservation of mass and of energy were believed to hold. In the more familiar cases of energy production and absorption, such as in chemical processes, the energy changes are of such magnitude that the corresponding changes in mass are undetectable. Thus, mass appears to be conserved. The same is true, of course, when one (conventional) form of energy, e.g., mechanical work, is converted into an equivalent amount of another form, e.g., electricity. However, when it comes to rearrangements within the atoms themselves, the energy changes are something like a million times as large as in chemical reactions. The changes of mass are then appreciable, and they have been shown, in various ways, to be in accord with the Einstein mass-energy equation.

INTERCONVERSION OF MASS AND ENERGY

3.79. A more detailed application of the mass-energy relationship to the subject of atomic energy will be given in Chapter IX, and various references to it will be made elsewhere. At this point, it will be sufficient to illustrate, by means of a few examples, the method of calculation and the general nature of the results obtained using the equation $E = mc^2$, where E represents the energy equivalent of a mass m, and c is the velocity of light. If c is expressed in centimeters per second, and m in grams, then E will be given in ergs (§ 3.32 footnote). Since the velocity of light is known to be 2.998×10^{10} cm. per sec., the Einstein mass-energy equation can be written as

E (ergs)

$$= m \text{ (grams)} \times (2.998 \times 10^{10})^2$$

$$= m \text{ (grams)} \times 8.99 \times 10^{20}. \quad (3.14)$$

In many measurements, particularly where there is an evolution or absorption of heat, as in chemical reactions, the energy is expressed in heat units or calories, 1 calorie being equivalent to 4.184×10^7 ergs. Making this substitution, it is readily found that equation (3.14) takes the form

E (calories)

$$= m \text{ (grams)} \times 2.15 \times 10^{13}. \quad (3.15)$$

3.80. Consider a process, such as the combustion of a hydrocarbon fuel, in which 100 grams of a chemical substance undergo reaction with the liberation of 1 million, i.e., 10^6, calories; this is an exceptionally large amount of heat for a chemical reaction. By means of equation (3.15) it is possible to calculate the decrease of mass to be expected. Substituting 10^6 calories for

E in the left-hand member, it follows that

$$10^6 = m \times 2.15 \times 10^{13},$$

$$m = 4.65 \times 10^{-8} \text{ gram.}$$

The loss of mass equivalent to the energy evolved will thus be 4.65×10^{-8} parts by weight in a hundred, which is less than one in a billion. Such a decrease is beyond the possibility of detection by even the most sensitive chemical balances. This is the reason, as indicated above, why the mass-energy effect has not been observed in chemical reactions.

3.81. As stated earlier, the electron volt and, particularly, the million electron volt units are commonly used for expressing energies in atomic studies. Utilizing the fact that 1 ev is equivalent to 1.60×10^{-12} erg and 1 Mev to 1.60×10^{-6} erg (§ 3.33), it follows from equation (3.14) that

$$E \text{ (ev)}$$

$$= m \text{ (grams)} \times \frac{8.99 \times 10^{20}}{1.60 \times 10^{-12}}$$

$$= m \text{ (grams)} \times 5.61 \times 10^{32}$$

$$E \text{ (Mev)}$$

$$= m \text{ (grams)} \times 5.61 \times 10^{26}. \quad (3.16)$$

3.82. In many calculations involving mass-energy equivalence in processes occurring within the interior of atoms, it is convenient to express masses on the atomic weight scale, i.e., relative to the oxygen atom as 16.0000.* Unit mass on this scale, referred to as an *atomic mass unit*, is then one-sixteenth of the mass of an oxygen atom. Since, as shown in § 1.57, the mass of any atom in grams is equal to its atomic weight divided by the Avogadro number (6.025×10^{23}), the mass of an oxygen atom is $16/(6.025 \times 10^{23})$. Hence, in view of the definition, an atomic mass unit, abbreviated to 1 a.m.u., is equivalent to $1/(6.025 \times 10^{23}) = 1.66 \times 10^{-24}$ gram. Upon inserting this factor into equation (3.16), the result is

$$E \text{ (Mev)}$$

$$= m \text{ (a.m.u.)} \times 5.61 \times 10^{26} \times 1.66 \times 10^{-24}$$

$$= m \text{ (a.m.u.)} \times 931, \quad (3.17)$$

where m (a.m.u.) represents the mass (or mass change) in atomic mass units, i.e., on the physical atomic weight scale. It is seen, therefore, that 1 atomic mass unit is equivalent to 931 Mev or, in other words, the energy equivalent in Mev is obtained upon multiplying the mass (or mass change) on the atomic weight scale by a factor of 931.

3.83. In several chapters of this book examples will be given of the use of the foregoing mass-energy and related equations. The agreement with experiment in so many instances has supplied abundant confirmation of the equivalence of mass and energy, at least for cases of this type. Even if in the course of time the theory of relativity should be amended or, as is probable, it is found to be an aspect of a much wider generalization, it seems certain that the Einstein equation $E = mc^2$ will remain essentially unchanged.

POSITRON-ELECTRON PAIR FORMATION AND ANNIHILATION

3.84. A simple application of the relationships between mass, on the one hand, and the energy or the wave length of electromagnetic radiation, on the other hand, for which the basic

---

* The physical, rather than the chemical, atomic weight scale (§ 8.61) is used, but the difference is of minor importance for calculations involving four significant figures or less.

information has been given in Chapter II, is concerned with the formation and annihilation of positron-electron pairs. The value of the annihilation energy (§ 2.77) is calculated in the following manner. As seen in § 2.56, the rest mass of the electron is close to 9.11×10^{-28} gram, and the positron has the same mass. Positron-electron annihilation, therefore, results in a loss of mass of $2 \times 9.11 \times 10^{-28}$ gram. Using equation (3.16), the accompanying liberation of energy should be

$$E = 2 \times 9.11 \times 10^{-28} \times 5.61 \times 10^{26}$$
$$= 1.02 \text{ Mev.}$$

Thus, the total amount of energy produced in the mutual annihilation of a positron and an electron is 1.02 Mev. If this energy were emitted as a single photon of radiation, the latter would lie in the gamma-ray region, since the wave length, as derived from equation (3.6), would be 1.21×10^{-10} cm. It will be seen shortly that the 1.02 Mev appears much more commonly as two or three photons; however, the resulting radiations may still be regarded as gamma rays.

3.85. By reversing the calculation made above, it is apparent that an energy of 1.02 Mev, at least, would be required to create a positron-electron pair. Two experimental facts may be mentioned in support of this value. First, the additional absorption of high-energy gamma rays, which was attributed in § 2.78 to the conversion of part of the energy into positron-electron pairs, does not become apparent until the gamma-ray energy quantum exceeds 1.02 Mev. The second is based on the fact that the gamma rays from thorium C″, which are known to have an energy of 2.62 Mev, can produce positron-electron pairs. If the creation of a pair requires 1.02 Mev, the excess energy of $2.62 - 1.02 = 1.60$ Mev should remain. This might be transferred to the electron or positron or, more probably, be shared by both. In complete agreement with this expectation, measurements show that the maximum energy carried by a positron formed in this manner is 1.6 Mev.

3.86. It was suggested by the Yugoslav scientist S. Mohorovičič in 1934 that, before a positron and an electron annihilated each other, they might exist, for a very short time, as a quasi-stable system held together by the attraction between the positive and negative electrical charges. In view of the similarity to a normal atom, as will be apparent in the next chapter, A. E. Ruark in 1945 proposed the name *positronium* for the temporary positron-electron combination.* A study of the system showed that actually two forms of positronium should be capable of transitory existence. This situation arises because electrons and positrons (and other fundamental particles) have a property most simply described as "spin" (§ 4.54). In one form of positronium, called orthopositronium, the electron and positron spin in the same direction, that is to say, their spins are parallel. In the other form, known as parapositronium, the spins of the particles would be in opposite directions, i.e., antiparallel.†

3.87. The difference between ortho- and para-positronium should be manifest in at least two ways. In the first place, theoretical calculations indicate

---

* The simplest stable atom, that of hydrogen, consists of a combination of a proton and an electron.

† Since protons possess spin, analogous ortho- and para-forms of a proton-antiproton combination should also be capable of transitory existence before annihilation occurs.

that the average lifetime of the ortho-form, before positron-electron annihi-lation occurs, should be about 1.5×10^{-7} sec., whereas that of the para-form, which has a much shorter life, should be only 1.3×10^{-10} sec. Further, when annihilation does take place, the distribution of the resulting 1.02 Mev of energy should be different in the two cases. The reason for this behavior is associated with the fact that the spins of the positron and of the electron can be only $+\frac{1}{2}$ or $-\frac{1}{2}$ unit (§ 4.54), whereas that of the photon of radiation, in which form the annihilation energy appears, is either $+1$ or -1; $+$ and $-$ signs indicate spins in one particular direction or in the opposite direction, respectively.

3.88. In orthopositronium, where the electron and positron have parallel spins, the resultant spin is either $+1$ or -1, but in the para-form, where the spins are antiparallel, the net spin must be zero. A basic requirement of the annihilation processes (and of atomic reactions, in general) is that spin should be conserved, i.e., the total spin should remain unchanged. This means that parapositronium (spin 0) can form two photons (spins $+1$ and -1), whereas orthopositronium (spin $+1$ or -1) must yield either one photon (spin $+1$ or -1) or three photons (spins $+1$, $+1$ and -1, or -1, -1 and $+1$) upon annihilation.

3.89. When two-photon annihilation occurs, the photons should be expelled in opposite directions, in order to sat-isfy the law of conservation of mo-mentum, each photon carrying half the total available energy, 1.02 Mev. Thus, gamma radiation with an energy quantum of $\frac{1}{2} \times 1.02 = 0.51$ Mev should be produced. Such radiation can always be detected whenever positron-electron annihilation occurs. However, this does not prove that

parapositronium is an intermediate step, for conservation of spin and momentum would lead to the same result, in any event.

3.90. Proof of the existence of posi-tronium would require a determination of the average lifetime. For the para-form this is too short to measure with any certainty; but that of the ortho-positronium, although less than a millionth of a second, is within the scope of modern techniques for ob-serving very small time intervals. By using such methods, M. Deutsch, of the Massachusetts Institute of Tech-nology, was able in 1951 to determine the time between the formation of positrons, by emission from a radio-active source, and their subsequent annihilation. This was found to be in excellent agreement with the calculated value given above, namely, 1.5×10^{-7} sec., thus providing good evidence for intermediate formation of orthoposi-tronium. Subsequently, confirmation was obtained by arranging three gamma-ray detectors symmetrically in a plane about a source of positrons. An event was registered only when a gamma-ray photon entered each of the three detectors simultaneously, thus recording the annihilation of ortho-positronium.

3.91. In a three-photon annihilation, conservation of momentum does not require the total energy of 1.02 Mev to be divided equally among the pho-tons. As a result, the energy quanta from orthopositronium annihilation cover a range from very small amounts up to 0.51 Mev. In principle, orthopositronium should also be ca-pable of emitting the whole 1.02 Mev as a single gamma-ray quantum. Radiation of this energy has been observed to accompany positron an-nihilation, but only to a relatively small extent. The reason is that, if momentum is to be conserved in a one-photon annihilation, another particle, preferably a heavy one, must be available to take up the recoil. Because of the very short life of parapositronium, two-photon annihilation occurs more readily, and the resulting 0.51-Mev gamma rays are the chief constituent of positron-electron annihilation radiation.

3.92. A number of gas molecules which have definite, although weak, magnetic properties, e.g., nitric oxide, nitrogen dioxide and oxygen, are known to be capable of causing spin reversal. It is of interest to mention, therefore, that these substances, particularly nitric oxide, can evidently bring about rapid conversion of ortho-into para-positronium. As a result, the phenomena due to the ortho-form are diminished and those due to the para-form are enhanced. For example, in the presence of nitric oxide, the number of events registered in a system which detects only the simultaneous production of three photons, as described above, is markedly decreased. Further, in nitric oxide the contribution of the 0.51-Mev gamma rays to the annihilation radiation is raised, whereas that of gamma rays of other energies is diminished. These observations lend support to the concept of the short-lived existence of two forms of positronium, distinguished by the difference in the direction of spin of the constituent positron and electron.

The Structure of the Atom   Chapter IV

EARLY THEORIES OF ATOMIC STRUCTURE

THOMSON'S CORPUSCULAR ATOM

4.1. During the nineteenth century most scientists would probably have regarded atoms as rigid spheres which were strictly indivisible, and consequently devoid of any internal structure. Nevertheless, there were a few who held different views. Thus, in his preface to the collected writings of Thomas Graham, published in 1876, the Scottish historian of chemistry, R. Angus Smith, wrote: "In using the word atom, chemists seem to think that they bind themselves to a theory of indivisibility. This is a mistake. The word atom means that which is not divided, as easily as it may mean that which cannot be divided, and indeed the former is the preferable meaning." Until 1897, however, when J. J. Thomson made the suggestion that electrons, which he called "corpuscles," are a universal constituent of matter (§ 2.50), there was no information available to provide the basis for a theory of atomic structure.

4.2. The first definite ideas concerning the interior structure of atoms were put forward by J. J. Thomson in 1898.* He said: "I regard the atom as containing a large number of . . . cor-puscles [i.e., electrons] . . . In the normal atom, this assemblage of corpuscles forms a system which is electrically neutral. Though the individual corpuscles behave like negative ions, yet when they are assembled in a neutral atom the negative effect is balanced by something which causes the space through which the corpuscles are spread to act as if it had a charge of positive electricity equal in amount to the sum of the negative charges of the corpuscles." Some years later, in 1904, he elaborated this view, thus: "We suppose that the atom consists of a number of [negative] corpuscles moving about in a sphere of uniform positive electrification . . . the corpuscles will arrange themselves in a series . . . of concentric shells. . . . The gradual change in the properties of the elements which takes place as we travel along the horizontal rows in . . . [the periodic] arrangement of the elements, is also illustrated by the properties possessed by these groups of corpuscles."

4.3. One of the unsatisfactory aspects of Thomson's theory of the structure of atoms was the vague nature of the "sphere of uniform positive elec-

---

* Some authors state that J. J. Thomson's theory is similar to one proposed by Lord Kelvin (William Thomson) a little earlier. It appears, however, that Kelvin's views are much less explicit than those of J. J. Thomson.

trification" in which the electrons were supposed to be embedded. Since the weight of an electron is about a two-thousandth part of that of a hydrogen atom, it would mean that a single atom, especially of the heavier elements, would contain many thousand electrons. However, in 1906, from considerations based on the dispersion of light, and the scattering and absorption of X-rays by gases, J. J. Thomson found that "the number of corpuscles is not greatly different from the atomic weight." This would mean that the negative corpuscles, that is, the electrons, contribute only a very small fraction of the mass of an atom, and consequently "the mass of the carrier of unit positive charge is large compared with that of the carrier of unit negative charge." These conclusions were later proved to be substantially correct, but it was very difficult to reconcile them with the supposed nature of the positive charge distribution.

4.4. It must be admitted that scientists in general, and chemists in particular, were not enthusiastic about these ideas on the nature of the atom, and Lord Rayleigh, in his biography of J. J. Thomson, indicates that Thomson himself was not too well satisfied with them. Nevertheless, some of his suggestions, particularly the one concerning the relationship between the change in properties of the elements in the periodic table and the groups of electrons, are not fundamentally different from those now accepted. Above all, Thomson's theory was important because it called attention to the uni-

versality of the electron, and indicated the possibility that the atom might consist of an arrangement of positive and negative electric charges.

OTHER EARLY THEORIES

4.5. Two other views on atomic structure which are worthy of mention were proposed in the early years of the present century. One, by the Hungarian, P. Lenard (1903), was based on his observation that swift cathode rays could penetrate sheets of aluminum and other metals (§ 2.19). It appeared, therefore, that a large portion of the atom consisted of empty space, and Lenard suggested that the material part was made up of neutral doublets, which he called "dynamids," each consisting of a positive and a negative charge.

4.6. The second theory, published in 1904 by the Japanese physicist H. Nagaoka, bears a striking similarity to the modern views on atomic structure. Its author compared the atom to the planet Saturn, where stability is maintained by the attraction of the heavy central body for the lighter particles in the surrounding rings. He then said: "The present case [i.e., the atom] will evidently be approximately realized if we replace these satellites by negative electrons and the attracting centre by a positively charged particle." Nagaoka used his picture of the atom to make some calculations relating to the spectra of the elements, but neither his speculations nor those of Lenard attracted any particular interest at the time.

THE NUCLEAR ATOM

THE SCATTERING OF
ALPHA PARTICLES

4.7. The modern ideas concerning the structure of the atom arose directly

from a study of the radiations emitted by radioactive bodies (see Chapter II). In 1906, Ernest Rutherford (§ 2.64), at that time in Canada, had noticed that when alpha particles from a radioactive source fell on a photographic plate, after penetrating a thin sheet of metal, the resulting trace is diffuse, fading off at the edges, instead of being sharp. This diffuseness was attributed to *scattering* of the alpha particles; that is to say, the particles were deflected from their course, presumably as a result of interaction with the atoms of the material through which they had passed.

4.8. Two years later, when Rutherford was in Manchester, England, he was experimenting with alpha particles in collaboration with his German assistant Hans Geiger, who later achieved unexpected fame as the inventor of the Geiger tube (§ 6.26), and his attention was once again drawn to the scattering phenomenon. In the words of Geiger: "In the course of experiments undertaken by Professor Rutherford and myself to determine accurately the number of alpha particles expelled from 1 gramme of radium, our attention was directed to a notable scattering of alpha particles in passing through matter."

4.9. The observation that aroused the interest of the investigators was that, although the majority of alpha particles in passing through a thin sheet of metal either continued in their original direction of motion or were scattered, i.e., deflected, to a slight extent, a small proportion of the particles were deflected through large angles, some even emerging on the side of incidence. In a detailed study of the scattering of the fast-moving alpha particles, H. Geiger and E. Marsden (1909) reported that when the radiations emitted by the radioactive element radium C impinged on a thin sheet of platinum, about one particle in 8000 was scattered at an angle of 90° from the direction of incidence. "If the high velocity [about 1.8×10^9 cm. per sec.] and mass of the alpha particle be taken into account," they said, "it seems surprising that some of the alpha particles . . . can be turned within a layer of 6×10^{-5} cm. of gold through an angle of 90°, and even more." [*] To produce the same effect by a magnetic deflection of the alpha particle would have required a field of enormous magnitude. In his lectures on the *Background to Modern Science*, given in 1936, Rutherford described the unexpected nature of the results in the following words: "It was about as credible as if you had fired a 15-inch shell at a piece of tissue paper and it came back and hit you."

RUTHERFORD'S NUCLEAR ATOM

4.10. The first interpretation of the large-angle scattering of alpha particles was that it was due to a succession of deflections through small angles, all in the same general direction. However, in his classical paper of 1911, in which he laid the foundation of the modern theory of atomic structure, Rutherford showed that it was highly improbable that this was the case. In view of J. J. Thomson's model of the atom as consisting of a number of electrons moving in a uniform sphere of positive electrification, it appeared possible that alpha-particle scattering might be due to encounters with the electrons. But, said Rutherford, "remembering that the mass, momentum and kinetic energy of the alpha parti-

---

[*] According to Rutherford, in whose laboratory and at whose suggestion the work was done, Geiger and Marsden found that "a small fraction of incident alpha particles, about 1 in 20,000, were turned through an average angle of 90° in passing through a thin layer of gold." This statement is frequently quoted, but the result does not appear in the published report of Geiger and Marsden.

cle are very large compared with the corresponding values for the electron . . . , it does not seem possible . . . that an alpha particle can be deflected through a large angle by a close approach to an electron." He therefore concluded that "considering the evidence as a whole, it seems simplest to suppose that the atom contains a central charge distributed through a very small volume." In other words, Rutherford postulated that the atom does not consist of a uniform sphere of positive electrification, as supposed by Thomson, but that the positive charge is concentrated in a small region, which he later (1912) called the *nucleus*, at the center of the atom.*

4.11. The scattering of alpha particles through large angles can then be readily accounted for by the marked repulsion experienced by these posi-

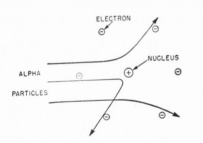

Fig. 4.1. Scattering of alpha particles which approach an atomic nucleus.

tively charged particles when they approach closely enough to the small positively charged nucleus of the atom. It will be seen shortly that, since the nucleus is very minute compared with the atom as a whole, only a minor proportion of the impinging alpha particles come close enough to suffer such strong repulsion. Hence, the number of these

particles which undergo large-angle scattering is definite but small (Fig. 4.1).

4.12. It will be seen that the proposed picture of the atom is not essentially different, as Rutherford pointed out, from the Saturnian atom of Nagaoka, mentioned earlier. Nevertheless, Rutherford is invariably given credit for originating the *nuclear atom*, because, to use Whitehead's apt phrase quoted in another connection in Chapter I, he made the nuclear atom "efficient in the stream of science."

4.13. By assuming Coulomb's law—that the force of repulsion between two similar charges is proportional to the product of the charges divided by the square of the distance between them—to apply to the interaction between the atomic nucleus and an alpha particle, Rutherford derived an equation relating the scattering at various angles to the charge on the scattering nucleus, the thickness of the scattering material and the velocity of the alpha particles. A very thorough test of this equation was made in Rutherford's laboratory in Manchester, England, by Geiger and Marsden, upon whose earlier studies the theory of the nuclear atom had been based. Reporting, in 1913, on their work, with seven different scattering materials and with alpha particles of different velocities, they said: ". . . the results of our investigation are in good agreement with the theoretical deductions of Professor Rutherford, and afford strong evidence of the correctness of the underlying assumption that an atom contains a strong charge at the centre, of dimensions small compared with the diameter of the atom."

* At first Rutherford was noncommittal as to the sign of what he called the "central charge," since the alpha-particle scattering could be explained irrespective of whether the charge was positive or negative. Subsequently, he concluded that the central charge was positive and that, in the neutral atom, the corresponding negative charge was distributed about it in the form of electrons.

MASS AND SIZE OF THE NUCLEUS

4.14. The data of Geiger and Marsden were not sufficiently precise to permit an accurate determination of the magnitude of the charge on the atomic nucleus—this was done a few years later, as will be seen below—but the indications were that the number Z of unit (electronic) positive charges carried by the nucleus of an atom was approximately half of its atomic weight. Since the atom as a whole is electrically neutral, the positive charge on the nucleus must be balanced by an equal number Z of negative charges in the form of electrons. It follows, therefore, that the number of electrons is roughly half the atomic weight, and hence would not greatly exceed 100 even for the heaviest elements. Further, since the mass of an electron is roughly a two-thousandth part of that of a hydrogen atom, the maximum number of about 100 electrons would represent no more than a twentieth of the mass of a hydrogen atom, i.e., 0.05 on the ordinary atomic weight scale. It is obvious, therefore, that essentially the whole of the mass of an atom, as well as all of its positive charge, must be concentrated in the nucleus.

4.15. According to Rutherford's calculations, the greater the angle through which an alpha particle has been deflected, the closer has it approached the atomic nucleus before being turned back. By determining the maximum scattering angle, the distance of closest approach between the centers of an atomic nucleus and an alpha particle may be calculated. This distance, which is found to be of the order of 10^{-12} cm., represents a maximum value for the sum of the radii of an atomic nucleus and an alpha particle. Since the alpha particle is itself the nucleus of a helium atom, as will be seen below (§ 4.30), it is evident that the radius of an atomic nucleus is somewhere between 10^{-12} and 10^{-13} cm.

4.16. An approximate evaluation of the size of the target nucleus* may be made in the following manner. As shown in § 2.109, an alpha particle carries two (positive) unit charges, i.e., $2e$, and since the (positive) charge on the nucleus is Ze, where Z is approximately half the atomic weight, the force of repulsion between the target nucleus and an alpha particle when their centers are at any distance d apart is given by Coulomb's law as $2e \times Ze/d^2$, i.e., $2Ze^2/d^2$. The potential energy or work of repulsion is obtained by integration over all distances from infinity to d, and the result is found to be $2Ze^2/d$.

4.17. Suppose that an alpha particle of mass m, moving with a velocity v, and hence having a kinetic energy $\frac{1}{2}mv^2$, is approaching the atomic nucleus along the line joining their centers. As the particle gets closer the potential energy of repulsion increases, since d is continually diminishing; eventually a point is reached when this energy ($2Ze^2/d$) just balances the kinetic energy ($\frac{1}{2}mv^2$) with which the alpha particle is moving toward the nucleus. At this point the alpha particle comes to rest instantaneously and is then turned back. The distance d_0 of closest approach between the target nucleus and the alpha particle may consequently be derived by equating the repulsive potential energy $2Ze^2/d_0$ to the kinetic energy $\frac{1}{2}mv^2$ of the alpha particle; thus,

---

* The term "target nucleus" will be used for the nucleus with which the alpha particle interacts, since the latter is itself an atomic nucleus.

$$\frac{2Ze^2}{d_0} = \frac{mv^2}{2},$$

so that

$$d_0 = \frac{4Ze^2}{mv^2}. \qquad (4.1)$$

4.18. The electronic charge e is known to be 4.80×10^{-10} e.s.u. (§ 2.41), and the mass of the alpha particle, which is virtually identical with that of a helium atom, is obtained by dividing the atomic weight of helium, 4.00, by the Avogadro number, 6.02×10^{23} (§ 1.60). The average velocity of an alpha particle is known to be about 1.5×10^9 cm. per sec., and if Z, the number of unit charges on the target nucleus, is taken as 20, so that the atomic weight is in the region of 40, it is found from equation (4.1) that d_0 is about 10^{-12} cm. The radius of the target nucleus, which must be less than this figure, should thus be of the order of 10^{-12} to 10^{-13} cm.

4.19. In addition to the approximate method based on the scattering of alpha particles, several other procedures, some of which will be described later (§§ 7.32, 12.57), have been used to determine the radii of atomic nuclei. Since the nucleus is so small and it is doubtful whether it can be regarded as a rigid sphere, it probably cannot be strictly considered as an entity of definite size. It is not surprising, therefore, that different methods for determining what are really "effective" radii should give different results. However, a review of the estimates made by about ten methods shows that essentially all the values fall into two groups. Except for the very lightest nuclei, such as those of hydrogen, helium, etc., the radius R

of an atomic nucleus can be expressed by

$$R = R_0 \times A^{1/3},$$

where A is the mass number of the element, that is, the whole number nearest to the atomic weight (see § 8.60), and R_0 is a constant which is found to be 1.2×10^{-13} cm. for one group of measurements and 1.5×10^{-13} cm. for the other group. The reason for this difference will be considered in Chapter XII, but for the present the former may be accepted, so that

$$R = 1.2 \times 10^{-13} A^{1/3} \text{ cm.}$$

On the basis of this relationship, the nuclear radius of carbon ($A = 12$) is 2.8×10^{-13} cm. and that of uranium ($A = 238$) is 7.4×10^{-13} cm. The radius of the smallest nucleus, namely, that of hydrogen, which is identical with a proton, is difficult to define exactly, but it may be regarded as being about 1×10^{-13} cm.* It is seen, therefore, that all nuclear radii lie within the range from 10^{-13} to 10^{-12} cm. This is still true even if the estimates are based on the larger value of R_0 given above.

4.20. It will be recalled that the radius of an electron is about 2×10^{-13} cm. (§ 2.59), so that atomic nuclei, in spite of being many thousand times heavier than an electron, are not very different in radius. It was thought at one time that the nuclear mass was essentially electromagnetic in nature, being, like that of the electron, due to its electric charge. If this were the case, nuclear radii would be very much smaller than are actually found. Consequently, the mass of the nucleus is governed by factors other than the

---

* It has been proposed that the unit of 10^{-13} cm., which is convenient for expressing nuclear radii, be called 1 fermi, in honor of E. Fermi, who made several outstanding contributions to nuclear physics (see, for example, §§ 7.50, 14.46).

charge. As will be seen below, it is the presence of protons and neutrons which accounts for nuclear masses; the neutron carries no charge and so its mass cannot be electromagnetic in nature.

4.21. The radius of an atom is about 10^{-8} cm. (§ 1.65), and since it consists of a single central nucleus, with a radius of the order of 10^{-12} cm. or less, and a relatively small number of electrons, each of which has a radius of 2×10^{-13} cm., it is obvious that an atom must have a very "empty" structure. For an atom with a (positive) nuclear charge of 20, for example, there are 20 (negative) electrons outside the nucleus, since the atom as a whole is neutral. The total volume of the nucleus and the electrons in a single atom is calculated to be about 10^{-36} cc., compared with the total effective volume of approximately 10^{-24} cc. for the atom as a whole. To the extent that nuclear and electronic volumes have any real significance—because of the operation of the uncertainty principle—it would appear that the actual volume of material, i.e., of the nucleus and the electrons, present in an atom is only about 10^{-12} of the effective atomic volume. It is not surprising, therefore, that fast-moving particles, e.g., beta particles, alpha particles and neutrons, can so easily pass through appreciable thicknesses of matter.

THE NUCLEAR CHARGE

4.22. Because of experimental difficulties, the accuracy of the scattering measurements made by Geiger and Marsden, referred to above, was such as to give the value of the nuclear charge with a possible error of some 20 per cent. As already mentioned, all that could be said was that the number of elementary positive charges on

the nucleus was approximately half the atomic weight. This result was in general agreement with a conclusion previously reached by C. G. Barkla (1911) following upon his experiments on the scattering of X-rays. According to a theoretical treatment by J. J. Thomson (1906), the extent of the scattering is determined by the number of electrons in the atom, and Barkla found this number to be roughly half the atomic weight for several light elements. The number of electrons in an atom should, of course, be equal to the number of unit positive charges on the nucleus.

4.23. Early in 1913, the Dutch physicist A. van den Broek, in a paper on *Radioelements, the Periodic System and the Constitution of the Atom*, made the suggestion that the number of positive charges on the nucleus of any given atom is equal to the ordinal number of the particular element in the periodic system, now referred to as the *atomic number* (§ 1.44). The same idea must have been in the minds of K. Fajans in Germany and of F. Soddy in Great Britain (§ 8.4), but van den Broek is accorded priority for the first publication of the view that has become universally adopted. It may be noted that for the lighter elements, up to molybdenum, at least, the atomic number is within about 10 per cent of half the atomic weight. The approximate estimates of the nuclear charge and of the number of electrons, made by Geiger and Marsden from alpha particle scattering and by Barkla from X-ray scattering, respectively, thus agreed fairly well with the suggestion that they should be equal to the atomic number of the element.

4.24. The next important step in connection with the determination of the magnitude of the nuclear charge was taken in 1913 in Rutherford's

Manchester laboratory, by the young English physicist, H. G.-J. Moseley, who was killed two years later in the battle of Gallipoli. Utilizing the then recent discovery that a crystal could act as a diffraction grating, and hence could be used to compare the wave lengths of X-rays (§ 2.97), Moseley made a study of the characteristic X-rays (§ 2.92) of a number of elements. A photographic method was used, so that the positions of the lines on the plate were directly related to the wave lengths of the particular X-rays. The results obtained for a series of consecutive elements in the

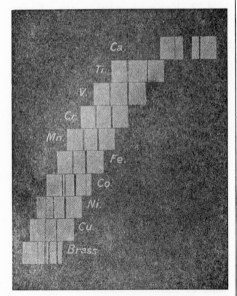

FIG. 4.2. Moseley's photograph of characteristic X-rays of consecutive elements.

periodic system, from calcium to zinc —with the exception of scandium, which follows titanium—are shown in the historic photograph in Fig. 4.2. It is apparent that the wave lengths of

the characteristic X-rays change in a regular manner with increasing atomic number of the element.

4.25. From the positions of the lines, Moseley determined the frequencies (§ 3.13) of the corresponding radiations, and then calculated a quantity, to which he gave the symbol Q, that was related to the square root of the frequency of the characteristic X-rays for each element. Upon examining the results he remarked: "It is at once evident that Q increases by a constant amount as we pass from one element to the next, using the chemical order of the elements in the periodic system . . . we have here a proof that there is in the atom a fundamental quantity, which increases by regular steps as we pass from one element to the next. This quantity can only be the charge on the atomic nucleus."

4.26. After referring to the conclusions drawn from alpha particle and X-ray scattering, that the number of unit charges on the nucleus of any atom is approximately half its atomic weight, Moseley went on to say: "Now atomic weights increase on the average by about two units at a time, and this strongly suggests the view that the . . . [number of charges] increases from atom to atom by a single electronic unit. We are therefore led by experiment to the view that . . . [the number of charges] is the same as the number of the place occupied by the element in the periodic system. This atomic number* is then for hydrogen 1, for helium 2, for lithium 3, . . . for calcium 20, . . . for zinc 30, etc."

4.27. The work described above was

---

* This is the first mention of the term *atomic number,* for the ordinal number of an element in the periodic system, that the present author has been able to find, although as long ago as 1864, J. A. R. Newlands (see § 1.40) employed the expression "the number of the element" for this quantity. Writers in the German language used the word "Ordnungszahl," which means "ordinal number."

interrupted by World War I, but after the war, James Chadwick (see § 2.116), in Rutherford's laboratory at Cambridge, England, set out to make an accurate study of the scattering of alpha particles with a view to calculating the number of unit charges carried by an atomic nucleus. From his measurements, reported in 1920, he estimated the nuclear charges of copper, silver and platinum to be 29.3, 46.3 and 77.4 units, respectively, with an accuracy of between 1 and 2 per cent. These figures are in excellent agreement with the respective atomic numbers of 29, 47, and 78. Similar accord was obtained by P. Auger and F. Perrin (1922) in France for argon, by E. S. Bieler (1924) in England for aluminum and magnesium, and by Rutherford and Chadwick (1925) for gold.

4.28. As a result of these observations, and of many others, it is now unquestioned that the number of unit positive charges carried by the nucleus of any atom is equal to the atomic number of the particular element.* The number of electrons surrounding the nucleus and maintaining electrical neutrality of the atom as a whole, frequently referred to as the *extranuclear electrons* or *orbital electrons,* must consequently also be equal to the atomic number. For this reason the symbol Z is used to represent both the atomic number, or the nuclear charge, and the number of the orbital electrons associated with the atom of a given element.

4.29. It follows, as a consequence of the foregoing arguments, that in the hydrogen atom the nucleus carries a single positive charge and there is one extranuclear electron. The helium atom has a nucleus with two positive charges and there are two external electrons. The nucleus of the lithium atom carries three positive charges and there are three surrounding electrons, and so on throughout the periodic system. The heaviest naturally occurring element, uranium, has an atomic number of 92; thus, its nucleus has 92 positive charges and there are the same number of extranuclear electrons.

4.30. As was seen in § 2.64, Rutherford concluded the proton was identical with a hydrogen atom that carried a single positive charge. Hence, it would be equivalent to such an atom which has lost one unit of a negative charge, i.e., one electron. As the hydrogen atom contains but a single electron, it is evident that the proton is identical with a hydrogen nucleus. Similarly it will be readily apparent that an alpha particle is actually a helium nucleus, that is, a helium atom minus its two electrons, so that it carries two positive charges.

4.31. It may be remarked that in the process of ionization, whereby an atom or a group of atoms acquires an electric charge and hence becomes a carrier of electricity, the orbital electrons are involved. If by some means, such as an electrical discharge or by the action of alpha or beta particles, one or more electrons are removed from an atom, or a molecule, the result is a positive ion. Thus a proton is a singly charged, positive hydrogen ion, while an alpha particle is a doubly charged, positive helium ion. On the other hand, when an atom or molecule acquires in some manner one or more additional electrons, which have been ejected from other atoms or molecules, a negative ion is formed. As a general rule, an *ion-pair* consisting of a positive and a negative ion or, more com-

---

* It is even becoming the practice to define the atomic number of an element as the number of unit positive charges carried by the nucleus.

monly, of a positive ion and an electron, is produced in every ionization act in a gas.*

THE STRUCTURE OF THE NUCLEUS

4.32. The problem of the structure of the atom thus divides itself into two virtually distinct parts: first, a consideration of the small, central nucleus which carries the positive charge and essentially the whole mass of the atom, and second, the arrangement of the extranuclear or orbital electrons within the considerably larger space available to them. The former aspect will be dealt with somewhat briefly here, but it will be taken up again later (§ 4.83) when further information has been presented.

4.33. Since the lightest positively charged particle known before 1932 was the proton,† it was naturally assumed that atomic nuclei were built up of a system of closely packed protons. The mass of the proton is approximately unity on the ordinary atomic weight scale and it carries a single positive charge. In order to account for the mass of a nucleus of atomic weight A, it was therefore necessary to suppose that it contained A protons. However, if this were the case, the number of unit positive charges on the nucleus would be the same as the atomic weight, whereas it has been shown to be equal to the atomic number Z, which is half, or less, of the atomic weight. It was suggested, therefore, that, in addition to protons, atomic nuclei contained $A - Z$ (negative) electrons; these would contribute a negligible amount to the total mass,

but would make the *net* positive charge, i.e., $A - (A - Z) = Z$, equal to the atomic number, although the total number of protons (A) would be the same as the atomic weight.

4.34. The view that electrons, as well as protons, were present in atomic nuclei appeared to receive support from the fact that beta particles, i.e., electrons, are emitted by certain radioactive elements, presumably from the nuclei of their atoms. Nevertheless, the stability of a closely packed system of protons and electrons was difficult to explain, and various other possibilities were considered from time to time. Among these was the suggestion, made independently, and almost simultaneously in 1920, by three scientists in different parts of the world, as mentioned in § 2.115, that a neutral combination of a proton and an electron, called a *neutron*, might exist as a constituent of atomic nuclei.

4.35. After the discovery of the neutron in 1932, W. Heisenberg (see § 3.46) immediately came forward with the idea that the nucleus contains only protons and neutrons; he showed, by means of wave mechanics, that the attractive forces existing between these elementary particles would be sufficient to account for the existence of stable nuclei. The theory was modified and improved in 1933 by the Italian physicist E. Majorana, and this has formed the basis of modern views on nuclear structure. Because they are the essential constituents of atomic nuclei, neutrons and protons are often referred to by the general name of *nucleon*.‡

* The expression "ion-pair" should not be confused with "positron-electron" pair, described in § 2.71.

† The discovery of the positron (§ 2.67) has not changed the situation; this particle is not a constituent of atomic nuclei, although it is emitted by certain unstable (radioactive) nuclei, as explained in § 10.82.

‡ The term "nuclon" was originally proposed by F. J. Belinfante in Holland in 1939, but this was changed to "nucleon," for etymological reasons, and used by the Danish physicist C. Møller in 1941. The use of the word "nucleonics," to describe the general field of nuclear science and technology, was proposed by Z. Jeffries in July 1944.

4.36. The mass of a neutron, like that of a proton, is close to unity on the atomic weight scale. Hence, an atomic nucleus, of atomic weight A and atomic number Z, contains A nucleons, consisting of Z protons and $A - Z$ neutrons. Since fractions of neutrons and protons do not exist, the number A is here not really the atomic weight but a whole number near to the atomic weight. This integer, equal to the number of nucleons (neutrons and protons) in the nucleus, is called the *mass number;* it will be defined more precisely in § 8.60. Some pictorial representations of the structures of a few of the simpler atomic nuclei are shown in Fig. 4.3. In ordinary hydro-

238 and its atomic number is 92, so that the nucleus consists of 92 protons and 146 neutrons. It will be seen in Chapter XII that these facts are important in trying to understand the factors which contribute to the stability of atomic nuclei.

4.38. There is one further point to be considered. If nuclei consist essentially of neutrons and protons, both of which have masses of almost unity, then the atomic weights of all elements should be very close to whole numbers. As stated in § 1.39, in connection with Prout's hypothesis, a surprisingly large proportion of the elements do in fact have atomic weights which differ from integral val-

H	He	Li	Be	B	C
$A = 1$	$A = 4$	$A = 7$	$A = 9$	$A = 11$	$A = 12$
$Z = 1$	$Z = 2$	$Z = 3$	$Z = 4$	$Z = 5$	$Z = 6$

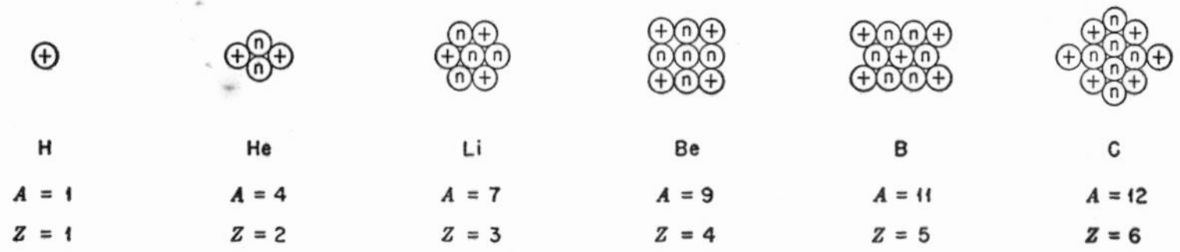

FIG. 4.3. Pictorial representation of neutrons (n) and protons (+) in simple atomic nuclei.

gen, mass number $A = 1$, and atomic number $Z = 1$, the nucleus consists of a single proton, as stated above; in helium, $A = 4$ and $Z = 2$, the nucleus contains two protons and two neutrons; the nucleus of the carbon atom ($A = 12$, $Z = 6$) is made up of six protons and six neutrons, and so on.

4.37. For elements of low atomic weight, the atomic number Z is approximately half the mass number A; atomic nuclei of such elements thus contain almost equal numbers of neutrons and protons. With increasing atomic weight, the atomic number Z becomes less than half of A; hence $A - Z$ is greater than Z, and the number of neutrons in a stable nucleus exceeds the number of protons. The mass number of uranium, for example, is

ues by no more than 0.1. The apparent exceptions are due to the fact that many elements actually consist of mixtures of atoms of different atomic weights, so that the average is not a whole number. Chlorine, for example, contains atoms with atomic weights close to 35 and 37, and they are present in such proportions as to give an average value of 35.46. This matter will be understood more clearly when the concept of "isotopes" has been discussed in Chapter VIII. In the meantime, it may be mentioned that if the protyle, which Prout thought to be hydrogen, were extended so as to include both protons and neutrons, the hypothesis, which he put forward on so little evidence over a hundred years ago, would be accepted at the present day.

STABILITY OF THE
ALPHA PARTICLE

4.39. Since alpha particles, i.e., helium nuclei of mass 4.00, are ejected from the nuclei of several radioactive elements, and since the nuclei of elements whose atomic weights are multiples of four are known to be exceptionally stable (§ 12.44), it was thought possible that alpha particles might be secondary units of nuclear structure. Helium has an atomic weight very close to 4 and an atomic number of 2, and so its nucleus would consist of two protons and two neutrons, as seen above. Such a combination would be expected to have great stability. One way of seeing that this must be so, is to examine the weights of the alpha particle and of its constituent nucleons. The mass of a proton is 1.00759 and that of a neutron is 1.00898,* so that the total mass of the constituents of an alpha particle would be as follows:

$$\left. \begin{array}{l} \text{Mass of two protons} \\ \quad = 2 \times 1.00759 \\ \text{Mass of two neutrons} \\ \quad = 2 \times 1.00898 \end{array} \right\} = 4.0331.$$

4.40. The actual mass of an alpha particle, i.e., a helium nucleus, obtained by subtracting the mass of two electrons from that of the helium atom, is 4.0028. There is consequently a decrease of mass, and hence a liberation of energy (§ 3.76), in the formation of an alpha particle from its constituent nucleons. The loss of mass is 4.0331 − 4.0028, i.e., 0.0303 atomic mass units, and by equation (3.17), based on the Einstein mass-energy relationship, this is equivalent to 28.2 Mev. Hence, in the formation of a single alpha particle from two protons and two neutrons, the considerable amount of 28.2 Mev of energy, referred to as the *binding energy*, will be released. Conversely, if it were required to break up an alpha particle into its constituent nucleons, this same large quantity of energy would have to be supplied. This means that the alpha particle is extremely stable, as implied above.

4.41. Although the combination of two protons and two neutrons has exceptional stability, it is believed at the present time that the alpha particle is not generally found in atomic nuclei. According to a theory developed by W. Elsasser in 1934, alpha particles could only exist in the nuclei of other atoms if the radius of the alpha particle were small compared with the distance between the particles in the nucleus. Actually, these distances would be much the same, so that the condition for the presence of alpha particles as secondary units of nuclear structure is not satisfied. When, as is the case with some radioactive elements, the circumstances are such that the binding energy of the alpha particle, as calculated above, exceeds the amount of energy required to remove two protons and two neutrons individually from the nucleus, an alpha particle can be ejected, although it may not be present as such in the nucleus.

* These values are based on the *physical* atomic weight scale which will be explained in § 8.61.

THE EXTRANUCLEAR (ORBITAL) ELECTRONS

ATOMIC SPECTRA

4.42. A great deal of information concerning the arrangement of the electrons surrounding atomic nuclei has been obtained from the study of atomic spectra. When a substance is heated sufficiently strongly in a flame or by means of an electric arc or spark, or, if it is gaseous, an electrical discharge is passed through it, radiation, mainly in the visible and ultraviolet range, is often emitted. If the rays are examined in a spectroscope, which is an instrument for splitting up complex radiation into its components of different wave length, a definite pattern of lines, known as a *spectrum,* appears. This spectrum is characteristic of the element or elements present in the material emitting the radiations; it is usually called an atomic spectrum, since it originates in the atom of the element. The lighter atoms, such as hydrogen and helium, yield fairly simple spectra, with a relatively small number of lines, but for some of the heavier atoms the spectra may consist of hundreds of lines. As a result of much painstaking work, the wave lengths of the spectral lines of most elements are now known with considerable accuracy, and various numerical relationships have been discovered to exist among them. These have proved of great value in the construction of a theory of atomic spectra, which is closely related to the problem of the extranuclear electrons.

4.43. According to Maxwell's electromagnetic theory of light (§ 3.23), the emission of radiation, such as the characteristic spectrum of an element, is due to an oscillating electrical system. Concurrently with the growth of the concept of the electron as the unit of charge, there was the parallel development of the idea that these spectra were related to a vibrating electronic charge within the atom. Suggestions of this kind were made in the early 1890s by several scientists, including G. J. Stoney, G. F. Fitzgerald, H. Ebert, and, in particular, J. Larmor (1894) and H. A. Lorentz (1895) who treated the mathematical aspects of the problem in some detail. Even before the publication of J. J. Thomson's work which established the existence of the electron as a definite entity, the Lorentz theory was used to explain the effect of a magnetic field in splitting spectral lines as observed by P. Zeeman (1896). This, somewhat fortuitously, led to a value of the specific charge of the electron, as stated in § 2.55, in agreement with that derived by more direct methods.

4.44. When Nagaoka proposed his Saturnian atom (§ 4.6), he suggested that atomic spectra might be due to "the oscillatory motion of electrons revolving in circular orbits," but this view was untenable, as will be seen from the following arguments. To account for the fact that electrons did not fall into the positively charged nucleus as a result of electrical attraction, Rutherford found it necessary to postulate a rapid rotation of the electrons around the nucleus, somewhat similar to the rotation of planets around the sun. The inward attractive force was supposed to be balanced by the outward centrifugal force. However, the analogy between an atom and the sun's planetary system is fallacious, because the particles in the atom are electrically charged. By the electromagnetic theory, the rotating electron should continuously emit energy as radiation during its motion, but if this were the case the radius of curvature of its orbit would steadily diminish. The electron would thus follow a spiral path and eventually fall into the nucleus. Further, if the spectrum were related to the energy radiated by the moving electron, this energy would be changing with the radius of curvature of the path. Atomic spectra would thus cover a continuous range of wave lengths instead of consisting of well defined lines.

BOHR'S THEORY OF STATIONARY STATES

4.45. In order to overcome these difficulties, the Danish physicist, Niels Bohr, then working in Rutherford's Manchester laboratory, made in 1913 the surprising suggestion that, contrary to the requirements of classical electromagnetic theory, an electron does not radiate energy while it is moving in a closed orbit. Such an orbit would consequently be stable, and it would represent what Bohr called a *stationary state* of the atom. It was postulated that several stationary states were possible, the energy being constant in each state, but differing from one state to another. The production of a spectral line of definite frequency was then attributed to the radiation of energy associated with the transition or "jump" of an electron from a state of higher energy to one of lower energy, the frequency (or wave length) being related to the energy change by means of the quantum theory equation.

4.46. If E_2 is the energy of the atom in a state of higher energy (initial state) and E_1 is the value in the state of lower energy (final state), then an electronic transition from the former to the latter state will be accompanied by the emission of energy $E_2 - E_1$. By Planck's quantum theory equation

(3.2), it follows that the frequency ν and wave length λ of the corresponding spectral line are given by

$$\nu = \frac{E_2 - E_1}{h} \qquad (4.2)$$

and

$$\lambda = \frac{c}{\nu} = \frac{hc}{E_2 - E_1}, \qquad (4.3)$$

where h is Planck's constant and c is the velocity of light. Each particular energy transition, from one state to another, should thus result in the formation of a spectral line whose frequency, or wave length, is given by equation (4.2), or (4.3). Since several different stationary states are possible in every atom, there should be a number of transitions and hence a series of lines should be observed in the spectrum.

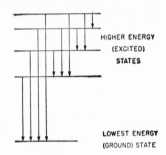

HIGHER ENERGY
(EXCITED)
STATES

LOWEST ENERGY
(GROUND) STATE

FIG. 4.4. Transitions of electrons from higher to lower energy states giving spectral lines.

4.47. If a substance is exposed to conditions under which the absorption of energy is possible, e.g., by the use of high temperature or a suitable electrical discharge, the electrons, which are normally in their lowest energy state, or *ground state*, are presumed to take up energy and to pass into states of higher energy. These are known as *excited states* of the atom. The spontaneous return of the electrons from the higher to the lower states should result in the liberation of specific amounts of energy, each such transition giving a line of definite frequency (or wave length) in the spectrum (Fig. 4.4). Since many different energy states are possible in every atom, numerous lines may be observed. It might be imagined that the spectra of atoms of high atomic number, which have a large number of electrons, would give extremely complex spectra. This is not altogether true, for it has been established that only a few—usually one, two or three—of the outermost electrons are concerned in the formation of ordinary, or optical, spectra. However, even this small number is sufficient to introduce many complications.

4.48. The energy differences of successive electronic states involved in the formation of optical spectra can be determined directly in some instances, and the values have been found to be of the order of 1 to 10 electron volts (§ 3.33). The frequency or wave length of the corresponding radiation can be calculated by means of the quantum theory equations (4.2) or (4.3), respectively. Utilizing the known values of h (6.62 × 10^{-27} erg sec.) and c (3.00 × 10^{10} cm. per sec.) and recalling that 1 ev is equivalent to 1.60 × 10^{-12} erg (§ 3.33), it is readily found from these equations that

$$\nu \text{ (per sec.} = \frac{E_1 - E_2 \text{ (ev)}}{4.13 \times 10^{-15}} \qquad (4.4)$$

and

$$\lambda \text{ (cm.)} = \frac{1.24 \times 10^{-4}}{E_1 - E_2 \text{ (ev)}}. \qquad (4.5)$$

Suppose, for example, the difference of energy between two electronic states involved in a particular transition is 2 ev; it follows immediately from equation (4.5) that the wave length of the emitted radiation should be 0.62 × 10^{-4} cm., or 6200 A. This would represent a line in the visible region of the spectrum (§ 3.16). A larger value of the energy difference would mean a shorter wave length, so that the spectral line might appear in the ultraviolet region.

4.49. According to the accepted ideas of the time, Bohr's approach was somewhat contradictory, for he had to make two assumptions: first, to use his own words, that "the dynamical equilibrium of the systems in the stationary states can be discussed by help of the ordinary mechanics . . . [and second, that] . . . the passing of the systems between different stationary states . . . is followed by the emission of a homogeneous radiation, for which the relation between the frequency and the amount of energy emitted is the one given by Planck's theory. . . . The second assumption is in obvious contrast to the ordinary ideas of electrodynamics, but appears to be necessary in order to account for the experimental facts." Bohr's justification was consequently that atomic spectra could not be correlated with the nuclear atom in any other way.

4.50. By assuming further that the electrons moved in circular orbits and that the angular momentum mvr—where m is the mass of the electron, and v is its velocity in the orbit of radius r—is *quantized*, that is to say, it is restricted to certain values which are integral multiples, e.g., 1, 2, 3, . . . , n, of a definite quantum, Bohr was able to evaluate the energies for the possible stationary states of the hydrogen atom. Upon inserting these results in equation (4.2) or (4.3), the frequencies or wave lengths of the lines in the hydrogen spectrum were determined and found to be in remarkable agreement with the experimental values. This agreement represented a great triumph for Bohr's theory, in spite of its foundation upon postulates which appeared to conflict with each other.

QUANTUM NUMBERS

4.51. The energy values calculated for the various possible stationary states were found to be dependent on the integral multiples of the momentum referred to above; hence, each postulated energy state could be associated with a *principal quantum number* (n). Further, each state corresponded to a definite circular orbit, the radius of which was also determined by the quantum number; thus, for any orbit of quantum number n, Bohr showed the radius r_n of a hydrogen atom to be given by

$$r_n = 0.53 \times 10^{-8} \times n^2 \text{ cm.} \quad (4.6)$$

In view of subsequent developments in wave mechanics (§ 4.56), it has become doubtful if these orbital radii have any real significance. The value of r for the innermost orbit, with $n = 1$, is seen to be 0.53×10^{-8} cm., which is very close to the accepted value for the normal radius of the hydrogen atom. In the higher energy states, i.e., for $n = 2, 3$, etc., the apparent orbital radii are seen to increase rapidly; thus, 2.12 A for $n = 2$, 4.77 A for $n = 3$, and so on.

4.52. In Bohr's original theory, the electron orbits had to be circular, but a later modification in 1916, due mainly to A. Sommerfeld in Germany, showed that by introducing a subsidiary quantum number, often called the *orbital quantum number*, elliptical as well as circular orbits became possible. This number is related to the angular momentum of the electron due to its motion around the nucleus. For each particular value of the principal quantum number n, only certain values of the orbital quantum number l were permitted; these varied, by steps of unity, from zero to $n - 1$.* Thus if n was 4, then l could be 0, 1, 2 or 3, but nothing else. The orbit with $n = 4$ and $l = 3$ was supposed to be circular, but the others were ellipses of increasing eccentricity as the value of l decreased. With the increased number of energy states permitted by the additional quantum numbers, it was found possible to account for the detailed structure of the lines of the hydrogen spectrum, and also for many of the characteristic features in the spectra of other atoms.

4.53. Subsequently, a *magnetic quantum number* m was introduced with permitted integral values, including zero, ranging from l to $-l$, that is, 3, 2, 1, 0, -1, -2, -3 for $l = 3$, to account for the behavior of spectra in magnetic fields. The different values of m were supposed to represent different orientations in space of the possible circular or elliptical orbits.

4.54. Finally, a fourth quantum number, the *spin quantum number,* had to be postulated to account for the previously unexplained close grouping of two, three or more spectral lines. Apparently every electron possesses a property which, in mechanistic terms, can best be described as spin. Since only two directions of spin are possible, the spin quantum number can have two values, and two values only, for every combination of the other three quantum numbers. These will be indicated by the symbols $+$ and $-$, to imply opposite directions of spin. It is a curious fact that, although the quantum numbers l, m and n can have various integral values, depending on cir-

---

* In Sommerfeld's original treatment this subsidiary quantum number was represented by k, and its possible values ranged from 1 to n. These have been changed in the text so as to conform with later developments based on wave mechanics.

cumstances, the spin quantum number is always ½, that is to say, it can be either $+\frac{1}{2}$ or $-\frac{1}{2}$. For simplicity, the numerical value will be omitted in the subsequent discussion and only the sign will be indicated.

4.55. If the principal quantum number n is 4, there can be four values of l, and a total of sixteen m values, each of which can be associated with positive or negative spin. There are thus 32 possible states, each with a slightly different energy, within the same (fourth) electronic level. Similarly there are 18 possible states in the third ($n = 3$) level, and eight in the second ($n = 2$) level. If transitions could occur between all these levels, the number of spectral lines would be enormous. Actually, certain transitions are "allowed," while others are said to be "forbidden," meaning that the probability of their occurrence is large or vanishingly small, respectively. The restrictions thus introduced, by certain well defined *selection rules,* as they are called, serve to limit, to a considerable extent, the number of lines in the spectrum of any given element.

WAVE MECHANICS AND ELECTRON ORBITS

4.56. Before proceeding to examine the consequences of the four quantum numbers described above, it is necessary to sound a note of caution. In the Bohr theory, and in its subsequent modifications, it was assumed that both the position, in a definite orbit, and the momentum of the electron are known. But according to the uncertainty principle (§ 3.46), this is impossible. If the momentum of the electron, and consequently its energy, is known exactly, then there must be an uncertainty with regard to the position of the orbit, and the extent of this indefiniteness is appreciable in com-

parison with the size of an atom. For this reason, it was stated above that the calculated radii of the electron orbits of the hydrogen atom are of doubtful significance.

4.57. By using the methods of wave mechanics which, as seen in § 3.50, should always be employed when dealing with particles of atomic, or smaller, dimensions, many of the apparent inconsistencies of the Bohr treatment have been removed. There is no longer any necessity to combine classical electrodynamics with quantum mechanics, and there is no need to make assumptions which were introduced in the original theory chiefly because they led to correct results. The same equations have now been developed in a much more consistent manner, and the quantum numbers n, l and m, instead of being somewhat arbitrary, emerge as a natural consequence. Further, the selection rules, which define the permitted and forbidden electronic transitions, mentioned above, are readily derived. It is true that Bohr had deduced similar rules in a very ingenious manner, but the arguments were less satisfactory than those based on wave-mechanical considerations.

4.58. However, the gain of mathematical consistency has been accompanied by a corresponding loss in terms of physical reality. The stationary electronic states of the atom are now referred to as its electronic *energy levels,* and the transition from one level to another is accompanied by emission of a spectral line whose frequency is still given by equation (4.2). But whereas in the older theory such a transition could be pictured as a jump of an electron from one orbit to another, this is no longer possible. For one thing, it is not permitted to think of an electron orbit as a specific path in which an electron moves round the nucleus. The definite orbit has been replaced by a mathematical function, sometimes referred to as an *orbital*, which represents the distribution of the electron in the space occupied by the atom. Some writers think of the electron as spread out into a cloud of electricity rather than as a particle, the orbital giving the density of the cloud at any location within the atom. The alternative point of view, as explained in Chapter III, is to regard the electron essentially as a particle, and to interpret the orbital as determining the statistical probability of finding the electron in any given position about the nucleus.

4.59. Although the latter interpretation will be adopted here, it is apparent that in neither case is there anything approaching a finite electron orbit. It may be noted that when the quantum numbers n and l are such that the state is equivalent to a circular orbit of the Bohr-Sommerfeld theory, the probability of finding the electron at any point is greatest at the distance represented by the corresponding Bohr radius. However, whereas the older theory requires the electron to remain at this distance, while in that particular energy state, wave mechanics implies that there is a definite, but smaller, probability that it will be found at points both nearer and farther from the nucleus. When the quantum numbers correspond to elliptical orbits, the correlation between the older and newer theories is less obvious.

4.60. The purpose of the foregoing remarks has been not so much to explain the physical significance of an electron orbit as to emphasize the difficulty of providing such an explanation. It is still the practice in many elementary books to picture an atom as consisting of a central nucleus

with a number of electrons moving around it in definite orbits, oriented in various directions in space. If the uncertainty principle and wave mechanics have any meaning, and it seems reasonably sure that they have, then such pictures are misleading. They attempt to give reality to a state of affairs within the atom to which, at least at present, no reality can be given. Perhaps if these atomic diagrams were to be regarded as purely symbolic their use might be justified; nevertheless, there is always the danger that they may be interpreted too literally.

4.61. It is true that physicists, while realizing its limitations, still frequently employ the Bohr-Sommerfeld atom model, because the calculations are simpler than those based on wave mechanics. The spectroscopist G. Herzberg has stated: "The fact that even in wave mechanics each stationary state of the atom has a perfectly definite angular momentum shows that the atom can still be regarded as consisting of electrons rotating about a nucleus, as in the original Bohr theory," but he is careful to emphasize that "we must not, however, speak of definite orbits."

THE PAULI EXCLUSION PRINCIPLE

4.62. Both wave-mechanical theory and the experimental facts of atomic spectra require the three quantum numbers, designated above by the letters n, l and m, to describe each energy level of an atom. In addition, the facts indicate the necessity of the spin quantum number s, which also finds a logical place in wave mechanics. It may be regarded as established, therefore, that, as far as is known at present, electronic energy levels, which are those concerned in atomic spectra, can be fully described by means of appropriate values of the four quantum numbers n, l, m and s. Those permitted by wave mechanics are the same as were derived from the older theory as given in § 4.51 *et seq.*, although they do not necessarily have the same physical significance.

4.63. So far nothing has been said about the distribution of the extranuclear (orbital) electrons among the permitted quantum states or about its physical equivalent, that is, the arrangement of the electrons in space. The higher the principal quantum number n, the more time will the electron spend at a farther distance from the nucleus, and so there is a relationship between these two aspects of electronic distribution. Even in 1897, when J. J. Thomson first realized that the electron might be a universal constituent of matter (§ 2.46), he compared the electrons in an atom to a system of floating magnets which formed a stable system of groups arranged in concentric rings. Later, in 1904, when he developed his theory of atomic structure, Thomson said that "the corpuscles [i.e., electrons] will arrange themselves in a series of . . . concentric shells." Furthermore, as stated earlier, he realized that there must be a connection between the variation in the properties of elements as exemplified by the periodic system and the arrangement of the electrons about the nucleus. In the years 1913 and 1914, Bohr, Rutherford and Thomson all pointed out that the extranuclear (orbital) electrons, and particularly those in the outermost groups or shells, were responsible for the chemical properties as well as for the spectra of the various elements. Hence, the problem of the arrangement or configuration of the electrons around the nucleus became of interest to the chemist as well as to the spectroscopist.

4.64. Although this problem was essentially solved by 1924, on the basis of a careful study, by many scientists, of the chemistry, the optical and X-ray spectra, and the magnetic properties of the elements, an important coordinating principle, known as the *exclusion principle,* was enunciated in 1925, by the Austrian-born, mathematical physicist W. Pauli. He based his conclusion on experimental observations, and the principle has, as yet, no theoretical basis. Nevertheless, in its most general form, expressed in the language of wave mechanics, it must represent something fundamental in the structure of matter. Here it will be adequate to state the exclusion principle in the special terms applicable to the problem of the distribution of the extranuclear electrons, thus: it is impossible for any two electrons in the same atom to have their four quantum numbers identical. In other words, no more than one electron can occupy each possible energy state, as defined by the four quantum numbers (§ 4.55).

4.65. This simple idea, in conjunction with the rules which give the permitted values for the quantum numbers n, l, m and s, leads to some interesting consequences. Consider, first, the group for which the principal quantum number n is 1; the only possible values of m, l and s which satisfy the conditions given in § 4.51 *et seq.*, as well as the exclusion principle, are then as follows:

n	1	1
l	0	0
m	0	0
s	$+$	$-$

There can consequently be no more than two electrons in the first ($n = 1$) quantum group.

4.66. In the second group, with $n = 2$, there are eight possibilities, thus:

n	2	2	2	2	2	2	2	2
l	0	0	1	1	1	1	1	1
m	0	0	-1	-1	0	0	$+1$	$+1$
s	$+$	$-$	$+$	$-$	$+$	$-$	$+$	$-$

It is seen that in no case are all four quantum numbers identical, so that there can be up to eight electrons, and no more, in the second principal quantum group. Of these eight electrons, two have $l = 0$, and six have $l = 1$.

4.67. Working in this manner, the results in the accompanying table may be derived for the maximum numbers of electrons corresponding to n values from 1 to 5, for each of the permissible l values. Attention may be called to the fact that the total maximum numbers in the successive principal quantum (n) levels are 2, 8, 18, 32 and 50, which may be written as 2×1^2, $2 \times$

DISTRIBUTION OF ORBITAL ELECTRONS
IN QUANTUM GROUPS

	$l = 0$	1	2	3	4	
	Maximum Number of					
	Electrons					*Total*
$n = 1$	2	—	—	—	—	2
2	2	6	—	—	—	8
3	2	6	10	—	—	18
4	2	6	10	14	—	32
5	2	6	10	14	18	50

2^2, 2×3^2, 2×4^2, and 2×5^2, respectively. The maximum numbers are thus proportional to $1^2, 2^2, 3^2, 4^2$ and 5^2. This is in general accord with the idea that the higher the value of the principal quantum number n, the more time do the electrons spend at an increasing distance from the nucleus. The greater the distance, the more the space available, and hence the larger the number of electrons that can be accommodated. As an approximation, therefore, the principal quantum numbers may be regarded as representing a series of spherical shells, of increasing radius, about the central nucleus. The first can accommodate a maximum of two

electrons; the second, eight; the third, eighteen; and so on.

THE PERIODIC SYSTEM AND THE ORBITAL ELECTRONS

4.68. By means of the results given in the foregoing table many of the general features of the periodic system of the elements can be interpreted. If, in addition, information obtained from atomic spectra, from the characteristic X-rays and from chemistry is utilized, it is possible to deduce the details of the arrangement of the extranuclear electrons in the atoms of most elements. The general procedure is to imagine the electrons, equal in number to the positive nuclear charge, i.e., to the atomic number of the element, to be added to the system one at a time until the complete atom is built up. It is then necessary to find in which quantum level each successive electron is accommodated. This apparently arduous procedure is greatly simplified by assuming that the main inner electron grouping of any atom is the same as that of the element preceding it in order of atomic number. All that is required, then, is to determine the position of the additional electron which distinguishes one element from the next in the periodic table. Thus, starting with hydrogen, which has one electron, its position is established as being in the $n = 1$ level; then with the next element, helium, the additional electron completes this group. In the third element, lithium, it is concluded from its chemical and spectroscopic properties that the extra electron must enter the second principal ($n = 2$) quantum level. This procedure is continued throughout the series of elements. In a few instances the assumption that the inner grouping is unchanged from one element to the next higher one does not hold, but there are definite indications when this is the case and due allowance can be made.

4.69. One of the many interesting results which has emerged from considerations of the type just described is that the principal quantum levels do not fill up with electrons strictly in the order 1, 2, 3, 4 etc. Whenever the outermost group, other than the first, contains eight electrons, the next electron goes into a higher principal quantum level, irrespective of whether any vacant places remain to be filled or not. The result is the regular repetition of properties at definite intervals, as exemplified by the periodic system, the completion of each period, after the first, being marked by the presence of eight electrons in the highest quantum level. The number of electrons in the various principal quantum levels for the elements of Group 0 of the periodic table, i.e., the inert gases of the atmosphere (§ 1.47), are shown below. It will be seen that with xenon, for exam-

ARRANGEMENT OF ELECTRONS
IN GROUP 0 ELEMENTS

Element	Atomic Number	$n = 1$	2	3	4	5	6
		Number of electrons in quantum levels					
Helium	2	2	—	—	—	—	—
Neon	10	2	8	—	—	—	—
Argon	18	2	8	8	—	—	—
Krypton	36	2	8	18	8	—	—
Xenon	54	2	8	18	18	8	—
Radon	86	2	8	18	32	18	8

ple, eight electrons have entered the fifth ($n = 5$) principal quantum level, although there are still fourteen vacancies in the fourth ($n = 4$) level. The same is true for radon, which contains electrons in the sixth ($n = 6$) level; although the fifth ($n = 5$) quantum level is far from complete.

4.70. Attention must be drawn to a number of aspects of the table given above. First, it will be seen from the last line that when completed the first four groups contain 2, 8, 18 and 32 electrons, respectively, as required by the exclusion principle. Second, the numbers of elements in successive periods of the periodic system, which are equal to the differences in the atomic numbers of the Group 0 elements, are 2, 8, 8, 18, 18 and 32. The increase from 8 to 18, and from 18 to 32, is evidently accounted for by the possibility of a larger number of electrons entering the higher quantum levels. Finally, it will be noted that the difference between 18 and 32 electrons in the fourth ($n = 4$) quantum level accounts exactly for the known number of elements in the rare earth (or lanthanide) series (§ 1.48). It is not unexpected, therefore, that a similar group—the actinide series—should exist beyond radon, as the fifth ($n = 5$) quantum level fills up from 18 to 32.

CHARACTERISTIC X-RAYS

4.71. The characteristic X-rays of the elements, or X-ray spectra, as they are often called, differ in one important respect from the ordinary or optical spectra considered above. In the former case, the wave lengths, or frequencies, for a particular type of X-ray, namely K, L, M etc., vary regularly from one element to the next, with increasing atomic number, as was first shown by Moseley (§ 4.24), and subsequently verified by others. With optical spectra, however, there is a periodicity, analogous to that observed with many other physical and chemical properties. The reason for this difference is that optical spectra are due to energy transitions involving the outermost electrons, and the arrangement of these among the quantum levels has a periodic character, as just indicated. The characteristic X-rays, on the other hand, must be caused by transitions of another kind. If an atom absorbs a sufficiently large amount of energy, very much larger than that required for the production of optical spectra, one or more of the electrons from an inner quantum level will be raised to a much higher level, or even completely ejected from the atom. The vacancy so created will then immediately be filled by another electron moving into the lower level from one of the upper electronic energy levels; in doing so an X-ray line characteristic of the element will be produced.

4.72. Calculations show that if the initial absorption of energy results in the ejection of one of the two electrons in the first ($n = 1$) principal quantum level, the X-rays produced, as another electron moves into the vacancy, belong to the K series. For this reason

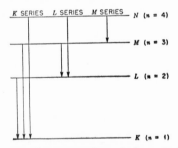

FIG. 4.5.   Interpretation of characteristic X-rays in terms of energy levels.

the first quantum level is frequently referred to as the K level. Similarly, X-ray lines in the L series are obtained when the absorption of energy by an atom causes an electron in the second ($n = 2$) quantum group, also called the L level, to be transferred to a higher level. Members of the M series result from the removal of an

electron in the third ($n = 3$) quantum level or M level, and so on (Fig. 4.5).

4.73. If any one X-ray series, say the K series, is considered, it can be seen that in passing from one element to the next of higher atomic number, the electronic transition responsible for the X-ray remains essentially unaffected. In each case, an electron from one of the higher energy levels must move into the vacant position in the K level. There will, of course, be small differences in the energy with increasing atomic number, and hence the wave lengths, or frequencies, of the characteristic X-rays should vary gradually from one element to the next, as is actually observed.

4.74. The amount of energy required to produce a particular characteristic X-ray line can be readily calculated by means of the Planck quantum theory, equation (4.4) or (4.5) being especially convenient for this purpose. One of the K lines of the element tungsten, for example, has a wave length of 0.213 A, i.e., 0.213 × 10^{-8} cm. Upon inserting this figure into equation (4.5), the corresponding energy change is found to be 58,200 ev. Consequently, at least 58,200 ev (or 58.2 kev) of energy must be supplied in order to excite this particular X-ray line of tungsten. Because the emission of the lines of the K series must be preceded by the ejection of an electron from the innermost energy level, where the electrons are held most tightly, large amounts of energy are needed. As might be expected, smaller energies are required to excite the L series, and still less for the M series, and so on, since the electrons are ejected from levels where they are less and less strongly held. The wave lengths increase accordingly and the corresponding X-rays have diminished penetrating power, i.e., decreasing hardness (§ 2.92).*

4.75. Attention should be called here to the fact that the foregoing interpretation applies only to the characteristic X-rays of the various elements. As usually produced, by permitting a stream of fast-moving electrons to impinge on a metal anticathode (§ 2.91), the X-rays invariably cover a considerable range of wave lengths, often including the characteristic rays of the metal. These continuous X-rays do not result from electronic transitions within the atom, as described above, but are due to the interaction of the high-speed electrons with the anticathode material. When a fast-moving electron approaches the nucleus of an atom the electrical interaction causes the electron to be accelerated and deflected from its original path. In accordance with Maxwell's electromagnetic theory, this process must be accompanied by the emission of energy as radiation. The loss of energy results in a slowing down of the electrons, so that the radiation is commonly referred to by the German name of *bremsstrahlung*, literally "braking (or slowing down) radiation." The continuous X-rays from an anticathode bombarded by high-speed electrons are thus bremsstrahlung. As a general rule, the fraction of the kinetic energy of the electron converted into radiation in this manner increases with the energy of the electron and with the atomic number of the material in which it is slowed down.

4.76. The frequency (or wave length) of the radiation is related, by means of the Planck equation, to the energy lost by the electrons. In an X-ray tube the electrons will have passed through a potential of a thousand to a million volts, so that their energies are 10^3 to 10^6 ev, i.e., about 1 kev to 1 Mev. It can be readily calculated from equation (3.6) that, if all the energy is converted into radiation, the corresponding wave lengths will be from 10^{-7} to 10^{-10} cm., which is the X-ray region (Fig. 3.4). Since various electrons lose different amounts of energy, the X-rays produced will cover a range of wave lengths, the values calculated above representing the minima for the respective electron energies.

MESONIC ATOMS AND MESONIC X-RAYS

4.77. A negatively charged pi- or mu-meson, such as may be present in cosmic rays or produced in the laboratory (§ 2.124), slows down very rapidly, in an interval of time that is small even compared to its very short life. The slow, i.e., low energy, negative meson can then be trapped by an atomic nucleus into a permitted (or stationary) energy level which is quite analogous to the energy levels (or orbitals), considered above, that can be occupied by electrons. The combination of nucleus and negative meson, which has but a transient existence, as will be seen below, is called a *mesonic* (or *mesic*) *atom*.

4.78. The energy levels in the mesonic atom, like the electronic levels in an ordinary atom, have definite quantum numbers, but they differ in one respect. For a given value of the

---

* The energies necessary to excite X-rays are much greater than those required to produce optical spectra, since the latter are associated with transitions between the outermost electronic levels. Thus, X-ray energies are generally in the kilo-electron volt range, whereas a few electron volts will excite optical spectra.

principal quantum number n, for example, the meson would be, on the average, very much closer to the nucleus than an electron. The effective radius of the so-called orbits of the mesonic atom can be readily obtained by means of the Bohr theory or its equivalent in wave mechanics. The mesonic atom, with a single meson, behaves like a hydrogen atom with a single electron, and so it is referred to as a hydrogenic (or hydrogen-like) atom. By applying the Bohr theory, it is then found that the effective radius, for the principal quantum number n, is given by equation (4.6) divided by Zm_0, where Z is the nuclear charge and m_0 is the rest mass of the meson relative to that of an electron. For a pion, m_0 is 273 and for a muon it is 207 (§ 2.126), so that a meson will be very much closer to the nucleus than would the corresponding electron. It may be mentioned that a hydrogen-like mesonic atom will also have orbital electrons, which originally surrounded the nucleus, but these are relatively so far away that they hardly affect the interaction of the nucleus with the meson.

4.79. At first, the negative meson will be trapped in one of the outer mesonic energy levels. As a result of the electrostatic attraction by the nucleus, it will then make a transition to the next inner level, and then to the next and so on. Every transition, as is the case in electronic transitions, will be accompanied by the emission of radiation of a definite energy and wave length. For electronic transitions, the corresponding energies would be in the electron volt range, and the wave lengths around 10^{-4} cm., so that the radiation would be in (or near to) the visual region of the (optical) spectrum. Because the mesons are closer to the nucleus, the energy changes accompanying the transitions are greater, and the wave lengths shorter, than for a hydrogen atom, roughly in proportion to the factor Z^2m_0.

4.80. Since m_0 is 207 for mu-mesons, and 273 for pi-mesons and Z, the nuclear charge, may range from 1 for hydrogen to 92 for uranium, it is apparent that Z^2m_0, which varies from one element to another, will be of the order of 10^3 to 10^6. The energy changes accompanying mesonic transitions may thus be expected to be in the approximate range of a thousand to a million electron volts, and the wave lengths of the radiations emitted should be in the vicinity of 10^{-7} to 10^{-10} cm. Such radiations will evidently lie in the X-ray region, and hence they have been given the name of *mesonic X-rays*. The production of these radiations was first reported by W. Y. Chang in the United States in 1949, and the discovery has since been confirmed by others. Mesonic X-rays, due to the trapping of pi- and mu-mesons by the nuclei of a number of different elements, have been observed. The energies and wave lengths of these radiations agree with the values calculated on the basis of the theory outlined above.

4.81. In a mu-mesonic atom, the negative mu-meson will usually stay in the lowest energy level for about a millionth of a second or so before it decays into an electron (§ 2.126). There are reasons for believing that in this state the meson actually spends some time within the nucleus, so that an occasional muon is captured by interaction with a proton. The negative charge of the mu-meson is neutralized, and the mass is annihilated. Energy is liberated and this leads to some minor disruption of the nucleus.

4.82. It was implied in § 2.125 that pions might be expected to interact much more readily with nuclei than do muons; this difference is manifest in the behavior of mesonic X-rays. The radiations corresponding to pi-meson transitions to the lowest levels are often missing, especially for heavier nuclei, whereas nuclear disintegrations are relatively common. Hence, it has been concluded that negative pi-mesons are often captured before they reach these low levels. In other words, a pion can be absorbed by the nucleus, although, according to classical mechanics, it is a relatively considerable distance away. At first thought, this might be attributed to the electrical attraction between the (positive) nucleus and the (negative) meson, but such is apparently not the case. A better explanation is the following. As just indicated, classical mechanics requires that the meson move in an orbit that is at a distance from the nucleus at all points. But wave mechanics implies that there is a small, but finite, probability that the pi-meson will spend some time near (or even inside) the nucleus. When this occurs, the strong interaction between the negative pion and the nucleons results in absorption of the meson followed by considerable disruption of the nucleus.

PROPERTIES OF THE NUCLEUS

NUCLEAR ENERGY LEVELS

4.83. The energy levels considered so far have been called electronic or mesonic levels since they represent different states of the orbital electrons or of mesons, respectively. There are also, however, *nuclear energy levels* which apply in an analogous manner to the states of the particles within the nucleus. There are good reasons for believing that various excited states of the nucleus exist (§§ 7.39, 10.118), with energy values in excess of the normal or ground state.

4.84. Transitions between pairs of nuclear energy levels give rise to radiations, but since the energy changes involved are considerably greater than for electronic transitions, the nuclear radiations have a much shorter wave length. In general, the energy separation of nuclear levels is of the order of a million electron volts, and if the energy difference $E_2 - E_1$ in equation (4.5) is set equal to 1 Mev (or 10^6 ev), the wave length of the corresponding radiation is seen to be about 1.2×10^{-10} cm. Such a wave length corresponds to very short X-rays, or, what is essentially the same thing, to gamma rays.* It will be seen in Chapter VII that the gamma radiation, which often accompanies the emission of alpha and beta particles in radioactivity, is probably due to the transition of an atomic nucleus from a higher (excited) energy level to a lower level (§ 7.101). Determination of the wave length of the gamma radiation permits the calculation of the corresponding energy change, and vice versa.

4.85. It has seemed probable for some time that definite quantum numbers could be assigned to the protons and neutrons in atomic nuclei,

* Although there is no fundamental difference between X-rays and gamma rays, the latter term is generally used for the short wave length radiations emitted by an atomic nucleus or accompanying particle annihilation. X-rays are produced by electrons (or mesons) outside the nucleus (§ 4.71 *et seq.*).

just as they have been to the orbital electrons. The problem has proved a difficult one because of the unexpected interactions occurring among the orbital and spin angular momenta, with quantum numbers l and s, respectively. As a result of this interaction, the order in which the energy levels for the nucleons are filled is quite different from the relatively simple situation existing for electrons (§ 4.68). However, considerable progress in the assignment of quantum numbers to protons and neutrons in atomic nuclei has been made in recent years, based on the Pauli exclusion principle, as will be explained more fully in Chapter XII. According to the "shell" model of the nucleus as it is called, the protons and neutrons each occupy a series of energy levels or shells, analogous to the electronic energy levels described above. Closed shells occur when the total number of protons or neutrons is 2, 8, 20, 50 and 82.

NUCLEAR SPIN

4.86. Since neutrons and protons manifest the property of angular momentum usually called "spin," every atomic nucleus has a definite spin quantum number, which is the resultant of the individual spins of its constituent nucleons. Several methods, some of them based on spectroscopic studies and others involving the behavior of nuclei in a magnetic field, have been devised for determining nuclear spins, and the values are known for a number of elements (§ 12.72). Individual nucleons can have spin quantum numbers of $+\frac{1}{2}$ and $-\frac{1}{2}$ only, and the combination of the spins

of these particles in the atomic nucleus means that the resultant spin quantum numbers may be 0, $\frac{1}{2}$, 1, $\frac{3}{2}$, 2, etc., i.e., an odd or even number of half integers. As is to be expected, nuclei with odd mass numbers, and hence containing an odd number of nucleons, have spin quantum numbers of $\frac{1}{2}$, $\frac{3}{2}$, $\frac{5}{2}$, $\frac{7}{2}$, or $\frac{9}{2}$, no value higher than $\frac{9}{2}$ having been observed for the ground state of any stable nucleus. On the other hand, when the mass number, and hence the number of nucleons, is even, the nuclear spin is usually 0 or 1, although larger integral values have been recorded in a few cases. In the event that the numbers of protons and neutrons are both even, the spin is apparently always zero, in the ground state, but may be 1, 2, 3, etc., in the excited states. It is important to mention that the nuclear spins in excited states are generally different from each other and from those in the ground state. But the general rule holds good that the spins of nuclei with odd mass numbers are odd numbers of half integers, i.e., $\frac{1}{2}$, $\frac{3}{2}$, $\frac{5}{2}$, etc., whereas those with even mass numbers are zero or integral, e.g., 0, 1, 2, 3, etc.

4.87. It may be remarked, in passing, that the nuclear spin quantum numbers provide one of the arguments against the presence of electrons in the atomic nucleus. The simple correlation between the number of particles in the nucleus and the nuclear spin would not then be possible. It will be seen in due course that nuclear spins have some interesting consequences; among other things, they play an important role in determining the allowed transitions between nuclear energy levels.

Natural Radioactivity   Chapter V

RADIOACTIVE ELEMENTS

EARLY RADIOACTIVE MEASUREMENTS

5.1. In an earlier chapter an account was given of the discovery of radioactivity, and the alpha, beta and gamma rays were described briefly. Studies of the behavior of alpha particles have led, as already seen, to the development of a theory of atomic structure, and also to the identification of the neutron, one of the most important of the fundamental particles of nature. Investigations of the phenomena associated with radioactivity have had striking consequences other than those just mentioned. It is, therefore, necessary to consider the subject of radioactivity in greater detail.

5.2. It will be recalled that, after his initial observation of the photographic effect of uranium salts, Becquerel found that these substances were able to discharge an electroscope. The instrument used by Becquerel was somewhat crude, and although he was able to show that several compounds of uranium, as well as the metal itself, emitted the active radiations, he could not make a reliable comparison of the relative activities of the various ma-

terials. It was to this quantitative aspect of the matter that the Polish-born Marie Sklodowska Curie, who was then in Paris studying the magnetic properties of iron and steel, turned her attention in 1898. Her husband, Pierre Curie, in cooperation with his brother, Jacques Curie, had discovered the property of *piezoelectricity** whereby certain crystals, quartz and some salts of tartaric acid in particular, are able to produce a difference of electric potential when subjected to pressure. Utilizing the fact that the electric current generated is proportional to the pressure, applied by means of weights, the Curie brothers were able to design a relatively simple form of electrometer for the measurement of very small currents.

5.3. It was a piezoelectric device of this type that Marie Curie used in her work on the activities of the radiations produced by various uranium compounds. The apparatus consisted of two parallel horizontal plates, connected through a high-voltage battery to a sensitive galvanometer. The uranium compound was placed on the lower plate, so that the radiations ion-

---

* From the Greek *piezein* (to press). The phenomenon is now extensively employed in telephonic communication and sound reproduction.

ized the air between the plates and thus caused a small electric charge to flow to the galvanometer. The magnitude of this charge, which was a measure of the ionizing power or activity of the radiations, was then determined by balancing it with the electricity produced by applying pressure to a piezoelectric quartz crystal, as described above.

5.4. In this manner, Madame Curie found that "all the compounds of uranium studied are active and, in general, the activity is greater the more uranium they contain." She also reported that thorium compounds possessed similar activity—a discovery made independently a few weeks earlier by G. C. Schmidt in Germany—and called attention to the fact that the active elements, uranium and thorium, are among those with the highest atomic weights.

DISCOVERY OF POLONIUM

5.5. While studying the ionizing power of the radiations from various uranium minerals, Marie Curie noted that two of these minerals, namely, pitchblende (uranium oxide) and chalcolite (copper uranyl phosphate), are much more active than uranium itself. "This fact," she went on to state, "is very remarkable and leads to the belief that these minerals may contain an element much more active than uranium." At this point, because of the challenging nature of the problem, Pierre Curie put aside his own work, and in 1898 he joined his wife in an attempt to discover the cause of the unexpected activity of the minerals pitchblende and chalcolite. In a joint publication* they reported: "Studies of the compounds of uranium and of thorium have shown . . . that the property of emitting rays, which make the air conducting and which act on photographic plates, is a specific property of uranium and of thorium found in all the compounds of these metals, being weaker as the proportion of the active metal in the compound is itself smaller. The physical state of the substance seems to have an altogether secondary importance. . . . Hence, it appears very probable that if certain minerals are more active than uranium and thorium, it is because they contain a substance more active than these metals. . . . We have attempted to isolate this substance in pitchblende, and the experiments have confirmed the foregoing conclusion. . . . The pitchblende [used] was about two and half times as active [in producing ionization] as uranium . . . it was attacked with acids and the solution obtained was treated with hydrogen sulfide. The uranium and thorium remained in solution, [but] the precipitated sulfide contained a very active substance, together with lead, bismuth, copper, arsenic and antimony."

5.6. The arsenic and antimony sulfides were dissolved out by means of ammonium sulfide, and from the nitric acid solution of the residue the lead was precipitated as sulfate. Ammonia was then added to separate the bismuth from the copper.† The active substance was found to be largely associated with the resulting precipitate of bismuth hydroxide. The separation from bismuth proved difficult, but fi-

---

* The title of this paper is "On a new radioactive substance, contained in pitchblende," and it is here that the word *radioactive* was used apparently for the first time, at least in print. However, in her life of *Pierre Curie,* Marie Curie said: "To define this new property . . . I proposed the term radioactivity." The implication is that Marie Curie was responsible for the name.

† The reader who is familiar with qualitative inorganic analysis will recognize in this procedure the conventional method used in the separation of metallic cations.

nally it was found that if the sulfides were heated to 700°C in an evacuated tube, the active sulfide was obtained as a black deposit in the cooler regions of the tube. The Curies then concluded: "By carrying out these operations, more and more active products are obtained. Finally, we obtained a substance whose activity is about 400 times as great as that of uranium. . . . We believe, therefore, that the substance we have isolated from pitchblende contains a hitherto unknown metal. . . . If the existence of this new metal is confirmed, we propose to call it *polonium*, after the name of the native country of one of us [Madame Curie]."

DISCOVERY AND ISOLATION OF RADIUM

5.7. In the course of further investigation, the Curies, together with an assistant, G. Bémont, found that pitchblende contained "a second strongly radioactive substance, entirely different from the first [i.e., polonium] in its chemical properties . . . this new radioactive substance . . . has all the chemical characteristics of barium. It is not precipitated by hydrogen sulfide, ammonium sulfide or ammonia; the sulfate is insoluble in water and in acids, the carbonate is insoluble in water; and the chloride is very soluble in water but insoluble in concentrated hydrochloric acid and in alcohol. . . . Although the [product] consists mainly of barium, it contains, in addition, a new element which confers radioactivity on it and which resembles barium in its properties. . . . Upon dissolving . . . [the mixed] chlorides in water and partly precipitating with alcohol, the precipitated portion is much more active than that remaining in solution."

5.8. By dissolving the precipitate in water and reprecipitating with alcohol, and repeating this procedure several times, a product was finally obtained with an activity 900 times as great as that of uranium. It was only lack of material, which diminished steadily in quantity as the barium chloride was removed, that prevented even higher activities being attained. The results were explained by the presence of a new element to which was given the name *radium*.* Since the most active product still contained a large proportion of barium it was concluded, quite correctly, that the "radioactivity of radium must be enormous," compared with that of uranium. The view that the highly active chloride did indeed contain a new element was supported by the spectroscopic observations reported in an accompanying note by M. Damarçay; he stated that the spectrum contained, in addition to the barium lines, a line that did not correspond with that of any other known element.

5.9. In order to confirm their claim to have discovered two new elements possessing marked radioactive properties, the Curies felt it necessary to work with larger quantities of material in the hopes that they might thereby obtain appreciable amounts of products of greater purity. Through the influence of the Academy of Sciences in Vienna and the cooperation of the Austrian Government, who then owned the famous St. Joachimsthal mines in Bohemia, the Curies secured a ton of pitchblende residues from which much of the uranium had been extracted. From these residues, working in an old shed, under the most primitive and difficult conditions, they obtained a specimen of radium chloride which they succeeded in separating from its

---

* From the Latin *radius* (ray).

associated barium chloride by repeated fractional crystallization. By 1902, Madame Curie reported, one tenth of a gram of radium chloride, of sufficient purity to be used for the determination of the atomic weight of radium, had been isolated from the pitchblende residues. This accomplishment represented the culmination of a supreme effort of scientific faith and perseverance.

Natural Radioelements

5.10. Following upon the identification of polonium and radium by the Curies, another new radioactive element, named *actinium*, was discovered in pitchblende residues by the French scientist A. Debierne in 1899, and independently, some two years later, by F. Giesel in Germany. In 1900, therefore, five different radioactive elements, including uranium and thorium, were known. By the end of 1904, largely owing to the fundamental discoveries made by Ernest Rutherford, then in Montreal, Canada, in collaboration with the English chemist Frederick Soddy, twenty elements possessing radioactive properties had been described; this number was extended to more than thirty by 1912, and at the present time over forty radioactive species or *radioelements,* as they are now called, of high atomic weight are known to exist in nature.

5.11. In addition, a few of the lighter elements, namely, potassium, rubidium, samarium, lutetium, rhenium and perhaps one or two others, possess feeble radioactive properties in their normal states. It should be emphasized that the elements referred to here are those which are radioactive in the forms in which they occur naturally. One of the outstanding achievements of modern atomic science has been the production of virtually every one of the known elements, and of some others previously unknown, in radioactive forms. This aspect of radioactivity and its important applications in science and medicine will be described in later chapters.

RADIOACTIVE DECAY AND RECOVERY

Uranium X and Thorium X

5.12. While studying the radioactive properties of uranium in 1900, William Crookes, whose work on cathode rays was mentioned in Chapter II, made a somewhat surprising discovery. He added ammonium carbonate to a solution of uranium nitrate in water until the precipitate which first formed had almost completely redissolved, leaving a small quantity of a flocculent residue. Upon examining the effect of this residue on a photographic plate, he found it to be very active, whereas the product obtained from evaporating the solution, which actually contained essentially all the uranium, was virtually inactive.

5.13. This unexpected result led Crookes to suggest that, contrary to the views of Becquerel and the Curies, radioactivity was not an inherent property of the element uranium, but of an extraneous substance associated with it. To this active substance Crookes gave the name uranium X. Apparent confirmation of this idea was provided by Becquerel himself when he observed that if barium chloride was mixed with a solution of a uranium salt and then sulfuric acid added, the precipitated barium sulfate, which contained none of the uranium, carried virtually all of the radioactivity.

5.14. However, Becquerel was not satisfied with Crookes's suggestion that the observed activity of uranium salts was due to an impurity. For, he said, "the fact that the radioactivity of a given salt of uranium, obtained commercially, is the same, irrespective of the source of the metal, or of the treatment it has previously undergone, makes the hypothesis not very probable. Since the radioactivity can be decreased [by suitable precipitation] it must be concluded that in time the salts of uranium recover their activity." This conjecture was verified by Becquerel in 1901, for having prepared some uranium salts whose activity had been removed in a barium sulfate precipitate, he put them aside for eighteen months. At the end of that time he found that the uranium compounds had completely regained their activity, as regards their ability to render air conducting and to affect a photographic plate. The barium sulfate precipitate, however, had become completely inactive. "The loss of activity," wrote Becquerel, ". . . shows that the barium [sulfate] has not removed the essentially active and permanent part of the uranium. This fact constitutes then a strong presumption in favor of the existence of an activity peculiar to uranium, although it is not proved that the metal be not intimately united with another very active product."

5.15. Observations analogous to those described above were reported by Rutherford and Soddy in 1902 as the result of experiments with thorium compounds. Thorium nitrate was dissolved in water and sufficient ammonia was added to precipitate the whole of the thorium as its hydroxide. The filtrate was evaporated to dryness and heated to drive off the ammonium salts. The small residue remaining, which Rutherford and Soddy called thorium X, by analogy with Crookes's uranium X, carried essentially all the radioactivity, whereas the thorium hydroxide precipitate was inactive. However, in the course of a few days, it was noted that the thorium X was losing its activity, while the thorium, which had been freed from thorium X, recovered its activity at the same rate, as shown in Fig. 5.1.*

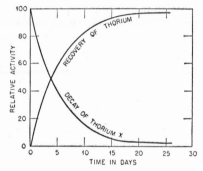

FIG. 5.1. Decay of thorium X and recovery of thorium, as observed by Rutherford and Soddy.

5.16. Rutherford and Soddy also made a quantitative study of the rate of decay of the activity of uranium X and of the rate of recovery of the activity of uranium after the uranium X had been removed. The curves obtained were similar in shape to those in Fig. 5.1, the only difference being that it required about six months for uranium to regain its original activity, although thorium recovered in about a month. Since the uranium (or thorium) recovers its activity at the same rate as the activity of the separated uranium X (or thorium X) decays, it can be understood why, in the ordinary way, uranium and thorium compounds do not exhibit any appreciable change of activity with time.

* When Rutherford was elevated to the British peerage, this diagram, which played an important role in the history of radioactivity, was incorporated in his escutcheon.

5.17. It was established, therefore, that uranium and thorium were associated with uranium X and thorium X, respectively, which differed in their chemical and radioactive properties from ordinary uranium and thorium. This fact alone is not in any way unusual, but the point that is remarkable is that after being removed, the active species is regenerated in the course of about six months by the uranium and one month by the thorium. After regeneration in this manner, the uranium X and thorium X can again be separated, and the almost inactive residue will once more recover its activity in due course. This removal and recovery of the activity can be repeated almost indefinitely. Before proceeding to consider the interpretation of these results, it is necessary to describe some other observations which have a bearing on the problem.

RADIOACTIVE EMANATION

5.18. In 1899, Marie and Pierre Curie had reported that substances placed in the vicinity of a radium preparation acquired an "induced" or "excited" activity; and in the same year, R. B. Owens, of Columbia University, working in Rutherford's laboratory in Montreal, noted that the radioactivity of thorium appeared to be affected by currents of air. An explanation of these diverse phenomena was provided by the work of Rutherford in 1900. He found that thorium salts continuously liberate a radioactive gas, which he called *emanation;* the activity of this emanation decays quite rapidly, but in doing so it leaves an "induced" activity on surrounding matter.

5.19. That radium salts emit an emanation was proved by F. E. Dorn

in 1900, and a corresponding actinium emanation was discovered in 1903 by A. Debierne. The emanations were found to behave like ordinary gases in all respects, and were even capable of being liquefied at low temperatures, their radioactivity remaining unaffected. In each case the decay of the activity of the emanation was accompanied by the development of an "induced" activity in the containing vessel or on materials in the immediate vicinity. This was later shown by Rutherford to be due to what he called an *active deposit*, left by the emanation as it decayed.

THEORY OF RADIOACTIVE DISINTEGRATION

5.20. With the object of correlating these perplexing facts, Rutherford and Soddy proposed in 1902 the theory of *radioactive disintegration*. It was suggested that the atoms of radioelements, unlike those of inactive elements, undergo spontaneous disintegration with the emission of alpha or beta particles and the formation of atoms of a new element. In the words of Rutherford and Soddy: "The disintegration of the atom and the expulsion of a . . . charged particle leaves behind a new system lighter than before and possessing physical and chemical properties quite different from those of the original parent element. The disintegration process, once started, proceeds from stage to stage with measurable velocities in each case." *

5.21. On the basis of these views, the observations recorded above find a ready explanation. Uranium, for example, which itself possesses only weak activity, may be supposed to undergo disintegration with the formation of the much more active uranium X, hav-

---

* The term "metabolon," from the Greek *metabolos,* meaning changeable, was suggested to describe a radioactive element, but it was not generally adopted and it is now obsolete.

ing chemical properties different from those of its parent.* Upon the addition of ammonium carbonate, the uranium X is precipitated, but the uranium is retained in solution. The liquid is consequently inactive, whereas the solid residue is highly active.

5.22. In the course of time the uranium X in the precipitate disintegrates further, the product being less active; hence there is a gradual decay of its activity. The disintegration stages may thus be represented, approximately, by the following scheme:

Uranium → Uranium X → Product.
(feeble   (strong   (feeble
activity)   activity)   activity)

The uranium in solution, however, continues to disintegrate, and in doing so produces more uranium X; the activity consequently increases until a certain equilibrium amount is attained. The uranium is then decaying to form uranium X just as fast as the latter is breaking up; the quantity of uranium X present, and hence the observed activity, remains essentially constant.

5.23. It should be mentioned that, although the product formed by the disintegration of uranium X appears to be almost inactive, it is actually undergoing further disintegration. It is now known that this process is extremely slow, and if the material were kept for a sufficient length of time, probably some hundreds of years, it would undoubtedly exhibit appreciable radioactivity.

5.24. The three radioactive emanations, similarly, are to be regarded as disintegration products of radium, thorium and actinium, respectively. The fact that they are gases is immaterial, since the physical and chemical properties are not necessarily related

to those of the parent elements. In a relatively short period, the emanations themselves disintegrate; the products are solids and so they are deposited on surrounding materials, thus causing the "induced" activity first observed by the Curies. These products also disintegrate in turn until, ultimately, an inactive end product is formed.

5.25. Becquerel, Pierre Curie and others had found that radioactive changes could not be affected by high or low temperatures, or by any other available physical means. The rates of ordinary chemical changes, on the other hand, are markedly influenced by changes of temperature, and sometimes by pressure. The implication of this difference between radioactive and chemical processes was realized by Rutherford and Soddy who wrote: "Since . . . radioactivity . . . is an atomic phenomenon . . . in which new types of matter are produced, these changes must be occurring within the atom. The results that have so far been obtained, which indicate that the velocity of the [radioactive] reaction is unaffected by the conditions, make it clear that the changes in question are different in character from any that have been before dealt with in chemistry. . . . Radioactivity may therefore be considered as a manifestation of subatomic change."

5.26. Although the theory of the spontaneous disintegration of radioactive substances is now accepted without reserve, it caused consternation in the realms of science during the early years of the present century. In spite of its undoubted ability to account for the facts of radioactivity, many chemists and physicists expressed strong opposition to the theory, because they felt that it was

* Uranium X is now known to be a mixture, resulting from successive disintegrations, but this does not affect the main argument given here.

contrary to the established views on the permanence of the atom.

5.27. However, in the course of time it became evident that radioelements were in fact unstable, and that the atoms were undergoing spontaneous change at a finite rate. The disintegration theory, as proposed by Rutherford and Soddy, consequently forms the basis for the interpretation of the properties of the forty or so naturally occurring radioactive species now known, as well as the several hundred which have been obtained in other ways. A fuller treatment of the fundamental implications of the theory in terms of atomic nuclear structure will be given later (§ 8.9).

5.28. It may be wondered how the concept of the spontaneous change of one element to another in radioactive disintegration can be reconciled with the view that the elements are the simplest forms of matter. It is for this very purpose that an element was described in § 1.14, as something which could not be split up by means of *ordinary chemical reactions*. Radioactive changes, as indicated above, differ fundamentally from chemical reactions, and so the fact that an element can break up *spontaneously* in a radioactive change, the rate of which cannot be altered in any known way,* is not contrary to the accepted definition of an element.

SEPARATION AND IDENTIFICATION
OF RADIOELEMENTS

5.29. By the use of various physical and chemical methods, the successive radioactive products have been separated from one another and identified. Some of these processes have already been mentioned, such as, for example,

the precipitation of polonium in the form of its sulfide, of radium as the sulfate, and of uranium X by means of ammonium carbonate. Since most radioelements are available in very small amounts only, the separation is usually performed in the presence of an appreciable quantity of a *carrier,* which is a nonradioactive substance having somewhat similar chemical properties. Thus, bismuth acts as a carrier for polonium, barium for radium, iron for uranium X, and so on. The carrier can usually be separated from the radioelement if desired, as described earlier for polonium and radium. Methods involving electrolytic deposition have been used to separate radioelements; so also has vaporization at high temperatures, which takes advantage of the differing volatilities of analogous compounds.

5.30. The phenomenon of *recoil* has been utilized in certain cases to separate a product from its parent. This depends on the fact that when an alpha particle is expelled with high velocity, the remaining radioactive atom must recoil, in the opposite direction. The mass of the alpha particle is 4, compared with about 220 for the atom of the radioelement, and so the recoil speed of the latter will be 4/220, i.e., 1/55, of the velocity of the alpha particle. The atom will thus recoil at about 3 to 4×10^7 cm. per sec. This relatively high speed allows the radioactive atoms to leave the plate or wire on which the parent element was deposited, provided the latter is in the form of a thin layer. The recoil atoms can be collected on an electrically charged plate or wire a short distance away. It may be noted that recoil, in principle, also accompanies the emis-

---

* There is evidence that, in special circumstances, a spontaneous nuclear change, known as *electron capture,* which is a kind of a reversed beta activity, is affected by the chemical state of the element. The situation is, however, somewhat unusual (§ 10.109).

sion of a beta particle, but the recoil velocity is too small to permit the remaining atom to travel any appreciable distance.

5.31. The production of a gaseous emanation provides a convenient means of separating this radioactive species from those which precede it in the disintegration series. The emanation soon breaks down to form the solid active deposit which can be collected on a negatively charged wire placed in the gas. By heating the wire, a partial separation may be achieved of the radioelements formed by disintegration of the initial deposit.

RADIOACTIVE CONSTANTS

RATE OF DISINTEGRATION

5.32. One of the most powerful methods for the determination and identification of a radioelement after separation is to measure the rate of disintegration. Because of its significance in the development of radioactivity, the subject merits some detailed consideration. From the shape of the curves, such as that in Fig. 5.1, representing the rate of decay of radioactivity, it appeared to Rutherford and Soddy (1902) that the activity was diminishing in what the mathematicians call an exponential (or logarithmic) manner. This would mean that the rate of disintegration of an active species, i.e., the number of atoms which disintegrate in a unit interval of time, is proportional to the total number of atoms of that species present at that time. Since disintegration is taking place continuously, the number of atoms present is changing, and so also is the rate of disintegration.

5.33. In order to deal with a situation of this kind it is necessary to make use of the methods of simple differential and integral calculus. Suppose that at a given instant there are present N atoms of a particular radioelement; suppose, further, that in the extremely small subsequent time interval dt, the number of atoms which disintegrate is dN, so that the rate of disintegration is represented by dN/dt. It was postulated above that the rate of disintegration is proportional to the total number of atoms N, so that

$$-\frac{dN}{dt} = \lambda N, \qquad (5.1)$$

where λ is a constant, which Rutherford and Soddy called the *radioactive constant* of the element under consideration.* The negative sign in equation (5.1) is necessary because the number of atoms of the radioactive element decreases with time, and hence the rate dN/dt is a negative quantity.

5.34. The radioactive constant λ is a definite and specific property of a given radioelement. Its value depends only on the nature of the species, and is independent of its physical condition or state of chemical combination. Within the limits accessible in the laboratory, it is also not affected by changes of temperature or pressure. The radioactive constant is thus a means of characterizing a radioelement.

5.35. Upon rearranging equation (5.1) into the form

$$\frac{dN}{N} = -\lambda dt,$$

---

* It is now frequently referred to as the *disintegration constant* or the *decay constant* of the radioelement.

and carrying out the process of integration, the result is

$$\ln (N_t/N_0) = -\lambda t, \qquad (5.2)$$

or, in the equivalent exponential form,

$$N_t = N_0 e^{-\lambda t}, \qquad (5.3)$$

where N_0 is the number of atoms present at any arbitrary zero time and N_t is the number remaining after the lapse of a further time interval t. The symbol ln is used to represent natural logarithms, in accordance with the general practice in scientific writings. The conversion to ordinary (Briggsian) logarithms may be made by introducing the conversion factor 0.4343, so that

$$\log (N_t/N_0) = -0.4343\lambda t, \qquad (5.4)$$

which may be written as

$$\log N_t = \log N_0 - 0.4343\lambda t. \qquad (5.5)$$

5.36. This expression means that if the logarithm of N_t, the number of atoms present at any time, is plotted on a graph against the time, with reference to any arbitrary zero, the results should fall on a straight line. The slope of this line will be equal to -0.4343λ, and hence it can be used to obtain the value of λ, the radioactive constant, for the given radioelement. The manner in which equation (5.5) can be employed for this purpose will be seen in § 5.51.

5.37. It may be mentioned here, however, that the logarithmic or exponential equations derived above have been found to represent very accurately the rates of disintegration of single radioelements for which the λ values differ by a factor of more than 10^{20}. In other words, the equations are applicable to species which disintegrate extremely rapidly, as well as to those which decay very slowly.

THE MEAN LIFE OF A RADIOELEMENT

5.38. Since dN is the number of atoms of the radioelement disintegrating in time dt, the quantity dN/N represents the *fraction* of the total number of atoms present which disintegrate in this time. Upon dividing by dt, and including a minus sign, the result, i.e., $-(dN/N)/dt$, will consequently be the fraction of the radioactive atoms present disintegrating in unit time. From equation (5.1) it will be apparent that this quantity is equal to λ, so that the radioactive decay constant is actually the fraction of the total number of atoms of the given radioelement disintegrating in unit time.

5.39. The atoms may be regarded as having a *mean life* or *average life*, as suggested by Soddy in 1904; then if the fraction λ decaying in unit time is multiplied by the average life, the result should be unity. Hence, the reciprocal of the radioactive constant, i.e., $1/\lambda$, may be taken as representing the mean life of the particular radioactive atoms. The average lives of the natural radioelements vary from 10^{-6} second to more than 10^{10} years, i.e., 10^{18} seconds, so that the range is enormous.

5.40. It is opportune at this point to consider the physical significance of the decay equations. The exponential nature of the disintegration implies that there is a definite probability, determined by the constant λ, that any particular atom will disintegrate at any given moment. The life of any atom, i.e., the length of time it can exist before it disintegrates, may have any value from zero to infinity, and it is impossible to tell in advance when it will disintegrate. However, it is known that a definite fraction λ will decay in unit time, although it cannot be foretold which particular atoms will disintegrate.

5.41. The situation is analogous to that existing among human beings; insurance companies cannot foretell the fate of any individual, but they have established an accurate pattern of the average expectation of life among persons of different types. In the case of a radioelement, the average expectation of future life of the atoms present at any instant is equal to $1/\lambda$, where λ is the radioactive decay constant of the particular element.* Human beings do not all die when they reach the average age as calculated by actuaries, and radioactive atoms behave similarly. Radioactive disintegration is thus an atomic process taking place at a definite rate, some atoms of a given element having a short life and others a longer life. The statistical average for a very large number of atoms, however, gives the mean life $1/\lambda$, as described above.

RADIOACTIVE EQUILIBRIUM

5.42. In the preceding treatment it has been supposed that the radioelement has been separated from its parent, so that it is not regenerated as it disintegrates. This condition applies to Fig. 5.1 for the decay of thorium X, and for the analogous case of uranium X. If the *parent element* and its disintegration product, or *daughter element*, are present together, a state of equilibrium will be attained, when the daughter element disintegrates as fast as it is being formed from its parent. According to equation (5.1), the rate of disintegration of a parent element, represented by the subscript 1, is equal to $\lambda_1 N_1$, where N_1 is the number of

atoms of the parent present and λ_1 is its decay constant. If every atom of parent produces one atom of the daughter element upon disintegration, as is undoubtedly the case in ordinary radioactive processes, this also represents the rate of formation of the daughter from its parent. Similarly, the rate of disintegration of the daughter element is given by $\lambda_2 N_2$, where N_2 is the number of atoms of the daughter present and λ_2 is its decay constant. In the equilibrium condition the rate of formation of the daughter from its parent will be exactly equal to its own rate of disintegration; hence,

$$\lambda_1 N_1 = \lambda_2 N_2, \qquad (5.6)$$

where N_1 and N_2 are here the numbers of atoms of parent and daughter, respectively, present at equilibrium.

5.43. Since the daughter element also disintegrates, it is itself the parent of a daughter, which may be represented by the subscript 3, so that when equilibrium is attained a relationship exactly analogous to equation (5.6) will apply, namely, $\lambda_2 N_2 = \lambda_3 N_3$. It can be seen, therefore, that if there are a number of successive disintegrations, the general condition for radioactive equilibrium is given by

$$\lambda_1 N_1 = \lambda_2 N_2 = \lambda_3 N_3 = \lambda_4 N_4 = \cdots, \quad (5.7)$$

where N_1, N_2, N_3, etc., are the numbers of atoms of the radioactive species 1, 2, 3, etc., present at equilibrium, and λ_1, λ_2, λ_3, etc., are their respective decay constants. Consequently, for any two members A and B of a radioactive series, irrespective of whether they are parent and daughter, or whether they are separated by several

---

* Radioactive atoms differ from human beings in a highly important respect. At any instant, the mean expectation of life for a given radioelement is independent of the time elapsed since the formation from its parent.

generations, it is evident that $\lambda_A N_A = \lambda_B N_B$, so that

$$\frac{N_A}{N_B} = \frac{\lambda_B}{\lambda_A} = \text{constant.} \quad (5.8)$$

Since λ_A and λ_B are both constants the quantity λ_B/λ_A is also a constant, and hence the ratio of the amounts of any two members of a disintegration series will be constant in the condition of radioactive equilibrium.

5.44. The results just derived have some interesting and useful applications. In 1903, Rutherford and Soddy made the suggestion that radium was itself a disintegration product of another element, and in 1904 Rutherford indicated that, since radium was always found in uranium minerals, it might be a descendant of uranium. He stated that, if this were so, the ratio of uranium to radium in these minerals should be constant, as required by equation (5.8). Shortly thereafter, B. B. Boltwood, of Yale University, H. N. McCoy, of the University of Chicago,* and R. J. Strutt (see § 2.105), independently, reported that this was in fact the case, so that radium and uranium were proved to be members of the same disintegration series. As far as is known, all uranium minerals contain 1 part of radium to 2.8 million parts of uranium.

5.45. If uranium is an ancestor (or precursor) of radium, then, upon keeping a pure specimen of uranium for some time, radium should gradually accumulate. An attempt to test this possibility was made by Soddy in 1905, but the results were unsatisfactory because of an impurity in the uranium. However, in 1907, Boltwood showed that an element, which he called *ionium*, that decayed very slowly, lay between uranium and radium. Consequently it would take many years to produce a detectable amount of the latter from the former, unless very large quantities were used.

The Half Life of a Radioelement

5.46. As an alternative to the radioactive decay constant, another constant, introduced by Rutherford in 1904, called the *half life*, is commonly employed as a characteristic property of a radioelement. The half life is the time required for the radioactivity of a given amount of the element to decay to half its initial value. This time, represented by the symbol T, can be readily evaluated from equation (5.4) in the following manner. After the lapse of time T, the number of radioactive atoms N_t will be half the initial number N_0, so that N_t/N_0 is $\frac{1}{2}$. Upon inserting this value for N_t/N_0 in equation (5.4), and replacing t by the half life T, it is seen that

$$\log \tfrac{1}{2} = -0.4343\lambda T$$

or

$$\log 2 = 0.4343\lambda T.$$

Since $\log 2$ is 0.3010, it follows that

$$T = \frac{0.693}{\lambda}, \quad (5.9)$$

and consequently if the decay constant λ is known, the half life of the radioelement, which is equally definite and specific, can be calculated very simply.

5.47. The fact that radioactive elements disintegrate in an exponential manner has some curious consequences. Suppose, for the sake of illustration, that a particular radioelement has a half life T of 1 hour. Starting, for ex-

---

* B. B. Boltwood and H. N. McCoy pioneered the study of radioactivity in the United States. McCoy's active interest in this field extended from 1903 up to the wartime atomic energy project in 1942.

ample, with 1 gram of the element, one half, i.e., 0.5 gram, will have disintegrated by the end of 1 hour, so that 0.5 gram remains. During the next hour one half of this amount, i.e., 0.25 gram, will disintegrate, leaving 0.25 gram. By the end of the third hour, another 0.125 gram will have decayed, and so on. In each successive hour the actual amount which disintegrates is less than in the preceding hour, although it is always the same fraction of the amount present at the beginning at that particular hour (Fig. 5.2). In general,

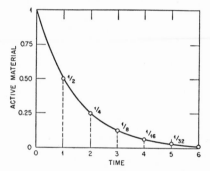

Fig. 5.2. Radioactive decay, illustrating the principle of the half life.

since the activity is reduced to one half of its initial value in the time T, the fraction remaining after n such intervals, i.e., after time nT, will be $(\frac{1}{2})^n$. Although this fraction may become very small, it can, theoretically, never fall to zero.* However, after ten times the half life the activity has fallen to $(\frac{1}{2})^{10}$, which is about 0.001, or 0.1 per cent, of the original amount, so that the remaining activity is negligible in comparison with the initial value.

5.48. By combining equation (5.8) with (5.9) so as to eliminate the λ's, it is found that in the state of radioactive equilibrium

$$\frac{N_A}{N_B} = \frac{T_A}{T_B} = \text{constant.} \quad (5.10)$$

Hence, if the ratio of the equilibrium amounts of two elements in a particular series can be determined, and the half life of one of them is known, the half life of the other can be calculated. It will be shown below (§ 5.51) that, for elements which disintegrate moderately rapidly, the half lives can be found by direct observation of the rate of decay; but when the disintegration is very slow, and the half lives are very long, direct measurements are not too accurate. In cases of this kind use may be made of equation (5.10). For example, uranium minerals, most of which are old enough for radioactive equilibrium to have been established, contain 1 atom of radium to every 2.8×10^6 atoms of uranium, so that if the latter is taken to represent A and the former B, the value of N_A/N_B at equilibrium is 2.8×10^6. The half life T_B of radium is known from direct measurements to be 1620 years, so that the half life T_A of uranium is given by equation (5.10) as

$$T_A = \frac{N_A}{N_B} T_B = 2.8 \times 10^6 \times 1620$$

$$= 4.5 \times 10^9 \text{ years.}$$

This is the accepted value for the half life of the common form of uranium.

5.49. In view of the fact that radio-elements are undergoing continuous disintegration, it may be wondered that any of these species still exist. The explanation is that each natural radioactive series has a precursor of very long half life. As seen from the calculation made above, the half life

* Since the law of radioactive decay is a statistical law, it may well break down when the number of atoms (or nuclei) is small. Hence, this statement, based on equation (5.3), may not be correct in actual practice.

of uranium is 4.5 billion years, which is about the same as the estimated age of the earth. This means that roughly half of the uranium present when the earth was formed still survives. Hence, as the various radioactive products decay, they are replaced by the disintegration of their parents, the supply being maintained by the vast reserve of uranium. It is of interest to note that only three series of radio-elements exist in nature, namely, the uranium, thorium and actinium series (§ 5.56), although four should be possible. It will be seen later (§ 5.65) that the longest-lived member of the fourth series has a half life of about 2 million years, so that in the time which has elapsed since the earth was formed it has decayed almost completely.

DETERMINATION OF THE DECAY CONSTANTS AND HALF LIVES

5.50. As already implied, the determination of the radioactive decay constant, and consequently of the half life, is one of the most significant measurements made with a radioelement. The methods employed depend on the assumption, which is in complete accord with all the known facts, that each radioactive atom of a given species expels from its nucleus either one alpha or one beta particle upon disintegration.* As a result the number of atoms disintegrating in a given time, and hence the rate of disintegration, could be evaluated by counting the number of alpha or beta particles emitted. The counting of such particles is an extremely important aspect of radioactive studies, and several instruments have been devised for the purpose. These will be described in Chapter VI. In the meantime, some

indication will be given of the methods of calculation usually employed.

5.51. For half lives that are neither too long nor too short, say of the order of a fraction of a second to several months, use may be made of equation (5.5). The rate at which particles are emitted in a small time interval may be taken as proportional to the number N of active atoms remaining at that instant, in accordance with equation (5.1). If this rate, which can usually be determined by automatic counting instruments, measured after time t, is represented by I_t, then equation (5.5) may be written as

$$\log I_t = \log I_0 - 0.4343\lambda t, \quad (5.11)$$

where I_0, which does not need to be known, is the disintegration rate at the arbitrary zero time. By plotting several values of the logarithm of I_t, determined after various time intervals t, against the time, as in Fig. 5.3,

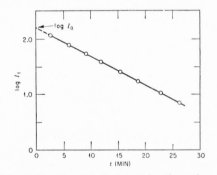

FIG. 5.3. Graphical determination of radioactive constants.

a straight line will result. From the slope of this line it is a simple matter to calculate the decay constant λ and the half life T. In the particular case shown, for example, the slope is -0.0517, with the time expressed in minutes; hence λ, which is equal to the

---

*When the phenomenon known as "internal conversion" of gamma radiation occurs (§ 7.106), an *orbital* electron is expelled in addition.

slope divided by −0.4343, is 0.119 reciprocal minutes, and the half life, by equation (5.9), is 5.82 minutes. The average life, i.e., $1/\lambda$, is 8.40 minutes.

5.52. If the radioactive substance is not pure, but consists of two or more elements with different half lives, the plot of log I_t against t is not a straight line, but rather a combination of such lines, with different slopes, merging into one another and forming a curve. By analyzing this curve it is frequently possible to determine the λ's for all the radioelements present. If two of these species should have very closely similar half lives, then such an analysis is not possible. Another circumstance which can arise is that the disintegration product of an element may contribute some activity, and thus confuse the results. In this event, the decay constant of the parent can be obtained from measurements made in the early stages, before perceptible amounts of the daughter element have accumulated. By the use of mathematical methods, it is possible to derive the decay constants of both parent and daughter.

5.53. When the radioelement has a moderately long life, the procedure described above is not satisfactory, because the values of I_t change very slowly with time, and it might be necessary to continue the measurements over several years to obtain sufficient data to make a plot such as that in Fig. 5.3. In cases of this kind, absolute measurements must be made. In the preceding method, it is not necessary to know how much material is used in the experiment, or the actual disintegration rate; all that is required is that the same sample remain in the same position relative to the counter while the measurements are being made. In the absolute method, the actual total number of particles emitted in a given time from a definite weight of the radioelement must be known. Such measurements are possible, although not very simple, and they have been made in a number of cases.

5.54. If ΔN is the number of atoms disintegrating, i.e., the measured number of alpha or beta particles emitted in a definite time interval Δt, say an hour or a day, which is appreciable although short in comparison with the half life of the radioelement, then the ratio $\Delta N/\Delta t$ may be taken as a good approximation to the instantaneous rate of disintegration dN/dt. It follows, therefore, from equation (5.1) that

$$\lambda = -\frac{\Delta N/\Delta t}{N}. \qquad (5.12)$$

The radioactive decay constant can thus be evaluated by dividing the measured quantity $\Delta N/\Delta t$ by the actual number N of atoms of the radioelement present in the sample used for the experiments. This number can be determined, of course, from the known weight of the element in the sample, its atomic weight, and the Avogadro number, as described in § 1.63.

5.55. For radioelements of extremely short or extremely long lives, accurate measurements of the decay rates are difficult to make. In some cases the half life may be derived from the ratio of the amounts of two elements present in radioactive equilibrium, as described earlier in connection with radium and uranium (§ 5.48). In other instances use may be made of certain equations relating the radioactive decay constant, or the half life, to the energy of the particles emitted by the particular element. These relationships, which will be given later (§§ 7.23, 7.78), are not exact, but they are sometimes useful, especially for disintegrations in which alpha particles are produced.

THE RADIOACTIVE SERIES

RADIOACTIVE DISINTEGRATION SERIES

5.56. As stated earlier, some forty species with different radioactive properties have been identified as occurring in nature. By making physical or chemical separations when possible, as described in § 5.29, by studying radioactive decay and growth curves, by determining the specific properties of the emitted radiations, and in other ways, it has been found that the naturally occurring radioelements of high atomic weight, at the end of the periodic system, fall into three distinct series. These are known as the *thorium series*, the *uranium series*, and the *actinium series*, respectively. In the first two cases, the series are named after the longest-lived precursors, thorium and uranium, with half lives of 1.39×10^{10} and 4.51×10^9 years, respectively. The parents of these elements undoubtedly had shorter lives, and consequently no longer exist in any detectable amounts. The parent of the actinium series is not, as was originally supposed, the element actinium, the first member of the series to be discovered, but rather a much longer lived element, sometimes referred to as actinouranium,* with a half life of 7.1×10^8 years.

5.57. Since an alpha particle is identical with a helium nucleus (§ 4.30), it has a mass, on the atomic weight scale, of 4, to the nearest integer. Consequently, it is evident that in any disintegration stage in which an alpha particle is emitted, the atomic weight of the daughter element must be four units less than that of the parent. On the other hand, a beta particle is an electron, the mass of which is negligible on the atomic weight scale. Hence, when there is a disintegration accompanied by the emission of a beta particle, the parent and daughter elements have virtually the same atomic weights. From actual determinations in certain cases, such as uranium, thorium, radium, etc., and by allowing for the change accompanying alpha decay, the atomic weights of all the known naturally occurring radioelements can be inferred.

5.58. In the accompanying tables there are recorded details of the thorium, uranium and actinium series, including the nature of the radiations, and the half lives of the respective members. In addition to the somewhat unsystematic names given to the various elements as they were discovered, but now becoming obsolete, each is associated in the table with the name of a familiar element; for example, thorium B, uranium B and actinium B with lead; thorium C, radium C and actinium C with bismuth; and so on. The reason for this correspondence and its significance will be explained in Chapter VIII.

5.59. The number given as a superscript to the symbol of each element is the atomic weight or, more correctly, the mass number (§ 4.36) of the radioactive species. It will be evident in due course that the combined symbol, given in the third column, is more systematic and more informative than the older mode of representation.

---

* This is another name for uranium-235, the key material for the utilization of atomic energy (Chapter XIV).

5.60. Attention may be called to the *branched disintegration* which occurs once, at least, in each series. Certain elements, such as thorium C, disintegrate in two ways, but with the same half life; one mode is accompanied by the emission of an alpha particle and the other by a beta particle. The two types of disintegration always occur in a definite proportion in any given case; thus 33.7 per cent of the thorium C atoms give off alpha particles to

THE URANIUM SERIES

Radioelement	Corresponding Element	Symbol	Radiation	Half Life
Uranium I ↓	Uranium	U^{238}	α	4.51×10^9 yr.
Uranium X_1 ↓	Thorium	Th^{234}	β	24.1 days
Uranium X_2* ↓	Protactinium	Pa^{234}	β	1.18 min.
Uranium II ↓	Uranium	U^{234}	α	2.48×10^5 yr.
Ionium ↓	Thorium	Th^{230}	α	8.0×10^4 yr.
Radium ↓	Radium	Ra^{226}	α	1.62×10^3 yr.
Ra Emanation ↓	Radon	Rn^{222}	α	3.82 days
Radium A 99.98% | 0.02%	Polonium	Po^{218}	α and β	3.05 min.
Radium B	Lead	Pb^{214}	β	26.8 min.
Astatine-218	Astatine	At^{218}	α	2 sec.
Radium C 99.96% | 0.04%	Bismuth	Bi^{214}	β and α	19.7 min.
Radium C′	Polonium	Po^{214}	α	1.6×10^{-4} sec.
Radium C″	Thallium	Tl^{210}	β	1.32 min.
Radium D ↓	Lead	Pb^{210}	β	19.4 yr.
Radium E ~100% | 2×10^{-4}%	Bismuth	Bi^{210}	β and α	5.0 days
Radium F	Polonium	Po^{210}	α	138.4 days
Thallium-206	Thallium	Tl^{206}	β	4.20 min.
Radium G (End Product)	Lead	Pb^{206}	Stable	—

* Undergoes isomeric transition (§ 10.123) to form uranium Z (Pa^{234}); the latter has a half life of 6.7 hr., emitting β radiation and forming uranium II (U^{234}).

form thorium C′, while the other 66.3 per cent emit beta particles and become converted into atoms of thorium C″. It will be noted that, upon subsequent disintegration, both thorium C′ and C″ yield the same product, namely, thorium D. The fact that the same type of behavior occurs in all three radioactive series must have some fundamental significance, which is not yet apparent.

5.61. It may be mentioned here, for the sake of completeness, that each of the natural radioactive series has a number of "collateral" members. These have been made artificially (§ 16.94), and do not exist in nature.

THE NEPTUNIUM SERIES

5.62. The atomic weight of thorium is 232, to the nearest whole number, and this is 4×58. Since an alpha-particle disintegration results in a decrease of 4 in the atomic weight, whereas there is no appreciable change accompanying beta-particle emission, it is evident that the atomic weights of all members of the thorium series may be represented by $4n$, where n is an integer varying from 58 (thorium) to 52 (thorium D). In exactly the same way, it can be readily seen that all atomic weights in the uranium series are given by the expression $4n + 2$, and those in the actinium series by $4n + 3$. It will be noted that there is no natural radioactive series of elements whose atomic weights are represented by $4n + 1$. The possibility that such a series might some day be discovered was suggested by the English chemist A. S. Russell in 1923, who even went so far as to put forward a decay scheme for

THE THORIUM SERIES

Radioelement	Corresponding Element	Symbol	Radiation	Half Life
Thorium	Thorium	Th^{232}	α	1.39×10^{10} yr.
↓				
Mesothorium I	Radium	Ra^{228}	β	6.7 yr.
↓				
Mesothorium II	Actinium	Ac^{228}	β	6.13 hr.
↓				
Radiothorium	Thorium	Th^{228}	α	1.91 yr.
↓				
Thorium X	Radium	Ra^{224}	α	3.64 days
↓				
Th Emanation	Radon	Rn^{220}	α	52 sec.
↓				
Thorium A	Polonium	Po^{216}	α	0.16 sec.
↓				
Thorium B	Lead	Pb^{212}	β	10.6 hr.
↓				
Thorium C 66.3% | 33.7%	Bismuth	Bi^{212}	β and α	60.5 min.
Thorium C′	Polonium	Po^{212}	α	3×10^{-7} sec.
Thorium C″	Thallium	Tl^{208}	β	3.1 min.
Thorium D (End Product)	Lead	Pb^{208}	Stable	—

the series. A somewhat different scheme was predicted in 1940 by the physicist L. A. Turner, in the United States, and this has proved to be remarkably accurate.

5.63. Although it is extremely improbable, for reasons which will soon be apparent, that the $4n + 1$ series of radioactive elements will be found in nature, the missing series has actually been obtained artificially in the laboratory. The production of these elements and the elucidation of the radioactive decay scheme represent one of the more noteworthy achievements of the wartime atomic energy project.* The methods used for making the elements which do not occur nat-

THE ACTINIUM SERIES

Radioelement	Corresponding Element	Symbol	Radiation	Half Life
Actinouranium ↓	Uranium	U^{235}	α	7.13×10^8 yr.
Uranium Y ↓	Thorium	Th^{231}	β	25.6 hr.
Protactinium ↓	Protactinium	Pa^{231}	α	3.43×10^4 yr.
Actinium 98.8% | 1.2%	Actinium	Ac^{227}	β and α	21.8 yr.
Radioactinium	Thorium	Th^{227}	α	18.4 days
Actinium K	Francium	Fr^{223}	β	21 min.
Actinium X ↓	Radium	Ra^{223}	α	11.7 days
Ac Emanation ↓	Radon	Rn^{219}	α	3.92 sec.
Actinium A ~100% | ~5 × 10⁻⁴%	Polonium	Po^{215}	α and β	1.83×10^{-3} sec.
Actinium B	Lead	Pb^{211}	β	36.1 min.
Astatine-215	Astatine	At^{215}	α	$\sim 10^{-4}$ sec.
Actinium C 99.7% | 0.3%	Bismuth	Bi^{211}	α and β	2.16 min.
Actinium C′	Polonium	Po^{211}	α	0.52 sec.
Actinium C″	Thallium	Tl^{207}	β	4.78 min.
Actinium D (End Product)	Lead	Pb^{207}	Stable	—

* The first five members of the neptunium series were discovered at Berkeley, Calif. (see Chapter XVI). The others were studied independently in the United States by F. Hagemann, L. I. Katzin, M. H. Studier, A. Ghiorso and G. T. Seaborg, and in Canada by A. C. English, T. E. Cranshaw, P. Demers, J. A. Harvey, E. P. Hincks, J. V. Jelley and A. N. May.

urally will be described in Chapter XVI, and for the present it will be sufficient to tabulate the results. The name *neptunium series* has been proposed for this series of elements whose atomic weights are represented by the formula $4n + 1$, because neptunium is the member having the longest life.

5.64. Like the naturally occurring radioactive series, the neptunium series exhibits branched disintegration near the end, but it differs in the respect that it contains no gaseous emanation.* Further, the stable end product of the neptunium series is ordinary

bismuth of atomic weight 209, whereas in the thorium, uranium and actinium series the nonradioactive end products are all forms of the element lead.

5.65. The half life of neptunium (Np^{237}), the longest lived member of the $4n + 1$ series, is seen to be 2.20 $\times 10^6$ years. Assuming, as is very probable, that this element existed when the earth was first formed, about 4.5×10^9 years ago, then the proportion now remaining can be calculated by means of equation (5.4), using equation (5.9) to relate the decay constant λ to the known half life. In

THE NEPTUNIUM SERIES

Element	Symbol	Radiation	Half Life
Plutonium ↓	Pu^{241}	β	13.2 yr.
Americium ↓	Am^{241}	α	462 yr.
Neptunium ↓	Np^{237}	α	2.20 $\times 10^6$ yr.
Protactinium ↓	Pa^{233}	β	27.4 days
Uranium ↓	U^{233}	α	1.62 $\times 10^5$ yr.
Thorium ↓	Th^{229}	α	7.34 $\times 10^3$ yr.
Radium ↓	Ra^{225}	β	14.8 days
Actinium ↓	Ac^{225}	α	10.0 days
Francium ↓	Fr^{221}	α	4.8 min.
Astatine ↓	At^{217}	α	1.8 $\times 10^{-2}$ sec.
Bismuth 98% | 2%	Bi^{213}	β and α	47 min.
Polonium	Po^{213}	α	4.2 $\times 10^{-6}$ sec.
Thallium	Tl^{209}	β	2.2 min.
Lead ↓	Pb^{209}	β	3.32 hr.
Bismuth (End Product)	Bi^{209}	Stable	—

* A collateral branch of the neptunium series does contain an emanation (Rn^{217}) as a member (§ 16.100).

this manner it is found that unless Np^{237} has a long-lived, but hitherto unknown, precursor, the amounts still present in nature must be so infinitesimally small as to be beyond the possibility of detection.* The existence of a precursor of higher atomic weight and much longer life is highly improbable, and hence it can be readily understood why the elements of the neptunium $(4n + 1)$ series do not occur naturally. Even if they did exist at one time, as they may well have done, all the members of this series have long since decayed virtually to completion, the final product being the nonradioactive element bismuth.

* Small amounts of Np^{237} have been found in uranium minerals, but they probably arise from the interaction of U^{238} with high-energy neutrons (§16.9).

Measurement of Nuclear Radiations

Chapter VI

MEASUREMENT OF RADIATION BY IONIZATION

SPECIFIC IONIZATION

6.1. Some of the most useful procedures for the detection and measurement of alpha and beta particles, and also of gamma-ray photons, are based on Becquerel's discovery (§ 2.100) that gases become electrical conductors, that is to say, they are ionized, as the result of exposure to radiations from radioactive substances. As seen in § 5.3, this fact was utilized by Madame Curie in her comparison of the radioactivities of various materials containing uranium. The fundamental principles were investigated in J. J. Thomson's laboratory in Cambridge, England, by J. S. Townsend in the closing years of the nineteenth century, but it is only in relatively recent times that they have been utilized in a wide variety of counters and detectors of radiations. It will be apparent in due course that radioactive radiations originate in the respective atomic nuclei and so they are referred to as *nuclear radiations*. They are also called *ionizing radiations* because they are capable of causing ionization, either directly or indirectly.

6.2. Since there is a strong electric field in its immediate neighborhood, a rapidly moving charged particle, such as an alpha or beta particle,* has the ability to eject orbital electrons from the atoms or molecules of a gas through which it passes, thus converting them into positive ions. The expelled electrons usually remain free for some time, although a few may attach themselves to other atoms or molecules to form negative ions. Thus, the passage of a charged particle through a gas results in the formation of a number of ion-pairs (§ 4.31).

6.3. The intensity of the ionization produced by a moving charged particle in its path through a gas is expressed by the *specific ionization;* this is the number of ion-pairs formed per centimeter of path. For particles of the same mass the specific ionization increases with the magnitude of the charge, and for particles of the same energy it increases with the mass, that is, with decreasing speed. The more slowly moving particle spends more time in the vicinity of an atom or molecule of the gas through which it

---

* The term beta particle includes both positive and negative electrons.

138

passes, and so the chances of ionization occurring are thereby increased.

6.4. Alpha particles from radioactive sources produce 50,000 to 100,000 ion-pairs per cm. of ordinary air, while beta particles of similar energy, having a higher speed and smaller charge, would leave no more than a few hundred ion-pairs per cm. However, since the total path of the beta particle would be of the order of a hundred times that of the alpha particle, the difference in total ionization would not be very great. Actually, the total number of ion-pairs produced by a charged particle is determined largely by its energy, since an approximately constant amount is lost for each ion-pair formed. For air at standard temperature and pressure the formation of a single ion-pair requires the expenditure of about 33.5 electron volts (§ 3.33) of energy by the moving charged particle.

6.5. Gamma rays and similar electromagnetic radiations, e.g., X-rays, are also capable of ionizing gases. They do so indirectly, however, by ejecting electrons with appreciable velocity from atoms or molecules present in the gas or in other substances subjected to the radiations. It is these rapidly moving, secondary electrons which produce ion-pairs in their paths. The specific ionization of the gamma radiation thus depends on the energy of the expelled electron.

BEHAVIOR OF ION-PAIRS IN ELECTRIC FIELDS

6.6. Quantitative measurements of nuclear radiations are based on the counting of individual particles, as well as on the determination of the total radiation received in a given interval of time. For these purposes,

instruments have been developed in which the positive and negative ions formed by the ionizing radiations are driven toward the collecting electrodes by means of an applied potential under various conditions. In order to understand the behavior of the ions in these circumstances, it is convenient to consider an apparatus consisting of a vessel, containing a gas, air for example, in which are fixed two parallel metal plates to act as electrodes, as shown at A in Fig. 6.1. The electrodes

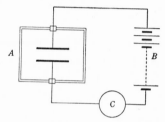

FIG. 6.1. Diagrammatic representation of apparatus used to study behavior of ion-pairs.

are connected to a battery B, so that the voltage can be increased steadily from zero to high values, and also to an instrument C capable of measuring electric current.

6.7. Normally, the air in the vessel does not conduct electricity,* and no current will be observed in the instrument C until the voltage becomes high enough—several thousand volts—to permit a spark to pass between the electrodes. Suppose now a single alpha or beta particle, or, in fact, any ionizing radiation, is permitted to enter the vessel A, while a small potential is applied to the plates by the battery B. A number of ion-pairs will be produced, and the applied potential will cause the positive ions to travel toward one electrode, while the negative

---

* Cosmic rays (Chapter XVIII) and other extraneous radiations cause some ionization the effect of which is neglected here.

ions (or electrons) move toward the other electrode. As a result, charges will collect on the electrodes, and the instrument C will indicate a pulse of current.

6.8. The magnitude of the charge collected and, hence, the size of the current pulse will depend on two factors in particular. These are (1) the number of initial (or primary) ion-pairs produced between the electrodes by the ionizing particles or radiation and (2) the applied voltage. The general nature of the results is indicated in Fig. 6.2, in which the pulse size, for

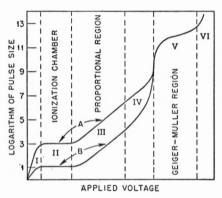

FIG. 6.2. Variation with applied voltage of pulse size due to an ionizing particle.

a given number of ion-pairs, is shown on a *logarithmic scale* as a function of the applied voltage. Curve B refers to a case in which the radiation produces

10 primary ion-pairs ($\log 10 = 1$) and curve A to one in which 1000 ion-pairs ($\log 1000 = 3$) are formed.

6.9. An examination of Fig. 6.2 shows that the curve can be divided into six more or less distinct regions, marked I to VI. Three of these regions, namely II, III and V, are made use of in various types of instruments for the measurement of radioactivity. In region I the size of the electrical pulse produced by a single alpha or beta particle increases with the applied voltage, but it attains a constant value in region II. In region III, the pulse size commences to increase again with increasing voltage, and this behavior continues through regions IV, V and VI. It will be noted that in regions II and III there is a constant vertical separation, equal to two logarithm units, between curves A and B. This means that the pulse size in both regions is proportional (or equal) to the number of initial ion-pairs; in region II the pulse size is independent of the voltage, but in region III it increases with the voltage. In region V, the curves A and B coincide, so that the pulse size, for a given voltage, is the same regardless of the number of ion-pairs initially produced between the electrodes. The explanation of the foregoing facts and their application to the measurement of nuclear radiations are given below.

IONIZATION INSTRUMENTS

THE IONIZATION CHAMBER

6.10. When the applied potential is small, the ions move slowly toward the respective electrodes, with the result that there will be ample time for many of the oppositely charged species to recombine, i.e., to meet and neutralize one another. The size of the pulse registered will consequently be

less than if all the ion-pairs originally formed succeeded in reaching the electrodes. As the voltage between the plates is increased, the ions travel faster, so that the number of recombinations is diminished and the pulse size is increased. Ultimately a point is reached, at the beginning of region II, when the ions move to the electrode so rapidly that virtually every ion produced by the alpha or beta particle reaches the electrodes. Since a further increase in the potential cannot cause any increase in the number of ion-pairs, the pulse size remains unchanged throughout region II. The actual voltage range over which the pulse size is constant depends on many factors, such as the nature and pressure of the gas, the spacing and shape of the electrodes, and so on, but it is roughly between 100 and 500 volts.

6.11. The conditions existing in region II are those which are employed in the *ionization chamber* method for the measurement of alpha and beta particles and also of gamma and X-rays. It can also be adapted for use with neutrons (§ 11.28). Simple forms of the ionization chamber method were employed by Madame Curie (1898) and by Rutherford (1900) in some of the earliest quantitative studies of radioactivity (Chapter V). The chamber itself is made of metal, and the electrodes, which are insulated from the walls, may be parallel (Fig. 6.1). Alternatively, a cylindrical chamber, the walls of which act as one electrode, may be used together with a thin metal rod or wire as the other electrode. The nature of the gas in the chamber depends on the particular purpose intended for the instrument; it may be air, carbon dioxide, nitrogen, argon or methane, among others. The battery voltage is adjusted so that the conditions correspond approximately to the middle of region II; a small change in the voltage will then not affect the pulse size. This represents one of the advantages of operating a radiation detector in the ionization chamber region II.

6.12. Ionization chamber instruments fall into two broad categories: the *nonintegrating* (or *pulse counting*) type, in which each particle capable of causing ionization is recorded separately, and the *integrating* type, in which the pulses are not separated with the result that there is a continuous accumulation of charge leading, according to circumstances, to either a steady decrease in the potential difference between the electrodes or to a relatively steady flow of current. The basic difference between the two types of instrument lies in the value of the *time constant** (or *response time*) of the system relative to the frequency of arrival of the ionizing particles. If the time constant is short, each pulse produced by an ionizing particle can be detected separately and counted. The requirement of a pulse-counting ionization chamber is, therefore, a detecting circuit with a very short time constant. On the other hand, a chamber of the integrating type must have a relatively long response time.

6.13. A simplified schematic arrangement of an ionization-chamber circuit is shown in Fig. 6.3. The cen-

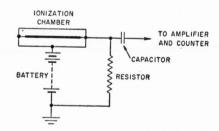

Fig. 6.3. Simplified circuit for ionization chamber particle counter.

tral electrode is connected to a suitable vacuum-tube (linear) amplifier, so that the pulses are amplified and modified before going to a counting

---

* The time constant (RC) is effectively equal to the product of the resistance (R) and the capacitance (C) of the detecting circuit.

instrument, as described below. In principle, a pulse counter of this type could be used for any ionizing particles or radiation, but it lends itself particularly to the counting of alpha particles and protons (and neutrons). In the ionization-chamber region II (Fig. 6.2), the amount of charge collected on the electrodes, which determines the pulse size, is equal to the total charge on the ion-pairs produced by the entering particle. Thus, the pulse size depends on the product of the specific ionization, i.e., number of ion-pairs per unit distance, and the distance between the electrodes. Since alpha particles (and protons) have a high specific ionization and a short range, they will produce significant pulses even in a small chamber. Because of the low specific ionization, counting of pulses due to beta particles and gamma rays, however, would require chambers of large size, as well as considerable external amplification.

6.14. The method described above is thus especially useful for counting alpha particles in the presence of beta and gamma radiations. For this purpose, a chamber with parallel-plate electrodes may be employed, the plates being about 1 or 2 cm. apart. The output pulses are fed into an amplifier which is adjusted so that it will respond only to the large pulses produced by alpha (or other highly ionizing) particles but not to the small pulses from beta particles or gamma rays. The substance under examination can be placed on the lower electrode plate within the chamber or the active material may be placed outside. In the latter event the alpha particles are allowed to enter through a "window" consisting of a very thin sheet of mica, nylon or plastic.

6.15. One of the most remarkable

instruments used in conjunction with an ionization chamber and linear amplifier for alpha-particle counting is the *pulse analyzer*, sometimes familiarly known as a *kicksorter*. It consists of a number of electronic circuits permitting only the passage of pulses exceeding a certain minimum, those rejected being due to beta particles, gamma rays and other extraneous radiations, and then sorting and counting them according to size. Since alpha particles from different sources generally have different energies and ranges (Chapter VII), they will produce different numbers of ion-pairs in the ionization chamber. The pulses will thus differ in size. Consequently, the alpha particles originating from several radioelements in a mixture can be counted independently and simultaneously.

6.16. Although the amplified pulses from an ionization chamber have been transmitted to an oscilloscope and photographed on a moving film, it is the more common practice to employ a mechanical counter. When the rate of arrival of pulses exceeds the maximum rate of response of the counter, which is about 5 to 10 per second, an electronic device called a *scaler* is included in the measuring system. A common form permits one pulse in every 2, 4, 8 or 16 etc., to be recorded on the counter. A scale of one in 64 is quite common, but instruments with much higher scaling factors are often used, since a pulse chamber can respond to individual particles arriving at the rate of 100,000 or more per second. Scalers based on a factor of 10 have also been constructed. The number of pulses indicated on the counter, multiplied by the appropriate factor of the scaler, gives the number of alpha particles entering the space between the electrodes in the ionization chamber. Instead of counting the total number of pulses, vacuum-tube circuits can be used to record the rate at which they are received, i.e., the number of pulses arriving in a specified short time interval. The data obtained with a *counting-rate meter* of this type can be employed directly in the determination of half lives.

6.17. In the integrating form, the conditions are such that what is measured is effectively the total ionization produced, rather than the number of individual particles. Two main forms of the instrument have been used in this connection, and measurements can be made with alpha, as well as with beta and gamma, rays. In the electrostatic form, of which the gold-leaf electroscope, used by Becquerel (§ 2.100) and others, is a simple example, the electrodes are charged up to a certain potential by means of a battery, and then the latter is removed. The instrument is so constructed that when charged in this manner, one of the electrodes, acting as an indicator, moves with respect to its discharged position. The entry of ionizing particles into the chamber results in the formation of ion-pairs, and each of the components is attracted to the electrode of opposite sign. As a result the electrodes are discharged and the change in position of the indicator electrode is observed. The rate of movement is a direct measure of the rate of entry of ionizing radiations, and the total change in position of the indicator is related to the total amount of radiation entering the chamber.

6.18. One of the simplest and generally useful devices of the electrostatic type of ionization chamber is the quartz-fiber electroscope invented by C. C. Lauritsen and T. Lauritsen in the United States in 1937. It consists of a very fine metal-coated, quartz fiber, about 6 mm. in length, parallel to a rigid horizontal metal wire to which it is connected. This is mounted within, but insulated from, a cylindrical aluminum case which acts both as the ionization chamber and one of the electrodes. The system of fiber and rigid wire, which represents the other electrode, is charged with respect to the metal case by connecting for a short time to a battery of 100 to 200 volts. As a result of the repulsion between the rigid metal wire and the flexible fiber, the latter, which acts as the indicator, is displaced from its normal position. When the electroscope is exposed to ionizing radiations, the charged wire and attached fiber collect ions which reduce the charge; hence the mutual repulsion decreases and the fiber gradually returns to its original position.

6.19. The rate of movement, observed by means of a microscope with a scale in the eyepiece, is roughly proportional to the rate at which the ions are collected, and hence to the rate of entry of the ionizing radiations. The Lauritsen electroscope is also used to determine the total amount of ionizing radiations emitted by a given material in a certain time. This is measured by the total movement of the flexible fiber indicator. As a general rule, beta and gamma rays can penetrate the thin aluminum wall of the ionization chamber, but for beta rays of low penetrating power, and particularly for alpha particles, a thin "window" may be used, or the specimen under examination may be placed within the chamber.

6.20. In the second type of integrating ionization chamber, which has found extensive use in the atomic energy field, the circuit is based on that shown in Fig. 6.4. In this instrument

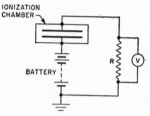

FIG. 6.4.   Simplified circuit for integrating (current measuring) type of ionization chamber.

the steady production of ion-pairs in the chamber results in a very weak, but continuous, flow of current through the resistance R. The magnitude of this *ion current*, as it is called, can be determined with the aid of a vacuum-tube voltmeter V connected across the resistance. Alternatively, the current can be measured directly by means of a sensitive instrument. The current strength is directly proportional to the rate at which ionizing (alpha, beta, gamma, etc.) radiation is entering the ionization chamber.

6.21. If it is required to determine beta radiation in the presence of alpha particles, the rays are permitted to enter the ionization chamber through a "window" made of a thin sheet of aluminum. This is sufficient to prevent the passage of alpha particles without appreciably hindering the beta radiation. However, allowance must be made for gamma rays if they are present. Ionization chambers for gamma rays usually contain a heavy gas, such as argon or difluorodichloromethane ("Freon"), often at high pressure, so as to facilitate the liberation, by each gamma-ray photon, of an electron capable of producing ionization. If alpha or beta particles are present, as they frequently are, they may be cut out by means of a thin sheet of lead which stops these particles but has little influence on the gamma rays.

PROPORTIONAL COUNTERS

6.22. Although the ionization chamber method of measuring nuclear radiations is very simple and convenient, it has the disadvantage of often requiring the use of a very sensitive electrometer or of a powerful vacuum-tube amplifier. Other ionization instruments have therefore been devised in which there is a considerable degree of internal amplification. It can be seen in Fig. 6.2 that, for a given number of initial ion-pairs, the pulse size in region III is greater than in region II. In other words, there is a certain amount of internal amplification of the pulse in region III and this amplification increases with the applied voltage. However, as noted in § 6.9, for a given voltage, the size of the pulse is proportional to the initial number of ion-pairs produced between the electrodes. For this reason, region III is called the *proportional region*. It is best attained by using a cylindrical chamber, which acts as the negative electrode (cathode), with a central wire as the positive electrode (anode). When the voltage is high enough the potential gradient near the central wire becomes so large that the electrons, produced in the primary ionization of the gas by an alpha or beta particle, will move toward it with a very high speed. In region III the speed becomes great enough for the electrons to cause the ionization of other atoms and molecules in the gas; the electrons so produced may cause further ionization, and so on. This multiplication effect is often referred to as a *Townsend avalanche* or *Town-*

send cascade, in honor of its discoverer, J. S. Townsend (see § 6.1).*

6.23. An electron from each original (or primary) ion-pair may consequently lead to the formation of a large number of secondary ion-pairs. The total number of ion-pairs produced by a single primary ion-pair is called the *gas-amplification* factor. This factor is unity in the ionization chamber (region II), but it may become as large as 10^4 or more in region III. The size of the pulse produced by a single particle is thus increased enormously, so that considerably less external amplification is required. In principle, the proportional region could be used in an integrating instrument in which the ion current is measured. But this would require such exact control of the potential difference between the electrodes as to be quite impractical. Consequently, pulse counting is always employed, and this is the reason for the name *proportional counter.*

6.24. As already indicated, the instrument consists of a cylindrical tube with a central wire, the latter being attached to the positive pole of the battery. The magnitude of the applied potential depends on the conditions, but it may be from 500 to 800 volts, or more, in order to take advantage of the increase of gas amplification with the voltage. Various gases have been employed for filling proportional counter tubes. As a general rule, a mixture is used consisting of a simple gas, such as hydrogen or argon, which favors high amplification, and a more complex one, such as carbon dioxide, methane, pentane, etc., to provide stability of operation. A fairly typical gas might be methane containing 10 to 25 per cent by volume of argon. The pressure of the gas is usually less than atmospheric, although a successful proportional counter for charged particles has been described in which methane gas at atmospheric pressure flows continuously, the experimental material being inside the counter tube.

6.25. Because of the proportional character of the amplification, an alpha particle will give a larger pulse than will a beta particle or a gamma-ray photon, just as in the ionization chamber. Hence proportional-counting instruments are particularly useful for counting alpha particles in the presence of beta particles and gamma rays. By means of suitable devices, the smaller pulses can be ignored and only the larger pulses produced by alpha particles recorded. If the applied voltage is maintained reasonably constant, the alpha-particle pulses can be sorted out by means of a pulse analyzer (§ 6.15). The proportional counter can also be used for the measurement of beta particles alone or in the presence of alpha particles, as described in connection with ionization chambers. Further, it can be adapted to the measurement of neutrons (§ 11. 26).

Geiger-Müller Counters

6.26. A type of instrument that has been widely used in radioactive counting is the *Geiger-Müller counter,* a name often abbreviated to *Geiger counter* or to *G-M counter.* Because the detecting portion is commonly in the form of a tube, the names *Geiger-Müller tube* or *G-M tube* are frequently used. These instruments operate in region V of the curve, in Fig. 6.2, showing the variation of pulse

---

* It was at one time thought that the avalanche ionization was produced by the positive ions. This view has now been discarded, since it is known that these ions do not generally acquire sufficient energy for the purpose.

size with the applied potential. The conditions in region IV, which lies between the proportional and Geiger-Müller ranges, have found no application in radioactive studies, and in region VI the potential is so high that once ionization takes place in the gas there is a continuous discharge of electricity, so that it cannot be used for counting purposes.

6.27. The essential difference between the proportional and the Geiger regions is that in the former an electron from an ion-pair probably produces an avalanche at one point only, whereas in the G-M region the avalanche spreads along the whole length of the central wire. The pulse size in the proportional region thus varies with the number of primary ion-pairs, but in the Geiger counter the amplification is so great that the size of the pulse is almost independent of the number of ion-pairs, as may be seen from Fig. 6.2. Although the amplification in the Geiger region is large, the discharge is not continuous, as it is in region VI. The negative members of the ion-pairs are mainly electrons, and these reach the central wire anode in a very short time. The positive ions, consisting of charged gas molecules, however, move much more slowly toward the walls of the tube, which act as the cathode. As a result a positive space charge is built up near the anode; the effective potential difference in its vicinity is consequently decreased and the discharge is terminated.

6.28. The characteristics of the Geiger region can be considered from another point of view. Imagine a weak source of ionizing (alpha, beta or gamma) radiation placed near an instrument, similar to a proportional counter, consisting of a cylindrical negative electrode (cathode) with a central wire as the positive electrode

(anode). This instrument is connected with a device capable of indicating only relatively large pulses, but not small ones. As the potential applied between the electrodes is increased the number of pulses recorded per minute will be observed to change in the manner depicted in Fig. 6.5. Until the

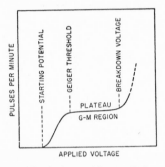

Fig. 6.5. Variation with applied voltage of number of pulses received per minute due to ionizing radiation.

voltage reaches the value indicated as the *starting potential*, the pulses are too small to be detected. But with rising potential the gas amplification increases, and pulses are recorded in increasing numbers. Eventually, when the Geiger *threshold potential* is reached, corresponding to the beginning of region V in Fig. 6.2, the number of pulses per minute becomes essentially constant, as indicated by the horizontal portion of the curve in Fig. 6.5. The range of potential over which this occurs is called the Geiger *plateau*. Beyond the plateau, continuous discharge (region VI) takes place, and counting is not possible.

6.29. The voltages of the threshold potential and of the plateau range depend, as may be expected, on the design of the counter and the nature and pressure of the gas it contains. Most G-M counters are filled with gas at pressures below atmospheric, when the plateau may extend over a range of two or three hundred volts in the region from about 800 to 1500 volts. The *operating voltage* is usually chosen so as to be somewhat less than the value at the middle of the plateau. The gas-amplification factor can then be as high as 10^8 or more for a weakly ionizing particle. In the curve shown in Fig. 6.5 the plateau is represented as horizontal; this is an ideal situation, but in actual practice there is often a slight upward slope. The slope must, however, be small if the G-M counter is to be satisfactory, for one of its important advantages is that the number of pulses registered per minute from a given source remains constant in spite of possible variations in the voltage; this condition can be realized only if the plateau is reasonably level, as in Fig. 6.5.

6.30. One of the troublesome features of the Geiger-Müller counter is that when an ionizing particle produces an avalanche the resulting discharge pulse may continue for some time. If another particle enters the counter tube before the discharge is complete, the pulse it should produce will be confused with the preceding one, and so on for subsequent pulses. In other words, the separate pulses are not *resolved*, and hence cannot be counted. The continuation of the discharge or, more correctly, the formation of a multiple discharge appears to be due to the positive ion members of the ion-pairs. When they reach the walls, i.e., the cathode, of the G-M tube, the positive ions cause electrons to be liberated; these move rapidly toward the central wire, and thus renew the discharge previously terminated, as described above.

6.31. There are two main procedures for suppressing or *quenching* the dis-

charge, so as to improve the resolving power of G-M counters. In the *self-quenching*, or internally quenched, type the filling gas is a mixture of argon and a few per cent of a polyatomic organic gas or vapor, such as methane, ethane or ethyl alcohol. The purpose of the argon is to provide high specific ionization and a low starting potential, whereas the organic molecules quench the discharge. Because the quenching compound ionizes more readily than argon, the positive argon ions initially formed transfer their charges to the organic molecules, so that virtually only ions of the latter reach the walls of the Geiger tube. As a result, the energy which would otherwise have caused the emission of electrons is now used to decompose the molecules of quencher.*

6.32. Some of the decomposition products deposit on the walls of the counter and on the central wire, and this sets a limit to the life of self-quenching counters. Nevertheless, a good tube may count as many as a billion, i.e., 10^9, pulses before becoming ineffective. It can then be opened, cleaned and refilled, if desired. A later development is the use of a halogen gas, such as chlorine or bromine, as a quencher in place of an organic compound. Self-quenched tubes of this type have a relatively low threshold potential; they are said to have a virtually unlimited life, since the atoms produced by decomposition of the halogen molecules recombine to form the molecules once again. A patented G-M tube containing argon, with small amounts of xenon, oxygen and nitrogen, is claimed to be self quenching and to have infinite life.

6.33. The gas in the nonself-quenching type of Geiger counter is argon of 98 per cent purity, the small amount

* Other factors, which need not be mentioned here, are also operative.

of impurity being possibly advantageous. The quenching of the discharge is now achieved by means of an external resistance or by the use of an auxiliary vacuum-tube circuit. These automatically reduce the voltage below the starting potential after each pulse, and then restore it in time for the next pulse. Since there is no decomposition of the gas, an externally quenched counter of this type has a very long life.

6.34. When properly quenched, internally or externally, a G-M counter will have a resolving time of about 2×10^{-4} second; that is to say, particles arriving at intervals of not less than 2×10^{-4} second will give separate pulses. If the particles were produced at a uniform rate, that is, at regular intervals, a maximum of 5000 pulses could be counted per second. However, the emission of radioactive particles is random in character and by no means uniform; consequently, the practical counting rate is below this maximum. In any event, there is always a probability that two or more particles will arrive at such short intervals that they are not counted separately, and a correction must be made for such losses. This "coincidence" correction increases with the resolving time of the tube and with the actual counting rate.

6.35. For very fast counting it is necessary to use a suitable scaler in conjunction with the Geiger counter. However, the G-M tube is almost invariably used to determine the rate at which radiation is being received at a particular point. For this purpose, the output of the tube, generally without further amplification, is applied to a counting-rate meter (§ 6.16).

6.36. Because of their versatility, G-M tubes have been made in a great variety of sizes and shapes, from 1 cm. to 1 meter in length and from 0.3 cm. to 10 cm. in diameter. The walls can be of metal such as copper, or a metal cylinder may be supported inside a glass tube (Fig. 6.6). Another

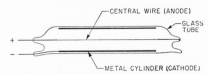

FIG. 6.6. Construction of simple Geiger-Müller tube.

possibility is to coat the interior surface of the glass tube with a thin layer of an electrical conductor, such as silver or graphite. The central wire which acts as the positive electrode (anode) is usually of tungsten, with a thickness of 0.02 to 0.05 mm. As indicated above, the nature of the gas depends on the type of counter; the pressure is usually less than atmospheric, but in some cases it is the same as that of the atmosphere. Geiger-Müller counters are mainly used for beta and gamma rays, partly because it is difficult to make tubes with windows thin enough to be penetrable by alpha particles. When the penetrating power of the beta radiation is small, the tube may have a very thin glass or mica window, which the particles can penetrate.

6.37. In view of the wide use of particle counters based on gas ionization, it may be noted that the principle was first used by Rutherford and Geiger in 1908 to count alpha particles with the object of determining their charge (§ 2.108). The apparatus consisted of a brass cylinder, about 20 cm. long and 1.7 cm. internal diameter, with a thin central insulated wire which was attached to the positive terminal of the battery. "In our experiments," they said, "it was arranged that the alpha particles could be fired through the gas at low pressure exposed to an electric field somewhat below the sparking value. In this way, the small ionization produced by one alpha particle in passing along the gas could be magnified several thousand times. The sudden current through the gas due to the entrance of an alpha particle in the testing vessel was thus increased sufficiently to give an easily measurable movement of the needle of an ordinary electrometer." With this apparatus, which apparently functioned in the proportional range, Rutherford and Geiger were able to count the alpha particles from a radium C source.

6.38. In 1913, some improvement in the design of particle counters, leading to operation in region V, was made by Geiger, but the modern highly sensitive G-M counter is essentially that developed by Geiger in collaboration with W. Müller in Germany in 1928. It should not be overlooked, however, that the wide sphere of usefulness of the G-M tube, as well as the ionization chamber and proportional counter, owes much to the developments in vacuum-tube circuits which have taken place in recent years. In this connection, mention may be made of the Swiss physicist, H. Greinacher who, in 1924, introduced the use of vacuum tubes to amplify the pulses produced by ionizing particles.

USES OF IONIZATION INSTRUMENTS

6.39. Instruments of the types described above are used either for the detection of nuclear radiations or for their quantitative measurement. In some circumstances, e.g., in prospecting for uranium minerals or in health protection operations (see Chapter XIX), it is required to know that radioactive material is present and, if possible, to obtain a rough indication of the quantity. For this purpose the Geiger counter with a rate meter is very convenient. The high voltage can be obtained with a small battery combined with a vibrator, and the large internal amplification makes vacuum-tube amplification unnecessary. Geiger tubes are rarely designed to detect alpha particles, because of their short range in air and small penetrating power. But both beta and gamma radiations can be detected, and if the tube is provided with a thin "window" and a thicker "shutter," it is possible to permit the beta particles to enter or to be excluded, as desired. For the detection and rough measurement of the intensity of alpha particles, some form of proportional counter is generally used.

6.40. For quantitative determinations, even of moderate reliability, the G-M counter is not always satisfactory. Accurate measurements can, however, be made with ionization chambers, either of the integrating or particle-counter types, and also with proportional counters. By the use of selector (or discriminator) circuits which reject small pulses, these instruments (or counters) can be used for alpha particles. They can also be adapted to measure beta or gamma radiation by means of suitable "windows." In general, ionization chambers would be used for the more highly ionizing radiations because there is no internal gas amplification. Both ionization-chamber and proportional counters have short resolving times, permitting high counting rates. In this respect they are greatly superior to the G-M counter which is not reliable, even for rough measurements, when the pulse rate is more than about 5000 per second.

6.41. When "absolute" counting is

being undertaken, it is necessary to know the geometrical efficiency, or *geometry,* of the counter, i.e., the fraction (or percentage) of the total number of particles emitted by the source that actually enter the counter tube. This can usually be determined by means of a standard radioactive source. Alpha-particle standards can be prepared from uranium and several beta and gamma standards, made from either natural or artificial radio-elements, are available. When the counter is used for comparative, rather than absolute, measurement, as is often the case, all that is required is that the geometry should always be the same. This is achieved by standardizing the operating procedure.

MEASUREMENT OF RADIATION BY OTHER METHODS

SCINTILLATION COUNTERS

6.42. Since the year 1947, there have been remarkable developments in one of the oldest methods of counting particles, namely, that based on the small flashes of light (or scintillations) which accompany the exposure of certain materials to nuclear radiations. The mechanism of formation of these scintillations is very complex, but essentially it involves the initial formation of a higher-energy (or excited) electronic state of the molecules (or atoms), or, in certain inorganic solids, of a small region of a crystal. The excess energy, which has been derived directly or indirectly from the nuclear radiation, is then emitted, within a very short time, as a flash of light.

6.43. In the course of his early studies of radioactivity H. Becquerel found, in 1899, that the radiations, like X-rays and cathode rays, are able to produce luminescence in a number of substances, such as zinc sulfide (Sidot's hexagonal blende), barium platinocyanide and diamond. This property of radioactive rays, which is mainly due to the alpha particles, was employed by Curie and by Debierne in the study of the gaseous emanations (§ 5.18). In 1903, W. Crookes in England, and J. Elster and H. Geitel in Germany, independently reported that the luminescence produced by alpha particles on zinc sulfide was not uniform but consisted of a large number of individual flashes which could be seen in a microscope.* A year later, in the first edition of his book on *Radioactivity,* Rutherford wrote: "In the scintillations of zinc sulphide, we are actually witnessing the effect produced by the impact . . . of single atoms of matter [i.e., the alpha particles]. . . . This would offer a very convenient means of actually counting the number of the particles . . . if each particle gave rise to a flash of light." At the time, Rutherford did not think this was very probable, but later, in collaboration with Geiger, he proved that such was actually the case.

6.44. The first attempt to count alpha particles, by observing the scintillations they generated in a diamond, was made by E. Regener in Germany in 1908. At about the same time, Rutherford and Geiger compared the

---

* Crookes devised a small instrument, which he called a "spinthariscope" (from the Greek, *spintharis,* a spark), for making these scintillations visible. It consisted of a brass tube with a zinc sulfide screen at one end, with a speck of radioactive salt 1 mm. from it, and a lens at the other end. Similar scintillations can often be seen by observing the figures on a luminous watch dial with a lens in the dark.

number of scintillations produced by a radium C source on a zinc sulfide screen with the pulses in an electrical (ionization) counter (§ 6.37). The numbers were approximately the same in both cases, so that if each alpha particle caused a single pulse in the counter, then it also gave rise to one scintillation. In this manner Rutherford and Geiger established the reliability of the scintillation method of counting alpha particles. The procedure was used by Geiger and Marsden in their original work in 1910 on the scattering of alpha particles during passage through thin sheets of metals (§ 4.9), and also later, in 1913, in their confirmation of Rutherford's equation, based on the nuclear theory of the atom (§ 4.13). It was also employed by Chadwick and others for the determination of the nuclear charge by the method described in § 4.27.

6.45. Prior to the 1930s, when the development of vacuum-tube circuits simplified the counting of electrical pulses, the scintillation method, involving tedious visual observation, was virtually the only procedure used for both quantitative and qualitative studies of alpha particles. As a result of the progress made in the methods of counting, described above, the scintillation procedure was largely discarded. However, in recent times there has been a revival of interest in the subject, mainly because of two factors. First, there was the discovery that certain organic compounds, either in the solid state or in solution, as well as inorganic solids, which produce scintillations when exposed to nuclear radiations, are transparent to the light they emit. As a result, relatively large quantities of the scintillator (or *phosphor*) can be used; this insures a high probability of interaction with the radiation and a high detection effi-

ciency. Second, was the advent of the electron-multiplier tube with a photoelectric cathode, generally called a *photomultiplier tube*. The light produced in a single scintillation, which is too feeble to measure directly, causes the emission of electrons from the cathode of the tube, due to the photoelectric effect. The number is greatly increased in successive stages, so that ultimately a measurable current pulse is produced. This can be recorded by means of a counter (or counting-rate meter) in the manner already described for ionization instruments.

6.46. A combination of scintillator and photomultiplier tube to count particles was apparently first used by the British scientists S. C. Curran and W. Baker in some wartime research,

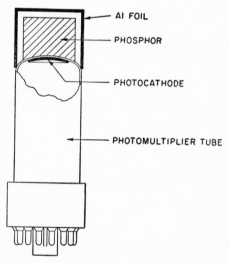

FIG. 6.7. Diagrammatic representation of a scintillation counter.

reported in 1944. However, the main stimulus to the present day interest came in 1947 from the work of H. Kallmann, then in Germany, who employed a large clear crystal of the organic substance naphthalene as phosphor, in conjunction with a photo-multiplier. A simple form of the system is shown diagrammatically in Fig. 6.7; the crystal of the phosphor, surrounded by thin aluminum foil, is attached to the top, close to the cathode, of the photomultiplier tube. The purpose of the foil is to reflect the light flashes on to the cathode. A particle of nuclear radiation (or a gamma-ray photon) entering the phosphor causes a flash of light, which falls on the photo-cathode. As a result, electrons are emitted and these are subsequently multiplied to produce a relatively large electrical pulse at the output of the tube.

6.47. Following the early use of naphthalene as the phosphor, it has been found that other, related organic compounds, consisting of several linked benzene rings, are better scintillators. They can be obtained as large clear crystals and the light flashes are more intense than those emitted by naph-thalene, so that they produce larger output pulses. Of the solid organic scintillators, anthracene appears to be the best. A further significant develop-ment has been the discovery that certain solutions of organic compounds are also capable of acting as phos-phors. Although they are not as ef-ficient as the pure crystals, the problem of growing good crystals is eliminated.

6.48. A liquid scintillator has two main components: the solvent, usually toluene or xylene, and the primary solute (or dissolved substance), e.g., a few per cent of diphenyloxazole or terphenyl. It appears that most of the energy is absorbed from the nuclear radiation by the solvent, which is itself not a scintillator, and is then trans-ferred to the solute, which actually emits the light. A small amount of secondary solute may be added to act as a *wave length shifter*, i.e., to in-crease the wave length of the light emitted. At the somewhat longer wave lengths, the transparency of the liquid is greater, so that less light is lost, and, in addition, the photomultiplier tube has a better response.

6.49. Another type of organic scin-tillator system, which lies somewhere between a solid crystal and a solution, has a plastic as the base. A solution is made of the primary solute, possibly with the addition of a wave length shifter, in a solvent like vinyltoluene or styrene which can be readily con-verted, by the process known as poly-merization, into a solid plastic; this acts as a satisfactory scintillator. The resulting transparent material can be made in large pieces and cut to any desired shape.

6.50. An important class of scin-tillators is related to those used in the early studies of radiations. They are inorganic substances which, unlike the organic compounds, do not scintillate when pure. The presence of a small amount of an activator is always necessary. One of the best inorganic scintillators, especially for gamma rays, is crystalline sodium iodide activated with thallium (about 0.1 per cent). Other alkali halides, such as potassium chloride and iodide, have also been used. Zinc sulfide, with a trace of silver as activator, is a highly efficient scintillator, but large single crystals are difficult to obtain. This material has, therefore, been chiefly used for the counting of alpha par-ticles, as these have a very short range, in any event.

6.51. Since 1954, the possibility of using gaseous scintillators has at-tracted interest because of their ex-tremely rapid response. When exposed to nuclear radiations, the inert gases of the atmosphere, e.g., argon, krypton and xenon, produce scintillations in the ultraviolet region of the spectrum. By means of a suitable wave length shifter, the flashes are converted into visible light, so that the photomultiplier responds most effectively. Liquid and solid xenon, which have the advantage over the gas in having a greater stopping power for the radiations, can also act as scintillators in the same manner.

6.52. In spite of the great variety of phosphors, there are generally circumstances in which one or another is preferred because of certain differences in behavior. Sodium iodide (with thallium) is a highly effective scintillator as far as light output is concerned, but the light pulse has a relatively long decay time, compared with the organic phosphors; hence, it is less satisfactory when a very rapid response is required. However, because of its high density, sodium iodide has a high stopping power for gamma rays, and hence is a very efficient counter for photons of this radiation. Further, the size of the output pulse is closely proportional to the energy quantum, so that, with the aid of a pulse analyzer, gamma rays of different energies, from a single substance or from a mixture, can be separated and counted. If required, the actual energies can be measured.

6.53. Organic scintillators give smaller light pulses, under equivalent conditions, than do sodium iodide (with thallium); but since they have a shorter decay time, higher counting rates are possible. The decay time in the liquid and plastic scintillators are even shorter than in the crystals, but the light emission is also decreased. Counters with liquid phosphors can be

made very large and in a great variety of shapes. The "human" counter at Los Alamos Scientific Laboratory, for determining the total radioactivity of the body, is large enough to contain a grown person. Three counters, each holding 420 gallons of liquid, were used in the detection of the elusive particle known as the neutrino (§ 7.61).

6.54. Because of their simplicity, great flexibility and versatility, high sensitivity to all forms of nuclear radiation, rapid response, very short resolving time, and the ability, in some forms, to discriminate between and measure photon energies, scintillation counters are finding ever-increasing uses. For general survey purposes, especially where gamma rays are being detected, they are superior to the Geiger counter because of their greater accuracy, higher efficiency and shorter resolving time. A G-M counter records about 1 per cent of the entering gamma-ray photons, but a sodium iodide scintillator will easily record 50 per cent, largely because of the greater density of the material. Further, even though the latter is slow compared to an organic phosphor, it has a very much shorter response time than a Geiger tube.

6.55. Aside from particle counting, there are many applications in the atomic energy field for which scintillation counters are especially suited because of their extremely rapid response. In many cases the light flash is over in a very few billionths of a second. Consequently, instruments of this kind are used for the accurate timing of nuclear (and related) particles moving with very high speeds. For example, scintillation counters were employed in the detection of the antiproton, described in § 2.83, in which it was necessary to count the particles traversing a distance of 40 feet in 51 billionths of a second.

ČERENKOV COUNTERS

6.56. For studies of various nuclear particles and photons of high energy, another type of light-emitting counter has attracted some interest. This is based on the production of what is known as *Čerenkov radiation*. In 1934, the Russian physicist P. A. Čerenkov reported that water and other transparent substances, such as glass and mica, emitted a weak bluish-white glow when exposed to gamma radiation.* The light was emitted mainly in the direction of the gamma-ray beam, and had a continuous spectrum from red to ultraviolet, at least. An explanation of this phenomenon was given, some three years later, by I. Frank and I. Tamm in Russia. It was shown that the production of Čerenkov radiation is a kind of electromagnetic shock-wave effect, arising when an electrically charged particle travels through a medium with a velocity greater than that of light in that medium.†

6.57. The idea of using the luminous Čerenkov radiation, in conjunction with a photomultiplier tube, to count individual charged particles (or photons) of high energy was put forward in the United States by I. A. Getting in 1947, and the first attempt to construct such a counter was made by R. H. Dicke shortly thereafter. Further development of the Čerenkov counter, as it has been called, was due to the work of J. V. Jelley in England in 1951. In its simplest form, a Čerenkov counter is similar to a scintillation counter, except that the light flashes are generally much more feeble in the former case. The high-energy particles or radiation photons enter a vessel containing a transparent liquid, e.g., water, or a block of glass. The interior walls of the vessel are silvered or painted white to reflect all the light produced on to the cathode of a sensitive photomultiplier. The output pulses can then be counted.

6.58. The Čerenkov counter, in various forms, has found application in the study of mesons, etc., in cosmic rays, and also of various particles and photons of high energy produced in the laboratory. In addition to having an exceptionally short resolving time, since the light pulse from a single particle usually lasts less than a billionth of a second, there are other special features of the counter which contribute to its value. Because the radiation in a given medium is produced only when the speed of the charged particles is greater than the velocity of light in that medium, the Čerenkov counter can be used as a threshold detector, i.e., to record only particles whose speed (or energy) exceeds a certain value.

6.59. The angle between the direction of light emission and the path of the initiating particle depends on the velocity of the latter. Consequently, the Čerenkov counter can be adapted to the determination of particle velocities (or energies). Particles of different mass can be distinguished in two ways: first, for the same velocity, i.e., the same Čerenkov angle, the brightness of the flash (and output pulse size) is proportional to the square of the atomic number and, second, for the same energy ($\frac{1}{2}mv^2$)

---

* Essentially the same effect was observed in water by L. Mallet in France in 1929.

† The velocity of light in a liquid or solid is considerably less than that in a vacuum or in air. In water, for example, the velocity of light is 2.25×10^{10}, and in ordinary glass about 2×10^{10}, compared with 3.00×10^{10} cm. per sec. in a vacuum.

or range, the velocity of the particle is inversely proportional to the square root of the mass number. There are other aspects of the Čerenkov counter which make it unique, but enough has been said to justify the interest in it as a device for studying high-energy particles.

CRYSTAL CONDUCTION COUNTERS

6.60. Another method for counting nuclear particles was proposed by P. J. Van Heerden in Holland in 1945. It has been known for some years that certain crystals, which are normally poor electrical conductors, become— like gases—conducting when exposed to ionizing radiations. If the crystal is placed between two electrodes, to which a potential is applied by means of a battery, each ionizing particle will produce a pulse of current which can be amplified and recorded. Van Heerden employed a silver chloride crystal, but this has to be cooled in liquid air in order to be effective. Later it was observed that some, but not all, diamonds can respond to gamma, and probably to beta, radiations at ordinary temperatures. It is claimed that extremely short pulses are obtained, so that much more rapid recording is feasible.

6.61. In addition to silver chloride, which requires low temperatures for its use, and diamond, which is costly, a number of inexpensive substances have been found which respond to radiation in the same manner at normal temperatures. A particularly good material is cadmium sulfide, with traces of impurities as activators, which has long been known as a *photoconductor,* i.e., it becomes an electrical conductor when exposed to

ordinary light as well as to radiations of shorter wave length, e.g., X-rays and gamma rays. The response time of cadmium sulfide is fairly long and so it does not lend itself to individual particle counting. However, it can be used in a simple integrating-type instrument (§ 6.20) for gamma-radiation surveys. It consists of the crystal, a battery and a current meter, which indicates the rate of arrival of the radiation.

STATISTICAL ERRORS OF COUNTERS

6.62. All individual nuclear events appear to be random in character, although when a large number of such events are examined a definite probability pattern is evident. If any single radioactive nucleus were considered, it would be impossible to say when it is likely to emit a particle. But, for a system consisting of a large number of nuclei of the given kind, the probability that any nucleus will expel a particle is determined by the decay constant (§ 5.33). The same general situation applies to nuclear events of all kinds.

6.63. One of the consequences of the random nature of nuclear processes is that, if two successive readings are taken on the same counter, exposed to a constant source of ionizing particles, the results will probably differ somewhat. This is referred to as the statistical error of the counter due to the random nature of the events recorded. The probable error can be calculated theoretically, but from the practical standpoint it is important to note that the magnitude of this error is decreased by increasing the number of counts.

TRACKS OF IONIZING PARTICLES

IONS AS CONDENSATION NUCLEI

6.64. Although ionization chambers, Geiger tubes, scintillation counters and other devices have proved invaluable for counting ionizing particles, another instrument—the Wilson cloud chamber—has been very useful in connection with somewhat different studies of such particles. The fundamental principles involved in the cloud chamber were discovered by the English physicist C. T. R. Wilson in 1896. Like J. S. Townsend, whose investigations led to the development of methods for counting alpha and beta particles (§ 6.1), Wilson was working in the famous Cavendish Laboratory, presided over at that time by J. J. Thomson. However, it was not until 1911 that Wilson devised the first form of the instrument which made possible the discovery of the positive electron, or positron, as described in § 2.67, and also of various mesons.

6.65. Air contained in an enclosed space can be saturated with the vapor of water or of any other liquid, the

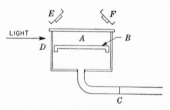

FIG. 6.8. Diagram of Wilson cloud chamber.

amount of the vapor necessary to produce saturation decreasing as the temperature is lowered. Imagine a vessel *A* containing air saturated with water vapor enclosed by a piston *B*, which is maintained in position by the pressure of the air below it (Fig. 6.8). Suppose that, by means of a valve *C*, the pres-

sure under the piston *B* is suddenly released so that it falls; this will result in an instantaneous expansion of the gas in *A*. The sudden (adiabatic) expansion will result in the air being cooled, so that it now contains more water vapor than is necessary for saturation at this lower temperature. If particles of dust are present in the air, they will act as condensation nuclei, and the excess of water vapor will separate out as fine droplets of liquid in the form of a cloud or mist. If, on the other hand, there are no dust particles, the air will become supersaturated with vapor, and no condensation will occur unless there has been considerable expansion accompanied by a marked fall of temperature.

6.66. In 1887, the versatile German physicist H. von Helmholtz, and others, had found that electrification brought about condensation in steam jets, and J. J. Thomson in 1893 had provided a theoretical interpretation of these facts. But it was C. T. R. Wilson who, in 1896, discovered that when dust-free air saturated with water vapor was exposed to X-rays, it behaved on expansion just as if it contained dust particles. Later he showed that the radioactive radiations from uranium and the electrons produced by the photoelectric effect of ultraviolet light on zinc (§ 2.48) had a similar influence. Wilson suggested that the positively and negatively charged ions formed in the air by the radiations acted, like dust particles, as condensation nuclei, and this was confirmed when he proved that no condensation would take place on expanding the saturated air after the ions had been removed by an electric field.

6.67. The background of Wilson's discovery provides a striking example of the consequences of scientific curiosity and observation. In the address which he gave following the award to him of the Nobel Prize for Physics in 1927, Wilson described how in 1894, when he was still a young student, he spent a few weeks during the summer in the observatory on the summit of Ben Nevis, in Scotland. "The wonderful optical phenomena shown when the sun shone on the clouds . . . ," he effect of ionizing radiations in facilitating the condensation of water droplets in saturated air cooled by expansion. Thus, he turned away from the study of the colors produced when light is scattered by clouds, to investigate the phenomenon of condensation on gaseous ions which has proved of such great value in many aspects of nuclear science.

THE WILSON CLOUD CHAMBER

6.68. C. T. R. Wilson's discovery

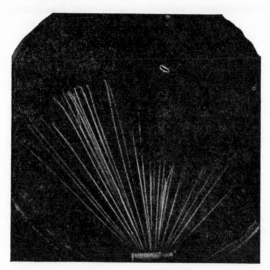

FIG. 6.9.   Cloud tracks produced by alpha particles from polonium.

said, "greatly excited my interest, and made me wish to imitate them in the laboratory. At the beginning of 1895, I made some experiments for this purpose—making clouds by expansion of moist air. . . . Almost immediately I came across something which promised to be of more interest than the optical phenomena which I had intended to study." At the beginning of 1896, Wilson had access to an X-ray tube, a novelty which was attracting great interest among scientists at the time, and it was then that he discovered the was first put to practical use in the early attempts to determine the magnitude of the electric charge carried by gaseous ions. Observations were made on the clouds produced when air saturated with water vapor was exposed to various ionizing radiations, as indicated in § 2.31. It was in 1911, however, that Wilson showed that the path of a single ionizing particle could be rendered visible. The apparatus, which has become known as a *cloud chamber*, for the obvious reason, is similar in principle to the device depicted in Fig.

6.8. The air is saturated with water vapor and the piston is allowed to drop to such an extent as will expand the volume of the air by a factor of 1.25 to 1.37, this being the range in which cloud formation can occur.

6.69. If an ionizing particle enters the chamber either immediately before, during or immediately after the expansion, the trail of ions left in its path will act as condensation nuclei, so that a close array of fine droplets, i.e., a kind of linear cloud, called a *cloud track*, will be formed. By using suitable strong illumination D from the side, the track appears as a white line on a dark background. This can be photographed by means of two cameras at right angles, as shown at E and F, so that a permanent record can be obtained from which the path of the single ionizing particle in three dimensions can be studied.

6.70. The cloud tracks produced by a group of alpha particles are shown in Fig. 6.9. It is seen that, in general, the particles travel in straight lines, although near the end of their paths, when their speeds have been greatly diminished, the particles may suffer sharp deflection, presumably as the result of impacts with the nuclei of oxygen or nitrogen present in the air.

6.71. Apart from their many applications in the study of ionizing particles, radiations and even neutrons, to which reference will be made in the course of this book, the Wilson cloud-chamber photographs have a significance that is fundamental to the atomic theory as a whole. As Lord Rayleigh (4th Baron) has pointed out, while it is true that the Brownian movement (§ 1.58) gives a magnified picture of molecular motion, that ionization counters permit individual alpha particles and electrons to be counted, and that flashes produced by single particles are rendered visible in various scintillation devices, it is the cloud track which provides perhaps the most convincing evidence of the reality of the atom. The track produced by an alpha particle indicates the path of a single helium nucleus, and deviations from a straight line show exactly where an encounter with another atomic nucleus has occurred.

6.72. Since the construction of the first Wilson cloud chamber in 1911, the apparatus has been improved in many ways, although the fundamental principle remains unchanged. In order to record rare nuclear phenomena, it is necessary to take many photographs, and in 1921 the Japanese physicist, T. Shimizu, working in England, devised a means for doing this automatically. The piston of the cloud chamber was attached to an electric motor so that the appropriate expansion, followed by compression to the initial volume, took place at regular intervals of a few seconds. After each expansion a photograph of such tracks as may have been formed was taken on a moving film, and then the chamber was cleared of charged particles by an electric field, so that it was ready for the next cycle of compression and expansion. Because the expansion was not sufficiently sudden, the cloud-track photographs were somewhat blurred, but this difficulty was overcome by P. M. S. Blackett, in England in 1927, by using a spring mechanism in place of the motor to move the piston of the cloud chamber at regular intervals.

6.73. Instead of operating the chamber regularly but intermittently, cloud chambers, particularly those used in the study of cosmic rays (Chapter XVIII), are frequently constructed so as to function automatically at the critical moment. Geiger (or other) counters are placed at the top and bottom of the chamber and when an ionizing particle passes through both of them, and hence through the chamber, a relay is operated which causes expansion of the gas and condensation of droplets of water on the ions left by the particle. The track of the latter is consequently revealed by a photograph taken at the same time.

6.74. In the earlier cloud chambers a chamber underwent sudden expansion. A cloud chamber of this type can be used in any desired position.

6.75. Although the foregoing description has referred to water as the liquid used to saturate the air in the Wilson cloud chamber, it is more common at the present time to employ ethyl or propyl alcohol or a mixture of alcohol and water. The use of alcohol in this connection gives better conden-

FIG. 6.10. Faint cloud tracks produced by beta particles from radium E. (The curvature of the tracks was caused by a magnetic field.)

layer of water or oil was used on the floor of the chamber as a seal for the piston, and this meant that the instrument could be used only in the horizontal position. A decided advance in design was made by C. T. R. Wilson in 1933 when he constructed a cloud chamber in which the piston was replaced by a thin rubber diaphragm fixed at its edge. The diaphragm was maintained in a state of tension by means of compressed air in the back (or lower part) of the chamber, and when this was released the gas in the sation on positive ions than does water alone and, in addition, the extent of expansion necessary for droplet formation is diminished from 1.25 to about 1.10 at ordinary pressures. While air is the usual gas, cloud chambers containing argon are sometimes employed, and the pressure may range from below to well above that of the atmosphere. The higher pressures are desirable for the study of high-energy (or long-range) particles which might otherwise pass right through the chamber without taking part in an event of interest, e.g., a nuclear disintegration.

6.76. For the study of radioactive radiations and for many similar purposes, relatively simple cloud chambers, with air at ordinary pressure, are quite adequate. Because of the low penetrating power of alpha particles, the source of the radiation must be inside the chamber, but a substance emitting beta particles can be placed outside and the rays allowed to enter through a "window." Gamma rays and X-rays yield cloud tracks because they liberate electrons which produce ionization in their paths (§ 6.5). These tracks are, however, very faint.

6.77. By making visible the actual track of an ionizing particle, the cloud chamber permits the measurement of the range of the particle from which its energy can frequently be calculated (§ 7.20). By counting the drops in the cloud track the specific ionization can be determined and the nature of the particle identified; it is thus possible to distinguish between an alpha particle, a proton, a meson and an electron. The alpha particle has the highest specific ionization and gives a short dense track, while an electron, unless it is moving with very high speed, leaves a track that is diffuse and tortuous (Fig. 6.10). By observing the curvature of the cloud track in a magnetic field the sign of the ionizing particle can be determined. As seen in § 2.69, this fact played an important role in the discovery of the positron.

Diffusion Cloud Chambers

6.78. A conventional cloud chamber has a relatively long recovery time— 5 to 10 sec.—after expansion, so that it may often miss an interesting nuclear event. The concept of a continuously sensitive cloud chamber was proposed by A. Langsdorf in the United States in 1939. The device he constructed, called a *diffusion cloud chamber,* was somewhat complex and it was not until 11 or 12 years later that simpler forms were designed and operated successfully.

6.79. Essentially, the diffusion chamber consists of a vessel, containing air or other gas, which is kept warm at the top and cold at the bottom; a supply of a volatile liquid is available, e.g., in a circular trough, near the top. The liquid vaporizes in the warm (top) region, where the vapor pressure is high, and continuously diffuses to the bottom (cold) region, where the vapor pressure is low and condensation occurs. Somewhere in between the air is supersaturated with vapor and the conditions are right for the growth of droplets around ions, just as is the case immediately after expansion of a conventional cloud chamber. The diffusion cloud chamber thus remains continuously sensitive to ionizing particles, until the supply of the volatile liquid is exhausted.

6.80. In order to increase the frequency of occurrence of nuclear events, the pressure of the gas in the chamber is increased. Diffusion chambers have been operated with hydrogen or helium gas at pressures up to about 35 atmospheres. The best volatile liquid has been found to be methyl alcohol, with ethyl alcohol only slightly inferior. In the former case, the temperature at the top of the chamber is about 30°C (86°F) and that at the bottom around −70°C (−94°F). For reliable functioning, reasonably good temperature control is desirable. The main drawback of the diffusion cloud chamber is that, at best, the sensitive region is no more than 3 inches deep. Nevertheless, the continuously sensitive chamber has found many uses, especially in the study of high-energy particles obtained in the laboratory.

THE BUBBLE CHAMBER

6.81. The basic disadvantage of condensation cloud chambers, both of the expansion and diffusion types, is that, due to the low density of the gas, significant phenomena are not very frequent. The situation can be improved by pressurizing the gas, as already noted, but it is still not too good. Photographic emulsions, described below, have much greater stopping power, but they have other limitations. In 1952, D. A. Glaser, at the University of Michigan, conceived the idea of using a superheated liquid to display the tracks of ionizing particles, just as a cloud chamber utilizes a supersaturated vapor. The instrument based on this concept is called a *bubble chamber* because the tracks consist of a series of closely spaced bubbles, analogous to the small droplets of liquid in the cloud chamber. A liquid hydrogen bubble chamber of more than 500 liters capacity is scheduled for completion in 1958; this may be compared with the few hundred cubic centimeter volumes of the chambers in use two or three years before.

6.82. Normally, a liquid will boil, with the evolution of bubbles of vapor, when the temperature reaches the boiling point. However, if the containing vessel is clean and has no rough surfaces, it is possible to superheat the liquid above its boiling point without ebullition (or bubble formation) taking place. Glaser found that when such a superheated liquid was exposed to nuclear radiation, the resulting ions acted as nuclei for the production of small bubbles. The bubbles are spaced at something like a hundredth of an inch apart, or less, depending on the specific ionization of the initiating particle, so that they appear as a fairly continuous track which indicates the path of the particle. As in the cloud chamber, the tracks can be photographed against a dark background (Fig. 6.11). The sign

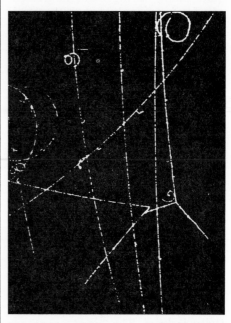

FIG. 6.11. Particle tracks in liquid hydrogen bubble chamber in a magnetic field. The spiral-like tracks are produced by low-energy electrons; for the origin of some of the other tracks, see § 18.92. (University of California Radiation Laboratory.)

of the electrical charges carried by the particles can be determined from the curvature of the track in a magnetic field.

6.83. In the first bubble chambers, the liquid employed was ordinary (diethyl) ether, but later liquid hydrogen, liquid nitrogen, isopentane and other liquids have been used successfully for different purposes. The density of the liquid is about a hundred (or more) times as great as the gas in a cloud chamber, even when under pressure. Hence, the stopping power is good and tracks, including those of particles of high energy, are reasonably short. Interesting nuclear events are thus of frequent occurrence. The earliest bubble chambers were quite small, having linear dimensions of a few inches only, but, with experience, chambers of larger and larger size are being constructed.

6.84. The operation of a bubble chamber is, in many respects, similar to that of an expansion cloud chamber. The liquid, in a smooth glass (or glass-walled) vessel, is compressed and the temperature raised to well above the standard boiling point. For example, isopentane, which normally boils at about 28°C (83°F), is heated to 157°C (315°F) at a pressure of roughly 23 atmospheres. The pressure is then suddenly released, so that the liquid becomes superheated. It is then sensitive to the passage of ionizing particles. Even if no such particles are present, boiling, with bubble formation, will inevitably occur within a short time, so that the period of sensitivity is brief. The liquid must then be cleared of ions by an electric field and recompressed before the chamber is again ready to operate.

6.85. Like the expansion cloud chamber, the bubble chamber has the drawback of not being continuously sensitive. However, one of the most important applications of the bubble chamber has been in connection with devices used in the laboratory to obtain charged particles of very high energy. It will be seen in Chapter IX that these devices operate intermittently, producing short bursts of particles at regular intervals. The compression of the liquid in the bubble chamber and the subsequent decrease in pressure, to bring the liquid into the superheated state, can then be timed exactly to correspond to the entry of the charged

particles. A flash of light permits a photograph of the tracks to be taken on moving film. The bubble chamber is thus proving to be a powerful tool in the field of high-energy nuclear physics.

PHOTOGRAPHIC DETECTION
OF IONIZING PARTICLES

6.86. In recent years there has been a marked revival of interest in the use of photographic films and plates for the study of ionizing particles. It will be recalled that the phenomenon of radioactivity was discovered by Becquerel because of the action of the radiations on sensitized plates (§ 2.99), and many applications of this effect have been made from time to time. It will be indicated in § 17.61 how photographic methods are used to obtain "radioautographs" which provide information on the distribution of radioactive elements in plant and animal tissue, and in § 19.39, the employment of film to determine the extent of exposure of a human being to radiation will be described. In the present section the matter to be considered is the direct recording on a photographic plate of the actual tracks of ionizing radiations.

6.87. In 1909, O. Mügge in Germany and in the following year, S. Kinoshita of Japan observed that the blackened regions of a developed photographic plate, resulting from exposure to alpha particles, appeared to be made up of individual grains. But they failed to note any connection between the arrangement of the developed grains and the tracks of the particles. It was shortly thereafter, however, in 1911, that M. Reinganum in Germany realized that the positions of the grains were related to the path of the alpha particle. In due course it was found that ionizing particles, in general, record their tracks in a photographic emulsion, as a series of closely spaced black specks of silver. Because of the relatively high density (and stopping power) of the photographic emulsion, the tracks produced by charged particles are very short compared with those obtained in a cloud chamber, although they do not differ greatly from bubble tracks. The photographic method was employed for various purposes during the 1920s and 1930s, but it is only in recent years that the procedure has come into general use, largely as a result of the development of special "nuclear track emulsions."

6.88. The early investigators used ordinary photographic plates in their work, but in recent years the composition of the emulsion has been changed so as to make it more suitable for the study of various ionizing particles, such as alpha particles, protons, mesons and even electrons. By adding boron or lithium to the emulsion, neutrons can also be detected (§ 11.27). The modern emulsions contain silver bromide to the extent of 80 per cent, or more, of the dry weight, this being about ten times the quantity present in plates or films used for normal photographic purposes. The silver halide grains are extremely small, ranging in diameter from 1 to 4 × 10^{-5} cm.; the larger the grain, the more sensitive is the emulsion to ionizing radiations. Originally the emulsions were deposited on glass plates, roughly one eighth of a centimeter thick. Now, however, stripped emulsions (or pellicles), as they are called, are available without backing. For exposure, the films can be stacked, one on top of another, to provide a large sensitive volume. Continuous tracks can thus be observed in various directions. Prior to development, the films are separated and later recombined as desired.

6.89. The tracks produced in a photographic emulsion are very short, e.g., a few thousandths of an inch for alpha particles from radioactive sources, but they can be magnified and photographed (Fig. 6.12). However,

Fig. 6.12. Magnified tracks in a photographic plate, produced by alpha particles from radiothorium and its successive decay products. (From "Nucleonics," a McGraw-Hill publication.)

the general practice is to examine the developed film (or plate) with a special binocular microscope, looking for and measuring particular or unusual tracks. This somewhat tedious procedure has become an art in which nontechnical personnel, with suitable training, have acquired considerable skill.

6.90. The photographic emulsion resembles the Wilson cloud chamber in the respect that it can record individual events involving atomic nuclei and other charged particles. Further, as with the cloud and bubble tracks, information concerning the particles involved can be obtained from measurements on the photographic tracks. As a general rule, it is required to know the mass of the particle and its charge and energy, and these can be derived from some of the following data: the range of the particle, the grain density (the number of silver grains per unit length of path or the spacing between grains when they are relatively far apart) and its variation along the track, and the small-angle

(Coulombic) scattering due to collisions of the particle with nuclei in the emulsion. Tracks caused by heavy, strongly ionizing particles have numerous thin, wavy tracks (or spurs) projecting from their sides. These are called *delta rays* and are produced by electrons ejected from the nuclei in the path of the particle. From the number of delta rays per unit track length, the magnitude of the charge on the particle can be estimated.

6.91. As compared with cloud or bubble chambers, photographic emulsions have one drawback. The chambers can be placed in a magnetic field and, from the resulting bending of the track, the sign of the electrical charge is immediately evident. In addition, the momentum of the particle can be determined if required from the curvature of the track. By the use of very strong magnetic fields, the deflection of long (but not short) tracks in photographic emulsions has been observed. This gives the sign of the charge, but the large amount of scattering makes the deflected tracks useless for calculation of momentum.

6.92. In addition to the high stopping power of emulsions, which increases the frequency of interesting events involving penetrating (high-energy) particles, an advantage of the photographic technique is its simplicity. Further, the emulsion is continuously sensitive, so that it is always available to record an event. These two favorable factors are offset, to some extent, by the numerous and complex track patterns which may result from an appreciable exposure, so that it is often difficult to discover and identify particular nuclear events. There are many investigations in nuclear physics in which photographic emulsions play an important part, not the least of these being studies of cosmic rays and mesons (see Chapter XVIII).

Properties of Nuclear Radiations

Chapter VII

THE PROPERTIES OF ALPHA RADIATIONS

RANGE OF ALPHA PARTICLES

7.1. In the preceding chapter the various methods for studying alpha, beta and gamma rays were described. It is appropriate, now, to return to a consideration of the properties of these nuclear radiations. It can be seen from Fig. 6.9, which is a cloud chamber photograph of the alpha particles emitted by the natural radioelement polonium, that the tracks are nearly all of the same length. It is thus said that alpha particles from a given source have a constant *range*, over which they are capable of producing ionization of the air through which they pass.

7.2. The process of ionization requires the expenditure of energy by the alpha particle—approximately 33.5 electron volts (§ 6.4) for each ion-pair formed—and so toward the end of its path the energy, and hence the speed, of the particle will have been greatly reduced. In these circumstances there is a considerable probability that first one and then two electrons will adhere to the alpha particle, which is a bare helium nucleus, i.e., He^{++} (§ 4.30), and thus convert it first to He^+ and then into a neutral helium atom. The neutral atom has no ionizing power,

and hence the condensation of water droplets in the cloud chamber no longer takes place. The range of an alpha particle may then be defined as the distance it can travel through air under standard conditions, usually a temperature of 15°C and a pressure of 1 atm., from its source to the point at which it can no longer produce appreciable ionization.

7.3. Even before the invention of the cloud chamber provided a means for

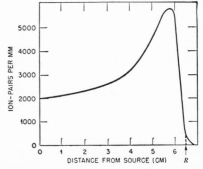

FIG. 7.1. Bragg curve showing number of ion-pairs detected at various distances from a source of alpha particles.

obtaining a picture of alpha-particle tracks, W. H. Bragg in England had produced evidence that these particles have a definite range. In 1904 he reported the results of an investigation, made by means of an ionization chamber, of the specific ionization, i.e., the number of ion-pairs per unit length of its path (§ 6.3), of an alpha particle in air at various distances from its source. When plotted on a graph and a line drawn through the points, a curve such as that in Fig. 7.1, frequently known as a *Bragg curve*, was obtained. Although the values for the points on the curve vary with the nature of the alpha-emitting radioelement, the shape of the curve is quite characteristic. As the distance of the alpha particle from its source increases the specific ionization increases, at first slowly and then more rapidly, reaches a maximum and then drops sharply almost to zero. The distance corresponding to the point R in Fig. 7.1 represents the (extrapolated) range of the alpha particles from the given radioelement.

7.4. It is not difficult to account, in a general way, for the shape of the Bragg curve. While the alpha particle traverses its path, producing ion-pairs as it proceeds, its energy, and consequently its speed, steadily diminishes. Because it moves more slowly, it spends more time in the vicinity of each of the molecules of the air which it encounters in its path and so the probability of removing an electron, and producing an ion-pair, increases. The specific ionization thus increases steadily, at first, as the alpha particle moves away from its source. Ultimately a point is reached when electrons attach themselves to the particle and convert it into a neutral atom which cannot cause ionization of the air, and so the specific ionization falls abruptly.

7.5. The reason why the end portion of the curve is not vertical, but slopes slightly to the right, and may even have a slight "tail," is that the alpha particles do not all lose exactly the same amount of energy in their encounters with the molecules in their path. Hence, they do not all cease to produce ionization at precisely the same distance from their source. This slight variation in the range, frequently referred to as *straggling,* is also partly due to the formation of He^+ ions, by the attachment of one electron to some of the alpha particles. These ions still possess ionizing power, and hence they cause a slight extension of the range before they take up a second electron and become neutral atoms.

7.6. Another way of studying the range of alpha particles is to determine the number which can be counted at various distances from the source. For this purpose the latter may be placed on one plate (electrode) of an ionization chamber (§ 6.14) and counts taken with the other plate at various dis-

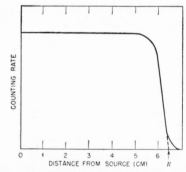

Fig. 7.2. Rate at which alpha particles can be detected at various distances from a source.

tances away. Alternatively, a scintillation counter, such as a zinc sulfide screen, can be employed (§ 6.43). If the counting rate, say in pulses or scintillations per second, is plotted against the distance from the radioactive source, the result will be of the form shown by the curve in Fig. 7.2. Up to a certain distance the counting rate remains essentially constant, and then it drops sharply to zero, apart from slight straggling. The extrapolated range is again indicated by the point R; at greater distances the alpha particles can no longer be detected.* Where cloud chamber studies have been made, the ranges observed are in close agreement with those obtained from direct ionization or counting measurements.

7.7. The extrapolated ranges, in air at 15°C and 1 atm. pressure, of the alpha particles from a number of radioelements are recorded in the accompanying table. For a reason which will soon be apparent, the half lives are also included. The ranges are seen to vary from 2.8 cm. for thorium, the longest lived, to 8.6 cm. for thorium C′, which has the shortest life of the natural radioelements. The significance of this inverse relationship between the half lives of alpha particle emitters and the ranges of the particles will be considered below.

RANGES AND HALF LIVES OF
ALPHA PARTICLE EMITTERS

Radioelement	Range	Half Life
Thorium (Th^{232})	2.8 cm.	1.39 × 10^{10} yr.
Radium (Ra^{226})	3.3	1620 yr.
Radiothorium (Th^{228})	3.9	1.9 yr.
Radium A (Po^{218})	4.6	3.0 min.
Thorium A (Po^{216})	5.6	0.16 sec.
Radium C′ (Po^{214})	6.9	1.6 × 10^{-4} sec.
Thorium C′ (Po^{212})	8.6	3.0 × 10^{-7} sec.

STOPPING POWER

7.8. It was mentioned in Chapter II (§§ 2.102, 2.111) that alpha particles are unable to penetrate a few sheets of paper or a thin aluminum foil, yet they can travel through several centimeters of air. It is evident, therefore, that different materials permit the passage of alpha particles to different extents. The same general conclusion can be drawn from the statement in § 6.89 that the tracks produced by alpha particles in a photographic emulsion are only a few thousandths of an inch in length; in a cloud chamber, on the other hand, the alpha particle tracks are usually from 1 to 3 inches long. The range of an alpha particle thus depends on the medium through which it travels.

7.9. A quantity called the *stopping power* of the medium has been defined as the rate of loss of energy by an alpha particle per unit distance as it travels through the medium. For practical purposes, however, it is more convenient to employ the *relative stopping power;* thus for any material,

Relative stopping power
$$= \frac{\text{Range of alpha particle in air}}{\text{Range of alpha particle in material}}, \quad (7.1)$$

the same source of alpha particles being used in both instances. Actually the relative stopping power depends to some extent on the source of the particles, but an approximate average value is generally employed. By finding the thicknesses of thin metal foils and of other substances, such as mica, which will just prevent the passage of alpha particles of known range in air, the relative stopping powers of these materials can be determined. Some of the values obtained in this way are as follows:

Mica	Aluminum	Copper	Gold
2000	1700	3800	4900

7.10. In many studies of the absorption (or stopping) of nuclear radiations by various media, it is often the

---

* The extrapolated range in Fig. 7.2 is slightly different from that in Fig. 7.1, but the discrepancy is no more than a fraction of a mm. and can be ignored for present purposes. A *mean range,* corresponding approximately to the middle of the rapidly descending portion of Fig. 7.2, is sometimes recorded; it is about 1.3 per cent less than the extrapolated range in the same figure.

practice to make use of a quantity which is the product of the thickness of the material, e.g., in cm., and its density, e.g., in gram per cc. The result is the mass per unit area, i.e., grams per sq. cm., which is equivalent to a certain thickness. It has been variously called the areal density, the thickness-density or the equivalent thickness.* In connection with the absorption of alpha (or beta) particles, especially, ranges expressed in grams/cm.^{2} are relatively small for solid materials, and so the result is multiplied by 1000 to give the equivalent thickness in milligrams per sq. cm., i.e., in mg./cm.^{2} Hence, the equivalent thickness, for present purposes, may be defined by

Equivalent thickness (mg./cm.^{2})
$$= \text{Actual thickness (cm.)} \times \text{density (grams/cm.}^3\text{)} \times 1000.$$

7.11. The equivalent range, in mg./cm.^{2}, of an alpha particle in any medium is thus obtained upon multiplying the range in that medium by its density and 1000. It follows, therefore, by combining this result with equation (7.1), that the thickness of the material which is equivalent in stopping power to 1 cm. of air is given by

Thickness in mg./cm.^{2} equivalent to
$$1 \text{ cm. of air} = \frac{\text{Density} \times 1000}{\text{Relative stopping power}}.$$

The values of this thickness for the substances whose stopping powers were given above are then as follows:

Mica	Aluminum	Copper	Gold
1.4	1.59	2.35	3.95 mg./cm.^{2}

This means that with aluminum, for example, a piece 1 sq. cm. in area of a sheet which has the same effect as 1 cm. of air in slowing down alpha particles weighs 1.59 milligrams, whereas

1 sq. cm. of an equivalent sheet of gold will weigh 3.95 milligrams.

7.12. From the conclusions concerning the stopping powers of various elements reached by W. H. Bragg in 1905, it can be shown that the equivalent thickness as defined above should be proportional to the square root of the atomic weight of the element. Thus, it is possible to state, as a fair approximation, that the thickness in mg./cm.^{2} equivalent to 1 cm. of air in the absorption of alpha particles is equal to $0.30A^{1/2}$, where A is the atomic weight in the case of an elemental substance, or the average of the atomic weights of the constituent elements for a compound material. This result is useful for calculating the extent of absorption of alpha particles in various media for which experimental data are not available.

7.13. In the study of alpha particles, and other radiations, it is customary to use thin sheets of metal foil, particularly of aluminum, as the absorber in place of air. The equivalent range in the metal can then be readily determined by weighing a piece of known area of the foil which can just stop the alpha particles. The actual range of the particles in the given material or in air can be calculated as follows. Suppose it has been found that an aluminum foil, weighing 4.32 milligrams per sq. cm., is required to stop the alpha particles from a given source. The equivalent range in aluminum is thus 4.32 mg./cm.^{2}, and, since the density of aluminum is 2.70 grams per cc, the actual range is found to be $4.32/(2.70 \times 1000)$, i.e., 1.60×10^{-3} cm. To obtain the range of the alpha particles in air, the equivalent range in aluminum is divided by the thickness of aluminum equivalent to 1 cm. of

* The same quantity is frequently referred to merely as the "thickness." The units, e.g., grams/cm.^{2}, indicate that it is really the actual thickness multiplied by the density.

air, i.e., by 1.59 mg./cm.² Thus, in the case under consideration, the range in air would be 4.32/1.59 = 2.72 cm. Alternatively, since the stopping power of aluminum, relative to air, is known to be 1700, the actual range in air is equal to the range in aluminum, i.e., 1.60 × 10⁻³, multiplied by 1700, i.e., 2.72 cm. The method of calculation used in any particular case will depend on which data are more readily available.

Velocity, Energy and Range of Alpha Particles

7.14. The direct measurement of the energies of alpha particles is made by determining the radius of their circular path in a magnetic field. As stated in § 2.43, the equation (2.8), which relates the charge e, carried by a particle of mass m, to the velocity v and the radius of curvature r of the path in a magnetic field of strength H (see Fig. 2.2), is applicable to any charged particle. For the present purpose it can be rearranged to take the form

$$v = \frac{e}{m} Hr, \qquad (7.2)$$

and since the charge on an alpha particle is known to be twice the unit electronic charge, and the mass is that of a helium nucleus, i.e., a helium atom minus two electrons, the evaluation of the velocity requires only the determination of the radius r of the path of the particle in a magnetic field of strength H.

7.15. The experimental arrangement used for this purpose, known as a 180° *magnetic spectrograph*, is shown diagrammatically in Fig. 7.3. The radioactive source is placed at R and the alpha particles emerge in a narrow beam through the slit S. As already seen, air slows down the alpha particles and so the apparatus is evacuated

by pumping out the air. A magnetic field of known strength, which acts in a direction perpendicular to the plane of the diagram, is then applied, and the alpha rays are bent through an angle of 180° so that they fall on a

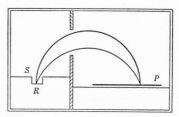

Fig. 7.3. Diagrammatic representation of a magnetic spectrograph.

photographic plate at P. From the position of the trace produced where the particles strike the plate the radius of curvature of the path can be determined, and hence the velocity of the particles can be calculated from equation (7.2).

7.16. In recent years the magnetic spectrograph has been improved by replacing the photographic plate by a suitable alpha-particle counter, the position of which is fixed, say at the point P. The magnetic field is then varied until the counter shows that the particles emerging from S are reaching P, and are then traversing a path of known radius. In the older, photographic method the magnetic field was constant, and the path radius was different for alpha particles of different energies; in the newer modification, which is simpler and more accurate, the radius of the path is constant but the field H is varied so as to make particles of different energies follow the given path.

7.17. The energy of an alpha particle is essentially kinetic in nature, that is to say, it is due almost entirely to the motion of the particle. Hence the energy of an alpha particle may be taken as equal to $\frac{1}{2}mv^2$ (§ 3.5), where, as above, m is its mass and v its speed.* It is for this reason that measurements of the velocity of alpha particles, as described above, are often referred to as energy determinations. The mass of an alpha particle on the atomic weight scale is 4.0028, and hence the mass of a single particle in grams is obtained upon dividing by the Avogadro number, 6.02×10^{23} (§ 1.57); the result is 6.65×10^{-24} gram. If the velocity v is expressed in cm. per sec., the kinetic energy of an alpha particle is $\frac{1}{2} \times 6.65 \times 10^{-24}v^2$ ergs. Making use of the conversion factor given in § 3.33, this becomes $2.08 \times 10^{-18}v^2$ Mev, with v still in cm. per sec. The initial velocities of alpha particles from radioactive sources vary from about 1.4×10^9 to 2.2×10^9 cm. per sec., and so the corresponding energies lie in the range between 4 and 10 Mev.

7.18. The size of the pulse produced by an alpha particle in an ionization-chamber counter coupled with a linear amplifier is a direct measure of the number of ion-pairs formed, and hence of the energy of the particle. This has been utilized in conjunction with the pulse analyzer, described in § 6.15, to determine the energies of alpha particles from a given source. To the source may be added small amounts of radioelements which emit alpha particles of known energies, or the instrument may be independently standardized with these substances. The analyzer then sorts out the pulses produced by the particles from the different sources, and, by noting which of the recording instruments respond, the unknown alpha-particle energies can be estimated from those which are known.

7.19. In 1910, H. Geiger, at that time in Rutherford's laboratory in Manchester, England, made some measurements of the relative speeds of alpha particles from radium C after they had passed through various thicknesses of mica of known stopping power relative to air. From the results, he concluded that the velocity v of the alpha particle at any point at a distance x from the source could be expressed by the equation

$$v^3 = a(R - x), \qquad (7.3)$$

where R is the usual range of the particles, as described in § 7.2, and a is a constant. If x, the distance from the source, is set equal to zero, the corresponding velocity, represented by v_0, will be the initial velocity of the alpha particles at the source, and then equation (7.3) becomes

$$v_0^3 = aR. \qquad (7.4)$$

This relationship, known as the *Geiger formula*, although derived from measurements on a single substance, radium C, was later found to be generally applicable to alpha particles from various sources, the constant a having the same value, namely, 1.03×10^{27}, in all cases, provided the initial velocity v_0 is given in cm. per sec. and the range R in cm. of air; thus,

$$v_0^3 = 1.03 \times 10^{27}R. \qquad (7.5)$$

There is consequently a direct connection, as might have been expected, between the velocity with which an alpha particle is ejected from its source, and the distance it can travel before losing its ability to produce ionization in air.

---

* The mass implied here is the ordinary or rest mass, which may be used provided v does not approach the velocity of light (§ 3.69). Since the speeds of alpha particles expelled in radioactive changes rarely, if ever, exceed one tenth of the speed of light, this condition is satisfied. The modification necessary for particles of high velocity is given by equation (3.9).

7.20. The energy E of an alpha particle, in Mev, is related to the velocity by $E = 2.08 \times 10^{-18}v^2$, as seen above; hence it can be shown from equation (7.5) that

$$E_0^{3/2} = 3.09R \text{ or } E_0 = 2.12R^{2/3}, \quad (7.6)$$

where E_0 is the initial energy of the alpha particle in Mev, and R is its range in cm. of air. From equation (7.6) it is possible to obtain a moderately accurate estimate of the energy of an alpha particle at its source, provided the range has been measured. Thus the alpha particles from radium have a range of 3.29 cm. of air, and upon substituting this figure for R in equation (7.6), the initial energy is calculated to be 4.70 Mev, the directly measured value being 4.79 Mev.

7.21. Actually, the Geiger formula and its equivalent equations (7.5) and (7.6) are approximate, at best, and in any event they are applicable only for alpha particles with ranges of from 3 to 7 cm. of air. At lower ranges R is approximately proportional to $v_0^{3/2}$ and $E_0^{3/4}$, and at higher ranges to v_0^4 and E_0^2. As a result of experimental investigations of the ranges and velocities, or energies, of alpha particles, and from theoretical considerations, curves have been constructed which give the energies of alpha particles as a function of their respective ranges. By means of these curves the energy of an alpha particle of known range can be estimated quite accurately. Such curves have found many uses, some of which will be indicated in Chapter X.

The Geiger-Nuttall Rule

7.22. It was pointed out in § 7.7 that the longest-lived radioelements emit alpha particles with the shortest ranges, whereas the elements of short life expel particles having long ranges. The possibility that a connection might exist between the life period of an alpha-active element and the range of the particles emitted was suggested by Rutherford in 1907, and four years later, when sufficient data had become available, an approximate relationship was brought to light by H. Geiger and J. M. Nuttall. These workers showed that if the logarithm of the alpha-particle range in air, i.e., log R, is plotted against the corresponding value of the logarithm of the radioactive decay constant, i.e., log λ, for a number of radioelements, an approximately straight line is obtained for each radioactive series. The *Geiger-Nuttall rule*, as it is called, is thus represented mathematically by the expression

$$\log \lambda = A \log R + B, \quad (7.7)$$

where λ is the decay constant of the radioelement emitting alpha particles of range R; the constant A is the slope of the straight line, which is virtually the same for each series, but the values of B are different.

7.23. Alternative forms of the Geiger-Nuttall rule can be derived from equation (7.7) by utilizing the relationship between the decay constant and the half life, e.g., equation (5.9), on the one hand, and between the range and the energy of the alpha particles, e.g., equation (7.6), on the other hand. These require that a straight line be obtained when the logarithms of the decay constants of radioelements are plotted against the logarithms of the alpha-particle energies, or the logarithms of the half lives against the logarithms of either the ranges or the energies. Thus, for example,

$$\log \lambda = \tfrac{3}{2} A \log E_0 + B', \quad (7.8)$$

where A has the same value as in equation (7.7) and B' is a constant for each radioactive series. Because of the limited applicability of the Geiger-Nuttall equation (7.7), these plots usually show a slight curvature, and some points lie above and some below the curve.

7.24. When Geiger and Nuttall proposed the general rule considered above, in 1911, they based their conclusions on measurements made on seventeen alpha-active radioelements. Since that time additional alpha emitters, making a total of about thirty, have been found to occur in nature. But, more important, something like a hundred others have been obtained since 1940 by means of various nuclear reactions, as will be described in Chapter XVI. Consequently, a considerable amount of information is now available for relating decay constants (or half lives) to alpha-particle ranges (or energies). The Geiger-Nuttall rule thus appears to be a restricted and approximate aspect of a much broader generalization which will be discussed later (§ 16.102).

THEORY OF ALPHA-PARTICLE
EMISSION

7.25. In reporting their correlation between the life of a radioelement and the range of the alpha particles emitted, Geiger and Nuttall wrote: "The connection . . . between the period and the range is at present only empirical, but it may depend on some simple relation which may ultimately be brought to light." It is true that several years later a theoretical relation between the life of a radioelement and the energy of the alpha particle was developed, but the approach was far from simple, as will soon be apparent.

7.26. In experiments on the scattering of alpha particles, such as those described in § 4.7, it was found that even the fastest of such particles from ra-

dioactive sources, having an energy of 10 Mev, are repelled by atomic nuclei. However, the more energetic the particle the more closely can it approach the nucleus before it is turned back. This conclusion applies to all nuclei, including those of radioactive atoms. Although alpha particles are prevented by repulsion from entering the nucleus from outside, it is an undoubted fact that radioactive nuclei emit alpha particles, so they must be able to exist, at least for a short time, within such nuclei. The interactions between a radioactive nucleus and an alpha particle, outside and inside the nucleus, can be represented pictorially by a *potential energy curve* such as that in Fig. 7.4.

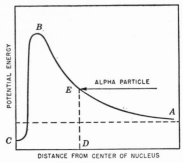

FIG. 7.4. Potential energy curve (hypothetical) for interaction between an atomic nucleus and an alpha particle.

The rising portion of the curve from *A* to *B* indicates increasing repulsion of an alpha particle as it approaches the nucleus. On the other hand, the sharp fall from *B* to *C*, which is essentially the region within the nucleus, implies attraction of the alpha particle by the nucleons in the nucleus.

7.27. Calculations have shown that the point *B*, at the maximum of the curve, corresponds to an energy of about 25 Mev, for an element of high atomic number. Hence, it may be concluded that an alpha particle with energy less than this amount will be repelled if it approaches the nucleus from outside, i.e., from right to left of the diagram. An alpha particle with energy E, about 10 Mev, approaching the nucleus, as shown in Fig. 7.4, will be turned back when it reaches a distance from the center of the nucleus corresponding to the point D. An energy of at least 25 Mev would be necessary for the alpha particle to reach the nucleus without suffering repulsion.

7.28. Scientists often speak of the conditions represented by Fig. 7.4 as being due to a *potential barrier*, since something analogous to a barrier is preventing the entry of alpha particles into the nucleus. However, it must be clearly understood that the term "barrier" is used in a figurative sense only; it is not meant to imply the existence of a material barrier, but rather of repulsive forces which are equivalent to a barrier. It is important to appreciate this point, because the shape of the potential energy curve, and hence that of the figurative "barrier," varies with the nature of the particle approaching the nucleus. When the particle is a proton, for example, the "barrier" is much lower than for an alpha particle, and when it is a neutron, the "barrier" is virtually not existent. In other words, the force of repulsion between a nucleus and a proton is less than for an alpha particle, while there is essentially no repulsion between a nucleus and a neutron.

7.29. So far there appears to be no objection to the foregoing discussion, but a more careful examination reveals a difficulty. If an alpha particle must have an energy equal to, or **greater** than, that corresponding to the maximum point B of the potential energy curve, i.e., 25 Mev, to get into the nucleus from outside, then an alpha particle from the interior of the nu-

cleus should have at least the same amount of energy to escape. That is to say, if a potential barrier prevents the access of alpha particles from outside the nucleus, the same barrier should prevent the emission of particles from the interior. It is surprising, therefore, to find that alpha particles are produced from radioactive sources with energy as low as 4.0 Mev, and for no natural radioelement does the alpha-particle energy exceed 10.6 Mev.

7.30. Classical mechanics provided no explanation of this state of affairs, but in 1928 the English physicist R. W. Gurney in collaboration with E. U. Condon of the United States, and the Russian-born G. Gamow independently showed that the paradox could be resolved by means of the then newly-developed wave mechanics (§ 3.50). According to classical theory, an alpha particle inside the nucleus cannot surmount the barrier and escape if its energy is less than 25 Mev, but wave mechanics requires there should be a definite, if small, probability that such a particle from the interior will be found outside the nucleus. In other words, there is a definite probability that the alpha particle will escape from the nucleus even when its energy is less than that of the top of the hypothetical barrier. If the energy of the particle is equal to (or exceeds) the value at the top of the barrier then the probability of escape amounts, of course, to a certainty, according to both classical and wave-mechanical theories.

7.31. By using the equations of wave mechanics, a complex expression can be derived for the probability that an alpha particle of given energy will escape when it reaches the exterior surface of the nucleus. In general, it can be said that this probability is greater, the larger the energy of the alpha particle relative to the top of the barrier, and the smaller the "thickness" of the barrier at the point corresponding to the given energy value. It can be seen from Fig. 7.4 that the higher the energy the less the thickness of the barrier; hence, both factors influencing the escape probability operate in the same direction. It follows, therefore, that the greater the energy of the alpha particle in a radioactive atom, the more likely is it to be found outside the nucleus. This is the fundamental basis of the fact that radioelements which disintegrate rapidly emit alpha particles of high energy and long range, whereas the long-lived elements produce particles of relatively low energy and short range (§ 7.19 *et seq.*).

7.32. An approximate value of the frequency with which alpha particles reach the exterior surface of the nucleus can be obtained upon dividing the radius of the nucleus by the estimated speed of the alpha particle. If this frequency, expressed as the number per second, is multiplied by the probability of escape, the result will give the frequency with which alpha particles actually escape; this is equivalent to the radioactive decay constant λ, in reciprocal-second (sec.$^{-1}$) units. It will be apparent from what has already been stated that the value of λ will, in general, be larger the greater the energy of the alpha particle. By making a number of simplifying assumptions, the wave-mechanical treatment leads to a relationship between the decay constant λ and the energy of the alpha particle which is somewhat similar to the Geiger-Nuttall rule in the form of equation (7.8). It may be remarked in this connection, that in order to make the theoretical equations fit the experimental results, the effective radius of the nucleus must be taken as approximately equal to 1.5 ×

$10^{-13}A^{1/3}$ cm., where A is the atomic weight (mass number) of the radioelement (see § 4.19).

7.33. An interesting conclusion from the wave-mechanical theory of alpha decay is that, for elements of high atomic number, such as the naturally occurring radioelements, the energy of the alpha particle must be at least 3.8 Mev if the decay constant is to be greater than 10^{-20} sec.$^{-1}$ (half life less than 10^{12} years). Smaller decay constants (or longer half lives) will mean that radioactive disintegration is so slow as to be undetectable. Of the heavy radioelements, thorium, with a half life of 1.39×10^{10} years, emits the alpha particle with the lowest energy, 4.0 Mev. It is possible, however, that other alpha-particle emitters, of longer half life, may exist, but present experimental methods are not adequate for their detection.

7.34. In view of the probability of the escape of alpha particles from radioactive nuclei even when their energy is insufficient to surmount the barrier, it might be argued that there should be a similar probability that alpha particles from outside with the same amount of energy should be able to reach the nucleus without being repelled. This argument is completely justifiable, and there is no doubt that such penetration does take place in the bombardment processes which cause nuclear rearrangements (Chapter IX).

7.35. It is instructive, however, to calculate the probability of an alpha particle escaping from, and of returning to, an atomic nucleus. The radius of a nucleus is about 10^{-12} cm., and the speed of an alpha particle moving in the nucleus is perhaps 10^8 cm. per sec. Consequently, as a rough approximation, an alpha particle will find itself at the exterior surface of the nucleus $10^8/10^{-12}$, i.e., 10^{20}, times per second. Upon multiplying this frequency by the escape probability, the result will give the decay constant λ, in sec.$^{-1}$ units, as seen above. The actual values of λ vary from roughly 10^7 sec.$^{-1}$ for thorium C' to 10^{-18} sec.$^{-1}$ for thorium; hence, the probability of escape ranges from 10^{-13} to 10^{-38}. This means that, even with the very short-lived radioelement thorium C', an alpha particle in the nucleus, with an energy of about 9 Mev, makes on the average 10^{13} attempts before it succeeds in escaping. For thorium, in only one attempt in 10^{38} does the alpha particle, of energy about 4.0 Mev, leave the nucleus.

7.36. It is because of the very large number of escape attempts made by the alpha particle, i.e., the large number of times it reaches the exterior surface of the nucleus, namely, about 10^{20} times per second, that radioactivity is an observable phenomenon. When a nucleus is bombarded by alpha particles from outside, however, the number of attempts at entry is very much less, and hence the effects are not so marked, although the probability of entering the nucleus is the same as the probability of escaping, for the same energy value.

ALPHA-PARTICLE SPECTRA

7.37. It has been assumed, so far, that all the alpha particles from a given source have virtually the same range and energy, but this is not strictly the case. It is generally true that a large proportion, if not all, the particles have identical energies, but in some instances particles with different energies have been detected.* The presence of a very small number of particles of exceptionally high energy was observed by E. Rutherford and A. B. Wood in 1916 in the radi-

ations from thorium active-deposit, probably originating from thorium C'. Three years later Rutherford noted that similar long-range particles were emitted from radium active-deposit. It was not until 1930, however, that S. Rosenblum, in France, proved definitely by means of a magnetic spectrograph, similar to that described in § 7.15, that the alpha particles from thorium C, all of which had been thought to have the same energy, actually consist of a number of groups of particles, with slightly different energies.

7.38. Since that time, several physicists have made detailed studies of the distribution of energy among the alpha particles from a number of radioelements. In a few cases, the particles were found to be monoenergetic, all having essentially the same energy, but in many instances there was a definite *alpha-particle spectrum*, consisting of two or more discrete groups —possibly as many as thirteen for radium C'—of different energies. A simple example is provided by thorium C which emits six groups of alpha particles whose energies are 6.086, 6.047, 5.764, 5.622, 5.603 and 5.478 Mev, respectively; the first group constitutes 27.2 per cent and the second 69.8 per cent, so that these two together make up 97 per cent of the total.

7.39. The occurrence of alpha-particle spectra can be accounted for by the existence of definite energy levels in atomic nuclei, as stated in § 4.83. In a radioactive disintegration the nucleus of the parent element, thorium C, for example, is almost invariably in its lowest energy state, but the nucleus of the daughter element, thorium C", formed as a result of the emission of

* The data in the table in § 7.7 refer to the main proportion of the alpha particles from any given source.

an alpha particle, may be either in its lowest (ground) state or in any one of five higher (excited) levels. The energy of the alpha particle thus depends on the energy levels of the parent and daughter nuclei involved in the disintegration. The six groups of particles observed for the transition from thorium C to thorium C″ are interpreted in this manner, as shown in Fig. 7.5, and the alpha-particle spectra

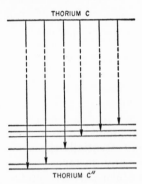

FIG. 7.5. Explanation of alpha-particle spectrum from thorium C.

of other radioelements can be explained similarly. The transition to the second level of thorium C″ is evidently the most probable, since the largest proportion of alpha particles have the energy corresponding to this particular change.

7.40. When the nucleus of the daughter element in a radioactive transition is formed in an excited state, it can change to a lower energy state by the emission of radiation. This appears as gamma rays, as will be explained in § 7.101. The fact that there is an almost exact correlation between the energies of the groups of alpha particles and the energies of the gamma rays is strong confirmation for the foregoing explanation, based on nuclear energy levels. Some reference will be made later to the circumstances which lead to gamma-ray emission and, hence, to groups of alpha particles.

7.41. In two or three instances, such as, thorium C′ and radium C′, a very small proportion of highly energetic alpha particles are due to the parent nucleus being in an excited energy state, whereas the daughter element, thorium D and radium D, respectively, is in its lowest (ground) level. The circumstances are here somewhat exceptional. An appreciable amount of thorium C′ is formed in an excited state upon decay of its parent, but the product has such an extremely short half life—3×10^{-7} sec.—that about one nucleus in a million will disintegrate to thorium D straight from the excited state before it has an opportunity to emit the excess energy as gamma radiation. Similar considerations apply to the disintegration of radium C′, which has a half life of 1.6×10^{-4} sec.

THE PROPERTIES OF BETA RADIATIONS

BETA-PARTICLE ENERGIES

7.42. It will be recalled that, whereas alpha particles are positively charged and have a mass of about 4 on the atomic weight scale, beta rays consist of electrons, so that they are very light, negatively charged particles. Apart from these distinctions, there is a highly important respect in which alpha and beta particles differ, to which attention must be called at the outset. It was seen in the preceding section that alpha particles are either monoenergetic or else there is a spectrum made up of a limited number of discrete groups having definite energies; beta particles, on the other hand, do not behave in this manner.

7.43. In 1900, H. Becquerel noted, from their behavior in a magnetic field, that the deviable radiations, i.e., beta rays, were complex, forming a continuous distribution of velocities, and hence of energies. But during the early years of the present century there was a difference of opinion among workers in the field of radioactivity: some thought the beta particles from a given source had a wide range of energies, while others were of the opinion that they were essentially monoenergetic. The latter view appeared to find support in the discovery, made by O. von Baeyer, O. Hahn and L. Meitner in Germany, in the years between 1910 and 1912, of the existence of homogeneous (monoenergetic) groups of electrons in beta rays. But doubt was cast on their significance when, in 1914, J. Chadwick found that they constituted a small fraction only of the total beta particle emission. The opinion was therefore expressed that the main portion of the electrons emitted by a radioactive element, which showed a continuous distribution of energy, were the true disintegration beta particles, and that the weaker monoenergetic groups were due to a secondary effect. A theory of the origin of these secondary electrons was proposed by E. Rutherford in 1914, and supported by Lise Meitner in 1922, after she and O. Hahn had shown that similar groups of monoenergetic electrons were sometimes found associated with alpha-particle disintegration. The nature of these secondary electrons, which are associated with the emission of gamma rays, will be considered in § 7.106.

7.44. Two main methods have been used for the study of the distribution of energy among the beta particles from a given radioactive source. The first makes use of the 180° (or semicircular) magnetic spectrograph which is quite similar in principle to that described in § 7.15 for the determination of the velocities of alpha particles. The best form of apparatus is that in which a particle counter is placed in a fixed position, such as P in Fig. 7.3. The magnetic field H is then varied, and the numbers of beta particles reaching the counter in a given time for the different values of H are recorded. From H and the fixed radius r of the semicircular path taken by the beta particles, the velocity v of the latter can be calculated by means of equation (7.2); each value of H thus corresponds to a definite velocity. In this way, the relative numbers of beta particles having various velocities can be determined.

7.45. Since the speeds of beta particles as they emerge from radioactive sources approach the velocity of light, allowance must be made in equation (7.2) for the relativistic increase of mass. If, as required by equation (3.9), m is replaced by $m_0/\sqrt{1 - v^2/c^2}$, where m_0 is the rest mass of the electron, v is the initial speed of the emitted beta particle, and c is the velocity of light, equation (7.2) becomes

$$v = \frac{e}{m_0} Hr \sqrt{1 - v^2/c^2}, \quad (7.9)$$

which is the form to be employed in the present instance. Further, the (kinetic) energy of the beta particle is no longer given merely by $\frac{1}{2}mv^2$, as is the case for the comparatively slow-moving alpha particles, but by

$$E = m_0 c^2 \left(\frac{1}{\sqrt{1 - v^2/c^2}} - 1 \right). \quad (7.10)$$

The calculations of the energy from the magnetic field and curvature of the path are thus somewhat more complicated, but they can be made without too much difficulty by means of equations (7.9) and (7.10).

7.46. The second method which has been employed in the determination of beta-particle energies makes use of what is known as the *magnetic-lens spectrometer.* The principle involved is essentially the same as that used for focusing in the electron microscope, and it is for this reason that the name magnetic lens (or electron lens) has been applied. In outline, the apparatus consists of a cylinder (Fig. 7.6)

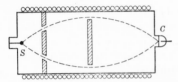

Fɪɢ. 7.6.   Principle of magnetic lens spectrometer for determining beta-particle energies.

around which is wound a coil (solenoid) of copper wire. When a current is passed through this wire a magnetic field is produced in the cylinder, its direction being parallel to the axis. The radioactive source is placed at one end of the cylinder at S, while at the other end, at C, there is a suitable charged-particle counter with a thin wall which the beta particles can penetrate. By means of the baffles shown at the left, the particles leaving the source S in a definite direction are permitted to enter the longitudinal magnetic field; this field constrains them to follow a helical (spiral) path, a projection of which is shown by the dotted lines in Fig. 7.6.

7.47. By suitably adjusting the current in the solenoid, and thus changing the magnetic field, beta particles from S can be "focused" so that they perform a single turn of the helix and just reach the wall of the counter. For a given value of the magnetic field, only those beta particles which have a par-

ticular velocity will reach the counter. The velocity can be calculated from the magnetic field and the dimensions of the apparatus. As a general rule, however, the instrument is standardized by means of electrons of known speed, and the velocity can then be determined directly from the current flowing through the solenoid. In this manner, the relative numbers of beta particles, as detected by the counter, with different velocities, and hence with different energies, can be determined.

7.48. The results obtained with a variety of different beta-active sources, both natural and artificial (Chapter X), are all of the same type. Apart from the few groups of monoenergetic electrons sometimes observed, the overwhelming proportion of the beta particles from any source exhibit a continuous distribution of energy, i.e., a beta-particle spectrum. The energies range from very small values up to a definite maximum, the latter varying with the source. If the relative number of particles possessing a particular energy is plotted against the energy, the points usually fall on a curve such as

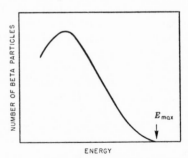

Fɪɢ. 7.7.   General form of distribution of energies among beta particles (beta particle spectrum).

that depicted in Fig. 7.7. The maximum energy, obtained by a short extrapolation, is indicated by E_{max}. The maximum velocities of beta particles range from about 25 to 99 per cent of the speed of light; the corresponding values of E_{max} vary from 0.025 to 3.15 Mev, most of them being in the vicinity of 1 Mev.

THE NEUTRINO THEORY

7.49. The problem of the continuous distribution of energy among beta particles concerned physicists for a number of years. It seemed highly improbable that it could be due to the existence of a continuous series of energy levels in either parent or daughter elements, since all the evidence points to the presence of a few discrete levels only. If the variation in energy among the beta particles were due to transitions between different energy states, then there should be a continuous distribution of gamma ray energies to correspond to that for the beta particles, but no such phenomena have been observed. A radioactive beta transition, like an alpha change, must be accompanied by a definite energy change, and this is undoubtedly equal to the maximum beta-particle energy, E_{max}. For example, when the masses of the parent and daughter elements are known, the energy change can be calculated (§ 3.79) from the decrease in mass, after allowing for that of the electron. This has been found to be the same as E_{max}. Further, it was seen in § 5.60 that thorium C undergoes branched disintegration, but the two branches rejoin at thorium D. The energy difference by the path thorium C → thorium C′ → thorium D should

be exactly the same as that for the alternative path thorium C → thorium C″ → thorium D. Careful measurements show that this is true only if in the transitions thorium C → thorium C′ and thorium C″ → thorium D the beta particle energies are those corresponding to E_{max} in each instance.

7.50. The problem is then: What happens to the additional energy in the case of the great majority of beta particles whose energy is less than the maximum? The situation was so desperate that some eminent physicists suggested that the law of conservation of energy might not hold in beta-disintegration processes, but this view could not be entertained seriously. Ultimately, in 1931, a way out of the difficulty was indicated by W. Pauli (see § 4.64), and this was elaborated by the famous Italian-born physicist E. Fermi in 1934. There is little doubt that the atomic nucleus does not contain free electrons, but only neutrons and protons (§ 4.35); hence, the electrons which are emitted as beta rays by radioactive nuclei must result from the spontaneous conversion of a neutron into a proton and an electron. Pauli suggested that this process was accompanied by the emission of another particle, now called a *neutrino**; this was assumed to be electrically neutral and to have a very small rest mass, small even compared to that of the electron. Thus, the creation of an electron in the nucleus, prior to its emission as a beta particle, would be represented by the process

$$\text{neutron} \rightarrow \text{proton} + \text{electron} + \text{neutrino.} \qquad (7.11)$$

	neutron	proton	electron	neutrino
mass	1	1	0	0
charge	0	+	−	0

* From the Italian, meaning a "small neutral one." The neutrino concept was proposed by W. Pauli at a Seminar in Theoretical Physics held in the University of Michigan in the summer of 1931. The name "neutron" was first used for the particle, but after the discovery of the real neutron of unit mass and zero charge (§ 2.118), the term neutrino was adopted by E. Fermi.

7.51. It will be seen that the two sides of the equation balance with respect to both mass—given to the nearest integer—and charge. In a beta-decay process, the proton remains in the nucleus, but the electron and the neutrino are ejected. In order to account for the continuous distribution of energy among beta particles Pauli supposed that the total available energy, equal to E_{max}, was divided between the electron (beta particle) and the neutrino. Thus the difference in energy between E_{max} and the actual value for any given beta particle would be carried off by the accompanying neutrino.

7.52. Even if it had not been necessary to postulate the formation of the neutrino to account for the beta-particle energy spectrum, it would be required for another reason. It was seen in § 4.86 that the spin quantum numbers of the neutron, proton and electron are each $+\frac{1}{2}$ or $-\frac{1}{2}$. Consequently, if there is to be a conservation (or balance) of spin in the beta-emission process, as in other nuclear reactions, an additional particle, also having a spin of $+\frac{1}{2}$ or $-\frac{1}{2}$, is required when a neutron changes into a proton and an electron. If this spin quantum number is assigned to the neutrino, spin can be conserved in the process represented in equation (7.11).

7.53. By applying the methods of wave mechanics to the neutrino hypothesis, as just outlined, Fermi was able to derive a complicated equation giving the probability of the emission from a radioactive nucleus of a beta particle with energy in the vicinity of any specified value. The plot of this probability function against the corresponding energy value should have given a curve similar to that in Fig. 7.7; although it was of the correct

form, the agreement with experiment did not appear to be too good. However, because of the lack of reliable experimental data at the time, the earlier tests of the theory were not conclusive.

7.54. More recent work, particularly with artificial beta-active radioelements of fairly low atomic weights, has given results which provide support for the neutrino theory. The tests have been facilitated by the use of a method of plotting suggested in 1936 by F. N. D. Kurie, J. R. Richardson and H. C. Paxton in the United States. They showed that the Fermi probability equation could be rearranged to take the form

$$K \, (N/F)^{1/2} = C - (E + 1), \quad (7.12)$$

where N is the number of beta particles of momentum (or energy) lying within a certain narrow range, F is a complex function of the corresponding beta-particle energy E as worked out by Fermi, and K and C are constants. The energy E of the beta particle is here expressed in units of $m_0 c^2$, where m_0 is the rest mass of the electron and c is the velocity of light. According to equation (7.12), the plot of $(N/F)^{1/2}$ against $E + 1$, often referred to in the scientific literature as a *Kurie plot*,* should be a straight line if the Fermi neutrino theory is to be substantiated. Where reliable data are available it appears that they do give a straight line, although a correction factor, which can be calculated, must be included for the so-called "forbidden" transitions (§ 7.78).

POSITIVE BETA ACTIVITY

7.55. All the beta-active elements existing in nature expel negative particles, i.e., electrons. But, there have been obtained in the laboratory a

* Also sometimes called a *Fermi plot.*

number of radioactive species that emit positive beta particles, i.e., positrons (see Chapter X). It will be seen in due course that the basic difference between the negative and positive beta emitters is that the nuclei of the former contain too many neutrons for stability, whereas the latter have too many protons. Consequently, just as a neutron will change into a proton and an electron, in the negative beta-active nuclei, as described above, so in the positive beta-active species, a proton is converted into a neutron and a positron. The latter is then emitted as a positive beta particle. Apart from the difference in sign of the expected particle, positive and negative beta emitters behave in exactly the same manner. All that has been stated above in connection with negative beta particles applies equally to positive beta particles.

7.56. The energies of the positive beta particles have a continuous distribution satisfying equation (7.12), so that the Kurie plot is linear, just as for negative beta particles. The production of a positron by the conversion of a proton into a neutron is thus represented by

$$\text{proton} \rightarrow \text{neutron} + \text{positron} + \text{neutrino}, \qquad (7.13)$$

$$\begin{array}{lcccc} \text{mass} & 1 & 1 & 0 & 0 \\ \text{charge} & +1 & 0 & +1 & 0 \end{array}$$

so that again it is necessary to postulate the formation of a neutrino, which shares the energy with the positive beta particle (positron) and also permits conservation of spin. For the present, the particles accompanying both negative and positive emission will be referred to as "neutrinos." The question of whether they are the same or different will be taken up shortly.

DETECTION OF THE NEUTRINO

7.57. Apart from the fact that the neutrino concept has proved useful in solving a difficult problem in nuclear science, it may be wondered if there is any direct experimental evidence for the existence of such a particle. In view of its very small mass, and the absence of electric charge, the neutrino would be expected to pass readily through matter and hence would be difficult to detect. It may be mentioned in this connection that when in 1927 C. D. Ellis and W. A. Wooster, in Rutherford's laboratory, determined the heat given out by the beta particles from radium E, the value corresponded to the average energy, and not to the maximum energy, of the particles. This result implies that if, as now supposed, the disintegration energy is shared between beta particles and neutrinos, the former gave up all their energy, while the latter escaped from the apparatus with virtually no loss of energy.

7.58. Two general procedures have been used to provide positive evidence for the supposition that neutrinos accompany beta decay; these may be described as indirect and direct methods. The indirect approach is to study the recoil momentum of the residual (or daughter) nucleus in a beta disintegration. When a radioactive nucleus emits one or more particles, the residual nucleus will recoil with a certain velocity determined by the law of conservation of momentum. If a beta (positive or negative) particle only is emitted, the direction and velocity of the recoil will be different from those associated with the emission of a beta particle plus a neutrino. A number of experiments on nuclear recoils have been made and the results are not contrary to the neutrino hypothesis. It is because the effects sought are small and difficult to measure, and also because they may perhaps be explained in other ways, that the conclusion is stated in this negative form.

7.59. The direct method for detecting the neutrino is based on the possibility of observing the results of its interaction with a neutron or a proton. For example, the neutrino produced in negative beta decay should react with a proton to produce a neutron and a positron; thus,

$$\text{proton} + \text{neutrino} \rightarrow \text{neutron} + \text{positron}. \tag{7.14}$$

mass	1	0	1	0
charge	+1	0	0	+1

Since each of the four particles concerned has a spin quantum number of $+\frac{1}{2}$ or $-\frac{1}{2}$, spin will be conserved in the process. The simultaneous formation of a neutron and a positron in this reaction would thus provide strong positive evidence for the existence of the neutrino. Theoretical calculations indicate, however, that the probability of a neutrino interacting with a proton is so small that, on the average, a neutrino would travel a total distance (although not in a straight line) of about a hundred light-years* through water before such interaction occurred!

7.60. The only hope of detecting this rare interaction is in a location where the number of neutrinos is expected to be extremely large. Such a situation should exist in the vicinity of a nuclear fission reactor (see Chapter XIV), since during operation of the reactor large amounts of negative beta-emitting radioelements are produced. In 1953, F. Reines, C. L. Cowan and their collaborators, of Los Alamos Scientific Laboratory, set up an experiment near the reactors at Hanford, Washington, and obtained preliminary results which, while positive, were not completely convincing. Consequently, the observations were repeated on a larger scale during 1956 at the Savannah River plant of the U. S. Atomic Energy Commission, where the neutrino density would be very high.

7.61. The apparatus consisted of five tanks, each $6\frac{1}{4}$ feet by $4\frac{1}{2}$ feet across. Two of these were "target" tanks, 3 inches deep, sandwiched between three "detector" tanks, 2 feet deep. The target tanks contained water in which a small quantity of cadmium chloride had been dissolved, whereas the detector tanks were filled with a solution of an organic scintillator (§ 6.48). Over a hundred photomultiplier tubes surrounded these tanks, so that flashes of light produced by gamma-ray photons would be detected.

7.62. The idea of the experiment was that a neutrino entering the water would occasionally interact with a proton, producing a positron and a neutron. Within an extremely short time, the positron will encounter an electron, of which there are many available, and then positron-electron annihilation will occur. This will be accompanied by the annihilation gamma radiation, consisting, in the main, of two photons each carrying 0.51 Mev energy (§ 3.91). The photons then enter the detector tank and produce scintillations which can be recorded.

7.63. In the meantime, the neutron

---

* A light-year is the distance traveled by light in 1 year; it is equivalent to about 5×10^{12} (five million million) miles.

will have traversed a more or less zig-zag (or random) path through the water. Several millionths of a second after its birth, it will encounter a cadmium nucleus and be captured (§ 11.98). One of the consequences of this capture is the release of about 8 Mev of energy which is divided among three or four gamma-ray photons. These will also enter the detector tank and produce light flashes, but the scintillations will appear after those caused by the positron-electron annihilation because of the appreciable time elapsing before the neutron is captured. The electronic counting system associated with the photomultipliers is therefore designed so that it will record only the production of scintillations (in pairs) separated by the appropriate time interval.

7.64. Ideally, such "delayed coincidences," as they are called, should result from the neutrino interacting with a proton. However, there are always extraneous circumstances which will produce such coincidences. In order to allow for these effects, observations were made with the reactor operating, so that neutrinos were being produced, and with the reactor shut down. The results showed that there was a difference of roughly 70 delayed coincidences per day which could be attributed to neutrinos. This is very much like the number that was expected under the existing experimental conditions. Exhaustive tests were performed to make sure that these delayed coincidences were not due to any other cause. The general conclusion was that the experiments provided positive proof for the existence of the neutrino, an elusive, uncharged particle with essentially no mass, but having a definite spin and capable of carrying off energy.

THE NEUTRINO AND ANTINEUTRINO

7.65. In view of the existence of electron and positron, proton and anti-proton, and neutron and antineutron, it is reasonable to ask: Is there an antineutrino to correspond to the neutrino? If the neutrino and anti-neutrino are different, then the particle accompanying negative beta decay, detected in the manner described above, really belongs to the class of antiparticles, so that it is the anti-neutrino. That such is the case may be most easily understood from the process represented in equation (7.14). The proton and the neutron are "normal" particles, and since the positron is an antiparticle, theory requires that the neutrino, on the other side of the equation, also be an antiparticle. The "normal" neutrino would then be the one produced in positive beta decay, as represented in equation (7.13).

7.66. Several methods have been proposed for determining whether the neutrino and antineutrino are really different particles or whether they are the same. Before outlining these tests, it may be stated that the results indicate that they are indeed different. One procedure is based on the existence of certain nuclei which, in theory, do not exhibit ordinary beta activity but which could, nevertheless, undergo *double beta decay*, that is, emit simultaneously two beta particles in each act of disintegration. This situation arises from the relative masses of the parent element, e.g., tellurium-130, and the daughters, either iodine-130 (one beta particle) or xenon-130 (two beta particles).* If the neutrino and antineutrino are different, then double negative-beta decay should be accompanied by the

---

* The significance of the (mass) numbers will be apparent in the next chapter.

emission of two antineutrinos. Theory shows that the radioactive half life of the parent should then be more than 10^{20} years. On the other hand, if the two particles are identical, there would be no neutrino (or antineutrino) associated with double beta decay. The energy could be distributed between the two beta particles and spins could be conserved without the neutrinos. The half life of the parent is then expected to be considerably shorter, namely, about 10^{12} years.

7.67. Although the direct measurement of such long half lives would be almost out of the question, another approach is possible. A search has been made for the expected daughter element in association with the parent in nature in minerals of known geological age. The results obtained so far indicate half lives of at least 10^{20} years, implying that the neutrino and antineutrino are different.

7.68. If the two particles are identical, then those coming from negative beta decay in a nuclear reactor should be capable of interacting with a neutron, as well as with a proton; thus,

conversion of chlorine to argon should be observed. In experiments with large volumes of the chlorine-containing compound carbon tetrachloride at the Savannah River reactors, no argon could be detected. This result, although negative, suggests that the neutrino and antineutrino are different.

7.69. Many of the nuclear reactions occurring in the sun, and which are responsible for its energy, are accompanied by the emission of positrons and, hence, of true neutrinos (§ 14.97). These neutrinos, unlike those from a reactor, which are really antineutrinos, should be capable of converting chlorine-37 into argon-37, as described above. The attenuation of neutrinos between the sun and the earth is negligible. Consequently, the conversion process should be observable on earth. Sea water contains much chlorine (as sodium chloride), and so it is to be expected that the radioactive argon-37 will be formed. As this will be present in minute traces only, its detection will be difficult, but if positive evidence is obtained it will provide convincing proof that the

$$\text{neutron} + \text{neutrino} \rightarrow \text{proton} + \text{electron.}$$

mass	1	0	1	0
charge	0	0	+1	−1

Suppose the neutron is in an atomic nucleus; the capture of a neutrino would convert the neutron into a proton, so that a new nucleus, one unit higher in atomic number, would be produced. One example of this would be the conversion of chlorine-37 (atomic number 17) into argon-37 (atomic number 18), which is radioactive. However, if the neutrino and antineutrino are different, the neutron will not interact with the particles (antineutrinos) from a reactor, and no

neutrino (from the sun) is different from the antineutrino (from a reactor).

7.70. Since the neutrino and antineutrino have no electrical charge and essentially zero mass,* it may be wondered how they differ. A possible clue has been provided by the results of some researches, reported in the early part of 1957, which were being performed for another purpose (§ 18.107). The magnetic element cobalt can be produced in an artificial radioactive form, called cobalt-60,

---

*It appears that the rest mass of the neutrino and antineutrino, like that of the photon, may actually be zero.

which emits negative beta particles. In a collaborative effort among (Miss) C.-S. Wu of Columbia University and E. Ambler and his associates at the U. S. National Bureau of Standards, a sample of cobalt-60 was subjected to the action of a magnetic field at extremely low temperatures (0.01°C above absolute zero). As a result, the nuclear magnets were aligned parallel to the field, with all the nuclei spinning in the same direction. By keeping the temperature very low, thermal agitation, which normally tends to favor a random arrangement of the nuclei, was kept at a minimum.

7.71. It was observed that, in these circumstances, the great majority of the beta particles, resulting from the radioactive decay of the cobalt-60 nuclei, were emitted in one particular direction. A repetition of the experiment with the positive-beta emitter cobalt-58 showed the same general effect, but the particles were now expelled predominantly in the other direction. In each case, conservation of momentum requires that the neutrino (or antineutrino) be emitted in the direction opposite to the beta particle. These results may be interpreted as implying a relationship between the spin of the neutrino (or antineutrino) and its direction of motion. If traveling in a given direction, the neutrino will spin one way, e.g., clockwise, whereas the antineutrino would spin the other way, e.g., anticlockwise. This example of right- and left-handedness represents an unsuspected aspect of the behavior of certain fundamental particles to which further reference will be made in Chapter XVIII.

ABSORPTION AND RANGE OF
BETA PARTICLES*

7.72. Cloud chamber photographs of beta particles (Fig. 6.10) are much less distinct than those produced by alpha particles, since the small mass of the former leads to a much smaller specific ionization in their paths. Further, it is found that the tracks are not straight lines, because the beta particles undergo frequent scattering. If the total length of the track of a beta particle could be measured in air it would probably be found to be several meters, as compared with a few centimeters for alpha particles. But such measurements are difficult, and so the range of a beta particle is usually defined in terms of the equivalent thickness (§ 7.10), expressed in mg./cm.^{2} or in gram/cm.^{2}, of an absorber, usually aluminum.

7.73. As the result of a series of circumstances, fairly good and reproducible results can be obtained in spite of the undoubted variations in actual range corresponding to the distribution of energy among the beta particles. It is an interesting and useful fact that, for light elements at least, the absorption thickness in mg./cm.^{2} is almost independent of the nature of the absorber. Hence, if a nuclear radiation detector is known to have a mica window with a thickness of 5 mg./cm.^{2}, the equivalent value for aluminum would be approximately the same. It is thus possible to make allowance for the absorption by the window when necessary.

7.74. The absorption of beta particles can be studied by placing the radioactive source near the thin wall of a suitable counter, and then recording the counting rate with various thicknesses of absorbing material inserted between the source and the counter. If a monoenergetic stream of electrons is used in such an experiment, it is found that the absorption

* The subsequent discussion applies equally to both positive and negative beta particles.

curve showing the number of particles passing through the absorber falls off steadily, in a roughly linear manner, as the absorber thickness is increased. This is quite different from the behavior of alpha particles, where, as indicated in Fig. 7.2, the counting rate remains almost constant until near the end of the range, when it falls quite sharply to zero. The reason why electrons act differently in this respect is partly because they lose energy by conversion into radiation, in addition to that used up in the formation of ion-pairs, but largely because they undergo very marked scattering, with frequent changes in direction, especially when passing through a solid absorber.

7.75. Since beta rays are not mono-energetic in nature, but consist of particles with a wide range of energies, the absorption curves are not linear but are more complicated in character. Because of a curious combination of factors, it so happens that if a graph is drawn of the *logarithm* of the counting rate for various absorber thicknesses against the thickness of absorber, the result is an approximately straight line, as depicted in

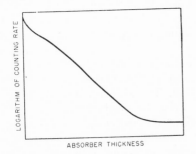

FIG. 7.8. Absorption of beta particles in matter.

Fig. 7.8. It will be noted that, beyond a certain absorber thickness, the counting rate no longer decreases but remains almost constant. This resi-

dual activity is due to the presence of the highly penetrating braking radiation (bremsstrahlung), analogous to continuous X-rays (§ 4.75), resulting from the deflection of the fast-moving beta particles by nuclei in the absorbing medium. The extent of the formation of this radiation increases with the atomic number of the absorber. If gamma radiation accompanies the beta rays, as is often the case, the curve for the residual counting rate is considerably higher, since it is now due to the gamma rays in addition to the bremsstrahlung.

7.76. From a cursory examination of Fig. 7.8, it might be concluded that the falling portion of the curve could be extrapolated to zero counting rate, as in Fig. 7.2, to give the effective range of beta particles in the absorber, apart from the extraneous radiation. The results obtained in this way are, however, very unreliable, especially if appreciable amounts of gamma radiation are present. A proposal for overcoming this difficulty, made by the English physicist N. Feather, in 1938, has been widely adopted. The absorption curves of the beta particles from the given sources are compared with the published data for radium E; the latter substance emits beta particles free from gamma rays and their maximum range is known to be equivalent to 476 mg./ cm.^{2} of aluminum. Consequently, by using the radium E as a standard, the maximum range of the beta particles under examination, in terms of mg./ cm.^{2} of aluminum, can be derived with the aid of a *Feather plot*, as it is called.

7.77. The importance of the maximum range R_{max}, as obtained in this manner, is that it is a characteristic property which can be used to identify the source and to determine the maximum energy E_{max} of the beta particles. A number of measurements have been made of both the maximum energy, using some form of magnetic spectrometer, as described in § 7.44 *et seq.*, and the maximum ranges of beta particles from a variety of sources; from them accurate data have been obtained from which a curve of E_{max} (in Mev) against R_{max} (in mg./cm.² or gram/cm.² of aluminum) has been plotted. Hence, if a value of R_{max} for beta particles from a given source is obtained by Feather's method, the corresponding maximum energy E_{max} can immediately be read off from the curve. As a less accurate alternative, use may be made of the relationship

E_{max} (Mev)

$$= 1.9\, R_{max}\,(\text{g./cm.}^2) + 0.17, \quad (7.15)$$

which is accurate within 5 per cent for E_{max} values, lying between 0.5 and 3 Mev.

BETA-DECAY TRANSITIONS

7.78. In seeking for a relationship between the radioactive decay constant λ of beta-emitting radioelements and the maximum energy E_{max} of the particles, analogous to the Geiger-Nuttall law for alpha decay (§ 7.22), the Canadian physicist B. W. Sargent found in 1933 that if the log λ values for various radioelements were plotted against the corresponding values of log E_{max}, most of the points fell on (or close to) two straight lines. These lines, known as *Sargent curves*, were approximately parallel and could be represented by the equation

$$\lambda = k\, E_{max}^5, \quad (7.16)$$

which was in agreement with the requirements of the Fermi theory of beta decay for large values of the

energy E_{max}. The values of k for the two curves differed by a factor of about a hundred, so that, for a given (maximum) energy of the beta particles, the decay constant (or half life) of a radioelement on one curve was roughly a hundred times as great as that on the other curve. This difference in behavior was attributed by G. Gamow to the transitions in the radioactive processes being either "allowed" or "forbidden" (§ 4.55). In the former case, the decay constant, for a given energy, would be greater than in the latter.

7.79. When Sargent made this correlation between decay constants and beta-particle energy, the only beta emitters known were those occurring in nature. As other beta-active species, both positive and negative, were discovered, from 1934 onward, it became apparent that there were many points which did not fall on the Sargent curves. Although the basic idea of allowed (or permitted) and forbidden transitions is correct, there are definitely more than two categories of such transitions.

7.80. The theory of beta decay shows that the decay constant (and half life) should depend upon (1) the energy available in the transition, (2) the charge on the product (or daughter) nucleus, (3) the difference in orbital angular momentum and intrinsic angular momentum (or spin) between the parent and daughter nuclei. The first two factors may be combined in a function f, which can be derived from the Fermi theory and, in 1943, E. J. Konopinski, in the United States, suggested that the product of f and the radioactive half life T, i.e., fT, be used as a basis for comparing beta-particle emitters. This quantity is called the *comparative half life*. Since it is usually a large number, it has been found more convenient to use its logarithm, i.e., log fT. The greater the value of fT (or log fT), the longer is the comparative half life, and the smaller the probability of the radioactive change.

7.81. A study of the log fT values for nearly three hundred beta emitters, both positive and negative, has shown that the results fall into a number of more or less well-defined groups. These can be correlated with the nature of the transition (allowed, first forbidden, second forbidden, etc.) and the changes in the angular momentum quantum numbers. As a rough, approximate rule, it may be stated that the greater the change in the nuclear spin quantum number, the larger is the log fT value and the more highly forbidden is the beta-decay process. For large values of the energy E_{max}, theory indicates that f is roughly proportional to E_{max}^5 so that for each type of transition TE_{max}^5 will be very roughly constant. This is in agreement with equation (7.16), since the decay constant λ is inversely proportional to T, the half life of the radioelement.

7.82. The smallest values of log fT occur in an interesting group of positive-beta emitters called *mirror nuclei*. The characteristic of these nuclei is that, in each case, the number of protons in the parent element exceeds the number of neutrons by unity. After emitting a positron, so that a proton is replaced by a neutron, in accordance with equation (7.13), the resulting (stable) nucleus contains one neutron in excess of the number of protons. It is because of this reversal in the neutron-proton numbers accompanying radioactive decay that the term "mirror" was applied to these nuclei. One consequence of this simple exchange between the numbers of neutrons and protons is that both parent and daughter nuclei, in their lowest energy (or ground) states, have the same angular quantum numbers. In other words, in the radioactive transition these quantum numbers are not changed, so that the transition is "allowed." Actually, the decay of mirror nuclei has such a high probability, i.e., low value of log fT, that the transition is said to be "allowed and favored" or "superallowed."

7.83. There are sixteen known mirror nuclei, from carbon-11 to scandium-41; their half lives range from 1230 sec. to 0.87 sec. and the corresponding maximum beta-particle energies are 0.99 Mev to 4.94 Mev. However, the values of fT (or of log fT) are very close together because, as stated above, the factor f makes allowance for the difference in the energies available for the transitions and the charge on the daughter nucleus, i.e., its atomic number. A few examples of the positive-beta decay properties of mirror nuclei are given in the accompanying table. The numerals to the left and right of the symbol for the element indicate the numbers of protons and neutrons respectively, in the specified mirror nucleus. A few other light nuclei, in addition to the mirror nuclei, exhibit allowed and favored transitions, the log fT values lying roughly between 3.5 and 4.0.

PROPERTIES OF MIRROR NUCLEI

Nucleus	T (sec.)	E_{max} (Mev)	log fT
$_6C_5$	1230	0.99	3.8
$_{10}Ne_9$	20.3	2.18	3.4
$_{14}Si_{13}$	4.9	3.64	3.7
$_{18}A_{17}$	1.88	4.4	3.7
$_{21}Sc_{20}$	0.87	4.94	3.6

7.84. As the change in the spin (and other) quantum numbers accompanying the radioactive decay increases, the transitions become less and less favored, as indicated by the increase in the log fT values. For allowed transitions which are not favored, log fT is roughly 4.5 to 6; for first forbidden transitions, it is about 6 to 10; and for higher forbidden transitions, log fT is generally greater than 10. One of the most highly forbidden transitions is that of indium-115, which exists in nature; both the spin and orbital quantum numbers change by four units and the log fT value is about 23.

THE PROPERTIES OF GAMMA RADIATION

GAMMA RAY INTERACTION WITH MATTER

7.85. As recorded in § 2.110, gamma rays are electromagnetic radiations similar to X-rays, but of shorter wave length. Actually it is not possible, as far as their behavior is concerned, to distinguish between the longest gamma rays and the shortest X-rays, but it is usual to employ the term gamma rays when the radiations originate within the nucleus. It was seen in § 4.71 that characteristic X-rays result from transitions between electronic energy levels; gamma rays, on the other hand, are associated with transitions between nuclear energy levels. But once the energy is liberated, the properties of the resulting radiation are determined by the frequency or wave length or, in other words, by the magnitude of the energy quantum. In this respect gamma rays and X-rays are very similar. Gamma rays accompany many radioactive changes, irrespective of whether alpha or beta particles are emitted.

7.86. Gamma rays, like X-rays, are highly penetrating; the effective range depends on the energy, but it might require several centimeters of metal to reduce the intensity of gamma radiation to such an extent that it becomes difficult to detect. In their passage through matter gamma rays lose their energy, and hence are absorbed, in several ways, three being important enough to require consideration here.

The first, which is most significant for gamma rays of low energy, and for absorbers of high atomic weight, is the photoelectric effect (§ 2.48), whereby electrons are ejected from atoms or molecules encountered by the radiation. If E is the energy of a gamma-ray photon (§ 3.35), then in a photoelectric encounter an amount P, equal to the binding energy of the electron in the atom, will be required to remove the electron, and the whole of the remainder $E - P$ is carried off by the electron in the form of kinetic energy.

7.87. The second factor contributing to the absorption of gamma rays is the Compton effect (§ 3.36); this plays a major role when the absorber is a material of low atomic weight, and the energy of the radiation is neither too high nor too low. Nevertheless, increase of the atomic weight of the absorber increases the extent of absorption caused by the Compton effect. When a gamma-ray photon collides with a free or loosely-bound electron, the latter removes some, but not all, of the energy of the radiation. The actual loss of energy depends on the scattering angle of the gamma rays, i.e., on the angle between the direction of the rays before and after collision with the electron. In any event, as a result of a series of Compton encounters, in passing through an appreciable thickness of absorber, the energy of the gamma rays may be so greatly diminished that they are no longer detectable.

7.88. For gamma rays of high energy the photoelectric and Compton effects are not so important for their absorption, especially in elements of high atomic weight, as is the third factor, the formation of positron-electron pairs (§ 2.71). As shown in Chapter III, the process requires a minimum energy of 1.02 Mev, and hence it can have no influence on gamma radiations with less than this energy. The effect increases rapidly, however, as the energy of the gamma-ray photon exceeds the minimum value. The probability of pair formation increases with the square of the atomic number of the absorber; this explains why gamma rays from thorium C″, with an energy of 2.62 Mev, readily produce positron-electron pairs when they pass through lead. For absorbers of high atomic weight and gamma rays of high energy, pair-production is the main cause of the energy loss.

7.89. As a result of the interactions leading to the photoelectric effect and to pair production, the gamma-ray photon loses the whole of its energy and ceases to exist. In a Compton encounter, on the other hand, the photon is deprived of a part only of its energy, as mentioned above; nevertheless, a fair proportion is transferred to the recoil electron (§ 3.36). Consequently, for each interaction between a gamma-ray photon and matter, the result is either the ejection of an electron or the formation of a positron-electron pair carrying a considerable amount of energy. It is the ionization (§ 6.5) caused by these secondary electrons, produced in the gas or ejected from the walls of the counter, which provides a means for the detection of gamma rays, as described in Chapter VI.

ABSORPTION OF GAMMA RAYS

7.90. The absorption of gamma rays is studied in a manner similar to that described for beta particles (§ 7.74), except that the greater penetrating power requires the use of a heavy metal of high atomic weight, such as lead, in place of aluminum, as absorber. For homogeneous gamma rays, consisting of radiations of a single frequency, or wave length, the plot of the logarithm of the counting rate (or intensity) against the thickness of the absorber is linear.* In mathematical language, this means that the intensity of the radiation falls off exponentially with the thickness of the absorber, so that if I_0 is the intensity (or counting rate) of gamma rays from a given source when no absorber is used, and I is the intensity after passing through a thickness of x cm. of absorber, then

$$I = I_0 e^{-\mu x}, \qquad (7.17)$$

where e is the base of natural logarithms, and μ is a characteristic property of the absorber, known as its *absorption coefficient*, for the given gamma rays. By measuring I, with a suitable counter, for various thicknesses x of the absorbing material, the value of μ can be determined from equation (7.17).

7.91. The absorption coefficient varies with the energy of the gamma radiation, and a linear plot of the intensity against the absorber thickness will be obtained only if all the radiations have the same energy. If

---

* This is strictly true only for what is called a "collimated" beam in which any rays that have been deviated (or scattered) from the original beam direction do not reach the detector.

several rays of different energies are present, the plot will not be a straight line, but rather a combination of two or more lines with different slopes. In some cases the curves can be analyzed so as to give the absorption coefficients for the individual components of the radiation.

7.92. One of the consequences of the exponential absorption of gamma rays is that, theoretically, the intensity of the radiation should not fall absolutely to zero no matter how much absorber is used. The situation is similar to that considered in § 5.47, in connection with radioactive decay. However, even if the absorption equation (7.17) held at very low intensities, which is doubtful, the radiation ceases to be detectable, so that its intensity is virtually zero, beyond a certain point.

7.93. Several modifications of the absorption coefficient are used in practice, of which two may be mentioned. One is the *half-value thickness*, i.e., the thickness of absorber necessary to reduce the gamma-ray intensity to half its initial value. This quantity is simply related to the absorption coefficient. If equation (7.17) is converted into the equivalent form involving ordinary (Briggsian) logarithms [see equation (5.4)], the result can be written as

$$\log (I/I_0) = -0.4343\mu x. \qquad (7.18)$$

When the intensity of the gamma rays is reduced by the absorber to half its initial value, I/I_0 is $\frac{1}{2}$, and x is the half-value thickness, represented by $x_{1/2}$; equation (7.18) then becomes

$$\log \tfrac{1}{2} = -0.4343\mu x_{1/2},$$

so that

$$x_{1/2} = \frac{0.693}{\mu}. \qquad (7.19)$$

Hence, if the absorption coefficient μ, in reciprocal centimeter units, is known, the half-value thickness of the absorber for the given radiation, in centimeters, can be readily calculated.

7.94. Another useful quantity is obtained upon dividing μ, called the *linear* absorption coefficient, by the density of the absorber; the result, known as the *mass absorption coefficient*, is expressed in cm.^{2}/gram. This quantity is important because it is almost independent of the nature of the absorber for low gamma-ray energies, although it increases somewhat for elements of high atomic weight. The corresponding *mass half-value thickness*, which also does not vary greatly with the absorbing material, is equal to $x_{1/2}$ multiplied by the density; it is then expressed in the familiar gram/cm.^{2} units used in connection with alpha- and beta-particle absorption. The absorber thickness in gram/cm.^{2} required to reduce the gamma-ray intensity by one half, is related to the mass absorption coefficient by an equation exactly similar to (7.19).

7.95. The fact that the mass half-value thickness, i.e., the actual (or linear) half-value thickness multiplied by the density, is almost independent of the nature of the material absorbing the gamma rays, means that the higher its density the smaller the thickness required of a given material to decrease the radiation intensity to a specified extent. For this reason, heavy metals, such as iron and, particularly, lead, are used for shielding from both gamma rays and X-rays.* It is of interest to note that the approximate constancy of the mass absorption coefficient and of the mass half-value thickness means that

---

* High atomic weight gives an added advantage, especially for radiations of high energy.

the weights of different materials required to decrease the radiation intensity by a definite fraction are very nearly the same. But for substances of higher density, the volume, and hence the actual (or linear) thickness, will be less than for materials of lower density.

7.96. In order to illustrate the application of some of the expressions given above, consideration will be given to the absorption of 1-Mev gamma rays by lead. Since it is the general practice to record linear absorption coefficients, determined experimentally, as the basic data, this information will be used for the present purpose. For the case chosen, μ is found to be 0.77 cm.$^{-1}$, and so by equation (7.19), the half-value thickness is $0.693/0.77 = 0.90$ cm. Thus, nine tenths of a centimeter of lead will decrease the intensity of 1-Mev gamma rays to half its initial value. Since the density of lead is 11.3 grams per cc., the mass absorption coefficient is $0.77/11.3 = 0.068$ cm.^{2}/gram; and the mass half-value thickness is $0.90 \times 11.3 = 10.2$ gram/cm.^{2} Approximately the same values for these last two quantities apply to the absorption of 1-Mev gamma rays by other elements of high atomic weight. The linear (or actual) half-value thickness, however, would vary inversely as the density of the absorbing material.

DETERMINATION OF GAMMA-RAY
ENERGIES

7.97. Several methods have been employed for ascertaining the energies of gamma rays. The most direct procedure is to determine the wave length, and hence the frequency, by using a (curved) crystal as a diffraction grating (§ 2.94). The energy of the photon is then given by the quantum theory relationship $E = hc/\lambda$, where h is Planck's constant, c is the velocity of light, and λ is the wave length of the radiation (§ 3.30). The result can be expressed in Mev by means of equation (3.6). Since the diffraction measurements become more difficult as the energy of the photon increases and the wave length of the radiation decreases, the method has been used for gamma rays of energy up to about 0.75 Mev only. Gamma-ray energies from radioelements occurring in nature range from about 0.04 to 3.2 Mev.

7.98. It was seen in § 7.86 that, in the photoelectric absorption of gamma radiation, the kinetic energy of the photoelectron is equal to $E - P$, where E is the energy of the gamma-ray photon and P is the binding energy of the electron. The kinetic energy of the electron can be measured by means of a suitable magnetic spectrograph (§ 7.44), or by determining its range in aluminum (§ 7.76); and the binding energy can be calculated from the wave lengths of the characteristic X-rays of the absorber, usually lead. From these two quantities the energy of the gamma ray can be obtained. The Compton recoil electrons (§ 3.36), resulting from the collisions of the gamma-ray photons with electrons from a light element, such as carbon or aluminum, can also be used for determining the energy of the photons. The energy of these electrons, measured by deflection in a magnetic field, or in other ways, is related in a fairly simple manner to the gamma-ray energy.

7.99. For gamma rays having energies in excess of 1.02 Mev, an excellent method for determining the energy is based on the formation of a positron-electron pair. In the instrument known as a *pair spectrometer*, the gamma rays impinge on a thin layer of material of high atomic weight, so that pair production occurs readily (§ 7.88). The emerging positrons and electrons then pass through a magnetic field, so that the positive and negative particles are deflected in opposite directions. From the radius of the curved path, the energy of the particle can be determined, just as in the magnetic spectrograph (§ 7.44). Upon adding to the sum of the energies of the positron and electron the 1.02 Mev required for their formation, the result would give the energy of the gamma rays.

7.100. A powerful tool for the study of gamma-ray energies is the *scintillation spectrometer*, now widely used in nuclear studies. It was mentioned in § 6.52 that the output pulse from a sodium iodide (thallium activated) scintillation counter is proportional to the energy of the gamma rays to which it is exposed. The actual energy can be determined by a method similar to that described in § 7.18 for alpha particles, utilizing a pulse analyzer. The instrument is standardized by means of gamma rays of known energy. For radiations of very high energy, use has been made of the Čerenkov detector, as outlined in § 6.59.

ORIGIN OF GAMMA RAYS

7.101. The gamma rays accompanying radioactive changes, irrespective of whether they involve alpha or beta decay, are almost invariably due to the same fundamental circumstances. The radioactive transition leaves the daughter nucleus in a high-energy (excited state) and the excess energy is emitted as gamma radiation (Fig. 7.9).* A good illustration of the correlation between the gamma-ray ener-gies and those of the groups of alpha particles is found in the thorium C → thorium C″ disintegration referred to in § 7.39.

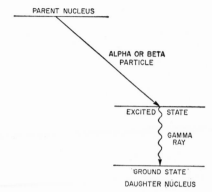

PARENT NUCLEUS

ALPHA OR BETA PARTICLE

EXCITED STATE

GAMMA RAY

GROUND STATE
DAUGHTER NUCLEUS

FIG. 7.9.   Emission of gamma radiation in radioactive decay.

7.102. Before proceeding to the calculations, however, it must be pointed out that the measured alpha-particle energy does not give the total energy accompanying a transition, because part of the energy is used up in the recoil of the daughter nucleus. The relative masses of the thorium C″ nucleus and of the alpha particle are 208 and 4, respectively, on the atomic weight scale; hence, it can be readily shown, assuming conservation of momentum, that the total energy liberated in a given transition, is (208 + 4)/208 times the energy carried off by the alpha particle. The values obtained in this way, together with the corresponding alpha-particle energies of the first five groups, are given in the accompanying table.† The third column contains the differences between the disintegration energy for a given group of alpha particles and the value for the first group. Since the latter is

* Positive-beta emission is invariably accompanied by the gamma radiation resulting from the annihilation of the slowed down positrons by electrons in matter. This radiation is, of course, of secondary origin and is not directly connected with the radioactive decay process.
† The sixth group, with energy 5.478 Mev, has been omitted since it constitutes only 0.16 per cent of the whole.

THORIUM C → THORIUM C″ TRANSITIONS

Alpha Particle Energy (Mev)	*Disintegration Energy* (Mev)	*Difference from First Group* (Mev)
6.086	6.203	—
6.047	6.163	0.040
5.764	5.875	0.328
5.622	5.730	0.473
5.603	5.711	0.492

the highest, it may be supposed to represent the transition from thorium C to the lowest nuclear energy level of thorium C″. The energy differences in the last column are then the energies of the higher (excited) levels of thorium C″, as compared with the lowest level.

7.103. If, as indicated earlier, the gamma rays arise from transitions between energy levels in the daughter nucleus, there should be a connection between the energies of the gamma rays accompanying the thorium C → thorium C″ process and the energies of the various levels derived above. Such is undoubtedly the case. Six gamma rays, with energies of 0.040, 0.327, 0.287, 0.471, 0.432 and 0.451 Mev, respectively, have been detected

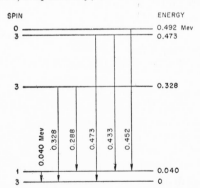

Fig. 7.10. Transitions between nuclear energy levels in thorium C″ correlated with gamma-ray energies.

in this radioactive change, and it can be seen from Fig. 7.10 that these values can be accounted for, within

about 0.001 Mev, by the transitions indicated by arrows.

7.104. Several instances of radioactive changes accompanied by gamma rays, some in association with the emission of alpha particles and others with beta particles, have been investigated in a manner similar to that described for the thorium C → thorium C″ disintegration. In every case the energies of the gamma rays can be explained quantitatively in terms of transitions between nuclear levels whose energies have been derived from those of the alpha and beta particles, as described above. Thus, gamma rays may be regarded as a form of nuclear spectrum which provides information concerning nuclear energy levels, just as optical and X-ray spectra permit the interpretation of electronic levels. It is of interest to mention in this connection that the analogy can be extended, in some measure, to nonradioactive elements. By supplying sufficient energy, the nuclei of a number of stable elements can be raised to excited energy states which then decay, at a measurable rate, to the normal state while emitting gamma radiation (§ 10.123).

7.105. It may be asked why some radioactive changes are accompanied by gamma radiations, whereas others are not. The answer is that the situation is determined largely, although not entirely, by the nuclear spins. In general, if the spin quantum number of the parent nucleus is the same as that of the daughter nucleus in the ground state, the transition is "allowed." There will then usually be no gamma radiation. A good example of this behavior is provided by the mirror nuclei referred to in § 7.82. In nearly all cases there is no (or very little) gamma radiation accompanying the radioactive decay. If the nuclear spins in the ground states of the parent and daughter differ, however, the transition is "forbidden," to some extent at least. There is a strong probability that decay will then occur to an excited state of the daughter nucleus. This will be followed by the transition to a lower energy state of the latter, accompanied by the emission of gamma rays.

INTERNAL CONVERSION OF GAMMA RAYS

7.106. Useful information concerning gamma rays has been obtained from the phenomenon now known as *internal conversion*. In 1914, E. Rutherford suggested the possibility that in emerging from a nucleus the gamma ray (photon) may produce a kind of photoelectric effect with one of the orbital electrons of the same atom. As a result, the whole of the energy is transferred to the electron. The gamma ray is then said to be internally converted. The electron which interacts with the gamma-ray photon is ejected from the atom with kinetic energy equal to $E - P$, where, as before, E is the gamma-ray energy quantum and P is the binding energy of the electron in the atom of the radioelement emitting the gamma radiation. This is presumed to be the daughter element in the given disintegration. If the ejected electron came from the first quantum level of the atom, usually called the K level (§ 4.72), then P can be replaced by E_K, where E_K, according to the theory of the origin of X-rays, is the energy of the K line of the characteristic X-rays of the daughter element. Hence, the electron should be ejected with a kinetic energy of $E - E_K$. Similarly, if the electron originates in the second (L) level, its kinetic energy should be $E - E_L$.

7.107. If the gamma-ray energy E has a definite value, then as a result of internal conversion there should be emitted a number of groups of electrons having discrete energies. There is no doubt that these are the secondary electrons, having definite energy values, that have long been known to accompany the primary beta particles which exhibit a continuous distribution of energy (§ 7.43). Because of their definite energies, the internal conversion electrons are said to give a *line spectrum*, as distinct from the continuous spectrum of the beta particles. It should be mentioned here that, as a general rule, only a small proportion of the gamma-ray photons have their energy internally converted; the fraction so converted, called the *internal conversion coefficient*, usually decreases with increasing energy of the gamma rays.

7.108. The validity of the preceding arguments can be checked in several ways. The energies of the internal conversion electrons have been determined in a number of instances, by the magnetic spectrograph, and adding to these the energy values for the appropriate K, L, etc., lines of the characteristic X-ray spectrum of the daughter element should give the energies of the gamma rays prior to conversion. A case which has been thoroughly studied is the electron line-

ELECTRON LINE SPECTRUM AND GAMMA RAYS FOR THE RADIUM B → RADIUM C TRANSITION

Energy of Electron (Mev)	Radium C X-Ray Line	Binding Energy (Mev)	Total Energy (Mev)	Gamma Ray Energy (Mev)
0.0368	L	0.0161	0.0529	0.0529
0.1510	K	0.0887	0.2397	0.240
0.1617	K	0.0887	0.2564	0.257
0.2041	K	0.0887	0.2929	0.293
0.2605	K	0.0887	0.3493	0.350

spectrum of the process radium B → radium C. A few of the measured kinetic energies are given in the table together with the binding energies derived from X-ray data of radium C; these are added and compared with the accepted values for the energies of five gamma rays. The excellent agreement of the figures in the last two columns provides support for the views presented above. Incidentally, the determination of the energies of the conversion electrons thus represents another method for evaluating gamma-ray energies.

7.109. It will be noted that the 0.0529 Mev gamma ray ejects an L electron but not a K electron; the reason is that the removal of the K electron requires 0.0887 Mev, which is greater than the energy available in this case. The other rays expel L, M and N electrons, in addition to the K electrons, but the results are not recorded here.

7.110. When a gamma ray is internally converted and ejects a K, L, etc., electron, it is to be anticipated that the vacancy will be filled by one of the other electrons in the atom. From what has been stated in § 4.72, it is apparent that this process should be accompanied by the emission of the K, L, etc., line of the characteristic X-rays of the daughter element. Such X-rays have, in fact, been observed in several instances of internal conversion, and the energies are found to be just as expected according to theory.

7.111. A final point is worthy of mention in conclusion. It has been tacitly accepted, so far, that gamma rays are due to transitions between energy levels in the daughter nucleus, rather than in that of the parent, for a given radioactive decay. That this assumption is justified is shown by the observations made in connection with internal conversion phenomena. The binding energies of the electrons, obtained by subtracting their measured kinetic energies from the known gamma-ray energies, and the observed frequencies of the characteristic X-rays, to which reference has just been made, are definitely those of the daughter, and not of the parent, element. These facts provide clear proof of the contention that the gamma rays are emitted from the excited daughter nucleus which remains after the parent has ejected either an alpha or a beta particle.

Isotopes
Chapter VIII

THE DISCOVERY OF ISOTOPES

RADIOELEMENTS AND THE PERIODIC SYSTEM

8.1. By 1911, nearly forty species with different radioactive properties were known, but only twelve positions were available to accommodate them in the periodic table (§ 1.44). The obvious question then was: How can forty elements be fitted into twelve places? It was apparent that, if the periodic classification was not to break down completely in the high atomic weight region, several radioactive species would have to occupy one position, at least in certain cases. Some evidence for this possibility had been obtained by a number of investigators, including H. N. McCoy and B. B. Boltwood in the United States (see § 5.44), W. Marckwald in Germany, and F. Soddy in Great Britain. It had been found that certain groups of "elements," having quite distinct radioactive properties, could not be separated by any chemical means available.* In spite of the difference in the nature of the disintegrations, the spe-

cies within each of the groups appeared to be identical chemically. Reviewing the situation at the end of 1910, Soddy said: "The evidence of chemical identity is not of equal weight for all the . . . cases, but the complete identity of ionium, thorium and radiothorium, of radium and mesothorium-1, and of lead and radium D may be considered thoroughly well established." In the same review, attention was called to the identity of the three gaseous emanations which have properties analogous to those of the inert gases of the atmosphere.

8.2. The chemistry of radium, being very similar to that of barium, presumably placed it in the alkaline-earth family, that is, in Group II of the periodic table (§ 1.46), whereas the properties of thorium appeared to make it fit best into Group IV.† The emanations undoubtedly belong to Group 0, and so it is possible to draw up the accompanying scheme for two of the alpha-emitting stages of the uranium and thorium series (§ 5.58),

---

* H. N. McCoy and W. H. Ross, at the University of Chicago, were apparently the first, in 1907, to show that two different radioelements might be identical chemically. In spite of nearly 200 precipitations, using oxalic acid, chromate, thiosulfate, hydrogen peroxide or ammonia, they were unable to cause any detectable separation of radiothorium from thorium.

† It is possible that thorium may be a member of the actinide series of elements (§§ 1.49, 16.65) and, consequently, not actually in Group IV; however, its most stable compounds have a valence of four, which is characteristic of Group IV, and this is really the point of the argument.

based on the identity of chemical properties mentioned above.

GROUP

IV   II   0

Thorium $\xrightarrow{\alpha}$ Mesothorium $\xrightarrow{\alpha}$ Emanation

Ionium $\xrightarrow{\alpha}$ Radium $\xrightarrow{\alpha}$ Emanation

8.3. This striking regularity led Soddy to suggest, in 1911, that "the expulsion of the alpha particle causes the radioelement to change its position in the periodic table . . . into the next but one [group] in the direction of diminishing group number." This was the first step in the development of an important generalization which could not be completed at the time, because of a lack of knowledge concerning the chemical properties of the elements involved in beta disintegrations. At Soddy's suggestion, therefore, A. Fleck undertook a systematic investigation of a number of radioelements for the purpose of supplying additional information. In the course of this work, part of which was published in 1912 and the remainder in 1913, he found that radium B, radium D, thorium B and actinium B were chemically identical with and entirely inseparable from lead (Group IV). The products resulting from beta-particle emission, namely, radium C, radium E, thorium C and actinium C, respectively, were completely identical with bismuth (Group V). It seemed, therefore, that the loss of a beta particle was accompanied by a change to the next higher group of the periodic table.

8.4. In the early days of 1913 interest in this subject ran high and there was keen competition among scientists to be the first to provide a satisfactory correlation between radioactive transformations and the associated changes in the periodic table. The events of the time may well be described in the words employed by Soddy in his contribution to the discussion on *Radioelements and the Periodic Law* held at the meeting of the Chemistry Section of the British Association, in Birmingham, England, in September 1913. "[On January 31, 1913] A. S. Russell, who knew of Fleck's results, put forward the view that in the beta-ray change the position of the element in the periodic table changes by one place, and he was the first to publish a complete scheme showing the passage of the radioelements through the periodic table. His scheme was in certain respects imperfect,* and it was followed almost immediately [February 15, 1913] by another by K. Fajans, who put forward the complete law in its present form, and made important and accurate deductions. . . . Soddy independently [February 28, 1913] arrived at a complete scheme similar to that of Fajans, but which in one respect possibly went somewhat further in regard to the generalization that all elements falling into the same place in the periodic table . . . are chemically identical, [and] nonseparable by chemical methods."

THE GROUP DISPLACEMENT LAW: ISOTOPES

8.5. The scheme referred to by Soddy in the foregoing quotation is called the *group displacement law*, and it may be stated in the following form: When an alpha particle is emitted in a radioactive change the product occupies a position two places to the left of

---

* Russell was evidently of the opinion that the change of two places in the table accompanying alpha emission and of one place associated with beta emission might be in the direction either of increasing or of decreasing group number. Actually, the former change always leads to a decrease, and the latter to an increase.

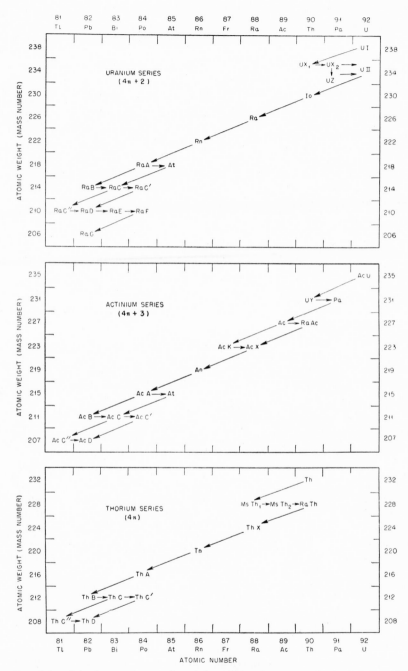

Fig. 8.1. Atomic number and atomic weight (mass number) changes in the natural radioactive disintegration series.

its parent in the periodic table, whereas the emission of a beta particle results in a shift of one place to the right. Since the atomic number of an element is its ordinal position in the periodic system (§ 1.44), the displacement law implies that an alpha-particle change is accompanied by a decrease of two units, and a beta-particle emission by an increase of one unit, in the atomic number. On the basis of this generalization, and recalling that the loss of an alpha particle means a decrease of four units of atomic weight, whereas the ejection of a beta particle leaves the mass virtually unchanged, it is possible to represent the changes of atomic number and atomic weight occurring in the three natural disintegration series in the manner shown in Fig. 8.1. An alpha-ray change is represented by an arrow sloping downward and to the left, and a beta-ray transition by a horizontal arrow pointing to the right. The symbols of the common names of the elements with atomic numbers from 81 through 92 are indicated in each case. The "corresponding element," recorded in the second column of the tabulations of the radioactive series in § 5.58, is thus the more common name for the element with the same atomic number as the given radioelement.

8.6. Since all the elements in any one vertical line of Fig. 8.1 have the same atomic number, it follows that they must occupy the same place in the periodic table. For example, there are seven elements, all with different radioactive properties, having the atomic number 84, so that they all fit into the position associated with the element polonium. In this manner all the known radioelements can be accommodated in the limited number of places available in the periodic table.

8.7. For elements occupying the same position in the periodic system, Soddy, in 1913, proposed the name *isotopes;*[*] thus radium A, radium C', radium F, actinium A, actinium C', thorium A and thorium C', in the 84th ordinal position, are isotopes. They are said to be isotopic with one another and also with the element polonium from which they are inseparable by chemical means. Isotopic elements are, therefore, chemically indistinguishable, although their radioactive properties, and even their atomic weights, are different.

8.8. As a consequence of this fact, the chemistry of short-lived elements, such as thorium C' with a half life of less than a millionth of a second, is well known, because they are isotopic with common elements. In 1908, before the development of the concept of isotopes, the English scientist A. Smithells had referred to radiochemistry as "the chemistry of phantoms." Little did he realize that within a few years the properties of such phantoms would be as familiar, in many cases, as those of lead, bismuth and thallium.

ISOTOPES AND ATOMIC STRUCTURE

The Nucleus and the Group Displacement Law

8.9. Since the emission from the atomic nucleus of an alpha particle, carrying two positive charges, is accompanied by a decrease of two units in the atomic number, while the emission of a beta particle, with a single negative charge, increases the atomic number by one unit, it appeared to Soddy that there was a relationship between the atomic number and the

---

[*] From the Greek, *iso* (same), *topos* (place).

positive nuclear charge. But before he was able to make an explicit statement on the subject, van den Broek put forward the idea—for which the work of Moseley on characteristic X-rays provided support—that the charge on the nucleus was equal to the atomic number (§ 4.23). Subsequently, Soddy expressed the opinion that the proof of the chemical identity of isotopes provided simpler and more convincing evidence than did that of Moseley for the contention that successive places in the periodic system represented unit differences of nuclear charge. Be that as it may, it is an undoubted fact that the group displacement law is in complete harmony with the accepted view that for any element the nuclear charge is equal to the atomic number.

8.10. A consideration of the changes occurring in the atomic nucleus upon the emission of alpha and beta particles is of interest in this connection. According to present-day views, an atomic nucleus consists of $A - Z$ neutrons (zero charge), and Z protons (unit positive charge), where A is the atomic weight of the element to the nearest integer, and Z is equal to the nuclear charge and hence to the atomic number. The atomic weight is then (approximately) equal to the total number of nucleons, i.e., to the total number of neutrons and protons (§ 4.36). An alpha particle, which is a helium nucleus, is made up of two neutrons and two protons, so that if A and Z refer to a radioactive parent, the corresponding numbers of neutrons and protons in the daughter element, after the emission of an alpha particle, will be $A - Z - 2$ and $Z - 2$, respectively. The atomic weight will thus be $(A - Z - 2) + (Z - 2)$, i.e., $A - 4$, and the nuclear charge, or atomic number, will be $Z - 2$. Thus, in accordance with the group displacement law, the loss of an alpha particle means a decrease of two units in the atomic number.

8.11. The expulsion of a beta particle involves first the conversion of a neutron into a proton and an electron, together with a neutrino (§ 7.50); the electron is then ejected, while the proton remains in the nucleus. In other words, as a result of a beta-ray change, a neutron has been replaced by a proton; there is thus the loss of one neutron and the gain of one proton to the nucleus. Considering the general case, once more, of a nucleus containing $A - Z$ neutrons and Z protons, the daughter nucleus after the emission of a beta particle will consist of $A - Z - 1$ neutrons and $Z + 1$ protons. The atomic weight will consequently remain essentially unchanged at $(A - Z - 1) + (Z + 1)$, that is, A, but the atomic number will be $Z + 1$. As required by the group displacement law, the atomic number is increased by unity.

ISOTOPES AND NUCLEAR STRUCTURE

8.12. It is evident from the preceding arguments or, in fact, from any form of the displacement law, that in any succession of one alpha-particle and two beta-particle emissions, irrespective of the order, the resulting element must have the same atomic number as, and hence be isotopic with, the initial parent. An illustration of this is provided by the three disintegration stages—alpha, beta, beta—at the beginning of the uranium series; the fourth element, uranium II, is isotopic with the first element, uranium I (Fig. 8.1). Since the expulsion of an alpha particle means the loss of two neutrons and two protons from the nucleus, whereas the emission of each beta particle results in the loss of a neutron but the gain of a proton, the changes in the nucleus accompanying one alpha- and two beta-particle processes are then as follows:

	Neutrons	Protons
Emission of alpha particle	−2	−2
Emission of two beta particles	−2	+2

8.13. The net effect of the three radioactive (alpha, beta, beta) changes is, therefore, the loss of four neutrons from the nucleus, but the number of protons, that is, the nuclear charge, is the same as for the original element. The difference between isotopes is, consequently, that their nuclei contain different numbers of neutrons, but the same number of protons. The result is that isotopic elements have the same nuclear charge, and hence the same atomic number, but different atomic weights, for the number of protons determines the former and the total number of nucleons (neutrons and protons) governs the latter.

8.14. In the type of isotopy considered above, the atomic weights differ by four units, but this is merely a consequence of the special case chosen to derive the general result. It can be seen from Fig. 8.1 that the elements of atomic number 84, which are isotopic with polonium, have atomic weights of 218, 216, 215, 214, 212, 211 and 210. The nuclei all contain 84 protons, but the numbers of neutrons are 134, 132, 131, 130, 128, 127 and 126, respectively. Other instances of the same general behavior will be given later.

8.15. Before the year 1913, which was notable for so many remarkable advances in atomic science, it was generally considered, especially in view of the success of the periodic system, that the chemical properties of the elements were determined by their atomic weights. The discovery of isotopes, having identical chemical properties but different atomic weights, and the correlation of the atomic number with the nuclear charge, established the fact that chemical properties are dependent on the atomic number and not on the atomic weight. The atomic number is fundamental, while the atomic weight is, in a sense, incidental. As the present chapter unfolds, the full significance of this statement will become increasingly evident. Attention may be called, in this connection, to the existence of several radioelements with the same atomic weight.* Such species were called *isobares*† by the British chemist A. W. Stewart in 1918, but the name *isobars* is now generally employed. Thus, radium B, radium C and radium C′ are isobaric, the atomic weight of each being 214, but their chemical properties are quite different, since they have different atomic numbers.

8.16. It appears that the chemical properties of an element are determined to a great extent by the number and arrangement of the extranuclear (or orbital) electrons (§ 4.68). Since isotopic elements have the same nuclear charge, they will have the same number of orbital electrons, undoubtedly arranged in the same manner. This is probably why isotopes are

---

* Strictly speaking, it is the "mass numbers," i.e., the integers nearest to the atomic weights (§ 8.60), which are the same.

† From the Greek, *iso* (same), *baros* (weight). The term "isobares," rather than the more obvious "isobars," was originally suggested, since the latter is generally employed to indicate lines of constant pressure on a weather map.

identical chemically.* Similarly, any properties which depend essentially on the extranuclear electrons, such as optical and X-ray spectra (§§ 4.42, 4.71), will be the same for isotopic elements. There are very slight changes in the spacings of the lines, which are significant in certain instances, but these are due to small differences in the masses of the isotopic nuclei; the main structure of the spectrum is, however, the same for the different isotopes.

8.17. Radioactive properties, on the other hand, are definitely associated with the nucleus; they are determined by the individual numbers of both protons and neutrons, and not merely by one or the other, or by their sum. It is obvious that isotopes, which have equal numbers of protons, exhibit different radioactive properties, and the same is true for elements, such as radium and actinium, for example, having equal numbers of neutrons.† Further, the nuclei of isobaric elements contain the same total number of nucleons, i.e., neutrons and protons, but they manifest differing radioactive behavior. It is evident, therefore, that radioactivity is governed by the particular combination of neutrons and protons in the given nucleus.

STABLE ISOTOPES

End Products of Radioactive Series

8.18. In 1905, Boltwood had called attention to the presence of lead in uranium minerals, and he thought that this metal might be an end product of the uranium series. In the same year, Soddy pointed out that, since the final product of radioactive disintegration is not undergoing change, it might be difficult to determine its identity, for it would probably prove to be one of the familiar stable elements. He suggested, on the basis of atomic weight considerations, that it might be either lead or bismuth. As the result of a study of the ratio of lead to uranium in a large number of minerals, Boltwood, in 1907, concluded that "on the basis of this evidence the assumption would appear to be justified that lead is the final product of uranium."

8.19. In the following years this view was generally adopted, and the realization, in 1913, that radium G, the end product of the uranium series, was actually isotopic, and hence chemically identical, with lead supplied the definite proof that had hitherto been lacking. At the same time, it was seen (Fig. 8.1) that actinium D and thorium D, the nonradioactive end products of the actinium and thorium series, respectively, also had atomic numbers of 82, and hence were isotopes of lead. This element is consequently the end product of the three natural radioactive series, and its universal association with uranium and thorium minerals can be readily understood. It is of interest to recall here that the end product of the $4n + 1$ neptunium series, which no longer exists in nature, is not lead, but bismuth (§ 5.64).

8.20. In the course of a consider-

---

* It will be seen later (§ 8.74) that there are some minor differences in the chemical reactivity of isotopes which have important consequences. These differences are not due to differences in the nature of the chemical reactions, but rather to their rates. The former depends on the electronic arrangement, but the mass of the atom affects the latter.

† Elements containing equal numbers of neutrons have been called *isotones* by K. Guggenheimer in 1934.

ation of the implications of the group displacement law. Soddy realized that, although the end products of the uranium and thorium series were both isotopic with lead, the atomic weights, as seen from Fig. 8.1, should be 206 and 208, respectively, as compared with 207.2 for ordinary lead. This astonishing conclusion was entirely revolutionary in character, since elements had previously been regarded as having definite atomic weights. But it seemed inevitable if the group displacement law and the concept of isotopes had any real basis of fact. Experimental proof that lead originating from uranium has a different atomic weight from that derived from thorium, while both differ from that of lead obtained from nonradioactive sources, would thus provide convincing evidence for the theory of radioactive decay and the existence of isotopes.

8.21. The mineral thorite, from Ceylon, consists mainly of thoruim with relatively little (1 to 2 per cent) uranium, and about 0.4 per cent of lead; hence, it seemed likely that the latter was produced entirely by radioactive decay of the thorium. Consequently, Soddy, in conjunction with H. Hyman, set out to extract and purify the lead from thorite, and then to determine its atomic weight. They obtained 1.2 grams of purified lead chloride, and determined the atomic weight by making comparison measurements with lead chloride from a nonradioactive source. In May 1914 it was reported that, in agreement with expectation, the atomic weight of the thorium lead was about one unit higher than that of ordinary lead.

8.22. Because of the difficulties associated with the accurate determination of atomic weights, especially when working with small amounts of material, M. E. Lembert came from Germany, at the suggestion of K. Fajans, to study the atomic weights of lead from various sources in the Harvard University laboratory of T. W. Richards, who was recognized as the leading authority in this field of investigation. In 1914, Richards and Lembert made direct determinations of the atomic weight of lead extracted from several uranium minerals, and in every case they found the values to be definitely lower than that of ordinary lead. The lowest result obtained was 206.40 for lead from uraninite, found in North Carolina; even though the figure was not down to 206, the theoretical value, probably because the lead was of mixed origin, the low value was nevertheless significant. The same conclusion, that the atomic weight of lead from uranium minerals was less than that of ordinary lead, was also reached independently by Maurice Curie in France, and by O. Hönigschmid and S. Horovitz in Austria during the year 1914, so that the accuracy of the result could not be in serious doubt.

8.23. In reporting, in the early part of 1915, on the work dealing with the atomic weight of lead from radioactive sources, Soddy wrote: "Bearing in mind that two of the four researches . . . have been carried out by chemists [Richards and Hönigschmid] experienced in atomic weight determinations, and that much of the mineral examined was no doubt of very mixed composition, so that not all the lead present can be reasonably assumed to have been of radioactive origin, it is clear that the theoretical predictions have received remarkable confirmation . . . that an investigator as experienced in atomic-weight work as Professor T. W. Richards should regard his results as definitely establishing a variation in the chemical equivalent of lead from different sources . . . is perhaps the chief result gained." Soddy indicated that the data available at that time were still of a somewhat preliminary nature, and he said that "further results with carefully selected minerals must be awaited."

8.24. Actually, subsequent measurements, made with the greatest care, have amply confirmed the earlier results. Some of the more interesting values are tabulated here; they may be

and having identical chemical properties, may perhaps not be considered surprising, but the remarkable fact is that an ordinary, nonradioactive element like lead can also exist in isotopic forms. Thus, although the various specimens of nonradioactive lead separated from uranium and thorium minerals have atomic weights differing by nearly two units, they are completely identical and indistinguishable in their chemical properties. The discovery of

ATOMIC WEIGHT OF LEAD FROM RADIOACTIVE MINERALS

URANIUM MINERALS	Source	Atomic Weight	Investigator
Cleveite...........................	Norway	206.08	T. W. Richards
Bröggerite........................	Norway	206.01	T. W. Richards
Pitchblende......................	W. Africa	206.05	O. Hönigschmid
Kolm.............................	Sweden	206.01	G. P. Baxter
THORIUM MINERALS			
Thorite..........................	Ceylon	207.8	O. Hönigschmid
Thorite..........................	Norway	207.9	O. Hönigschmid

compared with the atomic weight of 207.2 for lead from nonradioactive sources. The striking agreement with theoretical expectation, which predicted the atomic weights of lead from uranium and thorium to be 206 and 208, respectively, provides the strongest possible support not only for the group displacement law, but also for the whole theory of radioactive disintegration. It required the latter to predict the atomic weights of the end products, and it was a combination of both which indicated that they should be chemically indistinguishable from lead.

8.25. The results just described have an important significance apart from their bearing on the theories of radioactivity and the problem of the accommodation of the known radioelements in the limited number of places available in the periodic system. The existence of radioactive isotopes with different atomic weights, occupying the same position in the periodic table

the existence of stable isotopes of lead indicated the possibility that other nonradioactive elements might occur in isotopic forms, and in this connection concurrent developments in an apparently unrelated field were destined to play an important part.

POSITIVE-RAY ANALYSIS

8.26. As stated in § 2.62, the rays of positively charged particles formed by the passage of an electrical discharge through an evacuated tube had been shown by W. Wien to consist of atomic or molecular ions of the gas present in the tube. The nature of these ions can be investigated by studying the deflection of the positive rays in electric and magnetic fields, making use of a principle first employed by W. Kaufmann in 1901 for beta particles (electrons), and in the following year by Wien for positive rays.

8.27. A narrow beam of positively charged particles, such as constitute the positive rays, will normally travel in a straight line, but if subjected to an electric or magnetic field the beam will be deviated from its original direction. Imagine a single positively charged particle moving downward perpendicular to the plane of the paper, striking it at the point O in Fig. 8.2. Suppose a

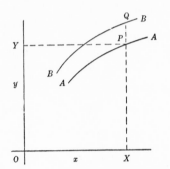

FIG. 8.2.   Principle of positive-ray analysis.

uniform electric field of strength E is applied, so that the particle is deflected to the right and strikes the paper at X; the distance x from O to X is then given by

$$x = k_1 \frac{Ee}{mv^2}, \qquad (8.1)$$

where k_1 is a constant depending on the dimensions of the apparatus, e is the charge on the particle, which must be a multiple of the electronic charge, and m and v are the mass and velocity, respectively, of the positive particle.

8.28. Suppose, however, that instead of the electric field, a magnetic field H is used to deflect the particle in a direction perpendicular to OX, so that it strikes the plane of the paper at Y; the displacement y from O to Y is now expressed by

$$y = k_2 \frac{He}{mv}, \qquad (8.2)$$

where k_2 is also dependent on the dimensions of the apparatus. By applying the electric and magnetic fields simultaneously, the particle is deflected to P, the coordinates of which are determined by x and y, as given by equations (8.1) and (8.2). If v is eliminated from them, it follows that

$$x = k \frac{E}{H^2} \cdot \frac{m}{e} y^2, \qquad (8.3)$$

where k is another constant related to k_1 and k_2.

8.29. If, instead of one positive particle, a beam of positive rays is considered, in which all the particles have the same ratio of mass m to charge e, so that m/e is constant, but not necessarily the same velocity, it follows from equation (8.3) that

$$x = \text{constant} \times y^2, \qquad (8.4)$$

provided the strengths of the electric and magnetic fields, that is, E and H, remain constant. The positively-charged particles, of constant m/e, which are deflected by these fields will thus fall on a series of points, of which P is one, whose coordinates satisfy equation (8.4). This expression is the mathematical representation of a parabola, and so it follows that the points when joined together will form a parabolic curve, such as AA in Fig. 8.2.*

8.30. An examination of equations (8.1) and (8.2) shows that, for a given particle, the displacements x and y depend on the velocity of the particle, the greater the velocity the smaller the displacement, and vice versa. The series of points making up the parabolic curve consequently represent positive particles with different velocities,

---

* It should be noted that the curve is not a complete parabola, but only a portion of one. It would, nevertheless, be described mathematically as a parabola, although the expression "parabolic curve" will be used here.

but having the same value of the mass-to-charge ratio, m/e. The fast moving particles are deflected only to a small extent, whereas the slower particles are deflected considerably more. The continuity of the curve AA would imply that particles having all possible velocities, between certain limits, are present in the positive rays.

8.31. A beam of particles for which m/e has a value that is constant, but different from the one considered above, will be deflected by electric and magnetic fields so that the particles fall on another parabolic curve BB. From equation (8.3) it can be seen that the smaller the quantity m/e, the larger will be the displacement y for a given value of x. The point Q, for example, corresponds to a particle whose mass-to-charge ratio, m/e, is smaller than that for the particle falling on the point P. In Fig. 8.2, therefore, the parabolic curve BB would be formed by the deflection of a stream of particles of varying velocity, but having a constant value of m/e which is smaller than that for the curve AA. If the ordinates of the points P and Q, for a constant value of the displacement x, are y_A and y_B, respectively, it follows from equation (8.3) that

$$\left(\frac{y_A}{y_B}\right)^2 = \frac{(m/e)_B}{(m/e)_A}, \qquad (8.5)$$

where the quantities $(m/e)_A$ and $(m/e)_B$ refer to the two sets of particles falling on the curves AA and BB, respectively. If the charges carried by the particles are assumed to be equal, it is seen from equation (8.5) that

$$\left(\frac{y_A}{y_B}\right)^2 = \frac{m_B}{m_A}. \qquad (8.6)$$

It should thus be possible to compare the masses m_A and m_B of particles present in positive rays by observing their deflections, y_A and y_B, for constant x, when subjected to the simultaneous action of electric and magnetic fields.

8.32. If a beam of positive rays contains particles of different masses then they will be sorted out in such a manner that all particles with the same mass or, more correctly, all having the same m/e value, will fall on one parabolic curve. A method of *positive-ray analysis* is thus available for detecting the presence of, and even for identifying, atomic and molecular particles whose masses differ from each other.

POSITIVE RAYS AND ISOTOPES

8.33. In the course of his extended studies of positive rays, J. J. Thomson (see § 2.21) made, in 1912, an interesting observation which has a bearing on the existence of isotopes of stable elements. An electric discharge was passed through a vessel containing the experimental gas at suitable low pressure. A narrow stream of positive rays was obtained in a manner similar to that described in § 2.61, using a pierced aluminum cathode connected to a fine-bore brass tube. After passing through electric and magnetic fields arranged so as to give deflections at right angles to one another, as in Fig. 8.2, the positive rays were allowed to fall on a photographic plate. Upon development, the latter showed a series of parabolic streaks, each corresponding to a definite value of the mass-to-charge ratio (m/e) of atomic and molecular particles present in the positive rays, in accordance with the discussion in the preceding section.

8.34. An illustration of the type of result observed is shown in Fig. 8.3. There are here three sets of positive-ray parabolas; one corresponds to Fig. 8.2, while the others are obtained by reversing, in turn, the direction of either the magnetic or the electric field. These three groups of curves are essentially reflections of one another in the x and y axes; hence, the positions of these axes can be found and the ordinates of points on the curves determined. Utilizing the curve produced by a substance of known mass, such as oxygen, as standard, the masses of other atoms and molecules can then be

of mass 22, on the atomic weight scale. In speaking of this matter in 1913, Thomson said: ". . . in addition [to the strong neon line] there is a line corresponding to an atomic weight of 22, which cannot be identified with the line due to any known gas. I thought at first that this line, since its atomic weight is one half that of CO_2, must be due to carbonic acid [molecular

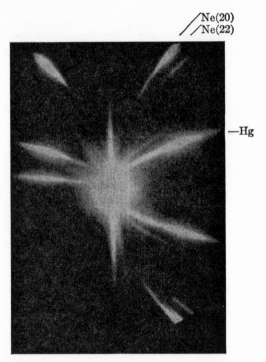

Ne(20)
Ne(22)

—Hg

FIG. 8.3. Thomson's positive-ray parabolas.

calculated by means of equation (8.6).

8.35. The positive-ray photographs obtained by Thomson exhibited a number of interesting features, but the aspects to be considered here will be restricted to those having a bearing on the subject of isotopes. It was noted that when the discharge tube contained neon gas, atomic weight 20.2, the photographs always showed, in addition to the expected neon line, the presence of a line indicating a particle

weight 44] with a double charge of electricity, [so that m/e would be 22], and on some of the plates a faint line at 44 could be detected. On passing the gas slowly through tubes immersed in liquid air [which would remove the CO_2] the line at 44 completely disappeared, while the brightness of the one at 22 was not affected. The origin of this line presents many points of interest; there are no known gaseous compounds of any of the recognized elements which have this molecular weight. . . . The fact that this line is bright in the sample when the neon line is extraordinarily bright, and invisible . . . when the neon [line] is comparatively feeble, suggests that it may possibly be a compound of neon and hydrogen, NeH_2, though no direct evidence of the combination of these inert gases has hitherto been found."

8.36. Although J. J. Thomson was not at all sure of the identity of the gas giving the mass 22 line in the positive-ray photographs, he felt that there could "be little doubt that what has been called neon is not a single gas, but a mixture of two gases, one of which has an atomic weight of about 20 and the other about 22. The parabola due to the heavier gas forms only a small percentage of the mixture." In order to throw some light on the situation, the English scientist F. W. Aston, who was then Thomson's assistant, set out to separate the constituents of neon gas. The first attempt, based on the fractional distillation of neon adsorbed on charcoal cooled in liquid air, failed to give any detectable separation, and so the possibility of separation by diffusion was tried.

8.37. It has long been known that a light gas will diffuse through a porous partition more rapidly than will a heavier gas; consequently, Aston passed neon gas through a pipe-clay tube, collected that portion of the gas which diffused through, and allowed this to diffuse once more, and so on. This procedure proved to be more successful, and at the historic meeting of the British Association in 1913, to which reference was made in § 8.4,

Aston announced that after repeated diffusion and rediffusion, he had obtained, from 100 cc. of ordinary neon gas, two extreme fractions of 2 to 3 cc., with atomic weights, calculated from their densities, of 20.15 and 20.28, respectively.

8.38. The difference in these atomic weights is small, nevertheless it is significant. The fact that the former value is less, while the latter is greater, than the atomic weight of ordinary neon showed that a partial separation of the two constituents of neon had been achieved. In his book on *Rays of Positive Electricity*, published in 1913, Thomson wrote referring to Aston's results: "He obtained sufficient alteration in the proportion between the two gases to produce appreciable changes in the relative brightness of the two lines [for the masses 20 and 22] in the positive-ray photograph, and changes in the density large enough to be detected. . . . No differences, however, could be observed in the spectrum of the mixture, and this . . . gives some grounds for the suspicion that the two gases, although of different atomic weights, may be indistinguishable in their chemical and spectroscopic properties."

8.39. In other words, it seemed possible that neon might exist in two isotopic forms with masses of 20 and 22, respectively; this interpretation of the results was later confirmed. It may be mentioned, however, that for several years Thomson was himself reluctant to accept this view, for he felt that the possible presence of a hydrogen compound, such as NeH_2, could not be ignored.

THE OCCURRENCE OF ISOTOPES

THE WHOLE NUMBER RULE

8.40. In the period from 1914 to 1918 the exigencies of the war in Europe interfered with the continuation of Aston's work on neon, but upon its resumption his initial efforts were devoted to an attempt at improving the degree of separation of the two forms of the element by diffusion. The results were not too promising, and Aston came to the conclusion that the best approach to the problem would be, as he himself stated, to make positive-ray studies "with such accuracy that it could be demonstrated with certainty that neither of the two atomic weights so determined agree with the accepted . . . figure." Consequently, with the object of improving the accuracy of the measurements, Aston redesigned the positive-ray deflection apparatus. In the instrument constructed in 1919, the electric and magnetic fields were so arranged that all particles having the same mass were brought to a focus so as to produce a fine line rather than a parabola. Since each line indicated the presence of atoms or molecules of a particular mass, the result was referred to as a *mass spectrum*, and the instrument was called a *mass spectrograph*.

8.41. With his first mass spectrograph Aston was able to confirm the supposition that two forms of neon exist with atomic masses almost exactly 20 and 22, respectively. The proportion of the former appeared to be approximately ten times the latter, so that the mean atomic weight should be 20.2, in excellent agreement with the accepted value. Turning next to the familiar element chlorine, whose atomic weight was known with considerable accuracy to be 35.457, Aston found that this also gave a mass spectrum with two lines corresponding to masses very close to 35 and 37, respectively, there being no indication of the presence of a particle with a fractional atomic weight. It appeared, therefore, that chlorine, like neon, consisted of a mixture of at least two isotopes.

8.42. By the end of 1920, Aston had examined nineteen elements in his mass spectrograph and found that nine of them consisted of two or more isotopic forms with masses which were close to integers. Further, it was observed that elements like helium, carbon, nitrogen, oxygen, fluorine and phosphorus, which have atomic weights close to whole numbers, are not composite, as are neon, chlorine, boron, argon and other elements.*

8.43. These results led Aston to formulate the *whole number rule*, which is essentially a modified form of Prout's hypothesis (§ 1.38). According to this rule all atomic weights are very close to integers, and the fractional atomic weights determined chemically are due to the presence of two or more isotopes each of which has an approximately integral atomic weight.† The constancy of the atomic weights of the elements as they occur in nature—with the exception of lead from radioactive sources—indicates essentially constant isotopic composition; that is to say, the constituent isotopes of a

---

* Later work has shown that small amounts of isotopes are present in helium, carbon, nitrogen and oxygen.

† The same general idea had been expressed in 1915 by W. D. Harkins and E. D. Wilson in the United States, and shortly thereafter by K. Fajans in Germany and by F. Soddy in England, but at the time it lacked experimental support.

given element are always present in substantially the same proportions.

8.44. The possibility that the chemical elements might consist of groups with virtually identical chemical properties, but different atomic weights, was considered during the 1880's by P. Schützenberger in France and by W. Crookes in England, both of whom thought it possible that the accepted atomic weights were mean values for the two or more members of the group. Crookes was influenced by the chemical similarity of the rare-earth elements which, at the time, could not be fitted into the periodic table. As this difficulty has since been overcome, the arguments for "meta-elements," as he called them, now lack force. It is to Soddy, therefore, that credit is due for being the first to envisage the situation correctly from the modern standpoint, for in 1913 he suggested "that each known element may be a group of non-separable elements occupying the same place [in the periodic table], the atomic weight not being a real constant, but a mean value, of much less fundamental interest than has been hitherto supposed. Although . . . matter is even more complex than chemical analysis has been able to reveal . . . the problem of atomic constitution may be more simple than has been supposed from the lack of simple numerical relations between the atomic weights."

8.45. In this latter conjecture Soddy was, of course, correct; but while there existed the possibility of fractional atomic weights, there could be no simple theory of nuclear structure. The discovery of the whole number rule removed, in the words of Aston, "the only serious objection to a unitary theory of matter." The fact that all nuclear masses are approximately integral is in complete accord with the

view that atomic nuclei are built up of neutrons and protons which have masses very close to unity on the atomic weight scale. As stated in § 8.13, the isotopes of a given element differ from one another by the number of neutrons in the nucleus; the isotopic atomic weights should thus differ by small integers, as is undoubtedly the case. It should be mentioned that, although the masses of isotopes approximate to whole numbers, or to the sum of the masses of their constituent neutrons, protons and electrons, certain differences do exist; these differences, although small, are definite and of great significance as will be seen in Chapter XII.

The Isotopic Composition of the Elements

8.46. In 1918, even before Aston had built his first mass spectrograph, A. J. Dempster in the United States had designed an instrument based on a somewhat different principle which will be described below. This instrument could be used to determine the relative proportions, as well as the masses, of the particles present, and with it Dempster examined the metals lithium, magnesium, potassium, calcium and zinc. Two years later, he reported that these elements, like many of the non-metals studied by Aston, consisted of mixtures of isotopes with atomic weights that were close to whole numbers.

8.47. Before the year 1921, therefore, it had been established that several elements, with atomic weights ranging from 10 to 238, existed in isotopic forms, and that the phenomenon of isotopy was quite general over virtually the whole of the periodic table. Since that time the mass spectra of all the known elements have been investigated and their isotopic compo-

ISOTOPES OF THE NONRADIOACTIVE ELEMENTS

Element	Atomic *No.*	*Isotopes*	*Element*	Atomic *No.*	*Isotopes*
Hydrogen.....	1	1, 2	Indium.......	49	113, 115*
Helium.......	2	3, 4	Tin..........	50	112, 114, 115, 116,
Lithium......	3	6, 7			117, 118, 119, 120,
Beryllium.....	4	9			122, 124
Boron........	5	10, 11	Antimony.....	51	121, 123
Carbon.......	6	12, 13	Tellurium.....	52	120, 122, 123, 124,
Nitrogen......	7	14, 15			125, 126, 128, 130
Oxygen.......	8	16, 17, 18	Iodine........	53	127
Fluorine......	9	19	Xenon........	54	124, 126, 128, 129,
Neon.........	10	20, 21, 22			130, 131, 132, 134,
Sodium.......	11	23			136
Magnesium ...	12	24, 25, 26	Cesium.......	55	133
Aluminum....	13	27	Barium.......	56	130, 132, 134, 135,
Silicon........	14	28, 29, 30			136, 137, 138
Phosphorus ...	15	31	Lanthanum...	57	138,* 139
Sulfur........	16	32, 33, 34, 36	Cerium.......	58	136, 138, 140, 142
Chlorine......	17	36, 37	Praseodymium	59	141
Argon........	18	36, 38, 40	Neodymium...	60	142, 143, 144,* 145,
Potassium.....	19	39, 40,* 41			146, 148, 150
Calcium......	20	40, 42, 43, 44, 46, 48	Promethium...	61	—
Scandium.....	21	45	Samarium.....	62	144, 147,* 148, 149-
Titanium.....	22	46, 47, 48, 49, 50			150, 152, 154
Vanadium.....	23	50,† 51	Europium.....	63	151, 153
Chromium....	24	50, 52, 53, 54	Gadolinium...	64	152, 154, 155, 156,
Manganese....	25	55			157, 158, 160
Iron..........	26	54, 56, 57, 58	Terbium......	65	159
Cobalt........	27	59	Dysprosium...	66	156, 158, 160, 161,
Nickel........	28	58, 60, 61, 62, 64			162, 163, 164
Copper.......	29	63, 65	Holmium.....	67	165
Zinc..........	30	64, 66, 67, 68, 70	Erbium.......	68	162, 164, 166, 167,
Gallium.......	31	69, 71			168, 170
Germanium...	32	70, 72, 73, 74, 76	Thulium......	69	169
Arsenic.......	33	75	Ytterbium....	70	168, 170, 171, 172,
Selenium......	34	74, 76, 77, 78, 80, 82			173, 174, 176
Bromine......	35	79, 81	Lutetium.....	71	175, 176*
Krypton......	36	78, 80, 82, 83, 84, 86	Hafnium......	72	174, 176, 177, 178,
Rubidium.....	37	85, 87*			179, 180
Strontium.....	38	84, 86, 87, 88	Tantalum.....	73	180,* 181
Yttrium......	39	89	Tungsten.....	74	180, 182, 183, 184,
Zirconium.....	40	90, 91, 92, 94, 96			186
Niobium	41	93	Rhenium......	75	185, 187*
Molybdenum..	42	92, 94, 95, 96, 97, 98,	Osmium......	76	184, 186, 187, 188,
		100			189, 190, 192
Technetium...	43	—	Iridium.......	77	191, 193
Ruthenium....	44	96, 98, 99, 100, 101,	Platinum.....	78	190, 192, 194, 195,
		102, 104			196, 198
Rhodium.....	45	103	Gold.........	79	197
Palladium.....	46	102, 104, 105, 106,	Mercury......	80	196, 198, 199, 200,
		108, 110			201, 202, 204
Silver.........	47	107, 109	Thallium......	81	203, 205
Cadmium.....	48	106, 108, 110, 111,	Lead.........	82	204, 206, 207, 208
		112, 113, 114, 116	Bismuth......	83	209

* Radioactive.
† Probably radioactive.

sitions have been determined.* The results for the nonradioactive elements are tabulated here; the masses of the naturally occurring isotopes are given to the nearest integers, on the atomic weight scale. It is seen that only twenty-one elements, about one fourth of the whole, are single species; all the others consist of two or more isotopes of different masses, tin having as many as ten isotopes.

8.48. The accompanying table lists over 280 isotopic forms of stable elements† and if to these are added the 40 or so radioactive isotopes, it is seen that a total of more than 320 isotopic species exist in nature. In addition there have been obtained in recent years some nine hundred or so which do not occur naturally, so that at the present time there have been identified considerably more than a thousand forms of the known elements.

8.49. With the increasing complexity of the subject there has been some feeling that a more precise terminology was desirable. Consequently, in 1947, T. P. Kohman, in the United States, proposed the term *nuclide* for a species of atom characterized by the constitution of its nucleus, that is, by the numbers of neutrons and protons it contains. Thus, the species whose masses are given in the table might be referred to as naturally occurring, stable nuclides. Similarly, every radio-element is a radioactive nuclide or radionuclide. An isotope would then be one of a group of two or more

nuclides having the same number of protons or, in other words, having the same atomic number. An element like fluorine, of which only one species exists in nature, would then be said to form a single stable nuclide, rather than a single stable isotope, since the word isotope seems to imply more than one species occupying the same place in the periodic system.

Mass Spectrographs

8.50. Following upon the pioneering work of Aston and of Dempster, which has been mentioned above, a great deal has been done with the object of improving the accuracy and simplifying the operation of the mass spectrograph. Both Aston and Dempster made important contributions in this connection, as also have several other physicists, notably K. T. Bainbridge, W. Bleakney, E. B. Jordan and A. O. Nier in the United States, and J. Mattauch in Austria. Many instruments have been constructed for determining both the masses of isotopes and their relative proportions. A limited number of these devices will be described here, the selection being based on features of special interest. Although the general term mass spectroscope is often used, a distinction can be made between "spectrometer," in which a meter measures an ion current, and "spectrograph," in which the record appears on a photographic plate.

8.51. In one form of Dempster's

---

* The isotopes of hydrogen, carbon, nitrogen and oxygen were discovered by means of optical spectra. They were not identified in the earlier mass spectrographs because their faint lines were very close to those of other substances which were, or might have been, present. Their existence has been confirmed, however, by means of the later instruments of greater resolving power.

† Actually, at least nine naturally occurring isotopes of these "stable" elements exhibit feeble radioactivity; these are K(40), Rb(87), In(115), La(138), Lu(176), Ta(180) and Re(187), which are negative beta emitters, and Nd(144) and Sm(147), which emit alpha particles. The isotope V(50) may also be radioactive. Based on the masses of the parent and daughter nuclei, about ten others should be capable of double-beta decay, e.g., Ca(48), Mo(100), Sn(124), Te(130) and Nd(150).

mass spectrometer, the element being studied is vaporized by heating it electrically, and the atoms in the vapor are then ionized by bombardment with electrons emitted from a hot filament. The positively charged ions so produced emerge from a hole in the plate P_1 (Fig. 8.4), and they are then ac-

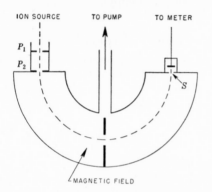

ION SOURCE   TO PUMP   TO METER

P_1

P_2

S

MAGNETIC FIELD

FIG. 8.4.   Dempster's mass spectrometer (direction focusing).

celerated by means of a variable electric field, of 1000 volts or more, applied between P_1 and P_2. The ions emerging from the narrow slit in P_2 thus all have virtually the same energy. If V is the potential difference of the electric field, the positive ions carrying a charge e will acquire energy equal to Ve, in passing from P_1 to P_2. This energy is kinetic in nature and hence it may also be represented by $\frac{1}{2}mv^2$, where m is the mass of the positively charged particle and v is the velocity with which it emerges from the slit in P_2; consequently,

$$Ve = \tfrac{1}{2}\,mv^2. \qquad (8.7)$$

The narrow beam of ions emerging from P_2 is then made to traverse a semicircular path by means of a constant magnetic field operating in a direction perpendicular to the plane of the diagram. The particles of suitable mass are thus able to pass through

the slit at S and on to a small plate connected to an electrometer or similar device for measuring the ion current.

8.52. It was seen in § 2.42 that, when a charged particle moves in a suitably oriented magnetic field H, the radius of curvature r of the path is related to the charge e, the mass m, and the velocity v of the particle by

$$\frac{e}{m} = \frac{v}{Hr}. \qquad (8.8)$$

Hence, by combining equations (8.7) and (8.8) so as to eliminate v, it follows that for the positively charged particles under consideration

$$\frac{m}{e} = \frac{H^2r^2}{2V}. \qquad (8.9)$$

8.53. In the apparatus depicted in Fig. 8.4, only those ions moving in a path of definite radius, can pass through the slit S and so be recorded on the electrometer. The m/e value for these particles is determined by V and H, according to equation (8.9), and hence if the electric and magnetic fields are kept constant, only ions of a particular mass can enter the slit assuming, for simplicity, that the charge e is the same in every case. The actual value of this mass can be calculated from equation (8.9) if V, H and r are known, but this is avoided in practice by standardizing the instrument with a substance of known mass. The potential V of the electric field necessary to cause these particles to follow the required path is measured and, since m/e is known, the quantity H^2r^2, which is characteristic of the particular apparatus, since H and r are both constant, may be readily obtained.

8.54. After the mass spectrometer has been standardized, the potential V is adjusted to any desired value, the magnetic field H being kept constant, and the corresponding ion current is measured in the electrometer. Since H^2r^2 is known and V can be determined, the mass—more accurately the m/e value—of these particular ions can be calculated from equation (8.9), and their quantity is proportional to the strength of the ion current. By using a number of different adjustments of the accelerating potential V, the masses and relative amounts of various isotopes present in the apparatus can thus be obtained.

8.55. The special feature of the Dempster mass spectrometer is that it gives what is known as *direction focussing*. Thus, charged particles emerging from the slit in P_2 in different directions are all brought to a focus at the slit S, provided they have the same m/e value. Other instruments, such as that of Bainbridge, on the other hand, give *velocity focussing*. In this case a beam of positively charged particles passing through the slits S_1 and S_2 (Fig. 8.5) is acted upon simultaneously

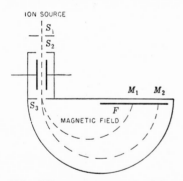

ION SOURCE

Fig. 8.5. Mass spectrograph with velocity focusing.

by opposing electric and magnetic fields. Only those ions remain undeflected, and so emerge from the third slit S_3, for which the displacements

produced by the two fields compensate exactly. It can be seen from the argument in § 2.44, in connection with J. J. Thomson's experiments on cathode rays, that the necessary condition for this to occur is that the velocity v of the charged particles shall be equal to E/H, where E is the strength of the electric field,* and H is that of the magnetic field. Since the field strengths are maintained constant, it follows that all the ions emerging from S_3 have the same velocity.

8.56. After leaving the slit S_3, the stream of charged particles enters another magnetic field which causes it to be deflected into a semicircular path, ultimately striking the photographic plate F. The conditions are now analogous to those in the Dempster apparatus so that an equation similar to (8.8) is applicable. The values of the magnetic field strength and of the velocity of the particles are, however, constant, and hence the radius of curvature of the path is seen to be directly proportional to the mass, assuming the charge to be the same for all the particles. Thus each set of particles, each isotopic species for example, having the same mass, will follow a particular path and will produce a definite line, such as M_1 or M_2, on the photographic plate. From the positions of the lines it is a relatively easy matter to determine the masses of the isotopic particles, in view of the direct proportionality between the mass and the radius of the path. Further, by comparing the intensities of the lines on the plate, the relative amounts of the various species can be determined.

8.57. For the sake of convenience, the foregoing descriptions have referred to mass spectrographs involving

* It may be noted that the electric field strength E is not the same as the potential V used earlier; E is equal to V/d, where d is the distance between the plates across which the potential is applied in order to produce the electric field.

one type of focussing or another. The more modern forms of the instrument employ both direction and velocity focussing; as a result, it is possible to obtain the well-spaced sharp lines, which are characteristic of direction focussing, together with the simple relationship between the position of the lines and the masses of the particles, which is a feature of velocity focussing. Since nothing especially novel is involved, it is not necessary to consider the matter further, except to indicate that a good mass spectrograph will give mass values with an accuracy of a few parts in a hundred thousand.

8.58. A mass spectrometer, capable of determining isotopic weights with great accuracy but based on an entirely different principle to those described above, was proposed by S. Goudsmit in the United States in 1948. It is seen from Figs. 8.4 and 8.5 that the positive ions follow a semicircular path in a magnetic field, but if there were nothing to stop them, the path would be a complete circle. More correctly, since the ions are emitted from the source in several directions, they would travel in a spiral. If r is the radius of curvature, the length of each circular turn of the spiral would be $2\pi r$. Since the velocity of the ion is v, the time T required to traverse a turn of the spiral would be $2\pi r/v$. According to equation (8.8), the value of r/v is m/He, and so it follows that

$$T = \frac{2\pi m}{He}$$

This means that, for a magnetic field of given strength H, the time required for an ion to complete a turn of its circular spiral path is independent of the radius of that path but is proportional to the mass of the ion.* This

is the principle of the time-of-flight mass spectrometer.

8.59. In the instrument, an ion collector is placed directly above or directly below the ion source. Thus, positive ions which have made one (or more) complete circular turns in the magnetic field will enter the collector. The ions are emitted from the source as a pulse of very short duration and their arrival at the collector is timed electronically. From the time of flight the mass of the ions is calculated; the instrument is calibrated by timing ions of known mass so that the magnetic field strength is not required. One significant advantage of the time-of-flight spectrometer is that the accuracy is essentially independent of the mass of the ions, whereas with the other mass spectroscopes the accuracy decreases with increasing mass.

ISOTOPIC WEIGHTS AND
ABUNDANCES

8.60. The accuracy of Aston's first mass spectrograph was inadequate to determine whether the masses of the isotopes were exactly integral or whether there were small deviations from whole number values. Consequently, he proceeded to construct a new instrument capable of greater precision, and his second mass spectroscope, completed about 1925, was capable of giving results accurate to about one part in ten thousand. With this apparatus, Aston showed that the masses of the individual isotopes (nuclides) on the atomic weight scale, commonly known as the *isotopic weights*, actually differed from whole numbers, although the differences were very small. Later work by Aston and others has confirmed this discovery. Some isotopic weights are slightly less than integers

---

* This is sometimes referred to as the *cyclotron principle*, for reasons which will be apparent in § 9.57.

and others are somewhat greater but, with the exception of the heavy radioactive elements, the maximum deviation is about 0.06 atomic weight unit, most of the differences being considerably smaller. The integer nearest the isotopic weight, which is commonly used to identify the isotope, Aston called the *mass number*.* The table in § 8.47 thus gives the mass numbers of the known stable nuclides of the elements.

8.61. It will be seen from this table that oxygen consists of three isotopes with the mass numbers of 16, 17 and 18, respectively. Of these, the first one is by far the most abundant since it constitutes 99.76 per cent of atmospheric oxygen. In the determination of isotopic weights by the mass spectroscope it is the invariable practice to take as the standard of comparison the value of 16.0000 for the weight of this common isotope of oxygen.† Unfortunately, the results so obtained are not exactly equivalent to those based on the ordinary chemical atomic weight scale. The reason for the discrepancy is that on the latter scale the figure 16.0000 is associated with ordinary atmospheric oxygen, which is actually a mixture of isotopes, whereas on the mass spectrographic, or *physical*, atomic weight scale this is taken as the isotopic weight of the single, most abundant isotope.‡

8.62. The relationship between the two scales may be determined in the following manner. Atmospheric oxygen consists of 99.76 per cent of the isotope of mass 16.0000, together with

0.04 per cent of the one of mass 17.0045, and 0.20 per cent of that of mass 18.0049, all on the physical atomic weight scale. The weighted mean of these values is 16.0044, so that this is the atomic weight of atmospheric oxygen on the physical scale, as compared with the postulated value of 16.0000 on the chemical scale. It follows, therefore, that

$$\frac{\text{Physical At. Wt.}}{\text{Chemical At. Wt.}} = \frac{16.0044}{16.0000} = 1.00027,$$

and hence isotopic weights obtained by means of the mass spectrograph must be divided by 1.00027 in order to convert the results to the chemical atomic weight scale. Although it is the invariable practice in nuclear studies to employ isotopic weights on the physical scale, there are occasions when it is of interest to compare mass spectrographic results with those obtained by chemical methods; in such instances the conversion factor is used.

8.63. In addition to giving the atomic weights of the isotopic constituents of an element, their relative amounts can also be obtained, as mentioned earlier, by means of the mass spectrograph. In fact, one of the most important uses of the mass spectrograph at present is for the quantitative analysis of both naturally occurring and partially separated mixtures of isotopic substances. The proportions of the various isotopes are referred to as the *abundance ratios* or the *relative abundances* or, in brief, as the *abundances*. The values are usually expressed as percentages, so

---

* While the atomic number of any species represents the number of protons in the nucleus, the mass number gives the total number of protons and neutrons i.e., the number of nucleons (§ 4.36).

† Although both mass spectrographs and mass spectrometers are used in this work, the results, following historical precedent, are generally referred to as mass spectrographic values.

‡ The physical atomic weight is sometimes referred to as the "atomic mass," reserving the expression "atomic weight" for the chemical value. However, this distinction between "mass" and "weight" is not in accord with the usual significance of these terms.

that the abundances of the three isotopes of oxygen, as recorded above, are 99.76, 0.04 and 0.20 per cent, respectively. The physical atomic weights and the relative abundances of the isotopes of some common elements, as they occur in nature, are quoted in the accompanying table.

ISOTOPIC WEIGHTS AND ABUNDANCES

Element	Mass Number	Isotopic Weight	Abundance Per Cent
Hydrogen.....	1	1.008145	99.985
	2	2.014740	0.015
Boron........	10	10.01612	18.7
	11	11.01280	81.3
Carbon.......	12	12.00380	98.89
	13	13.00748	1.11
Nitrogen......	14	14.00752	99.635
	15	15.00486	0.365
Oxygen.......	16	16.00000	99.76
	17	17.00453	0.036
	18	18.00486	0.204
Sulfur........	32	31.9822	95.018
	33	32.9819	0.750
	34	33.9786	4.215
	36	35.9784	0.017
Chlorine......	35	34.97990	75.53
	37	36.97754	24.47
Copper.......	63	62.9494	69.1
	65	64.9484	30.9

8.64. It is of interest to compare the atomic weights of elements as determined by chemical methods with the mean values derived from mass spectrograph results. For example, boron, as it occurs in nature, consists of two isotopes of atomic weights 10.0161 and 11.0128, whose abundances are 18.7 and 81.3 per cent, respectively. The weighted mean of these two physical isotopic weights is 10.826, and upon dividing by the conversion factor 1.00027, the atomic weight of ordinary boron is found to be 10.823 on the chemical scale; this may be compared with the accepted value of 10.82 obtained by chemical methods, as outlined in Chapter I. There is little doubt that at the present time the mass spectrograph provides the most reliable general method for the determination of atomic weights. The values obtained in this manner are accurate to better than one part in ten thousand, a precision which is rarely obtainable in chemical analysis. In several cases the previously adopted atomic weights have been proved to be incorrect as a result of studies with the mass spectrograph. During the 1920s, for example, the chemical atomic weight of boron was quoted as 10.90, but the isotopic analysis indicated an appreciably lower value. Subsequent redetermination by improved chemical methods gave 10.82, in agreement with the mass spectrograph value 10.823, as stated above.

8.65. For the majority of elements studied the relative abundances of their isotopes have been found to be independent of the source of the material. In some instances, however, variations have been detected. Lead, associated with radioactive minerals, is an outstanding example; as indicated in § 8.24, lead from uranium minerals contains more of the 206 isotope, whereas the thorium minerals have more of the 208 isotope. However, lead derived from apparently nonradioactive sources also exhibits slight differences in isotopic composition. The same is true of hydrogen, carbon, oxygen and, possibly, chlorine; the significance of some of these variations will be considered later.

HEAVY HYDROGEN: DEUTERIUM

8.66. For many reasons, one of the most notable of the stable isotopes is that of hydrogen; its discovery, in

1931, marked an important advance in understanding the chemical behavior of isotopes in general. In 1920, both W. D. Harkins and E. Rutherford, whose speculations concerning the neutron were mentioned in § 2.115, considered the possibility that there might exist a form of hydrogen with a mass approximately twice that of ordinary hydrogen. Subsequently, other scientists argued that such an isotope was to be expected to fit in with the mass regularities exhibited by the known isotopes of other elements of low atomic weight. However, as early as 1919, O. Stern and M. Volmer, in Germany, had sought, unsuccessfully, to detect the presence of a heavier isotope in ordinary hydrogen in order to determine whether the departure of the atomic weight from exactly unity might be accounted for in this manner. They tried to bring about a partial separation of the possible isotopes by diffusion, the procedure by which Aston had been successful with neon (§ 8.37), but they were unable to detect any change of density. Although it is now known that this failure was due to faulty experimental technique, it served the purpose of discouraging others from seeking for an isotope, the existence of which was in doubt. It may be mentioned that the earlier mass spectrographs were unable to shed any light on the problem, because with hydrogen in the apparatus there was invariably a line of mass approximately 2, due to molecular hydrogen (H_2), which could not be distinguished from that due to the isotopic atom of similar mass.

8.67. When, in 1927, Aston reported on the isotopic composition of hydrogen as determined by the mass spectrograph, he stated that it consisted of a single species of atomic weight 1.00778, apparently in excellent agreement with the chemical atomic weight 1.00777 accepted at that time. The discovery, two years later, by F. W. Giauque and H. L. Johnston, in the United States, that atmospheric oxygen is a mixture of three isotopes, showed that (physical) atomic weights obtained by the mass spectrograph could not be identical with the chemical values, as explained above. By making the appropriate conversion of Aston's mass-spectrographic atomic weight to the chemical scale, it would then become 1.00751, as compared with 1.00777 determined by chemical methods. The difference between these two values was appreciably greater than could be accounted for by the possible experimental errors, and in 1931 R. T. Birge and D. H. Menzel, in the United States, suggested it might be due to the presence in ordinary hydrogen of about one part in 4500 of a heavier isotope, concerning the existence of which there had been much speculation, as stated above. The lower result obtained by the mass spectrograph would then be the atomic weight of the lighter isotope, while that derived by chemical methods would be the weighted mean value for both isotopes normally present in hydrogen.

8.68. Encouraged by the calculations based on the difference in atomic weights, and also by the fact that a hydrogen isotope of mass 2 was required to complete a regular arrangement of the known isotopes, the American scientist H. C. Urey, in 1931, attacked the subject from a new angle. He considered the possibility that, in the liquid state, the two isotopes of hydrogen might have different vapor pressures, so that a separation would be possible. Calculations, made in conjunction with G. M. Murphy, showed that the lighter isotope (of mass number 1) should have the higher vapor pressure; hence, upon evaporation of liquid hydrogen, the heavier isotope (of mass number 2), if present, should concentrate in the residue. In view of the expected small proportion of the heavier isotope in ordinary hydrogen, Urey realized that it would be difficult to detect unless a large volume of liquid hydrogen could be used. Consequently, the collaboration of F. G. Brickwedde, at the U. S. National Bureau of Standards, was obtained in the evaporation of 4 liters of liquid hydrogen down to 1 cc. An examination of the optical spectrum* of this residue, by Urey and Murphy at Columbia University, exhibited very clearly a line in the precise position required for an isotope of hydrogen with a mass very close to 2 on the atomic weight scale.†

8.69. Subsequently, a careful study showed the same line to be present, although very much fainter, in the spectrum of ordinary hydrogen. Thus, definite proof was obtained of the existence of a heavier isotope of hydrogen. The concentration of this isotope by the distillation of liquid hydrogen was verified by a number of scientists in Europe; and further confirmation of its presence was obtained shortly afterward in the United States, when W. Bleakney found that the appropriate line could be detected in the mass spectrograph, and K. T. Bainbridge determined the isotopic mass.

8.70. Soon after the discovery of the heavier isotope of hydrogen, Urey, one of its discoverers, together with E. W. Washburn, of the U. S. National Bureau of Standards, thought that a partial separation of the isotopes might be achieved by the electrolysis of water,‡ that is to say, by decomposing water by means of an electric current. While the experiments to test this possibility were still in progress, a sample of water obtained from industrial electrolytic cells, which had been used for the production of hydrogen and oxygen, was examined by E. R. Smith, at Washburn's suggestion, and found to have a density appreciably higher than that of ordinary water. This difference was attributed to the presence in the former of an excess, above the normal proportion, of water molecules containing the heavier hydrogen isotope.

8.71. It thus appeared that upon the electrolysis of water—actually an aqueous solution was used—the lighter isotope of hydrogen is evolved more readily than the heavier one, so that the latter accumulates in the residual water. Consequently, by prolonged electrolysis, it might be possible to concentrate the heavier isotope. This was actually achieved in 1933 by G. N. Lewis and his collaborators at the University of California; by continued electrolysis of a large quantity of water from an old commercial electrolytic cell, they obtained ultimately a small residue in which almost all of the hydrogen was in the form of the

---

* Optical spectra, which are due to changes in energy levels and which are studied by the absorption of light (§ 4.42), should, of course, not be confused with mass spectra. The optical spectrum of a hydrogen atom of mass 2 is entirely different from that of a hydrogen molecule (H_2), although in a mass spectrum the respective lines are very close together.

† As a historical sidelight, it may be mentioned that, in 1935, Aston reported a revised value of 1.0081 for the mass-spectrographic atomic weight of hydrogen, stating that his earlier value had been in error due to imperfect resolution of certain lines. If the more accurate atomic weight had been available in 1931, the calculations of Birge and Menzel would have been invalid. However, as Urey has stated in his Nobel Lecture in 1935, "without it, it is probable we would not have made a search . . . and the discovery of deuterium might have been delayed for some time."

‡ The suggestion that isotopes might be separable by electrolysis was made in 1923 by J. Kendall and E. D. Crittenden in the United States.

heavier isotope. Other scientists, in the United States and elsewhere, soon followed up this work, using larger quantities of electrolyte and improved procedures, so that appreciable amounts of the isotope were isolated. Since ordinary hydrogen consists almost entirely of the lighter isotopic species, it meant that both isotopes were now available for experimental purposes in an almost pure state.

8.72. Because the atomic weights of the two isotopes of hydrogen are in the approximate ratio of 2 to 1, which is greatly in excess of that for any other element, the otherwise small differences in physical and chemical properties of isotopes are so much accentuated that it was considered desirable to ascribe different names to these isotopes. The name *deuterium** was suggested for the heavier isotope by its discoverers, and this, together with the symbol D, has been widely adopted. The nucleus of the deuterium atom is called a *deuteron,* by analogy with the term proton for the nucleus of the lighter isotope (§ 2.64). The deuteron, with a positive charge of one unit and a mass of approximately two units on the atomic weight scale, is evidently made up of a proton and a neutron.

8.73. The name hydrogen and the symbol H are used both for the lighter isotope and for the naturally occurring mixture which contains 99.985 per cent of this form. Where a distinction is necessary the expression "light hydrogen" is used, as against "heavy hydrogen" for deuterium, the heavier isotope. Ordinary water has the formula H_2O, whereas *heavy water,* as it is familiarly called, in which all the hydrogen consists of the heavy form, has the scientific name of deuterium oxide and is represented by D_2O. The density of heavy water is 1.108 as compared with 1.000 gram per cc. for ordinary water; it freezes at 3.82°C and boils at 101.42°C, the corresponding temperatures for normal water being 0°C and 100°C. The differences in the physical properties of light and heavy water are thus quite appreciable.

8.74. Prior to the discovery and isolation of deuterium, it was generally believed that the isotopes of a given element could not be separated by chemical methods, since they had identical chemical properties (§ 8.7). Although it is true that isotopes do undergo the same chemical reactions, experiments with deuterium drew attention to the fact that the different isotopes react at different rates. The difference is negligible for the isotopic forms of the heavier elements, but for elements of low atomic weight, and particularly for hydrogen, the effects are very significant.

8.75. The molecules of the lighter isotope of hydrogen (H_2), in the gaseous form, undergo what is known as an *exchange reaction* with liquid heavy water (D_2O), the two isotopic forms of hydrogen exchanging places with one another; thus, from left to right,

$$H_2 (g) + D_2O (l) \rightarrow D_2 (g) + H_2O (l)$$

where the symbols g and l indicate gas and liquid, respectively.† The reverse reaction, between deuterium gas (D_2)

---

* From the Greek, *deuteros* (second). The analogous term *protium* (from *protos,* first) was suggested for the lighter isotope, but this has not come into general use. Rutherford (1932) proposed the names *diplogen* and *haplogen* for the two isotopes, from the Greek combining forms *diplo* (double) and *haplo* (single), with the symbols D and H, respectively; the names met with limited acceptance and have now been discarded.

† The reaction actually also involves the intermediate isotopic forms HDO and HD, but for the sake of simplicity they will be omitted from consideration here.

and light water (H_2O) is also possible, as is to be expected if isotopes exhibit similar chemical behavior; thus,

$$H_2\,(g) + D_2O\,(l) \leftarrow D_2\,(g) + H_2O\,(l)$$

from right to left. The interesting point is that, provided the concentrations of the reacting substances are the same in both cases, the latter reaction takes place about three times as fast as the former, so that if the equilibrium

$$H_2\,(g) + D_2O\,(l) \rightleftarrows D_2\,(g) + H_2O\,(l)$$

is established between the isotopic forms of hydrogen gas and of liquid water, the substances on the left-hand side will be favored over those on the right-hand side. As a result, the ratio of deuterium to hydrogen in the liquid is found to be approximately three times as great as in the gas. If the specific rates* of the two isotopic exchange reactions had been identical, the relative proportions of the isotopes would have been the same in both gaseous and liquid phases. The foregoing reaction has been chosen for consideration because it has been utilized, as will be seen shortly, for the large-scale concentration of deuterium, but other chemical processes exhibit similar behavior (§ 8.112 *et seq.*).

THE SEPARATION OF ISOTOPES

THE SEPARATION FACTOR

8.76. Materials enriched in particular isotopic forms of certain elements have found numerous applications, as will be apparent in later chapters. Consequently, considerable interest attaches to the subject of the separation of isotopes. In the twenty or so years immediately following the first development of the concept of isotopes, partial concentrations had been achieved of the isotopes of a number of nonradioactive elements, such as neon, chlorine, mercury, zinc and potassium. The results were, however, not spectacular, and their main purpose was to provide confirmatory evidence for the existence of isotopes. The notable success achieved in the concentration of deuterium, in spite of its very small abundance (one part in about 6500 of ordinary hydrogen), and the useful scientific applications which were found for it, resulted in a revival of interest in the general problem of the separation of isotopes. This interest was stimulated by the necessity for obtaining uranium enriched in the 235 isotope for the wartime atomic energy project (Chapter XIV), with the result that, in the words of H. C. Urey, who has himself contributed largely to the subject, "it is [now] possible to separate the isotopes of any element, though the expense involved in certain processes is still greater than may be warranted by the particular objective sought."

8.77. The extent to which separation of isotopes is, or can be, achieved in a particular process is conveniently represented by means of the *separation factor*, defined as the ratio of the abundance of a given isotope in the enriched state to that in the initial state. For example, if an isotopic mixture contains a fraction (or percentage) f of a given isotope before treat-

---

* The rate of a chemical reaction depends on the concentrations of the reacting substances. The adjective *specific* implies that the concentrations are the same (unity) in each case, so that the results are comparable with one another.

ment,* and f' is the fraction (or percentage) present in the system after treatment, the separation factor s for this particular process is given by

$$s = \frac{f'}{f}.\qquad(8.10)$$

The larger the value of s in comparison with unity the more efficient is the separation. If it is only slightly greater than unity, the extent of separation is small, and many successive stages may be necessary to obtain an appreciable concentration of the desired isotope. If the separation factor is s in each stage, the over-all separation factor for n stages is s^n, which can become quite appreciable, if n is sufficiently large, even though s may be close to unity (§ 8.86).

THE GASEOUS DIFFUSION METHOD

8.78. Historically, the first successful method for the enrichment of isotopes, and one which is still of prime importance, made use of the different rates of diffusion of gases through a porous barrier.† Since the early years of the nineteenth century, it has been known that the rate of diffusion of a gas is inversely proportional to the square root of its density. The reason is that, at the same temperature, the molecules of a light gas move, on the average, with a higher speed than do those of a heavier gas. It was seen in § 1.33 that the gas density is directly related to the molecular weight of the substance, and so it follows that the rate of diffusion is inversely proportional to the square root of the molecular weight. Thus, a gas of lower molecular weight will pass through a particular porous barrier faster than one of higher molecular weight. Hence, in a mixture of two isotopic molecules, those containing the lighter isotope will diffuse more rapidly than the heavier species. This fact was utilized in 1913 by F. W. Aston to obtain a partial separation of the isotopes of neon, as mentioned earlier (§ 8.37); and in 1921 W. D. Harkins, in the United States, reported slight enrichment of the isotopes of chlorine by diffusion of hydrogen chloride gas through pipe clay.

8.79. If M_1 is the molecular weight of the form containing the lighter isotope, and M_2 is that of the form with the heavier isotope, the ideal separation factor for diffusion is represented by

$$s = \sqrt{\frac{M_2}{M_1}}.\qquad(8.11)$$

Actually this is a maximum value which can be realized only at the beginning of the process for, as diffusion continues, the gas is being steadily impoverished of the lighter, more rapidly diffusing, constituent. As a result, the *diffusate*, that is, the gas passing through the barrier, contains decreasing proportions of the latter. If diffusion were allowed to proceed long enough, the composition of the gas would, of course, be the same on both sides of the barrier, and there would be no separation of the isotopes. In practice, therefore, there has to be a compromise between the quantity of gas permitted to diffuse and the resultant separation factor; this is achieved by allowing about half of

---

* Strictly, f should refer to the depleted portion remaining after removal of the enriched material from the system. However, since the separation factor is usually close to unity, the depleted part has almost the same composition as the material before treatment.
† The passage of gas through fine pores, small in comparison with the distance between the molecules, is properly called *effusion*, rather than diffusion. However, the latter term is almost invariably used in the present connection, and so it will be employed here.

the gas to pass through the barrier.

8.80. It can be seen from equation (8.11) that the larger the ratio of the molecular weights of the two isotopic species the greater will be the separation factor, and hence the efficiency of separation by diffusion. The most favorable case for naturally occurring isotopes is that of hyrogen gas where the molecular weights M_1 and M_2 are approximately 2 and 4, respectively, so that the maximum (initial) separation factor is $\sqrt{2}$, i.e., 1.414. For the two most abundant isotopes of neon (mass numbers 20 and 22) this factor is 1.049, and for those of chlorine

through the barrier. The diffusate, which is richer in the lighter isotope, then passes into unit A; here it undergoes further diffusion, the diffusate containing a still higher proportion of this isotope. Turning attention once again to B, it will be seen that the gas which has not diffused, and which is consequently somewhat impoverished in the lighter species, is recycled; that is to say, it returns to unit C, where it joins the diffusate from D. The resulting gas then undergoes diffusion in C, the diffusate going on to B, while the remainder returns to D to be recycled. In this way, the gas

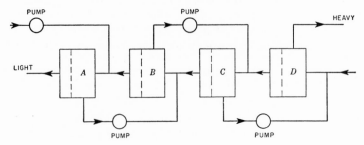

Fig. 8.6. Diagrammatic representation of cascade principle for separation of isotopes by diffusion.

(mass numbers 35 and 37), using hydrogen chloride as the diffusing gas, it is 1.028. It is apparent, therefore, that the extent of isotopic enrichment by diffusion decreases rapidly with increasing atomic weight of the element whose isotopes are to be separated.

8.81. In order to increase the overall separation by the diffusion process, G. Hertz of Germany introduced in 1932 the "cascade" principle with recycling, which may be illustrated by means of the diagram in Fig. 8.6. A number of units are shown, each containing a porous diffusion barrier represented by a broken line. Consider the unit B: the gas enters from the right, and the arrangement of pumps permits about one half to diffuse

moving to the left from one unit to the next becomes increasingly richer in the lighter isotope, while that traveling to the right contains an increasing proportion of the heavier species; thus, a kind of fractionation process is taking place.

8.82. In his work, Hertz used a closed system, so that the gas containing more of the lighter isotope collected in a vessel at one end, and that enriched in the heavier isotope accumulated at the other end. It is possible, however, to imagine a somewhat similar cascade of diffusion barriers in which gas is fed continuously into one of the intermediate units, and is drawn off steadily at the two extremes. At one end, the left-hand in

Fig. 8.6, the gas has a greater abundance of the lighter isotope, and at the other end a larger proportion of the heavier isotope, than does the feed gas.

8.83. Utilizing some form of the diffusion method, a number of investigators, both in Europe and America, achieved partial separation of the isotopes of hydrogen, carbon (in methane), nitrogen, oxygen, neon and argon. But the most remarkable application of the diffusion procedure is the concentration on a large scale of the 235 isotope of uranium, present to the extent of 0.72 per cent in ordinary uranium. The process was developed in the United States during World War II, and has been in successful operation since the spring of 1945. In his report on *Atomic Energy for Military Purposes*, written in that year, H. D. Smyth refers to this as "a notable achievement," although a full realization of the problems solved and the difficulties overcome, warrant it being described as a stupendous feat.*

8.84. In considering the possibility of separating the isotopes of uranium, it should be noted that uranium is a solid metal, and so it is first necessary to choose a compound of uranium that can be readily converted into a gas. A fairly obvious choice is uranium hexafluoride UF_6, for although it is a solid at ordinary temperatures, it is easily vaporized. An important advantage of the use of a compound of fluorine for this purpose is that this element consists of a single nuclide, as

can be seen from the table in § 8.47. Consequently, the course of the diffusion process will be determined only by the uranium isotopes, and not by the fluorine. On the other hand, uranium hexafluoride has the great disadvantage of being a highly reactive and corrosive gas, so that special materials would have to be used for pipes, vessels, pumps and even for lubrication purposes.

8.85. As found in nature, uranium contains three isotopic forms with mass numbers of 234, 235 and 238;† the proportion of the 234 isotope is only 0.006 per cent, so that its presence may be ignored. The uranium hexafluoride may thus be regarded as essentially a mixture of two isotopic forms, with molecular weights of 235 $+ 6 \times 19$ i.e., 349, and 238 $+6 \times 19$, i.e., 352, respectively; hence the maximum separation factor is given by equation (8.11) as

$$s = \sqrt{\frac{352}{349}} = 1.0043.$$

Close as this is to unity, the conditions in the diffusion cascade make it even closer. The first experimental measurements made by E. T. Booth, H. C. Paxton and C. B. Slade at Columbia University, indicated a value of about 1.0014, which would appear to be so near to unity as to be of no use for the practical separation of the uranium isotopes. However, the situation was not altogether hopeless, as the following considerations will show.

* The report on *Atomic Energy for Military Purposes*, subtitled *The Official Report on the Development of the Atomic Bomb under the Auspices of the United States Government 1940-1945*, often referred to as the Smyth *Report*, gives a full account of the development of this and other procedures which were considered for the separation of uranium-235. The discussion in this book will therefore be restricted to the essential principles required for an understanding of the more important methods used.

† The 238 and 234 isotopes are uranium I and II, respectively, of the uranium disintegration series, while the 235 isotope is actino-uranium, the parent of the actinum series (Chapter V). In the chemical preparation of uranium hexafluoride, or other compounds, the highly radioactive disintegration products are largely removed.

8.86. Since the proportion of uranium-235 is raised by a factor of only 1.0014 in each diffusion stage, it is clearly necessary to increase the number of stages in the cascade sufficiently to obtain the desired enrichment. If there are n successive stages, the overall separation factor will then be $(1.0014)^n$, and a simple calculation shows that a ten-fold enrichment of the lighter isotope could be achieved

foregoing simple method of calculation does not apply to an actual diffusion cascade, but it does indicate the orders of magnitude involved.

8.87. The nature of the diffusion barrier merits some attention. To obtain true diffusion, or rather effusion, which makes isotopic separation possible, it is necessary that the pores should be less than one tenth the mean free path of the molecules, that is, less

Fig. 8.7. Part of the plant for the separation of uranium-235 by gaseous diffusion at Oak Ridge, Tenn.

in about 1800 stages. In order to increase the abundance of uranium-235 from its normal value of 0.72 per cent to 99 per cent, n would have to be about 4000. Thus, using ordinary uranium hexafluoride as the process gas, a cascade of something like 4000 diffusion stages would be required to yield a product in which the uranium was almost entirely in the form of the lighter isotope. These numbers, although very large, did not appear to be beyond the bounds of possibility when the project was under consideration. It should be mentioned that the

than one tenth of the average distance a gas molecule travels before it collides with another molecule. Calculations based on the kinetic theory of gases show that at ordinary pressures the holes in the barrier would have to be about a millionth of a centimeter in diameter. One way in which such barriers could be made was by etching a thin sheet of silver-zinc alloy by means of hydrochloric acid. The acid would then dissolve out some of the zinc atoms, leaving a large number of submicroscopic holes in the sheet of metal.

8.88. "By 1942," says the Smyth *Report*, "the theory of isotope separation by gaseous diffusion had been well worked out, and it became clear that a very large plant would be required." In the summer of 1943 construction of a gaseous diffusion plant for the quantity production of enriched uranium-235 was started at Oak Ridge, Tenn. But it was not until nearly two years later, after many perplexing problems had been solved, that it came into full operation. With its thousands of miles of piping and hundreds of acres of diffusion barriers, the plant is one of enormous size (Fig. 8.7). It is indeed a monument, in the words of the Smyth *Report*, to the "courage and persistence, as well as the scientific and technical ability," of the physicists, chemists and engineers who were responsible for its planning, construction and operation.*

NOZZLE SEPARATION METHOD

8.89. A new method of separating isotopes, which has some features in common with the gaseous diffusion procedure, was proposed in 1955 by E. W. Becker and his collaborators in West Germany. The mixture of isotopic molecules in gaseous form is passed through an expanding air nozzle at pressures below atmospheric. The lighter component, having the faster moving molecules, then tends to concentrate at the outside of the gas stream with the heavier component in the inside. Opposite the center of the nozzle is a "paring tube," so that the gas entering this tube contains a larger proportion of the heavier molecules than does the remaining gas. Thus, a partial separation of lighter from heavier isotopes becomes possible. The combination of nozzle and paring tube is equivalent to a diffusion barrier, with a separation factor of about the same magnitude. The process, like gaseous diffusion, lends itself to the application of the cascade principle for increasing the over-all separation.

THE ELECTROMAGNETIC METHOD

8.90. The electromagnetic method of isotopic separation is of special interest as it was the first to yield appreciable amounts of uranium-235 for the wartime atomic energy project, although it is no longer used for that purpose. Because of its great convenience and adaptability for work on a moderate scale, however, the procedure is now being extensively employed for the production of the separated isotopes of over fifty stable elements for use in various research problems (Chapter XVII).

8.91. The principle of the electromagnetic method is essentially that of the mass spectrograph, in which each isotopic species present in a stream of ions is bent through a different path by a suitable arrangement of electric and magnetic fields (§ 8.51). If, instead of the photographic plate or other device used for detecting the positively charged ions, a number of small receivers are placed in the proper positions, the separate isotopes can be collected.† By using this method, which was suggested by F. W. Aston in 1919, the English physicists M. L. E. Oliphant, E. S. Shire and B. M. Crowther succeeded, in 1934, in obtaining very small quantities—less

---

* Additional gaseous diffusion plants for the enrichment of uranium-235 are now in operation at Paducah, Kentucky and at Portsmouth, Ohio. There are, presumably, similar plants in Great Britain and in the U.S.S.R.

† There is, of course, an actual separation of isotopes in any mass spectrograph, but the amounts are extremely small, being sufficient merely to affect a photographic plate or to be recorded as an ion current.

than one ten-millionth part of a gram —of the separated isotopes of lithium in virtually pure form. Almost simultaneously, W. R. Smythe and his collaborators in the United States described an improved form of the apparatus, using the same principle, by means of which they were able to separate appreciable amounts of the isotopes of several elements.

8.92. Because the mass-spectroscopic (or electromagnetic) method offered the advantage of efficient separation, even for isotopes of high atomic weight, it found application in certain instances where only minute amounts of the separated isotopes, provided they were in a fairly pure state, were adequate. A case of particular interest was that in which it was required to study the interaction of the isotopes of uranium with neutrons. By using the electromagnetic technique, A. O. Nier at the University of Minnesota, and K. H. Kingdon and H. C. Pollock, at the General Electric Laboratories, Schenectady, New York, were able in 1940 to obtain sufficient uranium-235 to provide the answer to a vital problem in connection with the utilization of nuclear energy (§ 13.68).

8.93. The advantage of the electromagnetic method is that it is capable of giving large separation factors, but the quantities of separated isotopes collected are extremely small. Strong beams of positive ions which are to be deviated in the magnetic field are difficult to produce and to manipulate, and the separation efficiency tends to diminish as the strength of the ion beam increases. Thus, an improvement in the amount of material handled by the apparatus could be achieved only at the expense of its efficiency, so that

there seemed little to be gained in this way. Consequently, when in 1940 the U. S. National Defense Research Council decided to investigate the feasibility of separating the isotopes of uranium, the electromagnetic method was rejected as impractical. In this connection, the Smyth *Report* states: "[H. D.] Smyth of Princeton had raised the question of possible large-scale separation of isotopes by electromagnetic means but had been told that it had been investigated and was considered impossible. Nevertheless, Smyth and [E. O.] Lawrence at a chance meeting in October 1941 discussed the problem and agreed that it might yet be possible."

8.94. At the time there was a great need for samples of relatively pure uranium-235 for experimental purposes, and E. O. Lawrence, of the University of California, thought that this could be most readily obtained by the use of the electromagnetic separation procedure. Therefore, toward the end of 1941, he and his associates set out to improve the design of the apparatus, devoting particular attention to methods for increasing the strength of the ion beam without impairing too seriously the efficiency of isotopic separation.*

8.95. The work proved so successful that, in spite of its apparent initial lack of promise, it was decided in September 1942 to build a large plant at Oak Ridge, Tennessee, consisting of a number of entirely independent units, for the electromagnetic separation of the isotopes of uranium. Subsequently, the yield of uranium-235 was considerably improved by using as feed material a compound of uranium which had been partly enriched in the 235

---

* The apparatus was called a *calutron,* a contraction of "California University cyclotron," because it made use of the magnet from one of the University of California cyclotrons (§ 9.67).

isotope by the thermal diffusion method to be described below (§ 8.102). Since the positive-ion beam consists of the unwanted uranium-238, as well as the wanted uranium-235, it is evident that for a given strength of the total ion current, the number of uranium-235 ions, and hence the quantity of this isotope collected, will increase as its abundance in the system is increased.

8.96. The type of electromagnetic unit at present in use at Oak Ridge, for the separation of the isotopes of elements other than uranium, is essentially equivalent to the Dempster mass spectrograph described in (§ 8.51). A stream of electrons, emitted from an electrically heated wire, passes through the vapor of a suitable volatile compound of the element whose isotopes are to be separated. A beam of positively charged ions thus produced at the ion source A (Fig. 8.8) passes

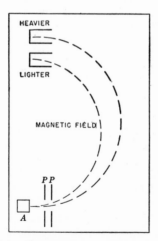

Fig. 8.8. Separation of isotopes by the electromagnetic method.

through slits in the plates PP; here they are accelerated by an electric potential V applied between these plates. The ion beam then enters a magnetic field of strength H, acting in

a direction perpendicular to the plane of the diagram, so that the beam is bent through a semicircle. The actual path of the positively charged particles depends on their masses, in accordance with equation (8.9), i.e.,

$$\frac{m}{e} = \frac{H^2 r^2}{2V},$$

so that, for a given electric and magnetic field, the square of the radius of the path is proportional to the mass of the particle. By placing collecting pockets in the proper positions, as calculated from this equation, the different isotopes of a given element can be separated. Although two such pockets are shown in the figure, three, four or more can be used when necessary, so that several isotopes of the elements can be collected simultaneously.

8.97. In order that the same apparatus may be easily adaptable to the separation of light isotopes, such as those of lithium, mass numbers 6 and 7, as well as of heavy isotopes, like those of lead, mass numbers 204, 206, 207 and 208, the positions of the ion source and the receivers are not changed, that is to say, the radii of the paths are kept approximately constant, but the magnetic field is altered as required. Since, by the equation given above, the mass m of the positive particles is proportional to H^2, i.e., to the square of the magnetic field strength, for a given path radius, it follows that a six-fold increase in the field strength will permit a thirty-six-fold increase in the mass of the isotopes that can be accommodated. The fine adjustment that may be necessary to bring the ion beams exactly on to the receiver, with its properly spaced pockets, is made by changing the accelerating voltage V. In this manner, elements covering a large range of masses can be readily handled in any one electromagnetic unit.

The Centrifugal Method

8.98. The gravitational force acting on a particle is proportional to its mass; consequently, under the influence of gravity there is a partial separation of the gases of the atmosphere, the lighter molecules tending to stay in the upper levels while the heavier ones concentrate in the lower levels. This accounts for the fact that at great heights there is more hydrogen and helium, which are the lightest constituents of the atmosphere, than at the surface of the earth. The suggestion that this principle might be applied to the separation of isotopic molecules, with different masses, was made by F. A. Lindemann and F. W. Aston in England in 1919. They showed that appreciable separation could be achieved by the use of a centrifuge, for this would provide a force analogous to gravity, but much more powerful. The theory of the subject was further examined in 1922 by R. S. Mulliken, in the United States, who proposed an improved procedure which, making use of combined centrifugal force and evaporation, would give better results than the former alone.

8.99. The basis of the centrifugal method of separating isotopes is that if a gas or vapor flows into a rapidly rotating cylinder the force acting on the molecules will result in an increased concentration of the heavier isotope at the walls, while the lighter isotope tends to collect nearer the axis of rotation. If the centrifuge is vertical, a current of vapor can be made to flow down near the walls and up around the central axis. It should then be possible to draw off a product richer in the lighter isotopic species at the top of the apparatus, near the center,

whereas the heavier species would be removed at the bottom near the periphery.

8.100. A particularly interesting feature of the centrifugal method is that the separation factor depends on the *difference* between the masses of the two isotopic elements, and not on their ratio. Thus, better separation should be obtainable, in principle, of the 235 and 238 isotopes of uranium than of the isotopes of hydrogen, with masses of 1 and 2, respectively. Further, since the difference in the isotopic weights is always the same for a given element, the efficiency is independent of the molecular weight of the compound whose vapor is being centrifuged.

8.101. The earliest attempts to make use of this principle for the separation of isotopes failed, probably because the speeds of rotation of the centrifuges were not high enough. But in 1939, J. W. Beams, and others, in the United States, using the high-speed centrifuge, which he had developed, and which produced a force of several hundred thousand times that of gravity, obtained appreciable separation of the isotopes of chlorine, in carbon tetrachloride, and of bromine, in ethyl bromide. Since the atomic weights of the two isotopes of uranium differ by three units, the centrifugal method seemed to offer an especially attractive possibility for the separation of uranium-235. A pilot plant for this purpose was constructed during the war, and although it operated successfully, large-scale production by the centrifugal method was not attempted because, as the Smyth *Report* says, "of the magnitude of the engineering problems involved."

The Thermal-Diffusion Method

8.102. Another plant for the separation of isotopes of uranium, which functioned for some time as a source of feed material for the electromagnetic plant, described in § 8.95, made use of the thermal-diffusion principle. The mathematical theory, which is applicable to any mixture of gases of different molecular weights, was worked out between the years 1911 and 1919 by D. Enskog in Sweden and by S. Chapman in England; later, in 1922, the possible application to the separation of isotopes was examined by R. S. Mulliken in the United States.

8.103. The general idea is that if a gaseous mixture of isotopes is placed in a vessel, part of which is hotter than the remainder, the lighter molecules should tend to concentrate in the regions of higher temperature. The experimental results were, at first, not very promising, but in 1938 the German scientists K. Clusius and G. Dickel introduced a simple modification giving a very decided increase in efficiency of the thermal-diffusion procedure. Their apparatus consisted of a long, vertical tube with a central wire which could be heated electrically to about 500°C or more, thus producing a temperature gradient between the hot wire and the colder wall of the tube. The gas containing the isotopes to be separated is placed in the tube and, as a result of thermal diffusion, the lighter molecules collect near the hot wire, whereas the heavier ones prefer to stay nearer the cold wall. At the same time, however, thermal convection causes the hotter gas in the center to rise and the colder gas at the wall to sink, so that there is a steady flow of gas, up at the center and down at the sides of the tube. This continuous streaming of the gas, together with the influence of thermal diffusion, results in a concentration of the heavier isotopic species at the bottom of the tube, while the lighter constituent tends to collect at the top. In this manner, Clusius and Dickel were able to make rapid and effective separations of the isotopes of chlorine and neon. Other workers, both in the United States and in Europe, applied the method to the elements carbon (in methane), nitrogen, oxygen, krypton and xenon.

8.104. Soon after the discovery of the combined thermal-diffusion and convection principles for separating gaseous isotopes, it was found that the method could be used for substances in solution and also for pure liquids. In 1940, P. H. Abelson, in the United States, suggested applying the procedure to liquid uranium hexafluoride for the purpose of separating the isotopes of uranium. After considerable experimental work had proved the feasibility of the method, a large-scale thermal-diffusion plant was built at Oak Ridge in the summer of 1944, its output, partially enriched in uranium-235, being used as feed material in the electromagnetic separation process. "In spite of some disappointments," wrote H. D. Smyth, "operation of this plant . . . succeeded in its purpose of considerably increasing the production rate of the electromagnetic plant." One of the principal drawbacks was its great power consumption, and so, when the gaseous diffusion procedure (§ 8.83) proved so efficient, and the electromagnetic separation became less important, the thermal-diffusion plant was closed down. Nevertheless, for isotope enrichment on the laboratory scale, it appears that the thermal-diffusion method has advantages over others, because of its simplicity, efficiency and wide applicability.

DISTILLATION METHODS

8.105. As a general rule, isotopic species have different vapor pressures (and boiling points), so that partial separation by fractional distillation should be a theoretical possibility. Aston's first attempt to separate the isotopes of neon was made by fractional distillation, but, as stated in § 8.36, his efforts met with failure. Subsequently, in 1919, F. A. Lindemann, in England, showed theoretically that separation of isotopes by distillation should be possible in certain circumstances, and in 1931, W. H. Keesom and H. van Dijk, of Holland, reported the successful enrichment of the isotopes of neon in this manner. In the same year, H. C. Urey and his collaborators used a form of distillation to concentrate the heavier isotope of hydrogen, as recorded in § 8.68. It has been claimed that, if the difficulty of operating at very low temperatures (about −250°C or −420°F) can be overcome, fractional distillation of liquid hydrogen should be capable of separating the deuterium at a lower cost than by any other method. Slight enrichment of oxygen-18 and nitrogen-15 has been achieved by distillation of liquid oxygen and of liquid ammonia, respectively.

8.106. It was seen in § 8.73 that the boiling point of heavy water (D_2O) is about 1.4°C higher than that of ordinary water (H_2O). This difference, although small, should make separation by distillation practical, provided an efficient fractionation column were used. Some success was reported in the United States by G. N. Lewis and R. E. Cornish in 1933, but the distillation method of separating the isotopes of hydrogen did not attract any great interest, because the relatively small amounts of heavy water or heavy hydrogen (deuterium) gas required for experimental purposes could be obtained much more readily by the electrolytic (§ 8.71) or by the gaseous diffusion (§ 8.78) processes. However,

in 1943, when it appeared that large quantities of heavy water might be needed in connection with the utilization of atomic energy for military purposes (§ 14.28), a plant for its production by fractional distillation of ordinary water was built and operated in the following year. But it was later superseded by more economical processes.

8.107. In addition to the isotopic forms of hydrogen, there are present in water, molecules which differ in the oxygen isotopes; thus, about 0.2 per cent of ordinary water consists of H_2O molecules containing oxygen-18. The boiling point of this isotopic species is slightly higher than that of the predominant form, with oxygen-16, and hence partial enrichment of the heavier isotopic form should be possible by fractional distillation. This expectation was verified, in the years from 1935 to 1937, by workers in Canada, the United States and England; water containing up to five times the amount of oxygen-18 normally present, for example, was obtained by Urey and his coworkers. The product was somewhat enriched in heavy hydrogen, but the actual percentage was quite small, probably of the order of 0.1 per cent.

8.108. It is of interest to mention, in passing, that a form of distillation was used in 1920 by J. N. Brønsted and G. Hevesy, in Denmark, to achieve a slight enrichment of the isotopes of mercury. The liquid element, kept at about 50°C, was allowed to evaporate into an evacuated space, and the vapor condensed on a surface cooled in liquid air placed from 1 to 2 cm. above the mercury. The condensate was then allowed to melt, partially evaporated again, and condensed once more. After several fractionations of this kind, the lighter isotopes of mercury were found to be present in small excess in the condensate, while the heavier isotopes collected in the residue. In subsequent years a similar evaporation technique gave detectable separation of the isotopes of the elements chlorine, zinc and potassium.

THE ELECTROLYTIC METHOD

8.109. It was recorded in § 8.71 that electrolysis of aqueous solutions results in preferential evolution of the lighter isotope of hydrogen, so that the deuterium concentrates in the residual water. The electrolyte generally employed is potassium hydroxide, and almost any electrodes, provided they do not dissolve, can be used. Nickel is a convenient material for this purpose. Separation factors of 6 or higher are readily obtainable, so that concentration of the deuterium from its initial value of 0.015 per cent, in ordinary water, up to 99.9 per cent in the product, is within the realm of possibility. The current consumption is, however, very large, thirty or forty thousand ampere-hours being required to yield one gram of heavy water. It is for this reason that large-scale plants for the production of heavy water by the electrolytic method were erected in Norway, where electric power is relatively cheap. During the war these plants fell into enemy hands, and so became the object of several attacks from the air. The purpose of these attacks was to interfere with experimental work by German scientists on the development of atomic energy, in which heavy water could be used (§ 14.28).

8.110. Although, in principle, the electrolytic method involves continued decomposition of the water by the electric current until only a very small fraction of the original amount remains, this simple procedure would be very impractical. For one thing, the dissolved electrolyte, potassium hydroxide, for example, would become more and more concentrated as the electrolysis proceeded, and for another, the hydrogen gas liberated toward the end would contain so much deuterium that it could not be wasted. It is the practice, therefore, to carry out the electrolysis in stages. When the volume of water has been reduced to about one tenth, the residue is treated with carbon dioxide to neutralize the potassium hydroxide and then the enriched water is distilled off. The distillate goes on to the next stage of electrolysis where the same procedure is repeated. About five to seven stages are required to yield relatively pure heavy water. The hydrogen gas evolved in the later stages, and which contains a high proportion of deuterium, is burnt in oxygen to form water; this is condensed and returned to the electrolytic cells.

8.111. During electrolysis hydrogen gas is given off at the negative electrode (cathode), and oxygen gas at the positive electrode (anode). Just as there is a preferential evolution of the lighter isotope at the cathode, there should be a somewhat similar behavior at the anode leading to an enrichment of oxygen-18 in the residue. The separation factor is, however, little different from unity, and although the enrichment effect has been confirmed experimentally, it is very small. Electrolysis of lithium salts, using a mercury cathode to collect the lithium metal, has also led to a partial separation of the isotopes of this element.

CHEMICAL EXCHANGE METHODS

8.112. All the methods described above for the separation of isotopes, with the possible exception of the electrolytic procedure, depend on differences in physical properties determined by the masses of the isotopic species. The discovery of the different reactivities of the isotopes of hydrogen, as described in § 8.75, encouraged Urey and his students, between 1935 and 1940, to investigate, both theoretically and experimentally, the isotopic exchange reactions of other elements with a view to their use in the separation of isotopes. These efforts met with remarkable success, and appreciable quantities of compounds enriched in carbon-13 and nitrogen-15, respectively, were made in the laboratories of Columbia University before the work was taken over by commercial organizations.*

8.113. The method used with nitrogen, for example, was to allow equilibrium to be established between the 14 and 15 isotopes of nitrogen in a system consisting of ammonia (NH_3) gas and ammonium (NH_4^+) ions. This was achieved by passing the gas up a column down which flowed a concentrated solution of ammonium nitrate. As a result of the isotopic exchange reaction, the heavy isotope (nitrogen-15) tends to concentrate in the ammonium ion in solution, while the ammonia gas contains relatively more of the unwanted lighter isotope. Part of the ammonium nitrate solution withdrawn at the bottom of the column is heated with sodium hydroxide, and this converts the ammonium ion into ammonia gas enriched in nitrogen-15. The resulting gas is then reprocessed with the remaining portion of the ammonium nitrate solution, thus obtaining further enrichment. Urey and his coworkers used a cascade system of three columns, operating on the countercurrent principle, the ammonium nitrate solution flowing downward and the ammonia gas upward. In this manner, they succeeded in increasing the abundance of the nitrogen-15 isotope to more than 70 per cent, as compared with the normal 0.38 per cent, in spite of the relatively low separation factor of 1.023.

8.114. Apart from its use as an isotopic tracer (Chapter XVII), interest has developed in nitrogen-15 because it captures neutrons to a negligible extent, whereas the probability of capture by the more abundant nitrogen-14 is considerable. In certain nuclear reactor applications (Chapter XV), it might be desirable to employ solutions of nitrates, e.g., of thorium, but this is not practical if the salt contains ordinary nitrogen. However, if this element were largely present as nitrogen-15, the situation would be very different. A chemical exchange method with certain operational advantages, based on ammonia gas and a solution of ammonium carbonate, appears to show much promise for the large-scale enrichment of nitrogen-15.

8.115. The chemical isotopic exchange procedure has also been used to concentrate carbon-13 from its normal proportion of 1.1 per cent to 22 per cent, by means of an isotopic exchange reaction between gaseous hydrogen cyanide (HCN) and the cyanide (CN^-) ion in sodium cyanide solution. In this case, however, the heavier carbon isotope concentrates in the gas phase, so that the desired product is withdrawn at the top of the column.† Some changes in the design of the apparatus are necessary but the principle is essentially the same as described for nitrogen.

---

* Isotopic exchange reactions probably account for the small variations in the isotopic compositions of some of the lighter elements, such as carbon and oxygen, in nature; thus, atmospheric oxygen contains 3 per cent more of the 18 isotope than does oxygen from Lake Michigan water, and 2.5 per cent more than that from ocean water.

† There is a simultaneous alteration in the proportion of the nitrogen isotopes, but this has been found to be very small.

8.116. As cyanides are poisonous, and consequently not too satisfactory for large-scale operation, an alternative process has been devised involving exchange of the carbon isotopes between carbon dioxide (CO_2) gas and the bicarbonate ($HCO_3{}^-$) ion, in ammonium bicarbonate solution. The attainment of equilibrium is accelerated by means of a catalyst, and excess of the carbon-13 isotope is then found to be present in the bicarbonate solution.

8.117. It was recorded in § 8.75 that in the isotopic exchange reaction between hydrogen gas and liquid water, the proportion of deuterium in the water is about three times as great as it is in the gas phase, when equilibrium is attained. In other words, the hydrogen-deuterium separation factor has the relatively high value of 3; consequently, appreciable enrichment of the heavy isotope should be possible by utilizing this reaction. One of the difficulties, however, is that the equilibrium is established slowly, and hence a catalyst is necessary in order to expedite the process.

8.118. The hydrogen-water exchange reaction has been employed for the production of heavy water on a large scale. The method used is to pass a mixture of hydrogen gas and steam upward through a tower containing the catalyst, while liquid water flows downward. In the presence of the catalyst, a rapid isotopic exchange reaction takes place between the hydrogen and the water molecules in the steam, with the result that the deuterium concentrates in the latter as deuterium oxide, that is, heavy water, molecules. The steam is condensed, and hence carried downward, by the flow of liquid water; the water emerging at the bottom of the tower is thus considerably enriched in the heavier isotopic form. Using a number of

towers in cascade, in a manner similar to that already outlined above, a product containing a large proportion of heavy water can be obtained.

8.119. With the development of nuclear reactors in which heavy water is an important component (Chapter XV), considerable effort has been devoted to the production of this material at a reasonable cost. One of the most successful methods utilizes the isotopic exchange reaction between liquid water and hydrogen sulfide gas. The equilibrium, which is established rapidly without the use of a catalyst, may be represented by

$$H_2O(l) + D_2S(g) \rightleftharpoons D_2O(l) + H_2S(g),$$

with the deuterium tending to concentrate in the liquid (water) phase. The *dual-temperature* process is based on the fact that at lower temperatures (about 25°C) the liquid contains relatively more deuterium than at higher temperatures (100°C).

8.120. In principle, water is first enriched in deuterium by interaction in a tower at the lower temperature with hydrogen sulfide with its normal content of deuterium. Part of the enriched water is removed as the product, and the remainder is sent to a hot tower where much of its deuterium is transferred back to the depleted hydrogen sulfide from the first tower. The hydrogen sulfide thus acts as a sort of carrier for deuterium, giving it up to the water at the lower temperature and regaining it at the higher temperature. The over-all result is that the water has been divided into two parts: one enriched in deuterium (heavy water) and the other impoverished in this isotope, whereas the hydrogen sulfide gas is restored (approximately) to its original composition. The depleted (or stripped) water may be discarded and the enriched water put through the process again, in a cascade system, to enrich it still further in deuterium.

8.121. Other instances of isotopic enrichment by methods which utilize differences of reaction rates have been reported. But, it may be noted, that it is only for the lighter elements that the procedure holds any promise at the present time. As the atomic weight increases, the difference in the rates at which the isotopic species undergo exchange reactions becomes very small, and the separation factor is then very close to unity. So far, sulfur-34 is the heaviest nuclide which has been concentrated by the isotopic exchange method, although there is little doubt that if it became necessary enrichment of even heavier isotopes could be achieved.

The Acceleration of Charged Particles

Chapter IX

NUCLEAR TRANSFORMATIONS

THE TRANSMUTATION OF ELEMENTS

9.1. It was mentioned in Chapter I that the Aristotelian theory, which regarded all matter as consisting of the same primordial substance associated with varying amounts of four qualities or principles, was probably responsible for the prolonged, but vain, efforts of the ancient alchemists to change base metals into gold. With the growth of the concepts of the individuality of the elements and of the indestructibility of the atom, particularly during the nineteenth century, it was natural that attempts to bring about the transmutation of metals should fall into disrepute. Only those completely ignorant of science, and sufficiently gullible to be attracted by the possibility of the easy acquisition of riches, fell victim to the wiles of charlatans claiming the ability to convert base metals into gold.

9.2. With the development of modern ideas concerning the structure of the atom, and the realization that all matter was made up of the same fundamental units, the possibility of transmutation, previously regarded as fantastic, was given serious consideration. In fact several reports—some of them from scientists of considerable repute—of success in changing or disintegrating various elements were published in the scientific journals, both in Europe and in America. With the exception of the results to be described shortly, all were subsequently proved to be unfounded, but one is worthy of special mention because of its apparently convincing nature. It was claimed that the passage of a high-tension electrical discharge through mercury vapor, atomic number 80, produced small amounts of gold, atomic number 79. The original mercury was apparently completely free of gold, yet the use of an extremely sensitive microscopic test showed the presence of traces of the precious metal, following the electrical treatment. After considerable controversy among the proponents and opponents of this plausible claim, it was ultimately proved that the gold was not being created but merely concentrated from the various materials used. Much of it, in fact, came from the gold-framed eyeglasses of one of the observers!

9.3. It was Rutherford, whose name has been frequently mentioned in these pages, who achieved the first deliberate, artificial transmutation of one atom into another. Although he did not convert a base metal into gold, his discovery was just as important to nuclear science.

TRANSMUTATION OF NITROGEN BY ALPHA PARTICLES

9.4. While working in Rutherford's laboratory, in Manchester, England, on the scattering of alpha particles, as described in § 4.7 *et seq.*, E. Marsden noted, in 1914, that when the radiations from radium C′ passed through hydrogen gas, they produced a number of high-speed, long-range particles, apparently protons. Some three years later Rutherford began a reinvestigation of Marsden's work, in the course of which he studied the effect of alpha particles on several gases, in addition to hydrogen. The apparatus used was very simple (Fig. 9.1); it consisted of a

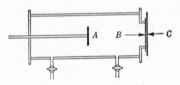

FIG. 9.1. Diagram of apparatus used by Rutherford to detect transmutation of nitrogen nuclei by alpha particles.

metal cylinder in which was supported the radioactive source *A* of alpha particles. A small hole at one end was closed with a thin metal disk *B* capable of stopping most of these particles, and one or two millimeters away was a zinc sulfide screen *C*. Any long-range particles formed by the action of the alpha particles on the gas in the cylinder were able to pass through the disk *B* and produce scintillations on the zinc sulfide (§ 6.43). Different gases could be admitted to the cylinder, and the effect of the alpha particles observed.

9.5. Reporting in 1919 on the results of his experiments, Rutherford wrote: "On introducing oxygen or carbon dioxide into the vessel, the number of scintillations fell off in amount corresponding with the stopping power of the column of gas. An unexpected effect was, however, noticed on introducing dried air. . . . Instead of diminishing, the number of [long-range] scintillations increased. . . . It was clear from these results that the alpha particles in their passage through air gave rise to long-range scintillations which appeared of about the same brightness as H-scintillations [i.e., the long-range scintillations produced by alpha particles in hydrogen]."

9.6. Careful investigation showed that neither oxygen, carbon dioxide nor moisture was responsible for the behavior observed with air, but the effects could be closely duplicated with nitrogen gas in the cylinder. Consequently, the interaction of alpha particles with nitrogen atoms or molecules results in the ejection of long-range, that is, highly energetic, particles similar to those obtained with hydrogen. "It is difficult to avoid the conclusion," said Rutherford, "that these long-range atoms arising from the collision of alpha particles with nitrogen are not nitrogen atoms but probably charged atoms of hydrogen. . . . If this be the case, we must conclude that the nitrogen atom is disintegrated under the intense forces developed in a close collision with a swift alpha particle."

9.7. Further work proved Rutherford's conclusions to be correct, and thus he achieved the first controlled artificial disintegration of an atomic nucleus. The extent of the disintegration was, however, extremely small, for it was estimated that only one alpha particle in about 300,000 expelled a long-range particle from a nitrogen atom. It is of interest to record that, in his successful realization of nuclear transmutation, Rutherford was able to confirm a possibility which he had considered in his William Ellery Hale lectures, delivered in Washington, D. C., in April 1914. "It is possible," he said, "that the nucleus of an atom may be altered by direct collision of the nucleus with very swift electrons or atoms of helium [i.e., alpha particles] such as are ejected from radioactive matter. . . . Under favor-

in a magnetic field, Rutherford and Chadwick proved that they were indeed positively charged hydrogen atoms, or protons, of high energy. All the elements from boron to potassium, with the exception of carbon, oxygen and, possibly, beryllium, were found to emit protons when subjected to the action of alpha particles. The energy of the protons, as determined from their range, was shown to be higher in some cases than that of the impinging alpha particle, thus indicating that

Fig. 9.2.   Blackett's photograph of alpha-particle cloud tracks in nitrogen. (From "Radiations from Radioactive Substances" by Rutherford, Chadwick and Ellis, The Macmillan Company, New York.)

able conditions, these particles must pass very close to the nucleus and may either lead to a disruption of the nucleus or to a combination with it."

MECHANISM OF THE NUCLEAR PROCESS

9.8. Following upon Rutherford's pioneer experiments, he and Chadwick, using an improved form of apparatus, made a more detailed study of the action of alpha particles on various elements. By observing the deflection of the resulting long-range particles

they resulted from a disintegration process, the additional energy being acquired in the accompanying nuclear rearrangement.

9.9. At the time this work was being done, between the years 1920 and 1924, the nature of the nuclear process which led to the emission of protons was uncertain. Two possibilities were considered: first, that the nucleus of the disintegrated atom merely loses a proton as a result of the severe impact accompanying collision with a fast-moving alpha particle; and, second, that the alpha particle enters the nucleus of the atom which it strikes, the resulting combined nucleus then ejecting a proton. The problem would have been solved if the nucleus remaining after emission of the proton could be identified, but there seemed no way in which this could be done, particularly in view of the very small number of atoms actually undergoing disintegration.

9.10. However, in 1925, P. M. S. Blackett, in England, and in the following year, W. D. Harkins, in the United States, independently obtained evidence which permitted of a decision between the two possible mechanisms indicated above. From photographs of the tracks produced by alpha particles passing through nitrogen in a Wilson cloud chamber (§ 6.68), it could be concluded that the alpha particle disappeared in the disintegrating collision, and so the second of the alternatives was probably the correct one. Blackett took over 20,000 photographs, depicting a total of more than 400,000 alpha-particle tracks; of these, eight were of the forked type, of which an example is shown in Fig. 9.2, taken by two cameras at right angles to one another. Each of these forked tracks undoubtedly represents a collision between an alpha particle and a nitrogen nucleus leading to disintegration. The long, thin track is that of the proton which is ejected, whereas the short, heavy track is due to the remaining (recoil) nucleus. This appears, from the cloud-track photograph, to have undergone a collision which changed its direction. It should be mentioned that since the nitrogen atom, before being struck by an alpha particle, is neutral and has no ionizing power, its path cannot be observed in the cloud-chamber photograph. The product, on the other hand, carries an electric charge, due to the loss of electrons in the collision; consequently it has the ability to produce ions in its path, and so forms a definite cloud track.

9.11. If the disintegration process had been the result merely of a disruption leading to the expulsion of a proton from the nitrogen nucleus, there should have been a total of four tracks, rather than the three actually observed. In addition to the tracks of the proton and of the recoil nucleus, the path of the alpha particle should have been apparent before and after the collision. Since the photographs do not show more than three tracks meeting at a point, it may be concluded that the alpha particle has entered the nucleus of the nitrogen atom with the formation of an unstable system, referred to as a *compound nucleus*, which immediately expels a proton.

NUCLEAR REARRANGEMENT

9.12. Assuming the foregoing mechanism to be correct, it is a simple matter to determine the nature of the recoil nucleus remaining after the proton has been emitted. The argument is based on the reasonable postulate that in the nuclear reaction there is no change in the total numbers of neutrons and protons, although the nucleons will be arranged differently before and after the collision. The sum of the neutrons and protons is equal to the mass number, and the number of protons is equal to the atomic number (§§ 4.36, 8.60 footnote). Both these numbers must, therefore, balance on the two sides of the equation representing the nuclear rearrangement. Thus, the interaction between an alpha particle and a nitrogen nucleus may be written as follows:

	Nitrogen Nucleus +	Alpha Particle →	Compound Nucleus →	Proton +	Recoil Nucleus
Mass number	14	4	(18)	1	17
Atomic number	7	2	(9)	1	8

9.13. It is seen that the residual nucleus must have a mass of 17 units and an atomic number 8; this is the atomic number of oxygen, and so it follows that the product is an isotope of oxygen with a mass of 17 on the atomic weight scale. Indicating the various nuclei by the symbols of the corresponding elements, and inserting the mass number as a superscript and the atomic number as a subscript in each case, the disintegration or, more correctly, the nuclear transformation or rearrangement, may be conveniently represented by the equation

$$_7N^{14} + {}_2He^4 \rightarrow {}_1H^1 + {}_8O^{17},$$

the mass numbers and the atomic numbers, respectively, adding up to the same amounts on the two sides of the equation.*

9.14. Processes of this and related types are frequently referred to as atomic (or nuclear) disintegration or, more colloquially, as "atom smashing." But it is in a few cases only that the nucleus is actually disintegrated, or smashed, in the sense of being broken up into small fragments. As a general rule, nuclear reactions involve a simple rearrangement of the protons and neutrons among the nuclei concerned. It is preferable, therefore, to speak of them either as nuclear rearrangements or as nuclear transformations or transmutations. They may be qualified as "artificial," to distinguish them from radioactive changes which are spontaneous nuclear transmutations.

9.15. Incidentally, it may be pointed out that, apart from the energy changes involved, a nuclear reaction and an ordinary chemical reaction are similar in principle. In the latter, the process is accompanied by a rearrangement of the atoms, whereas in the former the nucleons, i.e., the protons and neutrons, are rearranged. The change in the grouping of the nucleons associated with the interaction of the nitrogen nucleus and an alpha particle may be represented as follows:

	N	+ He	→ H	+ O
Protons	7	2	1	8
Neutrons	7	2	0	9

and it might even be written as:

$$p_7n_7 + p_2n_2 \rightarrow p + p_8n_9,$$

where p and n represent a proton and a neutron, respectively.

9.16. Although it is convenient to record for each participating nucleus both the symbol and the atomic number, this is really unnecessary since one includes the other; thus, the symbol N (for nitrogen) can refer only to the element of atomic number 7, and vice versa. On the other hand, the mass number must always be noted, for otherwise it would not be known which particular isotopic form is involved. Utilizing these facts, a very simple scheme, now widely used, was devised in 1935 by W. Bothe in Germany for describing nuclear processes. The reaction under consideration, for example, can be formulated as $N^{14}(\alpha,p)O^{17}$, which would be interpreted as follows:

* It will be noted that the alpha particle has been represented in the equation as a helium nucleus, with which it is, of course, identical.

a nitrogen (N^{14}) nucleus interacts with, and engulfs, an alpha (α) particle, a proton (p) is ejected and a nucleus of an oxygen (O^{17}) isotope remains. The general group of nuclear reactions studied by Rutherford and Chadwick can then be referred to as being of the (α,p) type; in these processes, the alpha particle is the incident particle, while a proton is expelled.

BOMBARDMENT OF ATOMIC NUCLEI BY CHARGED PARTICLES

9.17. By 1924, Rutherford and Chadwick had established that nearly all the lighter elements up to and including potassium emitted protons when subjected to the action of alpha particles. But with heavier atoms there was only scattering of these particles (§ 4.7) indicating that they did not have sufficient energy to penetrate the atomic nucleus. In reviewing the progress made during the years 1925 and 1926, on "the disintegration of nuclei by the impact of alpha rays," F. W. Aston (see § 8.36) wrote: "There has now come the inevitable period of quiescence awaiting the development of new weapons." Actually, some six years were to elapse before new methods of attacking the atom became available, with consequences that could certainly not have been foreseen.

9.18. It was shown in § 4.16 that, at any distance d, the energy of repulsion of an alpha particle, carrying two unit positive charges, by an atomic nucleus, with Z such charges—Z being equal to the atomic number—is $2Ze^2/d$, where e is the unit (electronic) charge. It is evident that the energy with which an alpha particle is repelled from a nucleus increases with the atomic number. Consequently, particles which might be sufficiently energetic to approach the nucleus of a light element would be turned back by a heavier nucleus, with higher atomic number. It was thus apparent to Rutherford, and others, in the late 1920s, that progress in the study of nuclear disintegration required the construction of devices which would provide particles with greater energy than the alpha particles obtainable from natural radioactive sources.

9.19. According to classical electrostatic theory the energy which an alpha particle would require in order to reach the nucleus of an atom, that is to say, to be able to surmount the so-called potential barrier (§ 7.28), for elements of higher atomic number, would be from 20 to 30 Mev. In 1930, such high energies, although now fairly commonplace, were quite out of reach. It was fortunate therefore that, at about the same time, the application of wave mechanics to the problem of nuclear penetration, as explained in Chapter VII, showed that particles could both leave and enter the atomic nucleus even though their energy was considerably less than that of the top of the hypothetical barrier.

9.20. The first experiments on nuclear transmutation were naturally carried out with swift alpha particles because of their availability, but the wave-mechanical calculations made by G. Gamow in 1928 suggested that other charged particles might be more effective. He showed that not only was the energy barrier lower, but the probability of penetrating it and reaching an atomic nucleus also increased, as the charge and mass of the incident particle decreased. Thus, for a given value of the particle energy, a proton, with unit charge and unit mass, was much more likely to enter the nucleus than an alpha particle, carrying two charges and having a mass of four units. In fact, it appeared that in order to attain a particular probability of reaching a given atomic nucleus, an alpha particle would need to have something like sixteen times the energy of a proton. A small number of fast-moving protons are, of course, ejected in the (α,p) type of process discovered by Rutherford, but the number is so insignificant as to be useless for practical purposes. Consequently, interest was aroused in many scientific laboratories in the possibility of developing methods for building up high potentials, of the order of hundreds of thousands, or even millions, of volts, whereby protons, i.e., charged hydrogen atoms, could be given sufficient energy to penetrate atomic nuclei.

DISINTEGRATION OF LITHIUM BY PROTONS

9.21. The more important of the devices by means of which high-energy particles can be obtained will be described below. In the meantime it may be stated that the first successful production of protons with sufficient energy to cause nuclear transformation was achieved in Rutherford's laboratory in Cambridge, England, by J. D. Cockcroft and E. T. S. Walton in 1932. Their work stands out in the history of nuclear science as being the first case of nuclear disintegration brought about by purely artificial means. Rutherford had used swift alpha particles from natural sources, but in the experiments of Cockcroft and Walton protons, obtained by the ionization of hydrogen in a discharge tube, were accelerated by means of high voltages. When the light element lithium, in the form of a layer of lithium oxide, was bombarded by fast-moving protons, bright scintillations, due to particles ejected from the lithium, were immediately observed on a zinc sulfide screen placed a short distance away. The scintillations were first detected when the accelerating potential was about 125,000 volts, the number increasing with increasing voltage. At 250,000 volts there was one scintillation for about a billion protons, and at double this voltage the number was increased ten-fold.

9.22. Subsequently, Cockcroft and Walton made observations of the tracks of the ejected particles in a cloud chamber, and they reported that "the brightness of the scintillations and the density of the tracks suggest that the particles are normal alpha particles. . . . It [therefore] seems not unlikely that the lithium isotope of mass 7 occasionally captures a proton and the resulting nucleus of mass 8 breaks into two alpha particles of mass 4." The nuclear reaction thus achieved may be written as

$$_3\text{Li}^7 + {}_1\text{H}^1 \rightarrow {}_2\text{He}^4 + {}_2\text{He}^4,$$

the proton being indicated by the symbol $_1\text{H}^1$ and the alpha particle by $_2\text{He}^4$. Utilizing the abbreviated method of formulation described above, the process would be represented as $\text{Li}^7(p,\alpha)$ He^4, although there is actually no difference between the alpha particle, represented by α, and the helium nucleus, indicated by He^4. It is particularly significant that, in agreement with the calculations of wave mechanics, the process occurred to a detectable extent with protons of about 125,000 ev, i.e., 0.125 Mev, a value considerably less than the height of the potential barrier between a lithium nucleus and a proton.

9.23. Support for the postulated disintegration was obtained from several different directions. Cloud-chamber photographs, made by P. I. Dee and E. T. S. Walton in England and by F. Kirchner in Germany in 1933, showed two tracks of equal length, evidently due to alpha particles, emerging in opposite directions from a lithium target bombarded by the high-energy protons. If the nuclear process resulted in the formation of two alpha particles, as postulated above, then they would, in fact, be expelled in opposite directions in order to comply with the requirement of conservation of momentum.

9.24. Proof of the supposition that it is the more abundant lithium isotope, mass number 7, that is involved in the production of alpha particles was provided in 1934 by Rutherford's students M. L. E. Oliphant, E. S. Shire and B. M. Crowther. Fairly pure specimens, a few millionths of a gram in weight, of the Li^6 and Li^7 isotopes of lithium were collected on small targets, using the electromagnetic separation procedure (§ 8.90), and bombarded with accelerated protons. The results showed definitely that the Li^7 isotope gave two alpha particles; the Li^6 isotope also exhibited a nuclear reaction, but it was of a different type, as might be expected.

NUCLEAR REACTION ENERGIES

9.25. Nuclear reactions, involving a rearrangement of the nucleons, resemble ordinary chemical reactions, in which there is a redistribution of whole atoms, in the respect that they are accompanied by energy changes. The nuclear energy changes are, however, usually very much larger; they are of the order of millions of electron volts, as compared with one or two electron volts for most chemical reactions. The over-all energy liberated or taken up in a nuclear process is called the *nuclear reaction energy*, and is generally represented by the symbol Q; for this reason the energy change is sometimes referred to, in brief, as the "Q" of the nuclear reaction. The value of Q may be positive or negative de-

pending on the nature of the process.

9.26. According to the Einstein theory of the equivalence of mass and energy, the nuclear reaction energy must be exactly balanced by the changes in mass associated with the reaction. Thus, if Q is positive, that is to say, if the process is accompanied by the liberation of energy, there must be a decrease of mass; the total mass of the products will then be less than that of the interacting nuclei by an amount equivalent to this energy. On the other hand, a negative value of Q means that energy is taken up and there is a gain of mass in the nuclear reaction; such a result implies that the total mass of the products exceeds that of the original particles.

9.27. In the course of their work, Cockcroft and Walton made a comparison between the changes of mass accompanying the interaction of lithium-7 and a proton to form two alpha particles, and the energy liberated in the nuclear reaction, assuming the applicability of the Einstein mass-energy relationship (§ 3.72) to such reactions. They showed that the agreement was consistent with their interpretation of the mechanism of the process, as given above. But there was no clear evidence, at the time, of the validity of the Einstein equation, and consequently, in 1933, K. T. Bainbridge, in the United States, used the energy data, together with the known isotopic weights of lithium, hydrogen and helium, to provide a quantitative verification of the mass-energy relationship.

9.28. In the reaction between protons and the lithium isotope of mass number 7, the nuclear energy liberated can be determined by measuring the range, and hence estimating the energy, of the alpha particles produced. Cockcroft and Walton found this range to be approximately 8 cm. in air, so that each alpha particle carried off about 8.5 Mev, making a total of nearly 17 Mev for the nuclear reaction energy. Later, more precise measurements of the alpha particle ranges showed that Q for the reaction was 17.2 Mev, after allowing for the energy of the incident proton; the energy of the bombarded lithium nucleus, which is a fraction of an electron volt, is quite negligible in comparison with the other quantities involved.

9.29. The mass equivalent of 17.2 Mev can be readily derived by means of the Einstein equation in the form of equation (3.17) which here becomes

$$17.2 \text{ Mev} = m \text{ (a.m.u.)} \times 931,$$

so that the mass equivalent in atomic mass units, is found to be 0.0185. Since there is a liberation of energy, that is to say, Q is positive, it may be concluded that in the nuclear reaction

$$\text{Li}^7 + \text{H}^1 \rightarrow \text{He}^4 + \text{He}^4$$

the sum of the masses of the products will be less than that of the interacting nuclei by 0.0185 atomic mass unit.

9.30. In an equation of this kind it is the masses of the respective nuclei which are implied, but the same final result is obtained by using the atomic or isotopic weights which include the masses of the electrons. The number of electrons is the same on both sides of the equation, and so when computing the loss or gain of mass in a nuclear reaction, the masses of the electrons, if they are included, will cancel.* The isotopic weights of Li⁷, H¹ and He⁴ are now known with considerable accuracy from mass-spectrographic determinations, so that the

change of mass may be computed as follows:

Interacting Particles		Product Particles	
Li⁷	7.0182	He⁴	4.0039
H¹	1.0081	He⁴	4.0039
	8.0263		8.0078

Difference
$$= 8.0078 - 8.0263 = -0.0185.$$

9.31. The nuclear reaction under discussion is therefore accompanied by a loss of 0.0185 unit of mass, on the atomic weight scale, and this is seen to be exactly equal to the mass equivalent of the energy liberated, as estimated from the energy of the alpha particles.

9.32. The identity of the figures in this case is partly fortuitous, but the fact that they are in agreement is a strong argument, as Bainbridge showed, for the applicability of the Einstein mass-energy relationship to nuclear reactions. This particular case is of special interest, not only because it was the first nuclear process brought about by artificially accelerated particles, but also because it provided one of the earliest, if not the earliest, verifications of the Einstein equation. Since 1932 numerous nuclear transformations have been studied in detail, and in every case for which sufficient data are available, the value of the nuclear reaction energy, as calculated from the measured energies of the incident and product particles, is exactly equivalent, within the limits of the experimental errors, to the change of mass accompanying the process. There can thus be no question as to the validity of the Einstein equation in these cases or of the reality of nuclear transformations.

* Processes in which positrons (positive electrons) are liberated are exceptional in this respect; each positron removes an electron.

DETERMINATION OF ISOTOPIC WEIGHTS

9.33. An interesting consequence of the study of the mass and energy changes involved in nuclear processes was the suggestion, made independently in 1935 by H. A. Bethe and by M. L. E. Oliphant, A. R. Kempton and E. Rutherford, that the mass-spectrographic isotopic weights of the lighter elements in use at that time required correction. These investigators found that, in certain nuclear reactions, the energy change differed from the equivalent of the mass change by amounts exceeding the probable experimental errors. It was felt that the source of the discrepancies was not in the mass spectrograph itself, but rather in the accepted isotopic weight of helium, mass number 4, which was used as a comparison standard for the lighter elements. The isotopic weights were consequently recalculated on the basis of an empirical correction in the helium value, and the results so obtained gave excellent agreement with the mass-energy principle. A more careful comparison by F. W. Aston of the isotopic weight of helium with that of oxygen, made in 1936, completely substantiated this correction, and thus provided striking evidence for the equivalence of mass and energy, at least in the nuclear processes.

9.34. It is of interest in this connection to mention that the isotopic weights of certain nuclides which are either too unstable or too rare to be measured by mass-spectrographic methods are actually determined from nuclear reaction energies. A case in point is that of the oxygen isotope O^{17} which, as mentioned in § 9.13, results from the interaction of an alpha particle with a nitrogen nucleus; this reaction, including the energy Q, may be written as

$$N^{14} + He^4 \rightarrow H^1 + O^{17} + Q.^*$$

From the known energy of the alpha particle and the measured range of the proton, the nuclear reaction energy Q is found to be -1.16 Mev; the mass equivalent on the atomic weight scale, obtained upon dividing by 931, as seen above, is then -0.00124.

9.35. It will be noted that since Q has a negative value in this case, the total mass of the products will be greater than that of the interacting particles. The isotopic weights of N^{14} and He^4 are 14.00752 and 4.00387, respectively, making a total of 18.01139, on the left-hand side of the equation. On the right-hand side there is 1.00814 for H^1 and -0.00124 for the mass equivalent of Q, i.e., 1.00690 in addition to the isotopic weight of O^{17}; the latter is consequently given by

$$O^{17} = 18.01139 - 1.00690 = 17.0045,$$

rounded off to six significant figures.

PARTICLE ACCELERATORS

THE VOLTAGE MULTIPLIER

9.36. Although it was not the first device for producing charged particles of high energy, the voltage multiplier system employed by Cockcroft and Walton (§ 9.21) is important historically because it was the first with which artificial nuclear transformation was

---

* It is the usual practice to write these equations in the algebraic form with $+Q$, although the actual value of Q may be positive or negative. Since in the case under consideration Q is -1.16 Mev, the equation becomes

$$N^{14} + He^4 \rightarrow H^1 + O^{17} - 1.16 \text{ Mev.}$$

achieved.* The principle had previously been used for accelerating electrons, and in 1929 it was adapted by Cockcroft and Walton for use with protons which were thus obtained with energies up to 380,000 ev. However, it was not until two years later that the disintegration of the lithium nucleus by protons with less than half this energy was definitely recognized.

9.37. The procedure may be illustrated by reference to Fig. 9.3. A

is open (Fig. 9.3, I); in the next half cycle, the alternations are reversed and S_1 is open while S_2 is closed (Fig. 9.3, II), and so on in successive half cycles. When S_1 is closed, the condenser C_1 is charged up to the potential V_1 (Fig. 9.3, I), which is virtually that supplied by the transformer T. Upon opening S_1 and closing S_2, part of the charge on C_1 is transferred to C_2, but in the next half cycle, C_1 receives more charge which it again shares with C_2

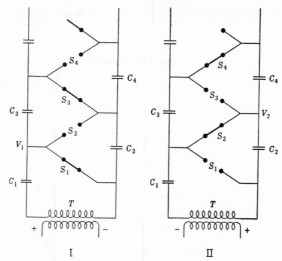

Fig. 9.3. Principle of the voltage multiplier used by Cockcroft and Walton.

number of condensers C_1, C_2, C_3, C_4, etc., of equal capacity, are arranged as shown, together with switching mechanisms S_1, S_2, etc.; the transformer T is the source of a high-voltage alternating potential. The switches S_1, S_2, etc., are actually vacuum tubes, and operate in such a manner that when the alternations in T are in one direction, the switch S_1 is closed while S_2

in the following half cycle. Eventually, both C_1 and C_2 are charged up to the potential V_1, so that V_2 (Fig. 9.3, II) is twice V_1. The arrangement of two condensers C_1 and C_2, and two vacuum tubes S_1 and S_2, acting as switches, is thus a *voltage doubler*, and several such doublers in cascade constitute a *voltage multiplier*.† In one stage the voltage is doubled, in two stages it is

---

* The voltage multiplier (or cascade rectifier) was apparently originated by H. Greinacher in Switzerland, in 1920.

† Strictly speaking, what has been called here, for simplicity, the switching action of the vacuum tubes S_1, S_2, etc., is really their ability to act as valves, which permit current to pass in one direction only. They thus act as rectifiers of the alternating potential supplied by the transformer. Consequently, the voltage multiplier is sometimes referred to as a *cascade rectifier*.

quadrupled, in three stages it is increased six-fold, and so on.

9.38. Starting with a potential of about 100,000 volts across the secondary coil of the transformer T, Cockcroft and Walton were able to obtain an output of nearly 800,000 volts. This high potential was then used to accelerate protons obtained by passing an electric discharge through hydrogen gas. In later forms of the apparatus, based on the voltage multiplication principle, particle energies up to 3 Mev have been obtained. The Cockcroft-Walton device has the advantage of simplicity, with no moving parts. The maximum energies obtainable are low compared with those from other accelerators, described below, but it provides fairly large ion currents at constant voltage, and hence it is very useful for experimental work requiring moderate potentials. The voltage multiplier can be used to accelerate other charged particles, such as alpha particles (helium nuclei), deuterons (deuterium nuclei), and others, produced by ionization of the corresponding gas.

THE ELECTROSTATIC GENERATOR

9.39. The essential principle of the high-voltage electrostatic generator, developed by R. J. Van de Graaff in the United States, is similar to that employed in various forms of apparatus, such as the Wimshurst machine, which have been used in laboratories for many years to obtain discharges of static electricity. The instrument makes use of two facts long familiar to physicists. The first is that a conducting sphere, or other hollow body, is able to accept any available charge, irrespective of its own voltage. It is thus possible to build up the potential by continuously supplying electric

charge to the sphere. The second fact is that discharge of electricity occurs readily at pointed objects.

9.40. The apparatus consists of a belt A, made of paper, silk, rayon or other flexible, nonconducting material, which is run, by means of a motor, at high speed over two pulleys, as indicated in Fig. 9.4. A direct current po-

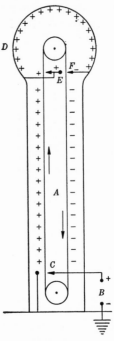

FIG. 9.4. Diagrammatic representation of the Van de Graaff electrostatic generator.

tential of from 5000 to 20,000 volts is applied at B, the positive pole being connected to a pointed comb-like conductor, and the negative to a rounded body, one on each side of the moving belt, as shown at C. As the moving belt passes by C, it picks up positive electricity* from the points, and conveys it upward toward the large metal sphere D, sometimes called the *corona*

* Actually negatively charged electrons pass from the belt to the points, thus leaving the belt with a positive charge.

cap, mounted on insulating supports. At *E* a set of points connected to the sphere draw off the charge from the belt and transfer it to the sphere, thus building up an electrical potential on the latter.

9.41. In the later forms of the Van de Graaff electrostatic generator, a pointed conductor *F*, also connected to the sphere, is placed opposite the rounded end of *E*. A discharge of negative electricity thus takes place from *F*, so that electrons are collected by and carried downward by the belt; these are eventually removed at *C* and pass to the source *B*. This additional device does not appreciably affect the maximum potential attainable, but it does increase the magnitude of the charged-particle current which the apparatus can supply.

9.42. As the generator operates, the voltage of the corona cap, with respect to the earth, steadily increases until it reaches a point where the electric charge leaks away as fast as it is collected from the moving belt. The leakage can be minimized, and the maximum attainable voltage thereby increased, by enclosing the apparatus in a gas-tight steel chamber and operating under pressures up to about 15 atmospheres. The gas in the chamber may be air or nitrogen alone or, better, methane, difluorodichloromethane ("Freon") or sulfur hexafluoride mixed with air or nitrogen.

9.43. In the first electrostatic generator constructed by Van de Graaff in 1931, the maximum potential attained was 1.5 million volts. In later forms this was increased in stages up to a considerably higher value. Electrostatic generators capable of reaching potentials of 12 million volts have been constructed, but operation beyond about 8 million volts is difficult. By changing the voltage supplied at *B*

(Fig. 9.4), the potential can be varied continuously over a considerable range. Although the maximum potentials attainable by means of the Van de Graaff accelerator are quite small compared with those from other machines described below, the former has some important advantages. It can provide a powerful beam of electrically charged particles, either electrons, protons or other positively charged ions, at voltages which can often be maintained constant within about 0.1 per cent.

9.44. In both the voltage multiplier and electrostatic generator methods of producing high potentials means must be devised for the application of these potentials to the particular ions, or electrons, being employed. For this purpose special accelerating tubes have been designed; they are usually made up of sections of glass, porcelain or other insulating material joined end to end by vacuum-tight seals. The complete tube has to be long enough to eliminate the possibility of a spark or other discharge passing from one end to the other when the potential is applied. The high-potential region of the voltage multiplier or electrostatic generator is connected to a hollow, cylindrical electrode at one end of the tube, and a similar electrode at the other end is connected to earth. Ions are then sent through the accelerating tube from a suitable source at the high-potential end to the target at the other end, acquiring increasing energy as they travel the length of the tube.

THE LINEAR ACCELERATOR

9.45. An instrument, known as a *linear accelerator,* for producing positive ions of high energy, was constructed by D. H. Sloan and E. O. Lawrence in the United States in 1931, utilizing a principle previously employed by R. Wideröe in Germany in

1929.* Because of certain limitations of the apparatus, which will be indicated shortly, it was used only for the acceleration of heavy ions, but the energies attained were not high enough to cause interaction with other nuclei. However, in recent years there have been important developments of the same general idea for producing charged particles of high energy. It is worth while, therefore, to consider the linear accelerator, especially as it was the forerunner of an instrument, to be described in the next section, which has played a highly significant role in the progress of nuclear science.

source S move from left to right along the common axis of the cylinders. While passing through the first (or any other) cylinder, they receive no acceleration, since this has a uniform charge,† but in traversing the gap between the first and second cylinders the ions are in a region in which there is a difference of potential. If the first cylinder is positive and the second is negative, the positively charged particles will be accelerated in the gap. The ionic particles then enter the second cyinder and travel through it at a speed which is constant but higher than the initial value. The length of

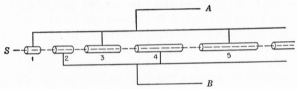

Fɪɢ. 9.5.   Linear accelerator for positively charged particles.

9.46. In essence, the *drift-tube type* of linear accelerator consists of a number of cylinders, of increasing length, arranged in a straight line, as represented in Fig. 9.5. Alternate cylinders are connected together, the first, third, fifth, etc., being joined to one terminal (A) and the second, fourth, sixth, etc., to another terminal (B) of a generator of high-frequency electrical oscillations. At any instant, therefore, alternate cylinders carry opposite electrical potentials; for example, in a particular half cycle of the oscillations, all the odd-numbered cylinders will be positive while those with even numbers will be negative. In the next half cycle the potentials will be reversed, so that the odd numbers become negative and the even numbers positive.

9.47. Suppose positive ions from the

this cylinder is such that just as the ions reach the gap between it and the third cylinder the potentials are reversed. The second cylinder is now positive while the third is negative, so that in passing through the gap the ions receive an additional impulse which accelerates them still further. By making the successive cylinders increasingly longer, to allow for the increasing speeds of the positive ions, it is possible for the ions to be kept exactly in phase with the alternations of potential. Thus, whenever the ions reach a gap between two cylinders, the one on the left has a positive potential whereas that on the right is negative; and so the ions acquire additional energy every time they pass from one cylinder to the next.

9.48. If V volts is the potential pro-

---

* The idea is said to have been first suggested by G. Ising in Sweden in 1924.
† It is for this reason that the cylinders are referred to as *drift tubes* or *shielding tubes*.

duced by the oscillator at the terminals *A* and *B*, the total energy in electron volts acquired by a singly-charged ion, such as a proton, will be approximately equal to *V* multiplied by the number of gaps traversed. In this way Sloan and Lawrence, using an apparatus with some thirty cylinders, were able to obtain mercury ions of 1.26 Mev energy, although the source of potential was only 42,000 volts. Subsequently, an energy of 2.85 Mev was obtained by raising the oscillator potential to 79,000 volts and using additional cylinders to increase the number of gaps.

9.49. Because the oscillation frequency of the high-frequency oscillators available in the early 1930s was not really high enough, it was necessary to work with relatively heavy, slow-moving ions, such as those of mercury. If the lighter ions, of hydrogen (protons) or helium (alpha particles), for example, had been used, the cylinders would have had to be made inconveniently long so as to allow sufficient time for the potential to be reversed while the fast-moving ions were passing through them. The advances made in the production of very high-frequency oscillations of considerable power for radar purposes suggested to the American physicist L. W. Alvarez the possibility of making a linear accelerator capable of yielding high-energy protons. In the apparatus constructed at Berkeley, California, in 1947, oscillations of about 200 million cycles per second frequency are employed in extremely short bursts, or pulses. The lengths of the cylindrical drift tubes vary from four to thirteen inches. Protons of about 4 Mev energy, obtained from a Van de Graaff electrostatic generator (§ 9.38), are introduced into the accelerator and their energy is steadily increased to 32 Mev

as they pass from one end to the other, a distance of about 40 feet.

9.50. When the plans for the new linear accelerator were being made in 1946, it was hoped to construct seven sections which would bring the energy of the protons up to nearly 300 Mev. However, contemporaneous theoretical developments showed that equally high (or higher) energies could be obtained with very much less power expenditure, and so no further work was done on the 300-Mev linear accelerator. This type of instrument has nevertheless found a number of applications in nuclear physics. One is to inject protons at moderately high energies, e.g., 10 Mev, into an instrument capable of accelerating these particles to much higher energies (§ 9.101). Another use, which is attracting interest, is for the production of large currents of positive ions, e.g., appreciable fractions of an ampere, many thousands of times greater than those attainable in other ways (§ 9.116).

9.51. A different kind of linear accelerator has been developed for the production of electrons of high energy. It is based on the principle that electrons can be made to travel with high-frequency radio waves and take up energy continuously from these waves. An accelerator of this type was constructed by D. W. Fry and his collaborators in England in 1946, and other designs were proposed by W. W. Hansen at Stanford University in 1947 and by J. C. Slater of the Massachusetts Institute of Technology about the same time. The Stanford traveling-wave accelerator is of particular interest. It consists of a 3-inch wide copper tube, divided into a number of sections by means of disks, with holes in the center, placed at intervals along the tube. This constitutes what is known as a traveling-wave guide.

Pulsed oscillations of extremely high frequency are introduced, and the wave length of a given phase is determined by the distance between the disks in the wave guide. Electrons entering the tube with the forward phase of the wave always remain in phase with the traveling wave and steadily increase in energy. In the first, 12-foot model of the linear electron accelerator, built in 1947, energies up to 6 Mev were reached, but a later (1957) form, for energies approaching 1000 Mev, the wave guide is 260 feet long, with high frequency (10-cm. wave length) power supplied from special klystron tubes* at 10-foot intervals. The electron beam is pulsed at the rate of sixty per second, each pulse having a duration of two millionths of a second.

9.52. Several linear accelerators, operating on a similar principle, for producing electrons of high energy, have been constructed in the United States and in England. Many of these devices make use of magnetrons, such as are employed in radar transmitters, as the source of high-frequency power. In Great Britain, in particular, linear electron accelerators of about 4-Mev energy have been developed commercially for the production of penetrating X-rays (bremsstrahlung).

THE CYCLOTRON

9.53. The method for producing positively charged particles of high energy which has attracted more world-wide interest than any other was a direct outcome of the earliest form of the linear accelerator. Instead of using shielding (or drift) cylinders of grad-

ually increasing length as the speed of the charged particles became greater, E. O. Lawrence, of the University of California, conceived the idea of using a magnetic field to make the particles move in a spiral of increasing radius, so that the length of the path automatically increased with the speed of the accelerated particle. The first report of the idea was made by E. O. Lawrence and N. E. Edlefson at the meeting of the National Academy of Sciences held in Berkeley, Calif., in September 1930, and the first experimental accelerator, using the new principle, was constructed by E. O. Lawrence and M. S. Livingston in 1931. The instrument, which has grown tremendously in size and power since that time, is now known as a *cyclotron*.† The original model produced protons with energy of 80,000 ev, but by increasing the size and power of the magnets, and introducing certain modifications to be described below, cyclotrons have been used to accelerate protons up to about 730,000,-000 ev (730 Mev).

9.54. In its most general form, the cyclotron consists of two flat, semicircular boxes, called *dees* because of their shape, which are indicated by D_1 and D_2 in Fig. 9.6, I. These are surrounded by a closed vessel, containing gas at low pressure, placed between the poles of a magnet as shown in the elevation in Fig. 9.6, II. A high-frequency, alternating potential, of several million cycles per second, is applied between the dees, which act as electrodes. At S an electrically heated filament produces a stream of electrons

---

* The klystron tube is an electronic (vacuum-tube) device for the generation of very high-frequency radio waves, i.e., radar waves (or microwaves) of short wave length.

† In 1935, E. O. Lawrence, E. McMillan and R. L. Thornton wrote: "Since we shall have many occasions in the future to refer to this apparatus, we feel it should have a name. The term 'magnetic resonance accelerator' is suggested . . . the word 'cyclotron,' of obvious derivation, has come to be used as a sort of laboratory slang." By 1936, however, the name cyclotron, because of its convenience, had come into general use.

which causes ionization of the gas, hydrogen, deuterium or helium, contained in the system; hence, S may be regarded as a source of positive ions, namely, protons, deuterons or alpha particles, respectively.

9.55. Suppose that at any particular instant the direction of the alternating potential is such that the electrode D_1 is positive and D_2 is negative. A positive ion starting from the source S will then be attracted to reaches the gap between the dees where it becomes subject to the action of the applied potential difference. If the oscillation frequency is such that in the time of passage through D_2 the sign of the potential is reversed, so that D_1 is negative and D_2 is positive, the positive ion will now be accelerated toward D_1. Since its energy is consequently greater than it was originally, the ion will move faster, that is, v will increase; hence, the circular path in

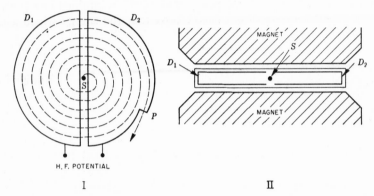

<table>
<tr><td>I</td><td>II</td></tr>
</table>

Fig. 9.6.   Simplified representation of cyclotron with two dees.

D_2, but as a uniform magnetic field acts in a direction at right angles (Fig. 9.6, II), the ion will move in a circular path. The radius of this path can be readily derived from equation (2.8) which, as stated earlier, applies to all types of charged particles in a magnetic field; the result is

$$r = \frac{mv}{He}, \qquad (9.1)$$

where m is the mass of the ion, e is its charge, v its velocity, and H is the strength of the magnetic field.

9.56. While it is in the interior of the dee, the speed of the ion remains constant, just as it does within the cylindrical drift tubes of the linear accelerator (§ 9.46). But after describing a semicircle through D_2, the ion D_1, under the influence of the magnetic field, will have a larger radius r, as can be seen from equation (9.1).

9.57. The striking and significant property of the cyclotron is that the time taken by the charged particle to traverse the semicircular path in the dee is independent of the velocity of the particle or of the radius of the path. That is to say, the increase in length of the path, due to the larger radius, is exactly compensated by the increase in the velocity of the particle. The length of the path is πr, where r is the radius, and π has its usual significance; since v is the velocity, the time T taken to traverse the semicircle is given by

$$T = \frac{\pi r}{v}.$$

Upon substituting the value of r from equation (9.1), it is seen that

$$T = \frac{\pi m v}{H e v} = \frac{\pi m}{H e}, \qquad (9.2)$$

which is independent of both v and r.

9.58. This means that if the oscillation frequency is adjusted to the nature of the given ion and to the strength of the magnetic field, the charged particle will always keep in phase with the changes of electric potential between the dees. Thus, each time the particle crosses the gap from D_1 to D_2 it will receive an additional impulse toward D_2; on the other hand, when it crosses from D_2 to D_1, it will be accelerated toward D_1, for the direction of the potential will then be reversed. The result of these repeated impulses is that the energy of the ion is steadily increased, and at the same time it describes a flat spiral of increasing radius. Eventually, the ion reaches the periphery of the dee and it can be brought out of the dee chamber by means of a deflecting plate at P (Fig. 9.6, I) which is charged to a high negative potential. The attractive force acting on the positive ion draws the latter out of its spiral path, so that it can be used to bombard any desired material.

9.59. Although the foregoing description has referred to a single ion, actually the source S supplies ions continuously, so that a stream of high-energy ions will emerge from the cyclotron. The value of the maximum energy may be calculated by making use of the fact that it is energy of motion, i.e., kinetic energy, and is consequently equal to $\frac{1}{2}mv^2$, where m is the mass of the particle and v is its maximum speed when it leaves the dee. According to equation (9.1), v is equal to Her/m, and if R is the radius of the dee, the maximum velocity, at the periphery, will be HeR/m. The kinetic energy E of the ion as it emerges from the cyclotron will then be

$$E = \frac{1}{2}m \left(\frac{HeR}{m} \right)^2 = \frac{H^2 R^2}{2} \cdot \frac{e^2}{m}. \qquad (9.3)$$

9.60. If the oscillation frequency of the potential is adjusted to the particular ion, the maximum energy attainable will be determined by the product $H^2 R^2$. If, for a given cyclotron, i.e., R is constant, the magnetic field strength H is also maintained constant, it follows that the energy which a charged particle will attain is proportional to the square of its charge, and inversely proportional to its mass. Protons, for which e and m are both unity in terms of electronic charges and atomic mass units, respectively, will thus acquire the same energy as alpha particles, with e equal to two and m to four units. Deuterons, on the other hand, for which e is unity and m is two, will attain only half this maximum energy.

9.61. The time for the ion to traverse any semicircular path is given by equation (9.2), and so the time to make a complete turn of the spiral is twice this quantity, that is, $2\pi m/He$. The frequency ω of the oscillations required to keep the ion in phase is the reciprocal of this time, so that

$$\omega = \frac{He}{2\pi m}, \qquad (9.4)$$

and upon combining this result with equation (9.3), the energy of the emerging ion is found to be

$$E = 2\pi^2 R^2 \omega^2 m. \qquad (9.5)$$

9.62. As a general rule it is more convenient to operate the cyclotron with the field strength H constant, as implied above, but an alternative possibility is to maintain constant the oscillation frequency ω of the voltage supply to the dees, and to adjust the magnetic field to satisfy equation (9.4) for different particles. It can be seen from equation (9.5) that, in contrast to the case in which the magnetic field is constant, the maximum energy will now be proportional to the mass m of the particle, and independent of its charge. Under the conditions of constant oscillator frequency, the energy attainable by an alpha particle will then be four times, and that of a deuteron twice, that of a proton.

9.63. Attention may be called to the fact that the voltage applied to the dees does not appear in either equation (9.3) or (9.5), so that the maximum energy which a given charged particle can acquire in a particular cyclotron is independent of this voltage. The reason is that when the voltage is small the ion makes a large number of turns before reaching the periphery, but when the voltage is high the number of turns is small. The product, which determines the total energy, is the same in each case, provided the magnetic field H and the maximum radius R of the path are unchanged.

9.64. No matter how the cyclotron is operated, it can be seen from equation (9.3) that the maximum energy acquired by a given particle is determined by H^2R^2, i.e., by the square of the product of the field strength and the radius, or diameter, of the dee. It is evident therefore that, in order to obtain ions of high energy, it is necessary to increase the strength and size of the magnet in the field of which the ions traverse their spiral path. The first cyclotron (Fig. 9.7) to yield high-energy charged particles usable for nuclear transformations, built by Lawrence and Livingston of the University

of California in 1931, had a magnet with pole faces 11 inches in diameter and this produced protons of 1.22 Mev energy. Subsequently, instruments with 27-inch, later extended to 37-inch, and 60-inch diameter pole faces* were constructed by Lawrence and his collaborators in Berkeley, Calif., and several cyclotrons were erected in the United States and elsewhere.

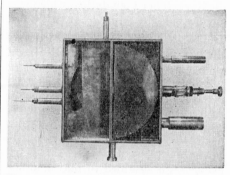

FIG. 9.7. The first cyclotron, about 11 inches diameter; the magnet is not shown.

9.65. Prior to 1946, the most energetic particles available were deuterons of about 20 Mev and alpha particles of 40 Mev energy obtained from the 60-inch Berkeley cyclotron, employing a magnet weighing about 200 tons. Although the cyclotron is capable of producing strong beams of high-energy ions, the voltage is neither as constant nor as uniform as it is for those from the other types of accelerators described above. The cyclotron is a powerful instrument for certain investigations requiring particles of very high energy, but where the exact value of this energy need not be precisely known. However, by passing the emergent beam through a magnetic field it is possible to sort out ions having definite energy values, if required.

* The diameter of the magnet pole faces is used to describe the size of the cyclotron. Thus a "60-inch cyclotron" would imply an instrument with pole faces 60 inches in diameter; the diameter of the dees is a few inches less.

THE SYNCHROCYCLOTRON

9.66. After the completion of the 60-inch cyclotron in 1939, Lawrence considered the possibility of designing an instrument of much greater power which would not only be able to bring about new types of nuclear rearrangements, but might be capable of actually creating particles. Encouraged by the gift of over a million dollars from the Rockefeller Foundation, which was augmented by funds from other sources, work on the construction of the new cyclotron was commenced in Berkeley, Calif., in August, 1940. It was to have a magnet containing 3700 tons of steel and 300 tons of copper, with pole faces 184 inches in diameter, and was to be capable of accelerating deuterons to 100 Mev and alpha particles to 200 Mev. However, this giant magnet was destined to play another role before it finally took its intended place in the world's largest cyclotron.

9.67. It will be recalled (§ 8.94) that in 1941 Lawrence had become interested in the separation of the isotopes of uranium by the electromagnetic method. After preliminary studies with the magnet of the 37-inch cyclotron had shown the procedure to be feasible, work on the 184-inch magnet, which had been set aside, was resumed and it was completed in May 1942. During the summer of the same year an apparatus employing the new magnet produced the first significant quantities of fairly pure uranium-235. It was the success achieved in this manner that led to the decision to erect a large-scale electromagnetic separation plant at Oak Ridge, Tenn., as stated in Chapter VIII. In 1945, the giant magnet was released from its wartime services in connection with the separation of isotopes and restored to its original purpose, the production of high-energy ions, after a lapse of nearly four years. But the delay was not altogether without compensation, for the discovery of a new principle made it possible for the 184-inch cyclotron to yield particles with twice the amount of energy originally expected.

9.68. When concluding, from equation (9.2), that the time taken for a given charged particle to describe the semicircular path in either of the dees of a cyclotron is independent of the velocity of the ion or of the radius of the path, the tacit assumption was made that the mass m of the particle remained constant. For energies of the order of 10 or 20 Mev, this is substantially true, but at higher energies, and hence higher speeds, the relativistic mass effect (§ 3.70) becomes important. The value of the mass m is given by equation (3.9), and this increases rapidly as the velocity v of the particle approaches the speed of light. A deuteron of 20 Mev energy, which is the fastest-moving particle produced in the 60-inch cyclotron, has a velocity about 0.145 times the speed of light, and its effective mass, by equation (3.9), is 1.01 times the rest mass. The change of mass is comparatively small, and so the operation of the cyclotron is not greatly affected.

9.69. At higher energies, the mass of the particle increases to such an extent that its effect becomes appreciable.* It can be seen from equation (9.2) that as the mass of the ion increases, so also does the time T of transit through the dee. As a result, the particle will no longer be in phase with the oscillating potential. Instead

---

* It was suggested by W. W. Hansen (see § 9.51) that when the speed of the particles approaches that of light and an increase of energy results in an appreciable increase of mass, rather than of velocity, the device should be called a *ponderator,* instead of an accelerator.

of reaching the gap between the dees at the exact instant required for it to receive an accelerating impulse, the ion will arrive too late and consequently will gain little or no additional energy. On account of the relativistic mass increase, therefore, an approximate limit is set to the energy that can be acquired by an ion in a conventional cyclotron operating under given conditions. In order to offset this limitation to some extent, it was proposed, when the 184-inch cyclotron was first planned, to use a very high potential—about a million volts—so that the ions would need to make only a comparatively small number of turns in order to attain higher energies.

9.70. In 1945, V. Veksler in Russia and, a few months later, E. M. McMillan in the United States, independently, showed that allowance could be made for the effect of the increase of mass of a particle moving at high speeds so as to keep it in phase with the oscillating potential. Two methods of compensation are possible. One is to increase the magnetic field H in proportion to the mass, so that m/H remains constant; it can be seen from equation (9.2) that the time T would then be unaffected by the increase of mass. The other possibility, which is more readily adapted to the cyclotron, is to leave the magnetic field unchanged, but to decrease the frequency of the oscillating potential as the mass of the particle increases.

9.71. In this connection, McMillan pointed out that if the oscillation frequency is continuously adjusted so as to coincide with the decreasing frequency of rotation of the particle, as the time T increases, the principle of *phase stability* can be utilized. This principle may be explained by reference to Fig. 9.8, which represents the variation with time of a cycle of the high-frequency oscillating potential. In normal operation the charged particle receives its acceleration at a point indicated by the time t_0, just beyond the potential peak. If the particle al-

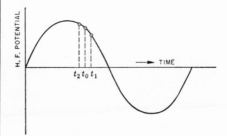

FIG. 9.8. Diagram to illustrate the principle of phase stability.

ways remained exactly in phase, it would always arrive at the appropriate time t_0 of the cycle to gain the proper amount of energy. However, if the particle arrives too late, for example at the time t_1, the potential will then have decreased, so that it will not receive the regular increment of energy, and hence of mass. It follows from equation (9.2) that the time T required to traverse the path will be less, and consequently its next arrival will be in time for it to receive the full accelerating effect of the potential at t_0. On the other hand, if the particle reaches the accelerating position too soon, at time t_2, for example, it will gain more energy and mass than normal, since the potential is now higher than at t_0. It will thus take a slightly longer time to return to the point where it receives the next impulse. The rotation of the charged particles is thus automatically synchronized with the changing frequency of the accelerating potential. The action is similar to that in a synchronous motor, and hence the name *synchrotron* was proposed by McMillan for a device using this principle.

9.72. About six months after construction of the 184-inch cyclotron had been resumed in 1945, it was decided to modify the instrument so that the frequency of the oscillations could be varied to compensate for the increase of the mass of the accelerated ions at high speeds. For this reason the machine (Fig. 9.9) is referred to as a *synchrocyclotron* or as a *frequency-modulated cyclotron.* It uses a single dee, instead of two dees as in the conventional cyclotron,† the oscillating potential being applied between it and a ground connection. Every time a charged particle enters or leaves the dee, it acquires additional energy, so that it follows a spiral path just as if two dees were employed. By means of a rapidly rotating, variable condenser, the frequency of the oscillating potential applied to the dee is decreased so as to compensate for the gain in the effective mass of the particle as its speed increases. A 200-Mev deuteron or a 400-Mev alpha particle has a speed of about 1.4×10^{10} cm. per sec., or about 0.47 times the velocity of light. It follows, therefore, from equation (3.8) that the mass is 1.14 times, or 14 per cent greater than, the rest mass at low energies. The frequency

FIG. 9.9. The 184-inch synchrocyclotron in the University of California Radiation Laboratory, Berkeley, Calif.

* In the Russian literature, it is called a *phasotron* because it utilizes the principle of phase stability.

† It may be mentioned that the 11-inch cyclotron, which was the first to produce useful acceleration, also had only one dee (Fig. 9.7). As a general rule, one dee electrode can be used when the applied potential is not too high; the other terminal of the oscillator is then grounded.

of the oscillator must consequently decrease in the same proportion if the charged particles are to be kept in phase with the alternating potential which causes the acceleration.

9.73. It is apparent from equation (9.2) that the time for a charged particle to traverse the dee does not depend solely on the mass m, but rather on the ratio of the mass m to the charge e of the ion. This ratio has the same value for deuterons ($m = 2$, $e = 1$) as for alpha particles ($m = 4$, $e = 2$); hence with a given oscillator, the same frequency modulation can be used for both of these ions. For this reason, the Berkeley synchrocyclotron, which went into operation in November 1946, was at first employed for the acceleration of deuterons to 190 Mev and alpha particles to 380 Mev. But early in 1949, the completion of a new oscillator, with a dual frequency range, made it possible to obtain high-energy (350 Mev) protons, in addition. Some years later, the 184-inch magnet was rebuilt, in order to increase the strength of the magnetic field, so that in 1957 protons of 730-Mev energy were produced. Following the successful operation of the University of California synchrocyclotron, about twelve others were constructed in various parts of the world. One in Russia has a magnet about the same diameter as that in Berkeley but weighs 7000 tons; it can yield protons having 680-Mev energy.

9.74. There is a difference between the output of a cyclotron and that of a synchrocyclotron which is worthy of mention. In the former the flow of accelerated ions is regarded as continuous, although it actually consists of a series of pulses corresponding to each half-cycle of the oscillating potential. For a frequency of 10 million cycles per second there would thus be 20 million pulses in this time interval. In the synchrocyclotron, however, a pulse of ions is carried from the ion source at the center to the periphery of the dee as the frequency of the oscillating potential is decreased from its initial to its final value. The frequency then returns to its original value and another pulse of ions is carried from the source to the periphery, and so on. The rate at which ion pulses are produced depends on the speed of rotation of the condenser controlling the oscillating potential. The high-energy protons are produced in bursts of 60 to 300 per second, the duration of each pulse being about one ten-thousandth part (10^{-4}) of a second. Because the pulses are of such short duration, the average ion current from a synchrocyclotron is quite small.

THE BETATRON

9.75. For certain purposes, such as the production of penetrating X-rays of high energy, it is desirable to obtain beams of energetic electrons. Both the voltage multiplier (§ 9.36) and the Van de Graaff electrostatic generator (§ 9.39) can be used to accelerate electrons, but the energies are limited to a few million electron volts. The linear type of accelerator, mentioned in § 9.51, however, can produce electrons of much higher energies.

9.76. The cyclotron, on the other hand, cannot be readily adapted to yield electrons of high energy because of the large relativistic increase of mass at fairly low energies. This happens because the rest mass of the electron is very small, compared with that of a proton or a deuteron; hence it must attain a much higher speed in order to carry the same amount of kinetic energy. At 1 Mev energy, the speed of an electron is more than nine-tenths of the speed of light and the relativistic mass is 2.5 times as great as the rest mass. In its present form even the synchrocyclotron could not be easily adapted to make allowance for such large increases of mass.

9.77. The idea of using magnetic induction to accelerate electrons was considered by R. Wideröe in Germany in 1928, and by E. T. S. Walton in England in 1929, but their attempts to put it into practice were not successful. In 1936, the German physicist M. Steinbeck secured a patent for an induction instrument with which he claimed to have obtained electrons of 1.8 Mev energy, although the beam intensity was admittedly small. The first successful induction accelerator with an appreciable output of electrons was designed and constructed by D. W. Kerst in the United States in 1940. To this he gave the name *betatron*, because it was used for electrons which are, of course, identical with beta particles (§ 2.104). The first betatron gave electrons with 2.3 Mev energy, but this was soon followed by one yielding 20-Mev electrons, constructed by Kerst in conjunction with the General Electric Company at Schenectady, N. Y. Subsequently, the latter organization constructed a 100-million volt instrument; this was completed in 1943, although details of its operation were not released until 1945. Several other betatrons have since been built for various purposes, with energies up to 300 Mev. It is claimed that for energies below about 100 Mev, the betatron is the simplest and most reliable type of electron accelerator.

9.78. The action of the betatron is based on the same fundamental principles as that of the familiar transformer in which an alternating current, applied to a primary coil, induces a similar current, usually with a higher or lower voltage, in the secondary windings. The effect is due essentially to the production by the alternating primary current of a time-variable magnetic field which, in turn, induces an oscillating current, that is, an oscillatory flow of electrons, in the secondary coil. In the betatron the secondary is an annular, i.e., ring-shaped, evacuated glass tube, often referred to, for obvious reasons, as the "doughnut," shown in section at *AA* in Fig. 9.10. This is placed between the poles

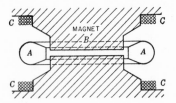

Fig. 9.10.   Schematic sectional diagram of a betatron.

of a specially shaped electromagnet *B*, energized by alternating, pulsed current passing through the coils *CC*. One purpose of this magnet is to produce a strong field in the central space or "hole" of the doughnut, and hence it is constructed with a large amount of iron in the core. Electrons are produced from a heated filament, and these are given a preliminary acceleration by application of an electric field having a potential difference of 20,000 to 70,000 volts. Even with the comparatively low energies thus acquired, the electrons travel at very high speeds, from one fifth to nearly one half the velocity of light.

9.79. The variation with time of the magnetic field strength, in a single cycle of the alternating current which energizes the magnet, may be represented by the sine-wave curve in Fig. 9.11. As the field strength starts to increase, i.e., near the point *O*, the partly accelerated electrons are injected into the doughnut. The effect of the growing magnetic field in the central space is to induce an electromotive force, or voltage, within the doughnut, which increases the energy of the moving electrons. Since they are traveling in a magnetic field, the electrons are forced into a curved path, but instead of being a spiral, as in the cyclotron, the increasing magnetic field keeps them moving in a circle of constant radius. Reference to equation (9.1) will show that this is possible provided the field strength H grows proportionately to the increase in the product of the mass m and the velocity v, i.e., to the increase in the momentum, of the electrons. Thus, the electrons are kept moving around the doughnut in a fairly stable, circular path, energy being acquired in each lap or turn.

9.80. When the field strength has reached the point P in Fig. 9.11, where

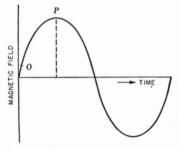

FIG. 9.11. Single cycle of sine-wave variation of magnetic field used in the betatron.

it ceases to increase and will subsequently decrease, a pulse of current is sent through an auxiliary coil which suddenly changes the magnetic field. As a result the high-energy electrons are displaced from their stable path and fall on a target, for the production of X-rays (bremsstrahlung), or the electron beam may be made to leave the apparatus and used for other purposes.

9.81. If the electrons had not been removed at the point P, the decreasing magnetic field from this point on would have induced an electromagnetic force in the opposite direction to that acting between O and P. This would have the effect of slowing down the previously accelerated electrons. Consequently, only the first quarter of the cycle is actually used for acceleration purposes, injection of electrons being always made at the point O, whereas removal occurs at P in each cycle.

9.82. A simple calculation will show how it is possible for the betatron to produce electrons with very high energies. As seen above, the electrons when introduced into the doughnut are already moving with speeds approaching that of light, and this is further increased as the electrons acquire additional energy. It may be assumed, therefore, that the average speed of the electrons between injection and removal is two-thirds the velocity of light, i.e., 2×10^{10} cm. per sec. The diameter of the circular path within the doughnut of a large betatron may be taken as 300 cm., so that the electrons will travel this path roughly $2 \times 10^{10}/300$, i.e., 6.7×10^7 times per second.

9.83. If the frequency of the alternating current used for the magnetic field is 60 cycles per second, the time for one cycle is 1/60 sec.; hence, the quarter cycle from O to P, during which the electrons are accelerated, lasts roughly 1/240 sec. During this period the electrons make $6.7 \times 10^7/240$, i.e., 280,000 turns of the circular path in the doughnut. If the electrons acquire an average of 250 ev of energy in each turn, due to the electromotive force produced by the magnetic field changing with time, they will have a total energy of about 70 Mev.

9.84. In the General Electric 100-million volt betatron, the diameter of the doughnut is about 180 cm. and the magnet weighs 135 tons. The electrons travel around the doughnut 250,000 times, covering a distance of about 900 miles, between injection and removal, and gaining 400 ev of energy at each turn. The 100-Mev electrons have a velocity which is more than 99.99 per cent of the speed of light, and their relativistic mass is nearly 200 times the rest mass.

9.85. Since the operation of the betatron is unaffected by the increasing mass of the electron as it gains energy, it at first appears that extremely high energies might be obtainable by means of this device. However, it has been shown theoretically that a charged particle, such as an electron, moving in a circle, as it does in the doughnut of the betatron, will lose some of its energy in the form of radiation. The effect of this phenomenon, which was confirmed experimentally in the General Electric Research Laboratory in 1947, is to set a limit to the energy which the gyrating electrons can acquire. The energy lost in each turn of the circular path is proportional to E^4/r, where E is the energy of the electron and r is the radius of the path; hence the amount lost increases very rapidly as the energy E becomes larger. Eventually, the electron loses just as much energy in the form of radiation as it gains from the electromotive force due to the time-changing magnetic field in each turn around the doughnut.*

9.86. Two possibilities present themselves for minimizing the loss of energy by radiation. Since this is determined by E^4/r, one solution to the problem is to employ a larger doughnut, so that the radius r of the electron path may be increased. The other measure which could be taken is to decrease the number of turns the electrons make between injection and removal, by altering the magnetic field so as to permit the acquisition of a greater amount of energy in each turn. The largest instrument based on these principles, and employing a magnet weighing 1000 tons, was constructed by Kerst, the inventor of the betatron, at the University of Illinois. It yields electrons with 300 Mev energy.

THE ELECTRON SYNCHROTRON

9.87. An alternative, and in many ways simpler, procedure for conferring high energies upon electrons is to make use of the synchrotron principle, enunciated independently in 1945 by Veksler and by McMillan, as mentioned in § 9.70. The first practical application of the idea is claimed by F. K. Goward and D. E. Barnes, in England, who in 1946 converted a 4-Mev betatron to yield 8-Mev electrons. Shortly thereafter, in 1947, H. C. Pollock and W. F. Westendorp of the General Electric Company designed and built a machine combining the action of both betatron and synchrotron. It produced electrons of 70 Mev energy, although the magnet weighed only 8 tons, as compared with 135 tons of the 100-Mev betatron. A somewhat similar device, capable of yielding 330-Mev electrons, was built in 1947 by McMillan in the Radiation Laboratory at Berkeley, California, and several others with about the same energy, have been constructed since that time. The highest energy attained in an electron synchrotron is 1200 Mev, which is

---

* This limitation does not apply to the linear electron-accelerator (§ 9.51), since the electron does not lose energy by radiation when moving in a straight line.

believed to be as high as is practical with this instrument.

9.88. Although electron synchrotrons vary in their detailed characteristics, the following description, which applies to the Berkeley instrument in particular, may be taken as fairly typical. It consists of an evacuated annular tube, or doughnut, shown in plan A in Fig. 9.12, between the poles

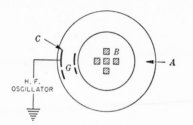

FIG. 9.12.   Diagrammatic plan of portion of a synchrotron.

of a magnet energized by alternating (pulsed) current, as in the betatron. But, in the electron synchrotron the magnet has cylindrical, i.e., ring-shaped, poles, and it does not extend into the central space or hole of the doughnut. For this reason, the synchrotron magnet is much lighter than that of a betatron having the same energy output.* In place of the central portion of the magnet, there are a small number of iron bars B, called *flux bars*, which serve an equivalent purpose, but only to a limited extent. In addition, the interior of one of the eight segments, of which the doughnut is constructed, is coated with copper C, leaving a narrow gap G, near one end, to form what is known as a *resonant cavity*. A grounded oscillator, producing an alternating potential of 3000 volts maximum, at the constant

high frequency of 47.7 million cycles per second, is connected to C. When the oscillator is turned on, a charged particle receives approximately 2000 ev of energy each time it passes the accelerating gap, provided it is in phase with the oscillations.

9.89. In the operation of the synchrotron, electrons produced by a heated tungsten wire are injected into the doughnut after being given a preliminary acceleration by means of an electrostatic field of about 90,000 volts. Due to the action of the increasing magnetic field, the electrons travel in a circular path, and the change with time of the field through the flux bars induces an electromotive force within the doughnut which adds energy to the electrons, just as in the betatron. However, the number of flux bars is such that when the energy of the electrons has reached about 2 Mev, the bars have become magnetically saturated, and are no longer able to induce an electromotive force; betatron operation then ceases.

9.90. At this point, the constant high-frequency, oscillating potential is applied to the resonant cavity C, and synchrotron action commences. Additional energy is now acquired by the electrons each time they pass the accelerating gap G. If the potential applied to C operates at the proper frequency, as will be described shortly, the electrons are kept in phase and receive an increment of energy in each revolution. These increments are larger than those in the betatron, and so the electrons can acquire a higher energy in the same (or smaller) number of turns.

* A 300-Mev nonferromagnetic synchrotron, in which the magnetic field is produced by passing current through specially designed coils, has been constructed by the General Electric Company in cooperation with the Office of Naval Research. It requires very large currents and the mechanical forces on the coils are so great that they must be rigidly clamped. This type of electron accelerator is probably most economical in the 100-Mev region.

9.91. At 2 Mev energy, when synchrotron operation is initiated, the velocity of the electrons is already 97.9 per cent of that of light. Since they cannot exceed, or even attain, the speed of light, it is evident that the subsequent increase of velocity cannot be more than about 2 per cent. Consequently, as the energy of the electrons is increased from 2 Mev to 300 Mev or more, their speed remains virtually constant. At the same time, the increasing magnetic field keeps the electrons moving in a circular path of constant radius, in spite of their increasing energy or momentum, as explained in § 9.79. Since the size of the orbit and the speed of the electrons remain essentially unchanged, it follows that the frequency with which they revolve around the doughnut stays constant. In order to utilize the principle of phase stability, which is a significant aspect of synchrotron action, it is necessary that the oscillating potential applied to the resonant cavity C should have constant frequency, equal to the frequency of revolution of the electrons. As a result, the electrons are kept rotating within the doughnut, gaining energy in each revolution.

9.92. It can be seen from equation (9.1) that if the velocity v of the electrons and the radius r of their path are both constant, the effective mass m will increase in proportion to the increase of H, the magnetic field strength. An increase in the mass means, of course, a gain in energy, since the speed is almost constant. In the synchrotron, the betatron function ceases and synchrotron action commences when the magnetic field strength is 80 gauss*; the field strength continues to increase to 10,000 gauss before the electrons are finally deflected from their path. Since the magnetic field increases by a factor of about 125, the effective mass of the electrons will be increased proportionately. At 2-Mev energy, the mass of an electron is five times the rest mass, and hence the electrons leaving the synchrotron will have a mass 625 times the rest mass, which corresponds to an energy of about 330 Mev. It will be observed that in the later stages, the synchrotron functions as a ponderator (§ 9.69 footnote), rather than as an accelerator; it is the electron mass, not the velocity, that increases appreciably, as the particle gains energy.

9.93. Just before the magnetic field has reached its maximum intensity, and the electrons have acquired their maximum energy, the oscillating potential is turned off. Since the magnetic field continues to increase, while the energy and mass of the electrons remain constant, the radius of the path must decrease [cf. equation (9.3)]. As a result the electrons travel in an orbit of gradually diminishing radius, so that they strike a target projecting from the inner edge of the doughnut. This leads to the production of highly-penetrating, i.e., short wave length, X-rays (bremsstrahlung) of equivalent energy. Since these rays are not affected by the magnetic field, they travel in a straight line from the target through the walls of the apparatus.

9.94. In the 300-Mev electron synchrotron designed by H. R. Crane and D. M. Dennison, at the University of Michigan, the doughnut is not circular, but consists of four quadrants connected by short straight pieces. The purpose of this design is to simplify

---

* The *gauss* is the unit of intensity, or strength, of magnetic field in the c.g.s. system of units.

construction of the magnet, which is made in four sections corresponding to the four quadrants. Further, the straight portions are used for injection and removal of the electron stream, and for application of the high-frequency, alternating potential in regions outside the magnetic field. In this synchrotron there is no initial betatron operation, so that the magnet, which is energized by alternating (pulsed) current, merely surrounds the four quadrants and does not extend into the central region; in addition, the flux bars are not necessary. The high-frequency, alternating potential is applied immediately upon injection of the electrons, but, in order to maintain them in phase in a circular orbit, the frequency is modulated until they attain a velocity approaching that of light. At this point the frequency is held constant and the mass, and energy, then increase with the increasing magnetic field, while the electrons gyrate in a path of constant radius, as in other synchrotrons. It will be apparent that the Michigan synchrotron combines the accelerating action of the synchrocyclotron adapted to a circular path, in the earlier stages, with the ponderating function of the synchrotron, in the later stages.

9.95. In concluding this section, it may be noted that all forms of betatron and electron synchrotron operate in pulses. Since the magnets are usually energized at a frequency of 60 cycles per sec., the output is pulsed at this same frequency.

THE PROTON SYNCHROTRON

9.96. Every extension in the energy range of charged particles used for experiments with atomic nuclei has usually been accompanied by the discovery of new phenomena, some of them expected, others unexpected. In the late 1940s, when the most energetic particles available had energies of 350 to 400 Mev, attention was turned to the possibility of attaining energies of thousands of Mev, i.e., in the billion electron volt (or Bev) range.* A cyclotron capable of conferring billions of electron volts in energy on positive ions would have to be considerably larger than the already enormous 184-inch machine with its 4000-ton magnet. To build even larger synchrocyclotrons, therefore, did not appear to be a very practical approach. Because electrons of high energy revolving in an orbit continuously radiate energy, as mentioned in § 9.85, it appears unlikely at present that any form of betatron or electron synchrotron will produce energies much in excess of 1 Bev. In principle, a linear (traveling wave) accelerator capable of producing electrons with energies of billions of electron volts is possible, but it has been estimated that a tube 2 miles long would be necessary for an energy of 10 Bev.

9.97. The idea of using a ring-shaped magnet for a positive-ion accelerator, somewhat similar to that employed in the electron synchrotron, with a varying magnetic field and frequency modulation was proposed by M. L. E. Oliphant in Great Britain in 1943, although the details were not published until 1947. The same possibility was studied independently by W. M. Brobeck in Berkeley in 1946. From these considerations came the next development in the field of parti-

* Because the term "billion" does not have the same significance in all countries, the symbol Gev (or GeV) is generally employed in Europe. This is an abbreviation for Giga-electron volt, derived from the Greek (and Latin) word *gigas* meaning giant.

cle accelerators, namely, the *proton synchrotron*, capable of attaining energies of several billion electron volts without the use of unreasonably heavy magnets.

9.98. The choice of protons for the particles was largely determined by the fact that they can acquire very high energies without losing appreciable amounts by radiation as do elec-

than the cyclotron, where the path is a spiral, means that the magnet can be much lighter in proportion. In the cyclotron, the magnetic field must cover the whole of the region in which the particles spiral around; consequently, the pole faces must be large. In the synchrotron, on the other hand, a ring-shaped magnet surrounding an annular tube or doughnut is all that is

Fɪɢ. 9.13. The Bevatron at the University of California Radiation Laboratory.

trons. The loss of energy of a charged particle per revolution is proportional to E^4/r, as stated in § 9.85, but it is also *inversely* proportional to the fourth power of the rest mass of the particle. Since the mass of the proton is nearly two thousand times that of an electron, the energy loss at 6 Bev will be quite negligible for protons.

9.99. The decision to use the synchrotron principle for acceleration, so that the particle moves in a circular path of almost constant radius, rather

required. Thus, protons of 3-Bev energy have been produced in a synchrotron with a magnet containing only 2000 tons of steel, compared with the 3700 tons of the Berkeley cyclotron.

9.100. Several proton synchrotrons have been (or are being) constructed. In order of increasing energy, five are of interest: (1) The one at Birmingham, England, which reached 1 Bev in July, 1953. (2) The Cosmotron, so called because the energies attained are of the same order as the primary particles in cosmic rays, at the Brookhaven National Laboratory, Long Island, New York. It was operated at 2.3 Bev in June, 1952, later increased to 3 Bev, and was the first accelerator to reach the billion electron volt mark. (3) The Radiation Laboratory (Berkeley) Bevatron shown in Fig. 9.13, which produced 4.9-Bev protons in March, 1954 and was later raised to 6.2 Bev. (4) An instrument, designed for protons of

be attained with an accelerator of proportionately smaller diameter.

9.101. In its general (iron magnet) form, and in fact in its principle of operation, the proton synchrotron is similar to the Michigan electron synchrotron, described earlier. There are four quadrants joined by straight pieces, as represented diagrammatically in Fig. 9.14, I. In the Cosmotron, for example, the external radius of the quadrants is about 35 feet and the

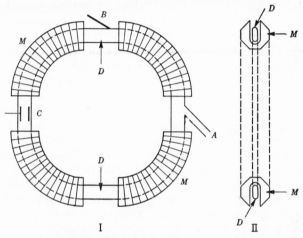

FIG. 9.14. Schematic drawing of a proton synchrotron.

10 Bev energy, completed in Russia during 1957. (5) Finally, an 11-Bev accelerator is being constructed at Canberra, Australia. The first four of these proton synchrotrons have steel (iron) magnets, but the last has been designed to use an air-cored magnet. With a steel core, the magnetic field strength is restricted by saturation effects to a maximum of about 20,000 gauss (or less); on the other hand, with an air core, it is hoped to reach 80,000 gauss, the limitation being set by the tremendous forces on the current-carrying coils (see § 9.88, footnote). With this stronger magnetic field, the same proton energy should

connecting pieces are about 10 feet long. The elliptical (or flattened) cross section of the doughnut *DD* is indicated in Fig. 9.14, II, which also shows the C-shaped cross section of the magnet, *MM*. The latter consists of a large number of plates surrounding only the quadrants of the doughnut, alternating (pulsed) current being used for energizing purposes. The protons, previously accelerated to 3.5 to 4 Mev in a horizontal van de Graaff machine in the Cosmotron and to 10 Mev in a linear accelerator in the Bevatron, are injected at *A*, in one of the straight portions of the doughnut. After having their energy increased, as a result of many rotations, the protons are removed by a deflector at *B*. Injection and removal thus take place outside the magnetic field.

9.102. The accelerating device *C*, equivalent to the dee of the cyclotron or the resonant cavity *C* (Fig. 9.12) of the electron synchrotron, is also inserted in one of the straight portions, outside the influence of the magnet. A high-frequency voltage is applied at the accelerating electrodes, so that the protons receive an increment of energy of about 1000 volts (or more) in each revolution. After making three or four million revolutions in the doughnut, the protons will have traveled a total distance of several hundred thousand miles and will have acquired energies of the order of billions of electron volts.

9.103. In order to keep the protons moving in a circular path of essentially constant radius, the field strength of the magnets is increased, as in the electron synchrotron. Since a proton does not attain a velocity within a few per cent of that of light until its energy is about 3 Bev, it is apparent that up to this point allowance does not have to be made for the steadily increasing speed with which the charged particles gyrate, as the strength of the magnetic field grows. The time required for the protons to make one turn of the doughnut gradually decreases so that the number of turns per unit time, i.e., the frequency of revolution, increases correspondingly. To maintain the condition of phase stability, which is essential for proper synchrotron action, the frequency of the high-frequency alternations applied to *C* is increased in the same manner. The rate at which the frequency is changed must be very accurately coordinated with the increasing magnetic field so that the particles maintain an orbit of constant radius.

9.104. The frequency is increased fairly rapidly at first, as the protons gain speed, but the rate is slowed down and the frequency becomes almost constant toward the end of their passage, as the speed approaches that of light. The period during which the magnetic field strength increases, and the frequency of the oscillations applied to *C* increases correspondingly, lasts a second or two. There is then a short delay to permit the magnet to recover, followed by another period in which the protons gain energy. The output of a proton synchrotron thus consists of a series of pulses at intervals of about five or six seconds. The intensity of the emergent beam, as measured by the total number of protons present, is not large, and the voltage, although high, is not very uniform. These properties are also characteristic of the electron synchrotron. A convenient feature of the proton synchrotron is that, by suitable adjustment of the ejector *B*, the beam can be removed at (approximately) any desired energy for particular experiments.

THE ALTERNATING GRADIENT
SYNCHROTRON

9.105. One of the purposes of accelerating protons (or other nuclei) to higher and higher energies is to create new particles, by the conversion of energy into mass. However, because of the necessity that momentum should be conserved, not all the energy is available for particle formation. For example, the creation of a proton-antiproton pair or of a neutron-antineutron pair, having a total mass of just over 2 a.m.u., should require roughly 2×931, or 1900 Mev, i.e., 1.9 Bev (§ 9.96). For this amount of energy to be available, the original accelerated proton would need to have about 6 Bev. The Berkeley Bevatron was designed to produce protons of such energy, and one of its purposes was the creation of the antiproton and antineutron. As seen in Chapter II, this objective has indeed been achieved.

9.106. In order to provide useful information concerning nuclear structure and nuclear forces, the next energy stage for proton accelerators should be about 25 to 30 Bev. A synchrotron capable of achieving this energy would require a magnet containing some 100,000 tons of iron, and the size and cost of the instrument would be prohibitive. In order to understand why such a large magnet is required, it is necessary to consider the nature of the path of the protons as they revolve in the doughnut-shaped chamber. It has been tacitly assumed earlier that the path is circular; actually, due to various minor fluctuations, the protons deviate to some extent about this circular path, and the amplitude of the deviations, i.e., the extent of departure from the circular path, increases with the energy acquired by the particles. The cross-sectional dimensions of the doughnut are determined by the area required to contain these deviating protons without touching the walls, and so the cross section will increase as the protons are accelerated to higher energies. Since the magnetic field must include the whole doughnut, as indicated above, the result is that the size (and mass) of the magnet needed is greatly increased.

9.107. A possible solution to this problem was to find a means of improving the normal, but small, focusing effect exerted by the magnet in a synchrocyclotron. If the straying of the protons (or other charged particles) from the ideal circular path could be restricted, by an improved focusing system, the doughnut vessel required to contain them would have a small cross-sectional area. The size of the magnet required in a machine to produce protons of a certain energy could then be decreased. Alternatively, for the same weight of iron, the magnet (and doughnut) could have a much larger diameter, thus permitting protons of higher energy to be obtained.

9.108. A suggested method for achieving "strong focusing" was published in 1952 by E. D. Courant, M. S. Livingston and H. S. Snyder of Brookhaven National Laboratory, based on the use of magnetic fields with alternating gradients.* It was shown that,

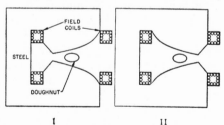

I   II

Fig. 9.15.   Principle of alternating gradient synchrotron.

by the application of a succession of alternate focusing and defocusing magnetic fields to a charged particle rotating in an orbit, the result is a strong net focusing effect. Suppose the alternate sections of the synchrotron magnet had their pole piece shaped as shown in Figs. 9.15, I and II. In the

---

* The same principle was enunciated in an article printed privately in 1950 in Athens, Greece, by a Boston-born, Greek electrical engineer, N. Christofilos, and an application was filed for a U. S. patent. The idea had been communicated to the Radiation Laboratory, Berkeley, but the scientists there were unable to follow the unorthodox mathematical approach used to explain it.

first case (Fig. 9.15, I), with the magnetic field strength decreasing from the inner to the outer edge of the doughnut, the beam of charged particles tends to converge (or be focused) in the vertical plane, while there is a tendency for divergence (defocusing) to occur in the horizontal plane. In the adjoining section, where the magnet is as indicated in Fig. 9.15, II, the gradient of the magnetic field is in the opposite direction, increasing from inner to outer edge. Now, there is defocusing in the vertical plane but focusing in the horizontal plane. If this alternation of magnetic field gradients is continued around the whole doughnut, the net result is a strong focusing effect, i.e., a marked decrease of the deviation of the particle beam from the ideal circular path.

9.109. The application of the alternating gradient concept to an actual synchrotron design involves a number of difficult theoretical and practical problems. Nevertheless, it is believed that these can be overcome and plans are being made for the construction of such an instrument at Brookhaven capable of accelerating protons to energies of 25 or 35 Bev. This energy region was chosen because it was felt that it would represent the best compromise between scientific usefulness and cost. In the proposed design, the radius of the (approximately) circular doughnut will be about 500 feet. The strong focusing should lead to the confinement of the protons within a region that is 2 inches wide and 1 inch high. The magnet, weighing less than 4000 tons, which is roughly the mass of the 3-Bev Cosmotron magnet, will be divided into 240 sections, each 7 feet long. Between the magnet sections will be field-free portions, 2 to 5 feet long, in which accelerating units, correction

(magnetic) lenses and other equipment will be located. Protons will be injected from a 50-Mev linear accelerator at regular intervals, just as in the more conventional synchrotron. However, additional energy will be applied, by variable high-frequency potentials, at several points in the path of the protons, instead of at one point as in the Cosmotron, etc.

9.110. An alternating-gradient 25-Bev proton synchrotron, similar to the Brookhaven machine, has been designed independently by the scientists of the eleven-nation European Council for Nuclear Energy (CERN). It is to be built in the Council's laboratories near Geneva, Switzerland, with completion scheduled for 1960. Other strong-focusing synchrotrons have been designed, although it is not yet certain whether these will be built or not. The principle is adaptable to charged particles other than protons, and its feasibility has been proved in an electron synchrotron.

9.111. From time to time, various ideas, some fanciful and others more realistic, have been proposed for attaining energies of many billions of electron volts. One of the most practical possibilities is based on the use of two intersecting beams of accelerated particles. It has been estimated that the energy available for the creation of matter in a head-on collison between two 15-Bev protons is equivalent to that of a 500-Bev proton striking a stationary target. The difficulty of realizing this effect lies in the fact that high-energy accelerators, such as synchrotrons, operate in pulses, so that the charged-particle (ion) currents are very small (§ 9.104). Hence, collisions among the particles in two such intersecting beams would be rare.

9.112. A possible solution to the problem of obtaining large ion currents has been worked out, and is being tested, in the United States by members of the cooperative organization for research in high-energy nuclear physics called the Midwestern Universities Research Association (MURA). This new idea is called the Fixed Field Alternating Gradient (FFAG) principle. It differs from the synchrotron in using a fixed (or steady) magnetic field, but with shaped pole pieces, so that the field strength increases rapidly from the inner to the outer edge of the doughnut. Because the field is steady, protons can be injected continuously (or in rapid successive pulses), instead of at intervals, as is necessary with an alternating magnetic (synchrotron) field. Hence, larger ion currents are possible. As a result of the strong gradient in the magnetic field, the injected protons spiral outward, from the inner to the outer edge of a wide doughnut, acquiring energy in each revolution. By the use of the alternating gradient principle, it is believed that the high-energy protons can be "stored" near the outer edge of the doughnut until ion currents of appreciable strength can be built up. With two such currents, circulating in opposite directions, from two separate accelerators, the number of very high-energy collisions should be large enough to lead to significant results.

Acceleration of Heavy Ions

9.113. Nearly all the work on the acceleration of charged particles has been done with the lightest elements, namely, hydrogen or its isotopes (deuterium and tritium) and helium. In recent years, however, the acceleration of nuclei of heavier atoms, e.g., carbon, oxygen and nitrogen, has attracted interest for a number of reasons (§ 10.48 *et seq.*). The acceleration of carbon (C^{+6}) ions to about 50-Mev energy, by means of the 37-inch fixed frequency cyclotron at the Radiation Laboratory, Berkeley, was reported briefly by L. W. Alvarez in 1940. Subsequently, carbon ions of higher energies, up to about 120 Mev, were obtained in the same laboratory with the 60-inch cyclotron, but it was not until about 1950 or so, that the acceleration of heavy particles began to attract more general interest.

9.114. It can be seen from equation (9.3) that, provided the oscillation frequency is properly adjusted, the energy that can be acquired in a cyclotron by a charged particle of given mass, for a certain magnetic field strength, increases with the charge on the particle. To accelerate heavy particles, it is desirable, therefore, to obtain highly charged ions, i.e., atoms which have been stripped of all (or nearly all) of their electrons. This is difficult to do directly, but advantage has been taken of the cyclotron effect to produce such ions in certain cases. For example, if the cyclotron frequency is adjusted for N^{+6} ions, it is possible to accelerate N^{+2} ions to a lower energy, by what is called the "third harmonic" method, in which the rotation frequency is one third of the actual cyclotron frequency. The accelerated N^{+2} ions then collide with other nitrogen ions (or atoms) in the cyclotron tank, with the result that completely ionized N^{+6} is produced. The acceleration of these ions in the cyclotron can then lead to high energies.

9.115. The drawback to the harmonic method of obtaining highly charged (or high-energy) ions is that the final beam current is very weak, and the energy distribution is far from uniform. Although such ion currents are useful for some purposes, there are experiments for which much stronger currents are desirable. One approach is to obtain a relatively strong source of particular ions, not necessarily those with the maximum charge, and then to adjust the cyclotron frequency so as to accelerate these ions to a given energy. For example, the 63-inch cyclotron at Oak Ridge National Laboratory was designed to accelerate N^{+3} ions to 25 Mev energy. A fairly strong source of these ions is produced by the passage through nitrogen gas of a high-intensity arc discharge, initiated and maintained by electrons emitted from a hot tungsten filament.

9.116. Another approach to the problem of obtaining larger ion currents, being followed at the Radiation Laboratory, Berkeley, appears to have considerable merit. It makes use of a linear (drift-tube) accelerator instead of a cyclotron. Ions of low charge are first accelerated and used, as described above, to cause further ionization, the resulting highly charged ions being further accelerated. However, since a linear accelerator can handle very much larger ion currents than a cyclotron, the emergent beam should be quite strong, although the energies of the charged particles may vary considerably. The instrument, called a Hilac (for heavy ion linear accelerator), will be capable of accelerating particles as heavy as argon ions.

Nuclear Transmutation and
Artificial Radioactivity Chapter X

TYPES OF NUCLEAR REACTIONS

THE PURPOSE OF NUCLEAR TRANSMUTATION STUDIES

10.1. Before 1932, when artifically accelerated particles were first shown to be capable of taking part in nuclear reactions, some ten transmutation processes were known. These were all of the (α,p) type, in which the incident particle was an alpha particle derived from natural sources. The availability, in recent years, of various charged particles, with energies up to very high values, has resulted in the detection of a large number of different nuclear reactions. Several hundred, involving virtually all the known elements, have already been identified, and many more undoubtedly remain to be discovered.

10.2. In considering the numerous investigations of nuclear transmutation, it is reasonable to ask: What is their purpose? There are several answers to this question. There is, for example, the basic interest in the way nuclei react, just as in the science of chemistry experiments are made on the way atoms interact. Further, the study of transmutation processes has thrown some light on the problems of nuclear structure and nuclear forces, and on the energy states of stable and unstable nuclei. Many nuclear reactions have led to the production and identification of previously unknown isotopes of the naturally occurring elements. These isotopic forms are almost invariably unstable and possess radioactive properties which have been utilized, as will be explained in Chapter XVII, to solve many problems of considerable theoretical and practical importance. In addition, numerous isotopes of elements which do not now exist on the earth have been obtained (Chapter XVI).

10.3. One of the by-products of the study of nuclear reactions was the discovery of the neutron (§ 2.117), and it was experiments on transmutations made with neutrons that led to the totally unexpected and surprising result that indicated the direction in which the release of atomic energy could be achieved. Success in this connection alone would have justified all the work that has been done in the field of transmutation.

FORMATION OF COMPOUND NUCLEUS

10.4. In the investigation of nuclear transformation processes the incident

273

particles or *projectiles*, as they are frequently called, have usually been energetic protons, deuterons and alpha particles accelerated by means of one or other of the devices described in the preceding chapter. In addition, numerous experiments have been made with neutrons as the incident particles. High-energy X-rays and, to a minor extent, electrons have also been used to bring about nuclear transformations. The lighter particle ejected in the course of a reaction may be a proton, deuteron, triton (§ 10.31 footnote), alpha particle, neutron or gamma-ray photon. In most cases studied only one of these is emitted, but several processes are known in which two or more are expelled. In certain nuclear reactions (§ 10.62), as many as twenty or thirty nucleons are ejected.

10.5. Although there are instances of exceptional behavior, which will be pointed out later, it is probable that in the majority of artificially produced nuclear transformations the first step is the formation of a *compound nucleus* due to the coalescence of the projectile with the struck nucleus, frequently referred to as the *target nucleus*. The compound nucleus is invariably unstable, because of its excess energy, and consequently it emits one or, occasionally, more particles of high energy in an attempt to attain stability.

10.6. The formation of a compound nucleus in the transmutation of nitrogen by alpha particles was established by cloud-chamber studies, around 1925, as reported in § 9.10. Nevertheless, for nearly a decade thereafter some scientists were of the opinion that nuclear disintegrations which did not involve capture of the projectile by the target nucleus were quite common. The general acceptance, at the present time, of a compound nucleus as an intermediate in most nuclear reactions is largely due to the experimental work of W. D. Harkins and D. M. Gans in the United States in 1935, and to the theoretical considerations of N. Bohr (§ 10.11) in the following year.

10.7. Before it can unite with the target to form a compound nucleus, the incident particle must overcome or penetrate the barrier due to electrostatic forces of repulsion. As stated in § 9.20, for a given amount of energy, the probability that an alpha particle will enter a specific nucleus is much less than for a proton. Consequently, if alpha particles are to be capable of producing nuclear transformations, especially for target nuclei having high atomic numbers and hence large positive charges, they will need to carry considerable amounts of energy. Since the deuteron, with a mass of two units and a single charge, is intermediate between a proton and an alpha particle, it would be expected, at first sight, that it should be on the whole less effective than a proton but more so than an alpha particle of the same energy.

10.8. It has been found, however, that the deuteron is capable of initiating several nuclear transformations, through the formation of compound nuclei, at relatively low energies. It will be seen in § 11.5 that it requires approximately 2 Mev to break up a deuteron into a proton and a neutron, but the addition of these individual particles to a nucleus of moderate or high mass number means an average increase in energy of about 8 Mev per nucleon (§ 12.7), or 16 Mev for the neutron and proton. Hence, the system will have made a net energy gain of 14 Mev as a result of the fusion of the deuteron with the target nucleus. This will tend to favor penetration of the potential energy barrier by the deuteron, and the consequent formation of the compound nucleus.*

10.9. With a proton as the projectile there is a gain of 8 Mev when it is taken up by a nucleus, and for an alpha particle the energy increase is only about 4 Mev, this being the difference between the 28.2 Mev energy required to separate it into two protons and two neutrons, as shown in § 4.40, and the approximately 32 Mev gained from the addition of four nucleons to the target nucleus. Because of the smaller energy increases, compound nuclei are less likely to be formed, and nuclear transformations are less probable with protons and alpha particles as projectiles than with deuterons of equivalent energy.

10.10. Since a neutron carries no electric charge there are no electrostatic forces operative, and there is virtually no potential energy barrier to prevent its entry into a target nucleus. At the same time, there is a gain of about 8 Mev of energy, provided the mass number of the target element is not too high or too low. It is to be expected, therefore, that nuclear transformations initiated by neutrons should be relatively common, as is indeed the case. The interaction of neutrons with various nuclei has an important bearing on the problems associated with the utilization of atomic energy, and some aspects of this subject will be dealt with more fully in the next chapter.

EMISSION OF PARTICLES FROM COMPOUND NUCLEUS

10.11. Having discussed the formation of the compound nucleus, it is now necessary to consider its subse-quent behavior. According to the views developed largely by N. Bohr (see § 4.45) in Denmark in 1936, when a particle enters an atomic nucleus the additional energy is very rapidly shared among the nucleons present in the resulting compound nucleus.† This redistribution of energy takes place continuously, so that in the course of time one particular nucleon, or combination of nucleons, in the compound nucleus acquires sufficient energy to permit it to escape, leaving a more stable residual nucleus. As far as its decay is concerned, a compound nucleus does not differ essentially from an ordinary radioactive nucleus, except that the former has a much shorter life. Calculations indicate that the average life of a compound nucleus is about 10^{-14} to 10^{-12} sec., and although this is very short in terms of measurable periods of time, it is long compared with that—less than 10^{-21} sec.—taken by a proton or neutron moving with a speed of 10^9 cm. per sec. to travel across a nucleus of 10^{-12} cm. diameter. There are thus sufficient collisions among the nucleons, even in 10^{-14} sec., to permit the conditions necessary for energy redistribution to be realized.

10.12. Since the barrier due to forces of repulsion is virtually nonexistent for neutrons, these particles will, in general, be able to escape from the compound nucleus much more readily than either protons, deuterons or alpha particles. This is especially true when the target nucleus has a high atomic number and, hence, a large positive charge; the potential barrier due to electrostatic forces is thus also high, and the probability that charged par-

* There is another reason, referred to in § 10.28, why deuterons are effective projectiles for certain nuclear transformations.

† More recent studies indicate that the entering particle does not necessarily share its energy very rapidly with the nucleons (see § 11.115), but this modification of Bohr's theory of the compound nucleus does not affect the general discussion presented here.

ticles will be emitted is very low. For target elements of small atomic number, on the other hand, neutrons are often more strongly bound in the compound nucleus than are protons, and since the energy barrier for the latter is then not too high, the ejection of a proton sometimes occurs. The energy required to form an alpha particle is only 4 Mev—the same as that gained when such a particle enters a nucleus— and so there is a fair chance that an alpha particle will be emitted from the compound nucleus, provided the atomic number, and hence the energy barrier, is not too high. The expulsion of a deuteron is, however, a rare event because, apart from the energy required to penetrate the potential barrier, some 14 Mev must be available for the formation of the deuteron as a separate entity. This process could take place only if the incident particle carried a sufficient quantity of energy which it contributed to the compound nucleus. In cases of this kind, when considerable energy is available due to the use of highly accelerated projectiles, two or more nucleons may be expelled virtually simultaneously.

10.13. In addition to protons, deuterons and alpha particles, compound nuclei on occasion emit other positively charged particles. Among those which have been observed are the nuclei of a hydrogen isotope and of a helium isotope, both with mass number 3, i.e., H^3 and He^3, respectively. A relatively large amount of energy is required for their liberation, and so the probability of their expulsion by a compound nucleus is small. It may be noted in passing that, although there is no obvious reason why heavier particles, such as Li^6 and Li^7, should not be emitted, the three positive charges carried by these nuclei makes

the electrostatic repulsion so large that the probability of their penetration of the barrier is quite negligible.* Other reactions, involving the emission of particles of small charge, consequently occur in preference.

10.14. When the energy of a compound nucleus, following the capture of an incident particle, is not sufficient to permit expulsion of a nucleon, some or all of its excess energy may be emitted in the form of gamma radiation. Processes of this kind are referred to as *radiative capture* reactions. These are of common occurrence when the incident particle is a neutron of low energy. Such transmutation processes, designated (n,γ), are very important, as will be seen in Chapter XI.

10.15. Another possibility which may be considered is that, like certain radioactive elements, a compound nucleus might acquire stability by expelling an electron, or even a positron. But, this rarely, if ever, takes place, because the formation of an electron requires the conversion of a neutron into a proton, together with an electron and a neutrino, as explained in § 7.50, and this change is slow compared with the direct emission of a particle or even of a gamma-ray photon. Radioactive decay processes accompanied by the expulsion of an electron or a positron occur when the unstable nucleus does not have sufficient excess energy to permit a nucleon to detach itself completely. Such unstable nuclei have relatively long lives compared with those of the compound nuclei under consideration.

GENERAL PROPERTIES OF
COMPOUND NUCLEUS

10.16. A particular compound nucleus can sometimes be formed in two or more different ways. The union

---

* There is some evidence that the unstable Li^8 particle is expelled in certain complex nuclear disintegrations (§ 18.54).

of an alpha particle with an N^{14} nucleus, a deuteron with O^{16} or a proton with O^{17} leads, for example, to the formation of the same compound nucleus, actually a high-energy (excited) state of an unstable fluorine isotope; thus,

$$\begin{array}{l} {}_7N^{14} + {}_2He^4 \searrow \\ {}_8O^{16} + {}_1H^2 \rightarrow [{}_9F^{18}]. \\ {}_8O^{17} + {}_1H^1 \nearrow \end{array}$$

The mass number of this compound nucleus is 18, since this is the sum of the mass numbers of the target nucleus and of the projectile in each case; similarly, the total charge is 9, which is the atomic number of fluorine.

10.17. Although it may not be strictly true, it can be assumed that, once a compound nucleus has been formed, its subsequent behavior, with special reference to the particle or particles emitted, depends only on the energy and not on its mode of formation. In general, a given compound nucleus is capable of breaking up in several different ways, the particular mode which predominates depending on the total amount of energy available, partly from the kinetic energy of the projectile, and partly from the gain of energy accompanying its fusion with the target nucleus. An interesting illustration is provided by the unstable compound nucleus $[{}_{30}Zn^{65}]$ which can be formed by the interaction of a deuteron ($_1H^2$) with the

$$[{}_{30}Zn^{65}] \begin{cases} \rightarrow (1)\ {}_{30}Zn^{65} + \gamma \\ \rightarrow (2)\ {}_{30}Zn^{64} + {}_0n^1 \\ \rightarrow (3)\ {}_{29}Cu^{64} + {}_1H^1 \\ \rightarrow (4)\ {}_{30}Zn^{63} + 2{}_0n^1 \\ \rightarrow (5)\ {}_{28}Ni^{61} + {}_2He^4 \\ \rightarrow (6)\ {}_{29}Cu^{62} + {}_1H^3 \\ \rightarrow (7)\ {}_{29}Cu^{63} + {}_1H^2 \end{cases}$$

nucleus of a copper atom of mass number 63, i.e., $_{29}Cu^{63}$. This compound nucleus can undergo several different reactions, as shown in the preceding column, their relative extents depending on the available energy.

10.18. The last four processes have a low probability, for reasons given earlier, although reaction (4) takes place to a considerable extent when the incident particle has a large amount of energy. It will be seen that process (7) is the reverse of that by which the compound nucleus has been supposed to be formed. In fact, all the processes indicated above, and similar nuclear reactions, are reversible, so that the same compound nucleus could, theoretically, be formed by reversing any of the reactions as written.* Actually Zn^{64} and Ni^{61} are the only stable species among the various product nuclides, and the formation of $[{}_{30}Zn^{65}]$ by the interaction of Zn^{64} with a neutron, i.e., the reverse of process (2), has been observed. There is no doubt that with alpha particles of sufficient energy reaction (5) could also be reversed, as could the others if the appropriate target nuclei were available.

10.19. In the interaction of an accelerated deuteron with the Cu^{63} nucleus, process (3), in which a proton is emitted, predominates at low deuteron energies, for a reason which will be given in § 10.28, but this becomes less important at higher energies, when reactions (3) and (4) occur at the same time. It is important to note that at suitable energies several nuclear reactions can take place simultaneously, although one particular process often predominates at low energies and another at higher energies. Consequently,

---

* There are, consequently, seven different ways in which the same compound nucleus $[{}_{30}Zn^{65}]$ could be formed, and six ways in which it could break up, omitting the reverse of the process of formation in each case. The formulation given above thus implies 42 different possible nuclear reactions. However, the formation of Zn^{65} by the simultaneous capture of two neutrons by Zn^{63}, i.e., the reverse of process (4), is not very probable.

the method of formation of the compound nucleus has an indirect influence on the nature of the subsequent process. For example, when $[_{30}Zn^{65}]$ is formed from Zn^{64} and a neutron of low energy, by the reversal of process (2), the only reaction which can take place to any appreciable extent is the radiative capture process (1); the relatively small amount of excitation energy is thus emitted as a gamma ray. When produced in this manner, the compound nucleus $[_{30}Zn^{65}]$ has insufficient energy for any of the other reactions indicated above to be possible. When high-energy neutrons are used as the incident particles, instead of those with low energy, some of the other reactions occur. It appears that whenever a compound nucleus has enough energy to make expulsion of a material particle possible, the probability of gamma-ray emission is extremely small.

TRANSMUTATION BY PROTONS

10.20. In the preceding sections a discussion has been given of the general principles underlying transmutation processes, in which a compound nucleus is formed as an intermediate stage. In this and the following sections reference will be made to specific cases of nuclear reactions with various projectiles, and some additional matters will be elucidated.

10.21. With protons as the incident particles, radiative capture processes, i.e., of the (p,γ) type, have been observed for a number of the lighter elements; thus,

$$_{13}Al^{27} + {}_1H^1 \rightarrow {}_{14}Si^{28} + \gamma,$$

which may be written as $Al^{27} (p,\gamma) Si^{28}$. The product is a nuclide with both atomic number and mass number one unit higher than those of the target material. Other instances of the same

kind are $Li^7 (p,\gamma) Be^8$, $N^{14} (p,\gamma) O^{15}$, $F^{19} (p,\gamma) Ne^{20}$ and $Cr^{50} (p,\gamma) Mn^{51}$. The bombardment of lithium by protons has been used as a source of high-energy (17 Mev) gamma radiations for experimental purposes.

10.22. As may be anticipated, the probability of the (p,n) type of reaction is relatively high, provided the proton has sufficient energy to penetrate the energy barrier and form a compound nucleus. Such a reaction is

$$_{11}Na^{23} + {}_1H^1 \rightarrow {}_{12}Mg^{23} + {}_0n^1,$$

where the neutron emitted is represented by $_0n^1$ since it carries no charge but has a mass of approximately one atomic mass unit. The product nucleus is seen to have the same mass as the target element but its atomic number is one unit higher. Several (p,n) reactions are known, although they are more common with the lighter than with the heavier elements, since higher energies are necessary for the nuclei of the latter to be penetrated by the protons.

10.23. For the sake of completeness, it may be mentioned that reactions of the $(p,2n)$ and (p,pn) types have been observed when using high-energy protons. In view of the results obtained with other particles of very high energy, in the range of several hundred million electron volts, there is no doubt that protons can initiate reactions in which three, four or even more particles are emitted.

10.24. Nuclear processes of the (p,α) and (p,d) types, where the particles expelled are an alpha particle and a deuteron, respectively, are comparatively uncommon because of the small probability of penetrating the relatively high energy barriers. The large binding energy of the alpha particle (§ 4.40) makes its emission more likely than that of a deuteron, but in any event, unless high-energy protons are used, the (p,α) reaction is to be expected only with target elements of low atomic number for which the electrostatic repulsion is not too high. The first transmutation process involving artificially accelerated particles to be discovered (§ 9.21) was of the (p,α) type, namely, $Li^7 (p,\alpha) He^4$; another example is

$$_7N^{14} + _1H^1 \rightarrow _6C^{11} + _2He^4.$$

One of the rare cases of a (p,d) reaction is

$$_4Be^9 + _1H^1 \rightarrow _4Be^8 + _1H^2,$$

but there are probably special circumstances which favor the emission of a deuteron in this case.

10.25. A few instances have been recorded of reactions of the (p,p) type, in which a proton is both the incident and the emitted particle; the product nucleus must then have the same mass number and atomic number as the target element. The only difference between target and product nuclei is that the latter is in a higher energy (excited) level than the former, the incident proton being deprived of some of its energy before it, or another proton, is ejected. An example of this kind of reaction, which is one instance of the more general phenomenon of *nuclear excitation*, is

$$In^{115} + _1H^1 \rightarrow In^{115*} + _1H^1,$$

where the asterisk (*) is used to indicate an excited state of the In^{115} nucleus. The excited nucleus soon loses its excess energy as gamma radiation; thus,

$$In^{115*} \rightarrow In^{115} + \gamma.$$

Such processes may be represented as (p,p') or $(p,p\gamma)$, the symbol p' implying the emission of a proton of different (lower) energy than the incident proton.

10.26. There are two ways in which an excited nucleus could be produced as a result of interaction with a proton (or other positively charged particle) of high energy. One involves the capture of the particle with the formation of a compound nucleus as the first stage. A particle of the same kind is then expelled within a very short time, but with less energy than it originally had. The (kinetic) energy which the particle has lost has been converted into excitation (or potential) energy of the target nucleus. A process of this kind is referred to as *inelastic scattering.** When the incident high-energy particle is a proton, the emission of a neutron from the compound nucleus, i.e., the (p,n) reaction, would appear to be more probable than the process described above. In this event, another method of nuclear excitation may be significant. The electrostatic (or Coulomb) interaction between the positive charges on the proton (or other charged particle) and the target nucleus (cf. § 4.13) may result in the transfer of energy from the former to the latter in a close encounter without the intermediate production of a compound nucleus. The amount of energy gained by the nucleus in this way may be sufficient to produce a definite excited state; the interaction is then referred to as a *Coulomb* (or *electrostatic*) *excitation*.

Transmutation by Deuterons

10.27. It was seen in § 10.8 that the deuteron is a particularly effective projectile for causing nuclear

---

* By contrast, the term *elastic scattering* is used for a collision in which kinetic energy is transferred from the projectile to the target nucleus, but the latter is not raised to an excited state.

transmutations because a relatively small amount of energy, about 2 Mev, is sufficient to cause its rupture into a neutron and proton. This small binding energy of the constituent nucleons of a deuteron has another significant effect in facilitating nuclear changes. In the course of a study, reported in 1935, of reactions of the (d,p) type resulting from the bombardment of various elements with deuterons accelerated by means of a cyclotron, E. O. Lawrence, E. M. McMillan and R. L. Thornton in the United States noted that the efficiency of the processes increased with increasing energy of the incident particle[*] at a rate that was appreciably greater than was to be expected from the wave-mechanical theory of barrier penetration by the deuteron (§ 9.20).

10.28. An explanation for this behavior was immediately proposed by the American mathematical-physicist J. R. Oppenheimer who, in conjunction with M. Phillips, derived certain theoretical consequences which were found to be in complete agreement with the observed facts. According to the *Oppenheimer-Phillips mechanism*, the deuteron behaves as a relatively loose combination of a neutron and a proton, since the binding energy is comparatively small. When the deuteron approaches a nucleus, the electrostatic repulsion of the positive charges tends to force the proton away, while the neutron is not affected. If the energy of the incident deuteron exceeds the neutron-proton binding energy, i.e., about 2 Mev, the proton portion will break off and be repelled, but the neutron will enter the target nucleus, since there is virtually no barrier to prevent this taking place. In a sense, the Oppenheimer-Phillips type of process

may be regarded as occurring in two stages: the break up of the deuteron into a proton and a neutron, followed by the reaction between the latter and the target nucleus. The resulting compound nucleus usually does not have sufficient energy to eject a particle, but as it is in an excited state it will lose its excess energy in the form of gamma radiation.

10.29. Nuclear reactions of the (d,p) type are quite common, for they have been observed with nearly all elements. At low deuteron energies the mechanism is presumably as described above, but at high energies it is probable that, as in most transmutations, a compound nucleus is formed by combination of the whole deuteron with the target nucleus, followed by the ejection of a proton. The end result is, of course, the same as in the Oppenheimer-Phillips processes. Examples of (d,p) nuclear transmutations, which include elements of low, medium and high atomic weights, are given below. It will be observed that the product is always an isotope of the target element, with a mass number one unit higher.

$$_{3}\text{Li}^{7} + {}_{1}\text{H}^{2} \rightarrow {}_{3}\text{Li}^{8} + {}_{1}\text{H}^{1}$$

$$_{48}\text{Cd}^{114} + {}_{1}\text{H}^{2} \rightarrow {}_{48}\text{Cd}^{115} + {}_{1}\text{H}^{1}$$

$$_{83}\text{Bi}^{209} + {}_{1}\text{H}^{2} \rightarrow {}_{83}\text{Bi}^{210} + {}_{1}\text{H}^{1}$$

10.30. Attention may be called to the last of these reactions, in which the product is an isotope of bismuth, of mass number 210 and atomic number 83. Reference to the table in § 5.58 and Fig. 8.1 will show that these are the mass number and atomic number of the naturally occurring radioactive element commonly known as radium E. Bombardment of ordinary bismuth by accelerated deuterons does,

---

[*] The variation with the energy of the incident particle of the efficiency, or yield, of a nuclear reaction is called the *excitation function* of the particular process.

in fact, yield a product which is identical with radium E; it emits beta particles and has a half life of 5.0 days.

10.31. Another (d,p) reaction of special interest was discovered by Rutherford, in conjunction with M. L. E. Oliphant and P. Harteck, in 1934, as a result of the bombardment by deuterons of deuterium itself, in the form of a solid compound. The process thus involves the interaction of an accelerated deuteron with a stationary one, and the result is the emission of a proton, leaving a third isotope of hydrogen, of mass number 3, as the residual nucleus; thus,

$$_1H^2 + _1H^2 \rightarrow _1H^3 + _1H^1,$$

where $_1H^3$ is the new isotope which has been called *tritium*.* The additivity of the subscripts, indicating the nuclear charges or atomic numbers, shows that the product, tritium, has an atomic number of unity, and hence must be isotopic with hydrogen. The atomic weight has been determined from the known isotopic weights of deuterium and hydrogen, and the reaction energy Q derived from the energy of the deuteron projectile and the ranges of the resultant particles. The value of Q is $+4.03$ Mev, which is equivalent to $+0.00433$ mass unit, and taking the isotopic weights of deuterium and hydrogen as 2.01474 and 1.00814, respectively, the isotopic weight of tritium is found, by the method described in § 9.33, to be $(2 \times 2.01474) - (1.00814 + 0.00433)$, which is 3.01701. It will be seen later that tritium is unstable and does not occur naturally; consequently, it can be obtained only in nuclear transmutation processes.

10.32. Competing with the proton-emitting nuclear changes induced by deuterons of moderate energies, are reactions of the (d,n) type, in which the deuteron enters the nucleus of the target element and a neutron is then ejected from the resulting compound nucleus. A large number of transmutations of this kind have been reported; in several cases, especially with target elements of low atomic weight, particularly beryllium, high-energy neutrons, useful for experimental purposes, are emitted. Among reactions of the (d,n) type are the following:

$$_3Li^6 + _1H^2 \rightarrow _4Be^7 + _0n^1$$

$$_{52}Te^{130} + _1H^2 \rightarrow _{53}I^{131} + _0n^1$$

$$_{83}Bi^{209} + _1H^2 \rightarrow _{84}Po^{210} + _0n^1.$$

In each case the mass number and atomic number of the product are both one unit higher than those of the target element. In the third example quoted above, the product has the mass number and atomic number of naturally occurring polonium, or radium F; its identity with the latter has been proved by a study of the radioactivity observed after bombardment of bismuth with deuterons. Both radium E, resulting from the (d,p) reaction, as mentioned earlier, and radium F, from the (d,n) process, are obtained simultaneously at moderately high (7 to 10 Mev) deuteron energies.

10.33. In addition to producing tritium, the interaction of deuterons with deuterons is accompanied by the formation of an isotope of helium of mass number 3, by the reaction

$$_1H^2 + _1H^2 \rightarrow _2He^3 + _0n^1,$$

which is a (d,n) process. This helium isotope is present to a very minute

---

* From the Greek *tritos* (third), by analogy with deuterium, from *deuteros* (second). A tritium atom is sometimes represented by the symbol T, and the nucleus, called a *triton,* is indicated by t.

extent in ordinary helium gas. By making use of the energy change Q of the $H^2(d,n)He^3$ reaction, and the known masses of the neutron and the deuterium atom, the isotopic weight of He^3 is found to be 3.01699. Mention may also be made of the analogous (d,n) reaction between accelerated deuterons and tritium, i.e., $H^3(d,n)He^4$. This process is of interest as a means of producing neutrons having an energy of at least 14 Mev (§ 11.89).

10.34. When the incident deuterons have high energies, of the order of 10 Mev or more, two neutrons are expelled from the compound nucleus, leading to a number of reactions of the $(d,2n)$ type with target elements of moderately high mass numbers; thus,

$$_{26}Fe^{56} + {}_1H^2 \rightarrow {}_{27}Co^{56} + 2{}_0n^1$$

$$_{52}Te^{130} + {}_1H^2 \rightarrow {}_{53}I^{130} + 2{}_0n^1.$$

At still higher energies, such as have been obtained by means of the 184-inch cyclotron (§ 9.72), reactions of the $(d,3n)$ type, and others of a still more involved nature, have been observed. The subject of disintegration by very high-energy particles will be considered separately in a later section (§ 10.58 *et seq.*).

10.35. Because of the high nuclear potential energy barrier for alpha particles, which increases with the atomic number of the target nucleus, reactions of the (d,α) type are observed only with deuterons of high energy and elements of fairly low atomic number. One example is

$$_{20}Ca^{40} + {}_1H^2 \rightarrow {}_{19}K^{38} + {}_2He^4,$$

and others are $Li^6(d,\alpha)He^4$, $Ne^{20}(d,\alpha)$ F^{18}, $Mg^{26}(d,\alpha)Na^{24}$ and $Ni^{60}(d,\alpha)Co^{58}$.

10.36. Although they are as unexpected as the (p,d) reactions referred to in § 10.24, a few instances are known

of processes of the analogous (d,t) type, where t represents the triton, or nucleus of tritium, i.e., of H^3 or T, the third isotope of hydrogen. One case, namely,

$$_4Be^9 + {}_1H^2 \rightarrow {}_4Be^8 + {}_1H^3,$$

indicated in brief by $Be^9(d,t)Be^8$, is of especial interest since the bombardment of beryllium by 10-Mev deuterons has been used as a source of high-energy tritium nuclei (§ 10.46).

10.37. Possibly due to the fact that there is a considerable gain of energy when a deuteron enters a nucleus, radiative capture (d,γ) reactions are not common. The excitation energy of the compound nucleus is so high that it can very quickly emit a neutron, at least, or even a proton. The re-emission of a deuteron, leaving the target nucleus in an excited state, is a possibility, provided the entering deuteron has sufficient energy. This inelastic scattering process is then followed by the emission of radiation from the excited nucleus. Just as with protons, excited nuclei can also be produced by deuterons as a result of Coulomb interaction (§ 10.26).

TRANSMUTATION BY ALPHA PARTICLES

10.38. It will be recalled (§ 9.4) that Rutherford first observed in 1919 the transmutation of the nitrogen atom as a result of interaction with alpha particles from radioactive sources. The nuclear reaction he discovered was of the (α,p) type which is common with elements of low atomic number. As the latter increases, the potential barriers preventing the entry of the alpha particle and the emission of the proton become higher and the probability of the (α,p) process decreases. However, with the availability of artificially accelerated alpha particles (helium ions), this reaction, which Rutherford was not able to observe for elements above potassium, has now been detected for nuclei with high atomic numbers.

10.39. Although it was not realized until 1932, the (α,n) reaction, which, incidentally, led to the discovery of the neutron (§ 2.117), frequently occurs at the same time as the (α,p) change. An important example of an (α,n) transmutation is

$$_4\text{Be}^9 + {}_2\text{He}^4 \rightarrow {}_6\text{C}^{12} + {}_0n^1,$$

which provides a useful laboratory source of neutrons; alpha particles of sufficient energy are obtained from radon gas, i.e., from radium emanation, from radium or from polonium. By using energetic alpha particles, (α,n) reactions have been observed with the heaviest elements, including uranium, and the artificial elements neptunium and plutonium (Chapter XVI).

10.40. When the energy of the alpha particle is large enough for it to penetrate a highly charged nucleus, other reactions, such as $(\alpha,2n)$, (α,np), $(\alpha,3n)$, $(\alpha,4n)$ and $(\alpha,3np)$, in which two or more nucleons are expelled, take place. Nuclear processes occurring with incident alpha particles of very high energy will be referred to in § 10.58 and in Chapter XVI.

10.41. Alpha particles are able to bring about nuclear excitation reactions as a result of inelastic scattering, in which the high-energy alpha particle is first captured by the nucleus and is then expelled with a lower energy. Just as with protons and deuterons, alpha particles can also produce excited nuclei due to Coulomb interaction. In every case, the excited nucleus eventually rids itself of the excess energy by the emission of gamma radiation.

TRANSMUTATION BY NEUTRONS

10.42. The production of neutrons of various energies and their properties will be described more fully in Chapter XI, and so only brief consideration will be given here to transmutation reactions induced by neutrons. The most common type of process is radiative capture, represented by (n,γ), in which a neutron is taken up by the target nucleus and the resulting compound nucleus then emits its excess energy as gamma radiation (§ 10.14). Neutrons of relatively low energy, frequently called *slow neutrons*, are particularly effective for the (n,γ) reaction, an instance of which is

$$_{29}\text{Cu}^{63} + {}_0n^1 \rightarrow {}_{29}\text{Cu}^{64} + \gamma.$$

Virtually all the elements, except some of the very lightest, exhibit radiative capture of slow neutrons; the product is always isotopic with the target element, but its mass number is one unit higher.

10.43. With fast neutrons, that is to say, with those having higher energies, the (n,p) type of reaction is fairly common; additional energy is here required to permit the proton to escape from the compound nucleus. Such reactions are $\text{N}^{14}(n,p)\text{C}^{14}$ and $\text{Cl}^{35}(n,p)\text{S}^{35}$, so that the product nucleus has the same mass, but its atomic number is one unit less than that of the target. For elements of atomic number of about 40 or less, and in a few instances where the atomic numbers are higher, (n,α) reactions have been observed; examples are $\text{F}^{19}(n,\alpha)\text{N}^{16}$ and $\text{Zn}^{68}(n,\alpha)\text{Ni}^{65}$. If the neutron energy exceeds about 8 Mev, processes of the $(n,2n)$ type, such as $\text{C}^{12}(n,2n)\text{C}^{11}$ and $\text{Hg}^{198}(n,2n)\text{Hg}^{197}$, become possible; the product is here isotopic with the target element, as in the (n,γ) reactions, but its mass number is now smaller by one unit. Because of the large amount of energy required to remove a deuteron, at least 14 Mev, reactions of the (n,d) type take place only with neutrons of very high energy (§ 11.56).

10.44. Since neutrons are not electrically charged, these particles cannot cause nuclear excitation by electrostatic interaction as can protons, etc. However, neutrons of sufficient energy can produce excited nuclei as a result of inelastic scattering reactions. The compound nucleus, formed when the target nucleus captures a fast neutron, expels a neutron of lower energy, leaving the original nucleus in an excited (high-energy) state. The excess energy is subsequently liberated as gamma radiation. The subject of neutron scattering, both inelastic and elastic, is of considerable importance and further reference to it will be made in Chapter XI.

TRANSMUTATION BY PARTICLES OF MASS THREE

10.45. With the availability of moderate quantities of tritium (§§ 10.31, 11.58), the isotope of hydrogen of mass number 3, and of He^3, an isotope of helium of the same mass number, a certain amount of work has been done using these nuclei as projectiles. The investigations have not been extensive for several reasons, e.g., the radioactive nature of tritium and the relative scarcity of both this substance and helium-3. In any event, the results obtained by bombarding various target elements with H^3 and He^3 ions have not been basically different from those described above for other isotopes of hydrogen and helium, respectively.

10.46. The first studies with accelerated tritons, i.e., tritium ions, were made in 1943 by C. P. Baker, M.

G. Holloway, L. D. P. King and R. E. Schreiber in connection with a wartime project at Purdue University. These experiments, with a gas containing only a very small proportion of tritium, were preliminary in nature, and were mainly concerned with reactions involving light elements. In 1948, M. L. Pool and D. N. Kundu, in the United States, used high-energy tritons, obtained by the action of 10-Mev deuterons on beryllium (§ 10.36), as projectiles in the bombardment of some heavier ions, e.g., Co^{59} and Rh^{103}. The reactions observed were of the (t,p) type, e.g.,

$$_{27}Co^{59} + {}_1H^3 \rightarrow {}_{27}Co^{61} + {}_1H^1.$$

Among other nuclear reactions involving accelerated tritons, mention may be made of the following: H^2 (t,n) He^4, which is the same as the one between accelerated deuterons and tritium; the (t,d) reaction with Li^6, namely, $Li^6(t,d)Li^7$; and a reaction of the (t,He^3) type, namely, Ag^{109} $(t,He^3)Pd^{109}$.

10.47. In 1939, L. W. Alvarez and R. Cornog showed that the helium-3 isotope was present to a very small extent in ordinary helium, by using the Berkeley cyclotron (§ 9.64) as an electromagnetic separating device. In these experiments they obtained evidence for the $Si^{28}(He^3,p)P^{30}$ reaction. A process of the same type, namely, $H^2(He^3,p)He^4$, was studied in 1943 by the Purdue group mentioned above, in which accelerated He^3 ions were used to bombard deuterium. More recently, other (He^3,p) reactions, e.g., $H^3(He^3,p)He^5$ and $He^3(He^3,p)Li^5$, have been observed. In the reactions $C^{12}(He^3,\alpha)C^{11}$ and $N^{14}(He^3,\alpha)N^{13}$, both incident and ejected particles are isotopes of helium, so that the products are isotopic with, but have one unit of mass less than, the target nuclei. Of interest also are the processes $He^3(He^3,2p)He^4$ and $C^{12}(He^3,d)$ N^{13}, which are alternative to some of the interactions noted above.

Transmutation by Heavy Ions

10.48. Since 1950, when a group at the University of California Radiation Laboratory showed that accelerated carbon ions caused the reactions Al^{27} $(C^{12},\alpha n)Cl^{34}$ and $Au^{197}(C^{12},4n)At^{205}$, there has been a growing interest in the transmutation processes brought about by relatively "heavy" ions, such as those of lithium, carbon, oxygen and nitrogen. Most of the reactions observed fall into two broad classes. The first type includes reactions in which there is apparently a simple transfer of a nucleon (or nucleons) from one nucleus to another. For example, the bombardment of a nitrogen target with high-energy nitrogen nuclei leads to the reactions

$$_7N^{14} + _7N^{14} \rightarrow _7N^{13} + _7N^{15}$$

and

$$_7N^{14} + _7N^{14} \rightarrow _6C^{13} + _8O^{15}.$$

In the first, a neutron is transferred from one nitrogen nucleus to the other, and in the second, a proton is transferred. In a somewhat similar reaction of nitrogen ions with boron-10, i.e.,

$$_7N^{14} + _5B^{10} \rightarrow _7N^{13} + _5B^{11},$$

a neutron is transferred to a nucleus of another kind.

10.49. In reactions of the second class, several nucleons (or other particles) are emitted as a result of bombardment of a target nucleus by an accelerated "heavy" ion. Although such processes are grouped together, there are probably several different types, some of which will be described

here. The interaction of 26-Mev nitrogen ($_7N^{14}$) ions with a nuclide of moderate mass number, e.g., aluminum ($_{13}Al^{27}$), leads to a variety of products, ranging from $_{14}Si^{31}$ to $_{19}K^{38}$; thus, from

$$_{13}Al^{27} + _7N^{14} \rightarrow 2\,_1H^1 + 2\,_2He^4 + _{14}Si^{31}$$

to

$$_{13}Al^{27} + _7N^{14} \rightarrow _1H^1 + 2\,_0n^1 + _{19}K^{38}.$$

There is some doubt whether a single compound nucleus, in the generally accepted sense, is formed in these reactions. It has been suggested that, owing to the strong electrostatic interaction between the nitrogen ion and the target nucleus, the former is split up into two or three helium ions (alpha particles) and some odd nucleons. The target is thus struck by a group of projectiles rather than by a single one. Varying numbers of these projectiles are then captured by the target nucleus to form several different compound nuclei, resulting in a number of different products.

10.50. Another type of reaction in the same general category occurs with heavy nuclei; the first stage is apparently the fusion of the projectile with the target to form a compound nucleus, which then expels a number of (generally four to six) neutrons. The particular interest of reactions of this kind lies in the fact that, with uranium as the target material, for example, it is possible to produce nuclides of higher atomic number which do not exist in nature. The minimum energy of the projectile in order to overcome the electrostatic repulsion of the uranium (or similar) target nucleus is about 100 Mev, but higher energies are desirable. Three fairly typical examples of the reactions that can occur are the following:

$$_{92}U^{238} + {_6}C^{12} \rightarrow 6n + 98^{244}$$

$$_{92}U^{238} + {_7}N^{14} \rightarrow 6n + 99^{246}$$

$$_{92}U^{238} + {_8}O^{16} \rightarrow 4n + 100^{250},$$

where the products are indicated by their respective atomic numbers, i.e., 98, 99 and 100. It is in the hopes of producing new elements of even higher atomic number, as will be discussed more fully in Chapter XVI, that reactions of this kind are receiving special attention. The compound nuclei formed are very unstable, and there is a considerable probability that they will break up into two (or more) much lighter nuclei, by the process of fission (§ 10.60). The yield of the new heavy nuclei is thus relatively small, and large ion currents are necessary in order to obtain appreciable quantities of the desired products (see § 9.113).

10.51. The capture of ions of sufficiently high energy may lead to considerable disruption of the target nucleus. Such reactions are apparent from the formation of "stars" in nuclear emulsions (§ 18.51). One of the nuclei in the emulsion, probably either silver or bromine, captures the bombarding ion and the resulting nucleus breaks up into a number of particles, each of which produces a track, like the prong of a star. In one well-defined instance, capture of a 750-Mev carbon ion led to the formation of a nine-pronged star. From the nature of the tracks, it was concluded that two of the particles emitted were protons, two alpha particles, and one possibly a lithium ion; the others were not identified.

Transmutations by Radiation and by Electrons

10.52. In 1934, using the gamma radiation from thorium C, having an energy of 2.62 Mev, J. Chadwick and M. Goldhaber in England found that a deuterium nucleus could be disintegrated into a neutron and a proton; thus,

$$_1H^2 + \gamma \rightarrow {_1}H^1 + {_0}n^1.$$

Since the binding energy of a neutron and a proton is a little over 2 Mev, the gamma ray from thorium C has sufficient energy to break up the deuterium nucleus. The binding energy of a neutron in beryllium of mass number 9 is also low, and the same gamma radiation is able to cause the (γ,n) reaction

$$_4Be^9 + \gamma \rightarrow {_4}Be^8 + {_0}n^1.$$

Reactions of this type, brought about by high-energy radiations, have been referred to as *photodisintegration** or *nuclear photo-effect*, the prefix *photo* implying light, or radiation, in the most general sense of the term.

10.53. In all elements, except the lightest, the energy required to remove a neutron from an atomic nucleus is about 8 Mev, and hence it is easy to understand why the gamma radiations from thorium C failed to cause any transmutations other than the two recorded above. When the 17-Mev radiations, produced by the bombardment of lithium by protons, were employed, however, a number of nuclei exhibited phototransmutation of the (γ,n) type. In several cases, where the energy is insufficient to cause actual transmutation, nuclear excitation has been observed; such processes may be described as being of the (γ,γ') type. Among the nuclides which have thus been obtained in excited states of moderate life are Kr^{83}, Sr^{87}, Cb^{93} and Hg^{199}.

10.54. By allowing electrons from a betatron (§ 9.75) or a synchrotron (§ 9.87) to fall on a tungsten target,

---

* *Phototransmutation* would perhaps be a better term to use here.

X-rays of energy from 20 to 330 Mev have been obtained, and these have been used to produce a variety of nuclear processes. Reactions of the (γ,n) and (γ,p) types* are most common at the lower energies, but at higher energies (γ,np), $(\gamma,2n)$, $(\gamma,n2p)$, (γ,α) and other processes involving the ejection of two, three or more particles have been observed. When high-energy X-rays interact with oxygen-16, one of the products is apparently carbon-11; this would imply that the reaction $O^{16}(\gamma,3n2p)C^{11}$, in which five nucleons are ejected, has occurred. Disintegration into four alpha particles has also been reported. Similarly, 25-Mev gamma rays can break up a carbon-12 nucleus into three alpha particles.

10.55. In the interaction of gamma rays or X-rays with matter, some or all of the energy of the absorbed radiation is transferred to the target nucleus which is thus converted into a highly-excited state resembling a compound nucleus. As with the latter, there is a continuous redistribution of energy among the nucleons present, and when any one of them acquires sufficient energy it can escape from the excited nucleus. When the energy derived from the radiation is of the order of 10 Mev, only one nucleon, either a proton or a neutron, can be emitted, but when the energy is of the order of 100 Mev or more it is not surprising that three, four or more nucleons are ejected.

10.56. Relatively few nuclear reactions induced by electrons have been observed; one reason is that the interaction probability of an electron with a nucleus is extremely small. However, it has been reported that electrons of about 1.8 Mev energy are capable of ejecting a neutron from the beryllium-9 nucleus. As seen above, the binding energy of the neutron is small in this case, so that the (e^-, ne^-) reaction

$$_4Be^9 + {}_{-1}e^0 \rightarrow {}_4Be^8 + {}_0n^1 + {}_{-1}e^0$$

does not appear unreasonable. It will be noted that the electron does not actually enter into the nuclear reaction, but its energy is utilized in some manner to detach the neutron.

10.57. Several cases have been described of nuclear excitation by means of high-energy electrons. The products are excited states identical with those obtained by means of X-rays or in other ways. The exact mechanism whereby the energy of the electrons is transferred to the nucleus is not clear; it is possible that the X-radiation (bremsstrahlung), produced as the electrons are decelerated (§ 4.75), is responsible for the nuclear excitation.

FISSION AND SPALLATION

10.58. It will be noted that in the nuclear transmutation processes already considered there are only a few cases of reactions associated with the expulsion of more than one particle. In the great majority of instances there is either radiative capture, when no material particle leaves the compound nucleus, or else a single particle is emitted. As a result, the products are very close, both in mass number and atomic number, to the target elements. This is, on the whole, to be expected because the binding energy of a nucleon is about 8 Mev, and hence an incident particle whose energy is of the order of 10 Mev is unlikely to bring about the ejection of more than one or two neutrons or protons. But if particles in a higher

* It will be recalled that high-energy X-rays differ from gamma rays in their origin only; for practical purposes, however, no distinction need be made, and so the symbol γ is used just as if actual gamma rays had been employed.

energy range, say in the region of 100 Mev or more, were employed, transmutations of other types, in which there are considerable differences between target and product nuclei, might be anticipated, and such reactions have indeed been observed.

10.59. It may be mentioned that the Bohr theory of the capture of the incident particle, followed by redistribution of its energy among the nucleons of the resulting compound nucleus (§ 10.11), requires modification for projectiles of high energy. Because of its high speed, such a particle can often pass through the target nucleus, being deprived of a fraction only of its energy (§ 11.112). Atomic nuclei are thus somewhat "transparent" to highly energetic projectiles.

10.60. The first of the high-energy transmutation processes to be considered is that known as *fission*, in which the target nucleus, in addition to emitting a small number of nucleons, usually neutrons, breaks up into two nuclei of approximately equal size. The phenomenon of fission forms the basis of the practical utilization of atomic (nuclear) energy, and so it will be discussed more fully in Chapter XIII; it is mentioned here only for the sake of completeness. Actually, the first instance of fission was not brought about by particles of high energy, but by slow neutrons interacting with the uranium-235 isotope. The more abundant uranium isotope of mass number 238 undergoes fission when subjected to the action of fast neutrons, of energy exceeding 1 Mev. Other naturally occurring elements of high atomic number, such as thorium and protoactinium, can be split by neutrons in a similar manner. Fission of uranium and thorium has been induced by protons, deuterons and gamma rays of energy from 1 to 10 Mev, and also

by 32-Mev alpha particles (§ 13.17). In the process of fission the nucleus of the target element breaks into two fragments in many different ways; thus, nearly eighty products, with mass numbers from about 72 to 160, have been detected in the fission of uranium-235. However, the major fraction of these products falls into two groups with mass numbers in the range of 80 to 108 and 125 to 153.

10.61. The examples of fission given above refer to the heaviest elements and do not actually represent very high-energy reactions, but the use of particles of higher energy has made it possible to induce fission of several somewhat lighter nuclei. Alpha particles accelerated to 400 Mev energy by the 184-inch synchrocyclotron have been found to cause fission of bismuth, lead, thallium, platinum and tantalum, while 200-Mev deuterons are similarly effective for bismuth, lead and thallium. Neutrons of 100 Mev energy produce fission of bismuth, lead and other heavy nuclei. A considerable number of nuclides of lower atomic weight have been detected among the products. It may be mentioned here, although the matter will be treated more fully at a later stage, that fission of uranium by particles of very high energy leads to an entirely different distribution of products from that observed in fission with neutrons of lower energy.

10.62. Another phenomenon, which differs from fission in being produced only with particles of high energy, was discovered in 1947 by G. T. Seaborg, I. Perlman and their collaborators at the Radiation Laboratory, Berkeley, California, using the facilities of the 184-inch cyclotron. When elements in the intermediate range of mass number and atomic number are bombarded by 400-Mev alpha particles or protons or by 200-Mev deuterons, they do not undergo fission and break up into two, more or less equal, parts. Instead, such nuclei emit various numbers, up to about twenty or thirty, or even more, of nucleons, leaving a series of products of lower mass and atomic number. The name *spallation** has been proposed for reactions of this kind.

10.63. Because of the tedious nature of the procedures necessary to identify the many products of spallation, the phenomenon has hitherto been studied with a few elements only. However, it has been observed for several elements, ranging from magnesium to antimony. Since it is not known whether alpha particles are split off in addition to neutrons and protons, a noncommittal method of representing spallation processes has been proposed. When arsenic ($_{33}As^{75}$) is bombarded by high-energy alpha particles ($_2He^4$), one of the numerous spallation products is an isotope of chlorine of mass number 38, that is, $_{17}Cl^{38}$; there has consequently been a net decrease of 18 units of atomic number and 41 units of mass, and this is indicated by writing $As^{75}(\alpha,18z41a)Cl^{38}$ to describe this particular reaction.

10.64. A nuclear process which represents a combination of fission and spallation was reported by the Berkeley scientists in 1948. When bismuth, lead, gold and other heavy elements are bombarded by high-energy protons or deuterons, ten or twelve nucleons are first expelled as in spallation, but the resulting nucleus is so unstable that it undergoes fission. Some of the reactions caused by accelerated carbon, nitrogen, oxygen, etc., ions are probably similar in nature (§ 10.50). It is of interest to mention that nearly all the known elements have been detected in the products of the fission-spallation of uranium.

10.65. The mechanism of fission is moderately well understood, as will be seen in Chapter XIII, but the basis of spallation is not altogether clear. Since products with atomic numbers higher than that of the target element have been detected, for example, $_{52}Te$ from $_{51}Sb$, it would appear that some, at least, of the incident particles enter the target nucleus to form an unstable compound nucleus. Because of the very high energy of the projectile, this nucleus is in a highly excited state, so that in an attempt to restore stability it rapidly emits a number of nucleons, each of which requires about 8 Mev for its release. With 400 Mev energy available, the emission of 41 nucleons from the compound nucleus, as in the spallation of arsenic referred to above, is not altogether surprising. Apart from the light that a study of the phenomenon must ultimately shed on the complex problem of nuclear structure, spallation of various elements has led to the isolation of a number of interesting, previously unknown, nuclides (§ 10.99).

TRANSMUTATION POTENTIALS:
RESONANCE AND ENERGY LEVELS

10.66. Certain nuclear transmutations, such as the $Li^7(p,\alpha)He^4$ reaction discovered by Cockcroft and Walton (§ 9.21), can be detected with incident particles of quite low energies, down to 0.025 Mev, although the yield increases markedly with increasing energy. On the other hand, some nuclear processes, for example $Li^7(p,n)Be^7$, are quite undetectable until the energy of the projectiles exceeds a certain mini-

* This term is based on the verb "to spall," meaning to break up by chipping off small fragments, which was suggested as appropriate by W. H Sullivan.

mum value. In reactions of the latter type there is said to be a *threshold energy,* below which transmutation cannot take place. The reason for the existence of such a threshold for the energy is not difficult to understand. If the nuclear reaction energy, i.e., the Q value, for a given process is negative, then this particular process cannot possibly take place unless an amount of energy Q, at least, is supplied from an external source. The source is, of course, the incident particle, which must carry with it the requisite nuclear reaction energy if the given process is to be possible.

10.67. The threshold energy in such cases is somewhat larger, numerically, than the reaction energy, the difference being the energy of the ejected particle and of the recoil nucleus, required for the conservation of momentum. For instance, the value of Q for the $Li^7(p,n)Be^7$ reaction is about -1.6 Mev, and the minimum energy which the protons must have for this process to be observed has been found to be 1.86 Mev. The neutron is evidently expelled with about 0.2 Mev energy, while the residual beryllium nucleus carries off a smaller amount. However, if the potential barrier for a particular reaction should happen to be much higher than the reaction energy, the threshold may greatly exceed the Q value.

10.68. Nuclear reactions of the (p,n), (γ,n) and (γ,p) types, as well as reactions in which two or more particles are emitted, such as $(d,2n)$ and $(n,2n)$, almost invariably have negative Q values and hence exhibit definite energy thresholds. When the energy of the incident particle or radiation exceeds this amount the efficiency

(or yield) of the process increases rapidly.

10.69. For reactions having positive Q values, there may be a detectable yield at low projectile energies if the potential energy barrier, either for the incident or for the emitted particles, is not high. If the barrier is high, there may be an apparent threshold energy, but it will probably not be very definite. In all cases, whether there is a threshold or not, the yield of a given nuclear process increases with the energy of the incident particle, provided there is no competitive reaction. A limit is reached as the energy approaches the maximum repulsion energy, that is, the value at the top of the hypothetical energy barrier (§ 7.28). Almost invariably, however, competing reactions cause the yield to decrease at high energies.

10.70. In certain instances it has been observed that instead of increasing regularly with increasing energy of the projectile, the efficiency of the process becomes exceptionally high in the region of certain particular energies. In the $Al^{27}(\alpha,p)Si^{30}$ reaction, for example, the yield of protons increases with the energy of the alpha particles, but for energies of 4.0, 4.49, 4.86, 5.25, 5.75 and 6.61 Mev the yields are markedly in excess of the general trend. This effect, which was predicted by the English physicist R. W. Gurney in 1929, is ascribed to a phenomenon known as wave-mechanical *resonance.** If the energy of the compound nucleus formed by the capture of the projectile happens to correspond fairly closely to one of its excited energy levels (§ 4.83), then there is an increased probability that the compound nucleus will be formed. In other

---

* The term is used in this connection because of the analogy with the phenomenon which physicists call resonance, whereby energy can be transferred from one vibrating system to another having the same vibration frequency.

words, when this energy condition exists, the incident particle has an exceptionally high probability of penetrating the potential energy barrier which resists its entry into the target nucleus. The alpha-particle energies recorded above, for which the proton yields in the $Al^{27}(\alpha,p)Si^{30}$ reaction are high, are presumably the resonance energies corresponding to the energy levels in the compound nucleus. It will be seen in Chapter XI that the resonance phenomenon is particularly common, as well as exceptionally important, in reactions of the (n,γ) type.

10.71. A study of the ranges of the particles emitted in nuclear reactions has revealed the fact that they do not necessarily all have the same range and, hence, the same energy. In some cases the particles are liberated in two or more groups; those in each group have the same energy, but the energies of the various groups are different. In the $B^{10}(\alpha,p)C^{13}$ reaction five groups of protons have been detected, and in $Al^{27}(\alpha,p)Si^{30}$ four such groups have been observed. It is probable that the emission of each group of protons leaves the product nucleus in a different energy state. When the protons of maximum energy are expelled, the product is presumably in its lowest nuclear energy level, that is, in the ground state. Each group with successively smaller energy corresponds to a successively higher energy level of the product nucleus. When the latter is in one of these excited states it will return to the ground state emitting, at the same time, gamma radiation. If the arguments presented here are correct, the energy of the radiation should correspond to the difference in energy of two proton groups. By studying the recoil electrons produced by the radiation (§ 6.5), this expectation has been confirmed.

10.72. The results described above provide information concerning the energy levels of the compound nucleus and of the product nucleus, respectively. Advantage has also been taken of nuclear excitation processes, caused by inelastic scattering of charged particles or neutrons and by Coulomb excitation, to throw light on the energy levels of many nuclei. The excited nuclear state formed may be extremely unstable, so that it loses its additional energy almost instantaneously, or it may exist for an appreciable time. In any event, the excess energy is ultimately emitted as one or more photons of gamma radiation. The energies of these rays, as determined directly or from internal conversion electrons (§ 7.106), are related to the energy levels of the nucleus, just as for the gamma rays accompanying radioactive changes (see Fig. 7.10).

NUCLEAR CROSS SECTIONS

10.73. The probability or (efficiency) of a nuclear reaction can be defined in terms of the number of particles emitted, or of nuclei undergoing transmutation, for a specified number of incident particles. A more general, uniform method, which has been widely adopted, is to express the relative efficiency by means of a quantity called the *nuclear cross section*. It represents the effective area of cross section of a single nucleus of a given species for a particular reaction. Thus, when the probability of the process is high, the so-called nuclear cross section will be large; on the other hand, when the probability is low, the cross section will be small.

10.74. If I is the number of incident particles striking in a given time a 1 sq. cm. area of the target material, containing N target nuclei (or atoms), and A is the number of these nuclei which undergo interaction in the specified time, then the nuclear cross section σ,* expressed as sq. cm. per nucleus, is defined by

$$\sigma = \frac{A}{NI} \text{ sq. cm. per nucleus.} \quad (10.1)$$

10.75. The description of σ as a nuclear cross section may be justified in the following manner. Suppose σ sq. cm. is actually the area per nucleus effective for a given transmutation process; since the material of the target surface contains N nuclei (or atoms) per sq. cm., the effective area per sq. cm. of total surface is consequently σN sq. cm. In other words, σN is the fraction of the surface which is capable of taking part in the nuclear reaction. This also represents the fraction of the incident particles I falling on the target surface which will be involved in the process. The number actually reacting is thus σNI, and this will be equal to A, the number of target nuclei undergoing transmutation, so that

$$A = \sigma NI.$$

Comparison of this result with equation (10.1), which provides the formal definition of σ, shows the two to be identical. Hence, it is justifiable to regard σ as the effective cross section of a single nucleus for a given nuclear reaction.

10.76. Since A is the number of target nuclei reacting, whereas N is the total number of such nuclei per sq. cm., the quantity A/N is the number of nuclei, and hence of incident particles, taking part in the process per single target nucleus. Upon dividing by the total number I of particles falling on 1 sq. cm. of the target, the result A/NI, which is equal to σ, by

equation (10.1), is the fraction of the particles falling on 1 sq. cm. of target that interact with a single nucleus. This represents a useful alternative definition of the cross section which brings out its relationship to the probability of the nuclear reaction; obviously, the larger the fraction of the incident particles reacting, the greater is the probability that the process will occur under the given conditions.

10.77. The value of the nuclear cross section depends not only on the nature of the target element, but also on the particular reaction under consideration, and the energy of the incident particle. A given nucleus, such as Li^7, for example, will in general have different cross sections for the reactions $Li^7(p,n)Be^7$ and $Li^7(p,\alpha)He^4$, which occur simultaneously. The values represent the probabilities of the two processes for protons of a specified energy, and the ratio will usually change with the energy of the incident particles.

10.78. When the nuclear cross section for a particular reaction is required, it is necessary to determine the number of nuclei taking part, either by counting the particles, such as neutrons or alpha particles, respectively, which are expelled, or by determining the number of product nuclei formed. Both of these methods have been used in different instances. On the other hand, if it is sufficient to know the *total* nuclear cross section for all processes in which the incident particles are absorbed, a simple procedure is possible. If I_0 is the number of incident particles, in a narrow (or collimated) beam, falling in a given time on 1 sq. cm. of the target material, which is in the form of a sheet of thickness x cm., and I is the corresponding number of these particles

* Greek *sigma*; this symbol is invariably used to represent nuclear reaction cross sections.

which emerge from the other side of the sheet, in the narrow beam, the difference $I_0 - I$ having been absorbed in various nuclear reactions, then

$$\frac{I}{I_0} = e^{-Nx\sigma}, \qquad (10.2)$$

where N is now the number of target nuclei per cc., e is the base of natural logarithms and σ is the *total* nuclear cross section. Hence, it is possible to determine the latter from measurements of the intensity of the beam of incident particles before and after passage through the target material.*

10.79. Experimental values for nu-clear cross sections are usually in the vicinity of 10^{-25} to 10^{-23} sq. cm. per nucleus, although in exceptional cases the results may be extremely small † or they may be as high as 10^{-20} sq. cm. per nucleus. The average diameter of a nucleus can be taken to be about 10^{-12} cm., and so the actual area of cross section is approximately 10^{-24} sq. cm. Since this represents the order of magnitude of many nuclear reaction cross sections, a unit, called a *barn*, equal to 10^{-24} sq. cm. per nucleus, has been adopted.‡ Thus, nuclear cross sections are frequently in the range of 0.1 to 10 barns, but they are known to vary from 10^{-8} (or less) to 10^6 barns for different reactions.

ARTIFICIAL RADIOACTIVITY

RADIOACTIVE PRODUCTS OF NUCLEAR PROCESSES

10.80. In the earlier experiments on nuclear transmutation, the process occurring was usually inferred from the nature of the emitted particle, special use being made of cloud-chamber photographs in this connection. Because nuclear reactions are generally performed on such a small scale, in comparison with the quantities commonly involved in most chemical work, the identity of the product could not be determined by conventional methods. Even mass spectroscopic procedures were hardly adequate to deal with the minute amounts of product that were usually obtained in nuclear processes. It was fortunate, therefore, that a notable discovery made it possible to identify, in many cases, the products of nuclear transmutations even when they were obtained in amounts which, if separated, would not have been visible under a microscope.

10.81. In the course of a study of the effect of alpha particles, from the naturally occurring radioelement polonium, on the nuclei of certain light elements, boron, magnesium and aluminum, in particular, I. Joliot-Curie and her husband, F. Joliot, to whose work reference was made in Chapter II (§§ 2.75, 2.117), found that, in addition to protons, there was an emission of neutrons and positrons (positive electrons). This result was not at all extraordinary, since the nuclear process appeared to be essentially of the (α,p) type discovered by Ruther-

* For further details, and the arrangements necessary for the inclusion or exclusion of scattering, see § 11.69 *et seq.*

† Values down to 10^{-32} sq. cm. per nucleus have been measured, but smaller values undoubtedly occur.

‡ The term "barn" was proposed in 1942 by the American physicists M. G. Holloway and C. P. Baker, as the result of a broadly humorous association of ideas. It served the purpose of a code word, which was desirable at the time, and seemed appropriate because "a cross section of 10^{-24} sq. cm. for nuclear processes was really as big as a barn" (Los Alamos Report, LAMS 523).

ford, and a neutron and a positron could together be regarded as the equivalent of a proton. But, early in 1934, the surprising fact was noted that, although the formation of protons and neutrons ceased when the source of alpha particles was removed, the positrons continued to be emitted. Reporting on their results, Joliot-Curie and Joliot wrote: "Our latest experiments have shown a very striking fact; when an aluminum foil is irradiated . . . [with alpha particles], the emission of positrons does not cease immediately when . . . [the source of the alpha particles] is removed. The foil remains radioactive and the emission of radiation decays exponentially as for an ordinary [naturally occurring] radioelement. We observed the same phenomenon with boron and magnesium. . . . The transmutation of boron, magnesium and aluminum by alpha particles has given birth to new radioelements emitting positrons. . . . It is probable that . . . [these species] are unknown isotopes which are always unstable."*

10.82. According to the Joliots, the nuclear process was actually of the (α,n) type, so that in the interaction of alpha particles with aluminum, for example, the reaction occurring was

$$_{13}Al^{27} + {}_2He^4 \rightarrow {}_{15}P^{30} + {}_0n^1.$$

The P^{30} isotope of phosphorus obtained in this manner, which is not found in nature, would then be the radioactive species which decayed with the emission of a positron. The latter is represented by the symbol $_{+1}e^0$, since it has a single positive charge but a virtually zero mass, and so the decay process would be

$$_{15}P^{30} \rightarrow {}_{+1}e^0 + {}_{14}Si^{30},$$

the final product being Si^{30}, a stable, naturally occurring isotope of silicon.

10.83. In order to confirm this suggested mechanism, aluminum foil was exposed to alpha particles, and then dissolved in hydrochloric acid solution. The hydrogen gas evolved was found to carry with it the positron emitting activity, presumably in the form of phosphine (PH_3) containing the radioactive phosphorus. Further, when the irradiated aluminum was dissolved in a mixture of hydrochloric and nitric acids, a small quantity of sodium phosphate added as carrier (§ 5.29), and then a zirconium salt, the precipitate of zirconium phosphate carried with it the radioactivity. The unstable species, which gives off positrons, hence appears wherever phosphorus, in the form of the appropriate compound, is to be expected. It is thus reasonably certain that the reaction of alpha particles on aluminum is of the (α,n) type, the product being an unstable isotope of phosphorus, decaying at a measurable rate. Similar transmutations occur with boron and magnesium, the products being radioactive nitrogen (N^{13}) and silicon (Si^{27}), respectively.

10.84. When the phenomenon of *artificial radioactivity*, as it is called, was first discovered, Joliot-Curie and Joliot suggested distinguishing the unstable isotopes by the use of the prefix *radio*, with the name of the corresponding element; for example, radiophosphorus, radionitrogen and radiosilicon. But this nomenclature, although still in use to some extent, has proved inadequate because many elements exist in several different radioactive forms. It is consequently the present practice to identify a radio-

---

* The possibility that artificial radioactive isotopes, and even new elements, might be synthesized by nuclear bombardment was envisaged by A. V. Grosse in the United States at the end of 1932.

nuclide by giving its half life period (§ 5.46) and its mass number, in addition to its name or symbol. Thus, the radionitrogen obtained by the interaction of alpha particles with boron would be described as 10.1-min. N^{13}, since its half life is 10.1 min. and its mass number is 13. It may be mentioned in this connection that the Joliots found the radioactivity of the substances obtained by nuclear bombardment to decay in an exponential manner, just as for the naturally occurring radioelements. It is thus possible to assign a half life to each species, and these have the general significance described in Chapter V.

10.85. In addition to bringing to light the existence of radioactive isotopes, commonly referred to as *radioisotopes*, of normally stable elements, the work described above was important for another reason. As its authors pointed out: "These experiments give the first chemical proof of artificial transmutation, and also proof of the capture of the alpha particle in these reactions." Evidence for nuclear reactions had previously been based largely on cloud-track photographs, and the nature of the product had to be inferred. When the latter is radioactive, however, it can be identified positively, and the mechanism of the process can be definitely established. Although the product is obtained in infinitesimal amounts, its path in chemical reactions can be followed by its radioactivity. Since it is an isotope of a familiar element, and hence has chemical properties which are virtually identical with the known properties of this element, its identification is a relatively simple matter. An indi-

cation of the procedure in the case of radiophosphorus was recorded above, and other instances will be given later.

10.86. The announcement of the formation of artificial radioisotopes of normally stable elements of low atomic number, as the products of alpha-particle bombardment, naturally aroused considerable interest among physicists in all parts of the world. In addition to confirming the results reported by the French scientists, it was soon found by others, as the Joliots had predicted, that radioactive isotopes were formed in many nuclear reactions.* Since 1934, a total of more than eight hundred different radioactive isotopes of all the known elements, from hydrogen to uranium, have been obtained as a result of a variety of transmutation processes, including fission and spallation. In addition, the elements of atomic number 43 and 61, which are not known to occur in nature—at least not with any degree of certainty—have been isolated in radioactive forms. Several elements beyond uranium in the periodic system, which may have once existed in nature but have now decayed almost completely, have been prepared, one of them, plutonium, in relatively large quantities. The major portion of this work has been carried out in the United States, and represents a remarkable achievement (see Chapter XVI).

IDENTIFICATION OF RADIOISOTOPES

10.87. When one or more radioactive nuclides have been produced as a result of a transmutation reaction, it is necessary to identify the element with which each is isotopic, and then

---

* In 1933, before the discovery of artificial radioactivity, W. D. Harkins, D. M. Gans and H. W. Newson, in the United States, had suggested that the transmutation of fluorine by neutrons occurred by the $F^{19}(n,\alpha)$ N^{16} process, and that the product N^{16} might decay to the stable O^{16} by the emission of a beta particle. This prediction was later confirmed; N^{16} is radioactive and emits beta particles.

to assign to it its proper mass number. If several active substances are formed, as in fission and spallation processes, a partial or complete separation is necessary. In any event, it is frequently desirable to separate a product from the target element in order to obtain material of higher specific activity, that is, with a greater activity per unit mass (§ 17.36). The methods of separation, which are quite similar to those employed for the natural radioelements (§ 5.29), will be referred to again later in connection with the identification of the products of nuclear fission (§ 13.76). For the present, all that is necessary is to suppose that the active material to be studied is available in a form in which the radioactivity is definite enough to be measurable, and that if more than one substance is present, the half lives are such that each can be distinguished from the other. These requirements are not too exacting, and are usually met without difficulty, except when fission and spallation products are involved.

10.88. Having secured the material in suitable form, the next step is to study the rate of decay, so that the particular species, characterized by its half life, may be identified. For this purpose a suitable radiation counter, as described in Chapter VI, is used. High-speed positrons, expelled from some artificially radioactive nuclei, produce ionization in their path, just as do electrons, so that they can be counted in the same manner. Since most artificial radionuclides have half lives which are neither extremely short nor excessively long, they can generally be evaluated by plotting the logarithm of the counting rate, determined after various intervals of time, against the time, as indicated in § 5.51

and illustrated in Fig. 5.3. If the substance under examination contains two or more active species, each can be identified by its half life, provided the values are sufficiently different.

10.89. Since the half life is a definite property of a particular nuclide which is independent of its physical condition or of its state of combination, it provides a simple and virtually infallible means for keeping track of the given species through a series of physical and chemical processes. Because radiation counters can record individual particles emitted by radioactive elements, the latter can be detected in amounts as small as 10^{-12} gram, or less (§ 17.35). Such amounts are, of course, far beyond the reach of ordinary conventional analytical procedures.

10.90. In order to determine the particular element with which the active species is isotopic, the experimental material is dissolved in a suitable manner, and stable compounds of two or three suspected elements are added to the solution. One or other of these elements should be isotopic with the radioactive substance, and hence should act as a carrier (§ 5.29) for it, since their properties will be identical. Familiar chemical and physical methods of separating the elements are then applied, and the behavior of the active material can be readily traced by determining the radioactivity of various parts of the system during the course of separation.

10.91. The procedure may be illustrated by means of a simple example.* A sheet of iron was bombarded with 5.5-Mev deuterons, when it was observed to develop a beta-particle activity with a half life of 45 days. The active species might possibly be isotopic with the target material, iron,

* Another case of a somewhat different type is described in § 10.116.

if the transmutation process were of the (d,p) type, or it might be a form of manganese, resulting from a (d,α) process, or of cobalt, if the nuclear reaction were of the (d,n) type. Hence, after exposure to deuterons, the iron sheet was dissolved in hydrochloric acid and oxidized to the ferric state by means of nitric acid. Small amounts of manganous and cobalt chlorides were then added so that the solution contained manganese, iron and cobalt, and it was necessary to find with which of these elements the 45-day activity would be associated when separated from the others. The solution was made 6N with respect to hydrochloric acid and then extracted with ether, which is able to dissolve the ferric chloride, but not the chlorides of cobalt and manganese. The activity was found to pass into the ether solution, indicating that the radioactive species was isotopic with iron. After extracting the solution several times with hydrochloric acid, to remove all traces of manganese and cobalt, the ferric chloride was converted into solid ferric oxide and the half life of the activity determined. It was found to be 45 days, as in the original material after bombardment, and so the active product was in all probability an isotope of iron.

10.92. Now the element has been identified, it is necessary to consider the more difficult task of determining its mass number. When appreciable quantities of material are available, as has been the case with the slow-neutron fission products of uranium-235, mass-spectrographic methods can be used successfully to yield unequivocal results. In other instances, however, indirect procedures must be adopted. The so-called *cross bombardment method* generally employed is to try to obtain the particular species

by a number of different nuclear reactions; from the results it is often possible to infer the mass number of the active nuclide. For example, in order to assign a mass number to the 45-day isotope of iron, cobalt oxide was exposed to the action of neutrons of moderate energy, when it was observed that a 45-day beta activity developed. Upon dissolving the resulting material in hydrochloric acid and adding ferric and manganous chlorides, it was found that the activity could be extracted together with the ferric chloride by means of ether, as described above. It is evident, therefore, that deuteron bombardment of a stable isotope of iron, and neutron bombardment of a stable isotope of cobalt, produce the same radioisotope of iron.

10.93. The process occurring in the former case must be of the (d,p) type, as stated above, since the atomic number remains unchanged, and so it follows that the mass number of the product must exceed that of the target nucleus by unity. The stable isotopes of iron have mass numbers of 54, 56, 57 and 58, and hence the respective products of the (d,p) reaction would have masses of 55, 57, 58 and 59. Since the mass numbers 57 and 58 are those of stable isotopes of iron, it follows that the unstable 45-day radioiron must have a mass number of either 55 or 59.

10.94. A choice between these values may be made by considering the neutron reaction with cobalt in which the same isotope of iron is obtained. This reaction must be either (n,p) or (n,d), since the atomic number of the product (iron) is one unit less than that of the target element (cobalt). However, the (n,d) reaction is improbable, since this requires neutrons of very high energy, and hence it must be concluded that the process under consideration is $Co(n,p)Fe$; the product must then have the same mass number as the transmuted isotope of cobalt. The stable isotopes of the latter have mass numbers of 57 and 59, and so the mass of the radioiron formed must be 57 or 59. Since the value, as seen above, is either 55 or 59, it is at once evident that the correct mass number is 59. The radioactive isotope of iron, with a half life of 45 days, is thus to be represented by the symbol Fe^{59}.

10.95. The foregoing example may be taken as more or less typical of the general cross bombardment procedure adopted for the assignment of mass numbers. When the particular radioisotope can be obtained in several different ways, the problem is simplified, but a decision may be more difficult when the target elements have many isotopes.

Decay of Artificial Radioisotopes

10.96. The first artificial radioisotopes to be identified decayed by the emission of positrons (§ 10.81), but later investigations showed that other types of decay were even more common. The emission of alpha particles has hitherto been detected for a few elements with atomic numbers less than 83, as will be indicated shortly. On the other hand, beta activity, accompanied by the emission of (negative) electrons, has been observed with the majority of artificial radionuclides. Prior to the year 1947, the known positron-emitting species were restricted to elements of moderately low atomic number, but nuclear transmutation by spallation has led to the isolation of several such radioisotopes of fairly high atomic number, and more are to be expected. In addition to decay by the emission of electrons and positrons, other types of radio-active change, which will be described below, have been observed.

10.97. It will be seen in Chapter XII that among the more than two hundred and seventy stable nuclides, existing in nature, the ratio of neutrons to protons in the nucleus falls within a somewhat limited range, which varies with the atomic number. If in a particular species the neutron-to-proton ratio is larger than the stability range, the isotope will be unstable. The latter could acquire stability, or at least become more stable, if a neutron were replaced by a proton, thus decreasing the ratio of neutrons to protons. As can be seen from equation (7.11), this is precisely what happens when a nucleus expels a negative electron, that is, a beta particle. Hence nuclei containing too many neutrons for stability are negative beta-active. Such species have mass numbers which are larger than those of the stable isotopes; for example, C^{14}, N^{16}, O^{19}, Al^{28}, Cl^{38}, Fe^{59} and Br^{83}. These nuclides are often obtained in (d,p), (n,p), (n,α), (n,γ) and (γ,p) processes, since the product in each case has a larger ratio of neutrons to protons than does the target element.

10.98. When the neutron-to-proton ratio of a nuclide lies below the range for stable existence, this *neutron-deficient nucleus* will tend to change in such a manner as to replace a proton by a neutron. There are three ways in which this can occur: one is the emission of a positron, the second is the expulsion of an alpha particle, and the third is the capture of an orbital electron (§ 10.105). Positron activity is commonly observed with isotopes having mass numbers smaller than the stable values. Examples of this type are C^{11}, N^{13}, O^{15}, Al^{26}, Cl^{33}, Fe^{53} and Br^{78}, which may be compared with the electron-emitting isotopes of the same respective elements given above. Nuclear reactions of the (p,n), (d,n), (α,n), $(n,2n)$, (γ,n) and $(\gamma,2n)$ types result in a decrease in the relative proportion of neutrons, so that the products are frequently positron active.

10.99. In high-energy, spallation reactions, it frequently happens that the nucleons which split off first are neutrons, leaving neutron-deficient nuclei with atomic numbers not very different from those of the target element. Such nuclei are radioactive and decay, as is to be expected, by the emission of positrons.

10.100. In a few instances, of which Cu^{64} is a notable example, discovered by C. C. Van Voorhis in the United States in 1936, radioactive decay occurs with the emission of both positrons and negative electrons. This is a type of branched disintegration (§ 5.60) in which some nuclei decay in one manner and some in the alternative manner, the half life being the same in each case. It is of interest to note that the mass numbers of the stable copper isotopes are 63 and 65, so that Cu^{64} has a neutron-to-proton ratio which lies between the values for the two stable species.

10.101. It was seen in Chapter VIII that when a radioelement emits a negative beta-particle, the product has the same mass number as the parent, but its atomic number is greater by one unit. This rule applies, of course, to any radioactive nuclide, natural or artificial. When a positron is emitted, the mass number is still unchanged, but the atomic number of the product is now one unit less than that of the parent. This conclusion follows immediately from the postulate made in § 7.55, that positron emission is associated with the replacement of a proton by a neutron. The change clearly leaves the total mass unaffected, but decreases the number of protons, and hence the nuclear charge and the atomic number, by unity. The same conclusion is reached by balancing the mass numbers and atomic numbers, as is the general practice in equations for nuclear reactions. Thus, considering the two modes of decay of copper-64, the equations are

$$_{29}Cu^{64} \rightarrow {}_{+1}e^0 + {}_{28}Ni^{64}$$

$$_{29}Cu^{64} \rightarrow {}_{-1}e^0 + {}_{30}Zn^{64},$$

where $_{+1}e^0$ and $_{-1}e^0$ represent a positron and an electron, respectively. The products are stable isotopes of nickel and zinc, both of which are found in nature.

10.102. For many years, the only known alpha emitters, apart from a naturally occurring samarium isotope, were nuclides of atomic number 83 or more. In September 1949, S. G. Thompson, A. Ghiorso, J. O. Rasmussen and G. T. Seaborg of Berkeley issued a preliminary report of the discovery of alpha-active isotopes of gold and mercury (atomic numbers 79 and 80), and, much more significantly, of certain rare-earth elements, with atomic numbers in the region of 60 to 66 and mass numbers of about 150. By bombarding the oxides of samarium, gadolinium and dysprosium with 200-Mev protons, several alpha-particle activities, possibly due to isotopes of gadolinium, terbium, and dysprosium, were detected. The capture of the high-energy proton is probably accompanied by the emission of several neutrons, leaving neutron-deficient nuclei, such as $_{65}Tb^{149}$ and $_{66}Dy^{150}$. A possible reason why these nuclides decay by the emission of alpha particles, as well as, in all probability, by positron emission or electron capture, will be indicated in § 12.110. In addition to neodymium-144 and samarium-147 which occur in nature, the following alpha-particle emitters have been obtained by nuclear reactions: samarium-146, europium-147, gadolinium-148, -149 and -150, terbium-149 and -150, and dysprosium-150, -151 and -152.

10.103. With the majority of, although not with all, artificial radionuclides, other than those obtained by nuclear fission and spallation, the immediate decay product is a stable species. The result is not surprising if it is recalled that the radioisotopes are usually obtained by a simple trans-

mutation in which a particle enters a stable nucleus and another particle is expelled. In spallation, however, the splitting off of several nucleons, as indicated earlier, may leave a product that is two or three, or possibly more, stages removed from stability. Short chains, involving two or three successive positron emissions, are then possible before a stable nuclide is reached; thus, representing the positron by β^+,

$$_{34}\text{Se}^{71} \xrightarrow{\beta^+} {}_{33}\text{As}^{71} \xrightarrow{\beta^+} {}_{32}\text{Ge}^{71} \xrightarrow{\beta^+} {}_{31}\text{Ga}^{71},$$

where Ga^{71} is a known stable isotope of gallium.

10.104. For reasons which will be made clear in Chapter XIII, the products of nuclear fission usually contain several more neutrons than is permissible for stability. These substances consequently decay by the emission of negative beta-particles (β^-), and several chains of four or five disintegration stages have been observed; one instance is the series

$$_{36}\text{Kr}^{90} \xrightarrow{\beta^-} {}_{37}\text{Rb}^{90} \xrightarrow{\beta^-} {}_{38}\text{Sr}^{90} \xrightarrow{\beta^-} {}_{39}\text{Y}^{90} \xrightarrow{\beta^-} {}_{40}\text{Zr}^{90},$$

the end product, being the most abundant stable isotope of zirconium.

ORBITAL-ELECTRON CAPTURE

10.105. In some instances, where the ratio of neutrons to protons is low, and hence positron activity would be expected, another type of decay has been found to occur with artificial nuclides. Instead of a proton being converted into a neutron with the emission of a positron, the nucleus captures one of the extranuclear (orbital) electrons, which immediately combines with a proton to form a neutron; thus,

$$\begin{array}{lcccc}
& \text{proton} + \text{electron} & \rightarrow & \text{neutron} + \text{neutrino} & \qquad(10.3) \\
\text{mass} & \quad 1 \qquad\quad 0 & & 1 \qquad\quad 0 & \\
\text{charge} & +1 \qquad -1 & & 0 \qquad\quad 0 &
\end{array}$$

with a neutrino being formed at the same time.* It will be seen that this process provides an alternative to that represented by equation (7.13) for the replacement of a proton by a neutron, thus increasing the neutron-to-proton ratio. The product of this type of radioactivity would have the same mass number as its parent, but its atomic number would be one unit lower, just as in the case of positron emission. The decay of an unstable species, such as Fe^{55}, by orbital electron capture, can be represented by the equation

$$_{26}\text{Fe}^{55} + {}_{-1}e^0 \rightarrow {}_{25}\text{Mn}^{55},$$

the electron which is captured by the iron nucleus being indicated by $_{-1}e^0$ on the left-hand side.

10.106. The phenomenon described above is referred to as decay by *orbital-electron capture*. The electron is usually captured from the first quantum level, i.e., the K level (§ 4.72), for such an electron is more likely than

---

* Since the orbital electron has a definite energy, the neutrino should also have a definite amount of energy, and not a range of energies as in positron or electron emission.

any other to be found near the nucleus; consequently, the expression *K-electron capture* or, in brief, *K-capture* is often employed. Instances of an electron being captured from the *L* level are known, although they are not common. The possibility of orbital-electron capture as an alternative to positron emission was predicted by the Japanese mathematical physicists H. Yukawa and S. Sakata in 1936, and proof of its reality was obtained in the United States by L. W. Alvarez in 1938.

10.107. The detection of orbital-electron capture depends on the fact that the removal of the extranuclear electron leaves a vacancy in the appropriate quantum level, usually the lowest (or *K*) level. An electron from one of the higher energy levels will then immediately move in to fill the vacant position, and the excess energy will be emitted as the corresponding characteristic X-ray, as described in § 4.72. Since the orbital-electron capture must precede the electronic transition and the emission of X-rays, the latter will be characteristic of the product nucleus with an atomic number one unit less than that of the radioactive species. A case in point is the 330-day vanadium isotope of mass number 49; the decay of this nuclide was found to be accompanied by the characteristic X-rays of the *K* series belonging to the element titanium which precedes it in the periodic system. The intensity of the X-rays falls off as the active material decays. It is evident, therefore, that V^{49} decays by *K*-electron capture.

10.108. If, as a result of orbital-electron capture, the product nucleus is left in its ground state, the change will not be accompanied by gamma rays; such behavior, of which the 330-day V^{49} provides an example, is referred to as *pure K-capture*. In most instances, however, the product nucleus is formed in a high-energy (excited) state and the excess energy is given off in the form of gamma radiation. Quite frequently, too, this radiation is internally converted (§ 7.106); that is to say, the energy of the gamma-ray photon is transferred to an orbital electron which is consequently ejected. The result is a "line" spectrum of electrons of definite energy, associated with X-rays characteristic of the product element. The latter would, of course, be indistinguishable from those due directly to orbital-electron capture.

10.109. Under all known conditions, the rates of spontaneous nuclear reactions, such as radioactivity, have been found to be independent of the physical or chemical state of the radioelement. However, a particular case of orbital-electron capture, namely, that by beryllium-7, provides an interesting exception. This element has only four electrons and, in 1947, E. Segrè in the United States and R. Daudel in France independently predicted that the rate of electron capture by the nucleus, i.e., the half life, might depend on the state of chemical combination, since this would affect the electron density close to the nucleus. The existence of a small but definite effect of this nature was demonstrated by several experimenters. In the uncombined (metallic) form, for example, the half life of beryllium-7 for orbital electron capture is about 0.013 per cent greater than in the oxide (BeO) and 0.074 per cent greater than in the fluoride (BeF_2).

CONDITIONS FOR POSITRON EMISSION AND ELECTRON CAPTURE

10.110. It will be shown presently that certain energy conditions are necessary for positron emission to be possible. Since orbital-electron capture leads to the same disintegration product, this process of decay may occur simultaneously with the positron activity. If the energy requirements are not met, however, orbital-electron capture takes place exclusively, with or without accompanying gamma radiation. Suppose that in a particular nuclide the ratio of neutrons to protons is smaller than the value needed for stability, so that positron emission is conceivable. If the nucleus ejects a positron, its mass will decrease by m_0, where m_0 is the rest mass of the electron, which is the same as that of a positron; the rest mass of the accompanying neutrino is neglected since it is essentially zero. Further, since the atomic number of the product is smaller by one unit than that of the parent radionuclide, the former will have one orbital electron less than the latter; this will also represent an additional decrease of m_0 in the mass of the atom as a whole. It follows, therefore, that, when positron emission takes place, the isotopic mass of the product must be smaller by the amount $2m_0$ than that of the positive beta-active parent.

10.111. Actually this is a minimum value, for the mass difference may be larger than $2m_0$, but it cannot be less, if positron decay is to be possible. Thus, if $M(A)$ represents the isotopic weight of the parent element A and $M(B)$ that of the product B, the condition for positron emission is

$$M(A) - M(B) > 2m_0.$$

The rest mass of the electron is 0.00055 on the atomic weight scale; hence, for positron emission to be possible, the isotopic weight of the parent must exceed that of the product by 0.0011,

at least. Since the mass difference eventually appears as energy, the quantity $2m_0$, i.e., twice the rest mass of the electron, may be replaced by its energy equivalent; this was shown in § 3.84 to be 1.02 Mev, so that the condition becomes

$$M(A) - M(B) > 1.02 \text{ Mev.}$$

It is seen, therefore, that for positron activity to be possible, at least 1.02 Mev of energy must be available, as a result of the loss in mass associated with the change from nuclide A to nuclide B. Energy in excess of this minimum will be shared between the ejected positron and the accompanying neutrino, although some may appear as gamma radiation.

10.112. When the mass difference $M(A) - M(B)$ is such that the minimum of 1.02 Mev of energy is not available, then the change from A to B will occur by orbital-electron capture, assuming as before that the neutron-to-proton ratio in the parent nucleus is smaller than requisite for stability. For this alternative process the energy demand is much less stringent. Instead of the positron being ejected from the nucleus while at the same time an orbital electron is expelled, as explained above, the same change from A to B is now achieved by the orbital electron going into the nucleus. The minimum mass difference $M(A) - M(B)$ is now equal to the mass of the neutrino, which is virtually zero; hence, the only requirement for decay by orbital-electron capture is that $M(B)$ should be less than $M(A)$, the actual difference being of no consequence. Any energy that is available due to the isotopic weight of the product being appreciably less than that of the parent will appear as gamma radiation, apart from some which may be carried off by the neutrino in equation (10.3).*

10.113. When competition between decay by electron capture and by positron emission is possible, the former process is favored by factors which increase the half life of the parent element. From the facts related in Chapter VII, it is apparent that, for similar beta transitions, the smaller the maximum energy of the positrons, the longer will be the half life. It is to be expected, therefore, that the extent of electron capture will increase as the positron energy decreases. In other words, as the energy of the radioactive change approaches the minimum value of 1.02 Mev, the probability of decay by positron emission decreases while that of electron capture increases. When the energy is less than 1.02 Mev, the latter process occurs exclusively. Two other factors tend to favor orbital-electron capture relative to positron emission: one is high atomic number and the other is a large difference in the nuclear-spin quantum numbers of the parent and product nuclei. Positron emission is very rare among the heaviest elements, although several cases of K-capture have been recorded.

NUCLEAR ISOMERISM

10.114. Another type of radioactive decay, i.e., by *isomeric transition,* has been brought to light by a study of artificial radionuclides, although it is actually an aspect of the familiar gamma-ray emission. The possibility that there might exist nuclides having the same mass number and also the same atomic number, that is to say, *isobaric isotopes,* but possessing different radioactive properties was envisioned by F. Soddy in 1917. Substances of this type have now become known as *nuclear isomers,* based on the suggestion made by (Frl.) L. Meitner in 1936, and the phenomenon has been called *nuclear isomerism.*†

10.115. The first evidence for the existence of nuclear isomers came in 1921 from the German radiochemist O. Hahn, who found uranium Z to be isotopic with and also have the same mass number as uranium X_2, although differing from it in its rate of decay. For several years this was the only case of nuclear isomerism which could be regarded as substantiated, but around 1935 indications came from several different directions that other nuclides, notably one of the artificial radioisotopes of bromine, exist in isomeric forms. Since that time about 150 examples of nuclear isomerism have been discovered, and the phenomenon of decay by isomeric transition, that is, by the spontaneous conversion of one nuclear isomer into another, has been elucidated. In most instances there are isomeric pairs only, but triple isomerism has been observed in a few cases.

10.116. When a target containing bromine was bombarded with slow neutrons the product was found to

---

* It may be remarked here that in negative beta-decay, i.e., in electron emission, the mass of the nucleus decreases by m_0, but there is a corresponding increase in the mass of the orbital electrons, the number of which is increased by unity. There are thus no energy restrictions, apart from the neutrino mass, and the conditions are similar to those for orbital-electron capture. Some writers in fact speak of the negative-electron emission and the orbital-electron capture processes as being the reverse of each other, but this is probably not strictly true.

† Chemists are, of course, familiar with the terms *isomer* and *isomerism,* from the Greek *iso* (same) *meros* (part), as applied to compounds having identical compositions and molecular weights but differing in their properties.

exhibit three different half-life periods of radioactive beta-decay, namely, 18 min., 4.5 hr. and 36 hr.* This result was surprising because the reactions of slow neutrons with moderately heavy nuclei are invariably of the (n,γ) type, and since ordinary bromine consists of only two isotopes, mass numbers 79 and 81, not more than two radioactive products, Br^{80} and Br^{82}, were to be expected; thus,

$$_{35}Br^{79} + _{0}n^{1} \rightarrow _{35}Br^{80} + \gamma$$

$$_{35}Br^{81} + _{0}n^{1} \rightarrow _{35}Br^{82} + \gamma.$$

10.117. The same three decay periods were also observed following the bombardment of bromine with deuterons; here again the products Br^{80} and Br^{82} were to be anticipated as a result of processes of the (d,p) type involving the stable 79 and 81 isotopes. It appeared certain, therefore, that the two radioisotopes of bromine Br^{80} and Br^{82} between them decay in three different ways, so that one of these nuclides decays at two different rates. The identity of the isotope exhibiting the dual decay was established in the following manner. The action of gamma rays on bromine according to the (γ,n) processes

$$_{35}Br^{79} + \gamma \rightarrow _{35}Br^{78} + _{0}n^{1}$$

$$_{35}Br^{81} + \gamma \rightarrow _{35}Br^{80} + _{0}n^{1}$$

leads to the formation of two products, Br^{78} and Br^{80}, with three decay periods, the half lives now being 6.4 min., 18 min. and 4.5 hr. Since the Br^{80} isotope is formed in both the (n,γ) and (γ,n) reactions, and the 18 min. and 4.5 hr. periods are observed in both cases, it is apparent that it is this isotope which is associated with two modes of decay.

10.118. The explanation offered for this behavior is that Br^{80} exhibits nuclear isomerism, each isomer having a different half life.† As will be seen below, a separation of the two nuclear isomers is possible; one is then found to decay with a half life of 18 min. and the other with a period of 4.5 hr. The difference between the nuclear isomers of Br^{80}, and in fact of all other cases of nuclear isomerism, is attributed to a difference in nuclear energy states: one isomer represents the nucleus in its ground state, while the other is the same nucleus in an excited state of higher energy. As a general rule, the transition from a higher to a lower nuclear energy level, which is associated with the emission of gamma rays, requires a very short time, probably less than 10^{-13} sec. The excited state then has an extremely short life. If the transition is "forbidden" to some extent, the high-energy (excited) state, referred to as a *metastable*‡ state, will have an appreciable life, varying from a small fraction of a second to several days. Such a metastable, excited state represents one isomeric form of the particular nuclear species, whereas the ground state, that is, the state of lowest energy, represents the other. In writing the symbols for isomeric states, the metastable form is distinguished by adding the letter *m* to the mass number, e.g., $Br.^{80m}$

---

* These are the most recent values which differ slightly from the original determinations.

† It should be noted that the two decay periods could not be due to branched disintegration (§ 5.60), since this is associated with one such period only, although there are two different decay products. Thus, Cu^{64} and As^{76}, which decay by both positive and negative beta emission and also by K-capture, have the same half life for each type of decay.

‡ The term *metastable* is used in physics and chemistry to indicate a state that is not the most stable possible under the given conditions, but is nevertheless sufficiently stable to have an appreciable independent existence.

Types of Nuclear Isomers: Isomeric Transition

10.119. For classification purposes, three types of nuclear isomers may be distinguished. In the first, referred to as *isomers with independent decay*, each isomer decays independently of the other with its own particular half life. In cases of this kind the transition from one isomeric state to the other, i.e., from the metastable to the ground state, is highly forbidden and takes place to a very small extent, if at all. The transitions are depicted in Fig. 10.1, with T_1 and T_2 represent-

emission of positrons and electrons, respectively, and KC implies decay by K-capture.

Mn^{52} (β^+, 5.55 days; β^+, 21.3 min.)

Co^{62} (β^-, 1.6 min.; β^-, 13.9 min.)

Zn^{71} (β^-, 3 hr.; β^-, 2.2 min.)

Mo^{91} (β^-, 66 sec.; β^-, 15.5 min.)

Ag^{106} (KC, 8.3 days; β^+, 24 min.)

Cd^{115} (β^-, 43 days; β^-, 53 hr.)

10.120. The second class consists of *genetically related isomers*, as represented in Fig. 10.2, in which the meta-

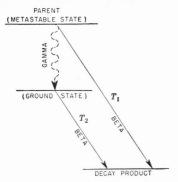

Fig. 10.1. Isomerism with independent decay.

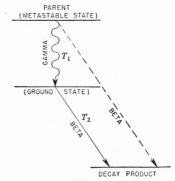

Fig. 10.2. Genetically related isomers: isomeric transition.

ing the different half-life periods. In the diagram both methods of decay have been shown to lead to the same (lowest) energy level of the product nucleus. But this is not necessarily the case, for one or other (or both) may yield an excited state of the product, which will then emit the excess energy as gamma radiation. Examples of nuclear isomers with independent decay, together with the type of activity and half lives, are given below; the symbols β^+ and β^- refer to the

stable state decays to the ground state with a definite half life T_1, a gamma-ray photon being expelled. This is the decay process known as *isomeric transition*, abbreviated to I.T. In the majority of cases the gamma radiation is internally converted, so that what is observed is a line spectrum of electrons, together with characteristic X-rays, as is usual with internal conversion (§ 7.106).* The ground state decays to form the product with a half life of

---

* The X-rays are here those of the radioactive element itself, since this is the species emitting the converted gamma radiation, and so isomeric transition can be distinguished from orbital-electron capture where the X-rays resulting from internal conversion are those of the product element.

T_2, which is different from T_1. As before, the product is not necessarily formed in its ground state, so that gamma radiation may accompany the radioactive change. There is also a possibility of some direct independent decay of the excited, metastable state of the parent, as indicated by the broken line. Some instances of genetically related isomers, which include those of Br^{80}, are the following:

Sc^{44} (I.T., 2.44 days; β^+, 3.96 hr.)

Zn^{69} (I.T., 13.8 hr.; β^-, 52 min.)

Br^{80} (I.T., 4.5 hr.; β^-, 18 min.)

Se^{81} (I.T., 56.8 min.; β^-, 18.2 min.)

In^{114} (I.T., 49 days; β^-, 72 sec.)

Te^{131} (I.T., 30 hr.; β^-, 24.8 min.)

10.121. It will be observed from the foregoing examples that the half life of the internal transition process is often longer than that of the beta decay, positive or negative, of the ground state. As a result, the radioactive substance emits two groups of beta particles, corresponding to two distinct half lives. One group, associated with the shorter half life, is due to decay of nuclei originally formed in the ground state, while the other group results from the decay of nuclei in the same ground state produced by isomeric transition from the metastable excited state. It is a well-known law that the over-all rate of any change taking place in stages is determined by the rate of the slowest of these stages; hence in the process

they actually originate from the ground state, appears equal to the rate of the isomeric transition, which is the slower stage.

10.122. Isomeric transition is frequently accompanied by the breaking of a chemical bond which may make possible a separation of the isomeric nuclei. An interesting illustration is provided by the isomers of tellurium, for example, Te^{131}. If to a tellurate (Te^{VI}) solution, containing this radioactive species, is added some ordinary inactive tellurite (Te^{IV}), then upon separating the latter chemically, it is found to contain the 24.8-min. isomer. The explanation of this behavior is that the gamma ray emitted by the upper (30-hr.) isomeric state undergoes internal conversion, resulting in the ejection of an electron from a K or L level of the product atom, that is, from the lower (24.8-min.) isomeric state. As a result of what is known as the *Auger effect,* the high energy of this inner (K or L) electron is transferred to one or more of the outer (valence) electrons, which are consequently removed from the atom. This detachment of valence electrons from the 24.8-min. isomer results in the breaking of some of the bonds between the tellurium and oxygen atoms; consequently, the isomeric transition is accompanied by a change from the VI to the IV oxidation state, i.e., from tellurate to tellurite. Other genetically related isomers have been separated chemically, and the general explanation of the behavior is analogous to that given here for tellurium.*

$$\text{Metastable State} \xrightarrow{\text{I.T.}} \text{Ground State} \xrightarrow{\beta} \text{Product,}$$

the rate of emission of the beta particles in the second group, although

10.123. The third category of nuclear isomerism is that in which the

---

* The name "hot-atom chemistry" is given to the study of chemical reactions resulting from the transfer to valence bonds of energy produced in nuclear processes of various kinds (see also § 17.42).

active species are *isomers of stable nuclei*. The decay process now merely involves an isomeric transition from the metastable excited state to the ground state of a stable nuclide, accompanied by the emission of gamma radiation. If this is internally converted, there will be a line spectrum of electrons, and the characteristic X-rays of the element will be emitted. More than thirty stable species, which are found in nature, among them Kr^{83}, Sr^{87}, Rh^{103}, Ag^{107}, Sn^{117}, Ba^{137} and Au^{197}, are known to form metastable states of appreciable life, from a few seconds to several days. In addition, isomers with very short lives, such as Sm^{152} and Dy^{160}, with half lives of the order of 10^{-6} sec., have been reported and it is probable that short-lived isomers of other stable nuclides will be discovered.

10.124. Isomers of stable nuclides are frequently the result of nuclear excitation accompanying inelastic scattering or Coulomb reactions, as already described in preceding sections. High-energy X-rays and electrons are able to produce similar excitation, so that the products are stable nuclides in metastable excited states of appreciable life. Isomers of stable species are also sometimes formed in other nuclear processes; examples are, $Sr^{86}(n,\gamma)Sr^{87m}$, $Kr^{82}(d,p)Kr^{83m}$ and $Se^{80}(\alpha,n)Kr^{83m}$. In the first two cases, one stable isotope of an element is converted into the metastable (isomeric) state of another stable isotope of the same element. As reported earlier, beta decay often leads to the formation of the product in an excited state; this may be a metastable state of a stable species, as is the case for the negative beta-decay of Br^{83} and Sr^{89}, the products being Kr^{83m} and Y^{89m}, respectively.

ISOMERISM AND NUCLEAR SPIN

10.125. The explanation accepted for the existence of metastable states, and hence of nuclear isomers, of both stable and unstable nuclides, is based on that proposed by the German physicist C. F. von Weizsäcker in 1936. If there is a considerable difference of angular momentum, that is, of resultant nuclear spin (§ 4.86), between an excited state and the ground state of a nucleus and the energy difference between the two states is small, then the transition from the upper to the lower energy state will be "forbidden." In other words, the probability of the transition will be small, and, on the average, an appreciable time will elapse before the excited state loses its excess energy and passes into the ground state. When this occurs, the nuclear state of higher energy is metastable and can have a detectable, independent existence; nuclear isomerism will then be observed.

10.126. In recent years, considerable effort, both theoretical and experimental, has been expended in elucidating the behavior of nuclear isomers. The transitions leading to the emission of gamma radiation are found to fall into two general classes, called magnetic and electric, respectively. Electric radiations arise from changes in the distribution of the electric charge in the nucleus; magnetic radiations, on the other hand, are due to changes in the distribution of magnetic poles. For the same difference in the spin and energy between the nuclear states, the magnetic (or M) transitions are more highly forbidden than those of electric (or E) character.

10.127. For the great majority of isomeric nuclei of relatively long life, the transitions to the ground (or lower energy) state are of the M4 type, i.e., magnetic transitions accompanied by a change of four units in the nuclear spin. Examples of transitions of other types, e.g., E1, . . . , E4 and M1, . . . , M3, have been observed, but, in general, for a given excitation energy, the life of the metastable isomeric state decreases with the change in the nuclear spin. Thus, very few M1, and still fewer E1, transitions have been observed, because of the extremely short life of the metastable state.

10.128. One consequence of the relationship between nuclear spin change and the life of the metastable state is the fact that very few isomers have been detected among nuclides having even numbers of neutrons and of protons. Because of the pairing of nucleons with opposite spins, the resultant spins of these nuclei in the excited and ground states are either zero or a small integer (§ 4.86). Consequently, the basic condition for a metastable state of relatively long life, i.e., a large difference in the nuclear spins, is not often realized. When a nucleus contains an odd number of protons or neutrons (or both), theory and experiment show that the resultant half-integral spins can be quite large, e.g., $1\frac{1}{2}$, especially in the excited states. The occurrence of moderately long-lived nuclear isomers is thus to be expected.

10.129. It is of interest to mention that the isomeric nuclei with odd mass numbers, i.e., having an odd number of either protons or neutrons, fall into three groups, often referred to as the *islands of isomerism*.* The (odd) mass numbers in these groups are mainly (1) from 39 to 49, (2) from 69 to 81

and (3) from 111 to 125. It will be seen in Chapter XII that the numbers 50, 82 and 126 represent closed shells of nucleons, so that the islands of isomerism occur just before the shells are complete. It is in these circumstances that the nuclei contain appreciable numbers of nucleons with unpaired spins, so that fairly large resultant nuclear spins are common.

10.130. The observed lifetime of a metastable state apparently depends on the extent to which an alternative process, namely, internal conversion of the gamma radiation (§ 7.106), can occur. The greater the competition from the latter, the shorter is the life of the nuclear isomer. The extent to which internal conversion takes place depends on the exact nature of the electronic environment of the nucleus, and this can be affected, to a minor degree, by the state of chemical combination of the atom. An example of this behavior has been observed with the nuclear isomer of radioactive technetium-99, i.e., Tc^{99m}, which has a half life of 6.0 hr. for decay to the ground state. In the compounds Tc_2S_7 and $KTcO_4$ the half life of Tc^{99m} was found to be 0.03 and 0.3 per cent, respectively, less than in the metallic (elemental) state.†

Decay by Neutron Emission

10.131. It may be wondered why, in view of the fact that atomic nuclei contain protons and neutrons, radioactive decay does not occur with emission of these particles. The answer is that if a nucleus has sufficient energy to release a proton or a neutron, that is, at least 8 Mev, the emission usually takes place extremely rapidly, prob-

---

* The existence of these "islands" was pointed out in 1949 by E. Feenberg and K. C. Hammack in the United States.

† Technetium (atomic number 43) does not exist in nature, but it has been obtained artificially (§ 16.75).

ably in much less than 10^{-12} sec. In other words, the particular nuclide would be so unstable that it would not be regarded as having any real existence. A few instances have been found of unstable nuclei which apparently decay by emitting neutrons at a measurable rate, but this result is due to incidental circumstances. The phenomenon is of the greatest significance for the design of nuclear energy reactors,

bromine isotope of high mass number, probably Br^{87}. This decays with a half life of 55.6 sec. emitting a negative beta-particle to yield Kr^{87}. The latter can be formed in a highly excited state with sufficient energy to permit it immediately to eject a neutron (Fig. 10.3), and form a stable Kr^{86} nucleus. The observed rate of emission of neutrons is determined by the slow stage in the over-all process,

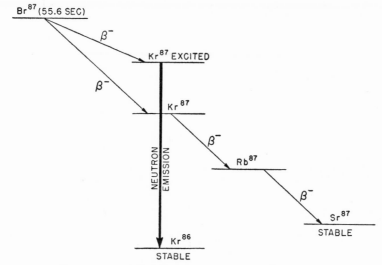

FIG. 10.3. Mechanism of delayed neutron emission.

as will be seen in later chapters, but it is sufficient to state here that the fission of uranium and plutonium by neutrons is accompanied by the delayed expulsion of neutrons. Five or six half-life periods, namely 55.6 sec., 22.5 sec., 4.51 sec., 1.52 sec., 0.43 sec. and, possibly, 0.15 sec., have been identified. By making rapid chemical separations, it has been found that the 55.6-sec. period follows the chemistry of bromine, and the 22.5-sec. period follows that of iodine.

10.132. The explanation suggested, in the former case, for example, is that one of the products of fission is a

namely, the decay of the Br^{87}. The half life for neutron liberation thus appears to be 55.6 sec., although the actual process in which the neutrons are emitted probably occurs very rapidly. The 22.5-sec. group of neutrons probably originates in an analogous manner from I^{137} produced in fission; this emits a negative beta-particle, with a half life of 22.5 sec., leaving a highly excited Xe^{137} nucleus. It is the latter which instantaneously expels the neutron to form stable Xe^{136}, although the apparent decay half life is 22.5 sec.

10.133. A somewhat similar type of

behavior was discovered in an entirely different connection by L. W. Alvarez and his collaborators in 1948. Upon bombarding various light elements from oxygen to chlorine by means of 200-Mev deuterons obtained from the 184-inch Berkeley synchrocyclotron, the emission of neutrons, associated with a half life of 4.1 sec., was detected. After making a series of care-

beryllium with deuterons, boron with protons and in other ways. The Li^9 has a half life of 0.17 sec., emitting a beta particle to yield the excited state of Be^9 which immediately expels a neutron.

ISOTOPE CHARTS

10.134. The information concerning the known isotopic species, both stable

	33	34	35	36	37
30	Zn 63 β^+, K 38 m	Zn 64	Zn 65 β^+, K 250 d	Zn 66	Zn 67
29	Cu 62 β^+ 10.5 m	Cu 63	Cu 64 β^+, β^-, K 12.8 h	Cu 65	Cu 66 β^- 5 m
28	Ni 61	Ni 62	Ni 63 β^- 300 y	Ni 64	Ni 65 β^- 2.6 h

NUMBER OF PROTONS (vertical axis)

NUMBER OF NEUTRONS

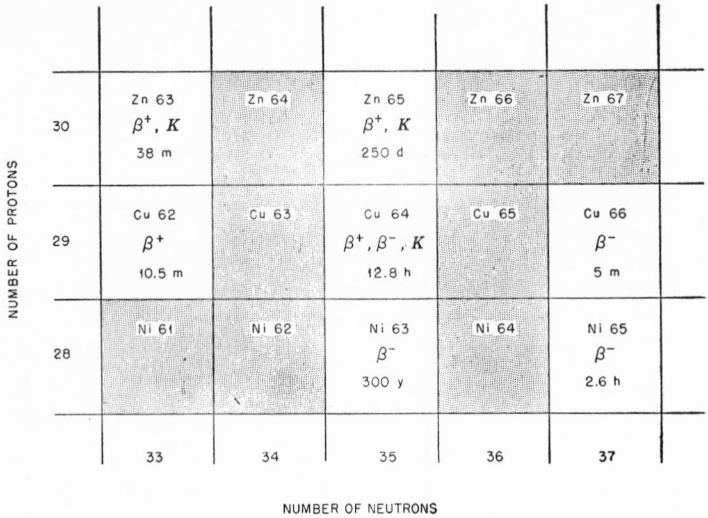

FIG. 10.4.   Portion of an isotope chart.

fully planned experiments the conclusion was reached that the results could be accounted for by the following scheme:

$$N^{17} \xrightarrow[\text{4.1 sec.}]{\beta^-} O^{17} \to O^{16} + n^1.$$

The unstable species N^{17} is formed in the bombardment; this decays with a half life of 4.1 sec. emitting an electron, and leaving a highly excited O^{17} nucleus. The latter then instantaneously ejects a neutron, with the stable oxygen-16 isotope as the final product. A similar example of neutron emission has been observed in connection with lithium-9, formed by the reaction of

and unstable, is usually summarized in the form of an isotope chart, as it is generally called. In one type of chart the atomic number Z, that is, the number of protons in the nucleus, is plotted as the ordinate, against the number of neutrons, equal to $A - Z$, where A is the mass number, as the abscissa. A simplified portion of such a chart is represented in Fig. 10.4. Each nuclide is seen to occupy a square; those with a shaded background refer to stable species occurring in nature, while artificial radioactive isotopes have a white background. The symbol and mass number are indicated in each case, as well as the types of decay and half lives of the unstable nuclides. All species on the same horizontal line have the same atomic number and hence are isotopic with one another. Nuclides with the same mass number, i.e., isobars, are seen to lie on a series of 45° diagonal lines running from upper left to lower right of the diagram.

10.135. Certain features of this isotope chart will be described subsequently; for the present it will be utilized to consider nuclear transmutation and radioactive decay processes. When a particular target nucleus combines with a proton, the resulting compound nucleus is represented by the next higher square in the same vertical line. Similarly, combination with a neutron gives a nucleus occupying the next square to the right on the same horizontal line. Uptake of a deuteron, which consists of a proton and a neutron, results in a shift of one position vertically upward, and one to the right, and so on for other particles. Emission of a proton, neutron or deuteron, of course, results in a reversal of these moves on the chart. The expulsion of an electron in radioactive decay, i.e., negative beta-decay, gives a product nucleus in which the number of protons is increased and the number of neutrons is decreased by unity. The product therefore occupies the adjacent upper-left diagonal position from that of the parent. On the other hand, in positive beta-decay, i.e., when there is positron emission, or in orbital-electron capture, the product nucleus is found in the adjoining lower-right diagonal square.

10.136. It is of interest to return, at this point, to the case discussed in detail in § 10.17 *et seq.*, namely, the combination of a deuteron with Cu^{63}; from the chart, the compound nucleus is seen to be the radioisotope [Zn^{65}],

undoubtedly in a highly excited state with considerable excess energy. If this energy is emitted as a gamma ray [reaction (1)], the product is Zn^{65} in its ground state; the chart shows this to be radioactive, decaying by positron emission, or by K-capture, to yield stable Cu^{65} as the product. A second possibility [reaction (2)] is the ejection of a neutron by the [Zn^{65}], leaving Zn^{64}, which is stable. In reaction (3), a proton is emitted, and hence the product is Cu^{64}; as stated in § 10.100, this exhibits branched disintegration, decaying by the emission of a positive or a negative beta-particle, the product being the stable nuclide Ni^{64} or Zn^{64}, respectively. According to reaction (4), two neutrons are expelled, so that Zn^{63}, which the chart shows to be a positron emitter, remains; its decay product is seen to be stable Cu^{63}. If the compound nucleus ejects an alpha particle [reaction (5)], the compound nucleus [Zn^{65}] loses two protons and two neutrons, with formation of the stable Ni^{61}. The tritium nucleus consists of one proton and two neutrons, and so the product of reaction (6) is Cu^{62}; from the chart it follows that this decays by the emission of a positron and is thereby converted into the stable Ni^{62} isotope. The last process does not need to be considered since it is the reverse of that by which the compound nucleus was supposed to be formed, in the first place.

10.137. In addition to the isotope chart described here, in which the number of protons is plotted against the number of neutrons for all the known nuclides, other types have been used for different purposes. For example, in one the atomic number Z is plotted against the mass number A, or vice versa; and in another, the excess of neutrons over protons, that is $A - 2Z$, is plotted against the atomic number Z. An especially convenient scheme makes use of axes inclined at an angle of 60°, the mass number A being plotted along one of those axes and the atomic number Z along the other.* Each type of chart has features of special interest, but, in general, familiarity with the use of one provides sufficient experience for the use of any other. It is consequently unnecessary to enter into further details here.

* *Trilinear Chart of Nuclides,* by William H Sullivan, U. S. Government Printing Office, Washington, D. C., 1957.

The Neutron

Chapter XI

PROPERTIES OF THE NEUTRON

MASS OF THE NEUTRON

11.1. When, in 1920, E. Rutherford considered the possible existence of a particle of unit mass and zero charge (§ 2.115), now called a neutron, he thought that, since it would not be repelled as it approached an atomic nucleus, "it should enter readily into the structure of atoms, and may unite with the nucleus." As indicated in the preceding chapter, this expectation has been abundantly confirmed; the nuclei of virtually all the elements have been found to interact with neutrons. In addition, the neutron has served a purpose which was entirely unforeseen: it provided the key that made possible the achievement of a long-sought objective, the release of energy from the atomic nucleus. In this respect, the various interactions of neutrons with atomic nuclei are of the greatest significance. For these and other reasons, the study of the production and properties of neutrons has attracted much interest, and the subject merits detailed consideration.

11.2. It was mentioned in § 2.118, when reporting briefly on the discovery of the neutron by J. Chadwick in 1932,

that he explained certain apparently paradoxical observations of previous workers by attributing them to the presence of an uncharged particle with a mass close to that of a proton. Since the evidence was not recorded earlier, it will be outlined here. The absence of charge associated with the neutron was established, of course, by the inability to deflect it in electric and magnetic fields; the mass was estimated in several ways. Suppose a particle of mass m_1, moving with a velocity v, collides with another particle, mass m_2, which is virtually stationary. The speed with which the latter recoils depends on the direction of recoil relative to that of the incident particle, but it is known from mechanics that it will be a maximum in a head-on collision, that is, when the struck particle recoils in exactly the same direction as that in which incident particle approached it. For such a collision, the recoil velocity v_2, which is the maximum possible for the specified conditions, is given by[*]

$$v_2 = \frac{2m_1}{m_1 + m_2} v. \qquad (11.1)$$

---

[*] This is readily derived from the equations for the conservation of (kinetic) energy, which is here $\frac{1}{2}m_1v^2 = \frac{1}{2}m_1v_1^2 + \frac{1}{2}m_2v_2^2$, and for the conservation of momentum, namely, $m_1v = m_1v_1 + m_2v_2$ for a head-on collision; v_1 is the velocity of the incident particle after the collision.

If the incident particle were a neutron and the struck particle were a nucleus of known mass m_2, the mass m_1 of the neutron could be calculated from equation (11.1) if the velocity v of the neutron before collision, and the maximum speed v_2 of the recoiling nucleus were known.

11.3. Unfortunately, Chadwick did not have reliable data concerning the speed of the neutron, and so this had to be eliminated from equation (11.1). If neutrons of the same velocity v collide with a particle of mass m_3, the maximal recoil velocity v_3 of the latter is determined by an expression exactly analogous to equation (11.1), namely,

$$v_3 = \frac{2m_1}{m_1 + m_3} \, v, \qquad (11.2)$$

where m_1 and v are the same as before. Upon dividing equation (11.1) by (11.2) it is seen that

$$\frac{v_2}{v_3} = \frac{m_1 + m_3}{m_1 + m_2}, \qquad (11.3)$$

thus permitting m_1, the mass of the neutron, to be evaluated if m_2, m_3, v_2 and v_3 are available. The recoils of hydrogen and nitrogen nuclei, after being struck by neutrons, were observed in cloud-chamber experiments and, from the lengths of the accompanying tracks, the maximum velocities were estimated to be 3.3×10^9 and 4.7×10^8 cm. per sec., respectively. These results were known to be approximate, but they should be sufficient to give some indication of the mass of the neutron. Thus, taking m_2 and m_3 to be the masses of the hydrogen and nitrogen nuclei, namely 1 and 14, respectively, in atomic mass units (§ 3.82), the corresponding values of v_2 and v_3 are then 3.3×10^9 and 4.7×10^8; upon substituting these data in equation (11.3), the mass m_1 of the neutron is found to be roughly 1.16 on the atomic mass scale, compared with unity for the proton.

11.4. The approximate result obtained in this manner showed, at least, that the mass of the neutron was similar to that of the proton, but a more accurate determination was desirable. Such a determination was made by Chadwick utilizing the energy and mass changes involved in the reaction between an alpha particle and a boron nucleus, in which a neutron was apparently liberated. If the reaction is of this type, then it should be

$$_5B^{11} + _2He^4 \rightarrow _7N^{14} + _0n^1,$$

and since the isotopic weights of the stable nuclides B^{11}, He^4 and N^{14} are available, it should be possible to obtain the weight of the neutron, provided the nuclear reaction energy (Q) were known (§ 9.25). The alpha particles, obtained from polonium have 5.25 Mev energy, equivalent to 0.00565 atomic mass unit, and the energies of the product N^{14} nucleus, calculated from its range in a cloud chamber, and of the neutron estimated from the maximum recoil of a proton after collision, were found to be 0.00061 and 0.0035 atomic mass unit, respectively. The energy of the boron target nucleus is negligible, and hence the energy change Q of the reaction in mass units is $0.00061 + 0.0035 - 0.00565 = -0.00154$. Taking the isotopic weights of B^{11} as 11.01279, of He^4 as 4.00387 and of N^{14} as 14.00752, it is seen that the mass of the neutron must be given by

Mass of neutron
$$= 11.01279 + 4.00387 - 14.00752$$
$$-0.00154 = 1.0076 \text{ a.m.u.}*$$

---

* This is lower than the mass (1.008986) now accepted, probably because of errors in the energy values.

Using the isotopic weight data available in 1932, Chadwick obtained 1.0067 for the mass of the neutron, but because of the uncertainty in the energy terms, he estimated the value to lie between 1.005 and 1.008.

11.5. Another procedure, which was first used by J. Chadwick and M. Goldhaber in 1934, has provided a still more precise result for the neutron mass. The method is based on the discovery that gamma rays of sufficient energy are able to disintegrate a deuteron into a proton and a neutron (§ 10.52); thus,

$$_1H^2 + \gamma \rightarrow {}_1H^1 + {}_0n^1.$$

The minimum energy necessary to break up the deuteron is now known to be 2.225 Mev, which corresponds to 0.00239 mass unit. It follows, therefore, that the mass of the deuteron plus 0.00239 should give the sum of the masses of the proton and the neutron. The isotopic weights of deuterium and hydrogen are 2.01474 and 1.008145, respectively, so that

Mass of neutron
$$= 2.01474 + 0.00239 - 1.008145$$
$$= 1.008985 \text{ a.m.u.}$$

11.6. Since neutrons are involved in many nuclear reactions, either as projectiles or as ejected particles, there are evidently numerous possibilities for calculating the mass of the neutron, provided the isotopic weights of the target and product nuclides, and the reaction energy are known. From an examination of the best data available in 1957 it appears that the neutron mass is 1.008986 atomic mass units. It may be noted, in passing, that the existence of an electrically neutral particle of appreciable mass seems to dispose of the theory, formerly held by many scientists, that all mass is electromagnetic in nature (§ 4.20).

RADIOACTIVITY OF THE NEUTRON

11.7. In the discussion of negative beta-decay in § 7.50, it was postulated that this type of radioactivity involves the conversion of a neutron into a proton and an electron, together with a neutrino. The sum of the masses of the proton, electron and neutrino is virtually equal to the mass of a hydrogen atom, i.e., 1.008145 atomic mass units, since this atom consists of one proton and one electron while the mass of the neutrino is negligible. It will be observed that the total mass is less than the mass of the neutron by 1.008986 − 1.008145 = 0.00084 unit, equivalent to 0.782 Mev of energy, and so it is possible to write

$$_0n^1 \rightarrow {}_1H^1 + {}_{-1}e^0 + 0.782 \text{ Mev.}$$

11.8. The fact that the conversion of a free neutron into a proton and an electron, together with a neutrino, is associated with the liberation of energy indicates that this process should take place spontaneously. In this event, the neutron would be the simplest radioactive species, decaying with the emission of a negative beta-particle, i.e., an electron, leaving a proton as the product. Since both the neutron and the proton have one half unit of spin (§ 4.86), it is probable that the decay will correspond to an "allowed" beta transition (§ 7.78). On this basis, it can be calculated that the half life of the neutron should be roughly 20 min.

11.9. The difficulty in detecting the radioactive decay of the free neutron lies in the fact that such neutrons are readily captured by nuclei; consequently, the average life of a free neutron is short in comparison with its expected radioactive half-life period. Nevertheless, an attempt to study the decay of neutrons was initiated by

L. W. Alvarez of the Radiation Laboratory, Berkeley, California, but the work was interrupted by the war. Since 1948, the problem has attracted the interest of A. H. Snell and his collaborators at the Oak Ridge National Laboratory, and of J. M. Robson and his associates at the Chalk River Laboratory in Canada. The experimental procedure consists in passing a strong beam of neutrons through a cylindrical tank which has been highly evacuated. An electrostatic field is so arranged that protons resulting from the beta decay of the neutrons are deflected in one direction and the accompanying electrons (beta particles) in another. A coincidence counting system, with a delay of about a millionth of a second to allow for the lower speed of the proton, responds only to the (almost) simultaneous arrival of a proton on one side of the neutron beam and an electron on the other. From the frequency of these coincidences, it has been estimated that the rate of formation of protons and electrons corresponds to a half life of about 13 min. for the free neutron, in general agreement with the calculated value given above. It is reasonably certain, therefore, that the free neutron is radioactive, in the sense that it disintegrates spontaneously with the emission of an electron, leaving a proton as the residual particle.*

DIFFRACTION OF NEUTRONS

11.10. One of the most striking arguments for the wave-particle duality of matter, which was discussed in Chapter III, has been provided by the diffraction of neutrons. It has been known for some years that electrons, in particular, and also protons and alpha particles, exhibit the characteristic wave property of interference resulting in the production of definite diffraction patterns (§ 3.41). While this evidence for the wave nature of matter is quite striking, some objection might perhaps have been raised on the grounds that the aforementioned particles are all electrically charged, and that the same phenomena would not be observed with neutral matter. All doubts of this kind have been dispelled by the clear proof that wave properties are also associated with neutrons. In 1936, W. M. Elsasser in France predicted that neutrons would exhibit the phenomenon of diffraction, and in the same year experimental proof was obtained by H. von Halban and P. Preiswerk in France and independently by D. P. Mitchell and P. N. Powers in the United States. Since that time the technique has been very greatly improved, thanks largely to the neutron beams obtainable from nuclear fission reactors. A photograph, taken at the Oak Ridge National Laboratory, showing the neutron diffraction pattern of a sodium chloride

Fig. 11.1. Laue type diffraction pattern of sodium chloride obtained with neutrons from the Oak Ridge nuclear reactor.

* The *bound* neutron in a nucleus is in a different energy state and does not exhibit this behavior.

crystal, is reproduced in Fig. 11.1; this may be compared with Fig. 2.8 for the diffraction of X-rays.

11.11. According to the de Broglie equation (3.7), the wave length λ cm., equivalent to a particle of mass m grams, moving with a velocity v cm. per sec., is equal to h/mv, where h is the Planck quantum theory constant, 6.62×10^{-27} erg sec. Since the energy E of a neutron is essentially all kinetic energy, it is equal to $\frac{1}{2}mv^2$, and so mv in the de Broglie equation may be replaced by $\sqrt{2mE}$; the equivalent wave length of the neutron is then given by

$$\lambda = \frac{h}{mv} = \frac{h}{\sqrt{2mE}}. \qquad (11.4)$$

Upon inserting the value of m, the actual mass of the neutron, which is approximately 1.67×10^{-24} gram, and introducing the factor 1.60×10^{-12} for converting electron volts to ergs (§ 3.33), it follows that

$$\lambda = \frac{6.62 \times 10^{-27}}{\sqrt{2 \times 1.67 \times 10^{-24} \times 1.60 \times 10^{-12}E}}$$

$$= \frac{2.87 \times 10^{-9}}{\sqrt{E}} \text{ cm.,} \qquad (11.5)$$

where E is the neutron energy expressed in electron volts.

11.12. It is of interest to see what order of energy would be requisite for a neutron beam if the associated wave train were to be capable of diffraction by a crystal. The wave length would have to be about 2×10^{-8} cm., and hence it follows from the equation (11.5) that neutrons with energy of about 0.02 ev should exhibit diffraction phenomena with crystals. This is precisely what has been found experimentally, and in § 11.84 it will be shown how reflection from a crystal surface is used to sort out neutrons of specific energies or velocities.

11.13. To the chemist, an application of neutron diffraction of exceptional interest is in connection with the study of molecular structure. Diffraction of X-rays by crystals and of electrons by gases has been very widely used to determine the distances between atoms in a molecule. But these methods have one great drawback: because the diffraction of X-rays depends almost entirely, and that of electrons largely, on the number of orbital electrons of the atom, it is not feasible to identify the positions of hydrogen atoms with their single electrons. In the diffraction of neutrons, on the other hand, it is the scattering by the nucleus which determines the extent of diffraction, and in this respect the effect of hydrogen is quite considerable. Hence, neutron diffraction by crystals makes possible the determination of interatomic distances involving hydrogen atoms. The strong neutron beams required for diffraction studies are available only from nuclear reactors (Chapter XIV), but since these neutrons have a range of energies (and wave lengths), the results are not too exact. Consequently, neutron diffraction is to be regarded as complementary to, rather than as a substitute for, X-ray diffraction. In addition to its usefulness in detecting hydrogen and other light atoms, e.g., beryllium, neutron diffraction can generally discriminate between atoms of approximately the same weight, e.g., manganese, iron, cobalt and nickel, and magnesium and aluminum, which X-rays cannot.

PRODUCTION AND DETECTION OF NEUTRONS

Neutron Sources

11.14. The first recognized formation of neutrons was the result of reactions of the (α,n) type, with beryllium, boron and lithium. Subsequently, other light elements, such as nitrogen, fluorine, sodium, magnesium and aluminum, were found to emit neutrons when bombarded with alpha particles. Although none of these can be regarded as strong sources of neutrons, from the present-day standpoint, a fair yield of neutrons can be obtained from the (α,n) reaction with beryllium. A convenient means of producing neutrons is a mixture of metallic beryllium with a small quantity of an alpha-particle emitter, such as a radium or a polonium compound. A sealed capsule containing radium emanation, that is, the gas radon, and beryllium provides an inexpensive source of neutrons; the use of radium, in place of radon, is more costly, but the neutron intensity is much stronger and more lasting.

11.15. The neutrons obtained from the reaction

$$_4\text{Be}^9 + _2\text{He}^4 \rightarrow _6\text{C}^{12} + _0n^1$$

are not monoenergetic; that is to say, they do not all have the same energy. The reaction energy of the $\text{Be}^9(\alpha,n)\text{C}^{12}$ process is about 5.5 Mev, and this, less the recoil, and possible excitation, energy of the C^{12} nucleus, represents the minimum energy of the emitted neutron. However, neutrons could be obtained with this energy only if the incident alpha particle had zero energy, and the probability of such particles entering the beryllium nucleus is quite negligible. The alpha particles from radioactive sources have appreciable energy, and most of this will ultimately appear as energy of the emitted neutrons. The yield from the bombardment of beryllium by alpha particles from 1 gram of radium is about 10 to 15 million neutrons per second.

11.16. A number of reactions of the (d,n) type have been employed as neutron sources, the accelerated deuterons being generally produced by means of a cyclotron (§ 9.53). With a cooled beryllium target, it is possible to use relatively strong deuteron currents, so that neutrons are obtained at the rate of many billions per second from the reaction $\text{Be}^9(d,n)\text{B}^{10}$. Another reaction of the same type, but somewhat less efficient, is $\text{Li}^7(d,n)\text{Be}^8$; since the reaction energy in this case is about 15 Mev, it is possible to obtain neutrons of fairly high energy by bombarding lithium with deuterons of moderate speed.

11.17. It was stated in § 10.33 that bombardment of deuterium by deuterons gives rise to the reaction

$$_1\text{H}^2 + _1\text{H}^2 \rightarrow _2\text{He}^3 + _0n^1 + 3.2 \text{ Mev},$$

and this (d,n) process has been used as a source of neutrons, the target being ice obtained by freezing heavy water, i.e., solid deuterium oxide (§ 8.73). The reaction energy is positive, by about 3.2 Mev, and a good yield of neutrons is possible even with deuterons of relatively low energy, for example, down to 0.2 Mev. A valuable source of neutrons of high energy results from the analogous (d,n) reaction of deuterons with the heavier isotope of hydrogen, tritium; thus,

$$_1\text{H}^3 + _1\text{H}^2 \rightarrow _2\text{He}^4 + _0n^1 + 17.6 \text{ Mev}.$$

Further reference to this source will be made in § 11.89.

11.18. Several light and moderately heavy elements undergo (p,n) reactions, but only one of these processes, namely,

$$_3Li^7 + {}_1H^1 \rightarrow {}_4Be^7 + {}_0n^1 - 1.62 \text{ Mev},$$

has been used to any extent as a source of neutrons. Although the reaction energy is here negative by 1.62 Mev, the actual threshold energy for the protons is about 1.88 Mev, the additional 0.26 Mev being mainly recoil energy of the Be^7 nucleus.

11.19. Photonuclear reactions, namely, reactions of the (γ,n) type, have proved to be particularly valuable for the production of homogeneous, i.e., monoenergetic, neutron beams (§ 11.87); these are called *photoneutron sources*. Processes of the (γ,n) type invariably have negative reaction energies; consequently, the gamma rays must have a definite minimum (or threshold) energy before the process can take place. The energy of the neutron is then roughly equal to the energy of the gamma radiation used minus the threshold energy of the particular (γ,n) reaction. If these two quantities are not very different, the neutrons will evidently have relatively low energies.

11.20. Two photonuclear reactions mentioned in § 10.52, namely, $H^2(\gamma,n)H^1$ and $Be^9(\gamma,n)Be^8$, for which the theoretical minimum energies are 2.225 and 1.66 Mev, respectively, have been largely used to produce neutrons. Any radioactive species emitting gamma rays of sufficient energy may be employed, in conjunction with a deuterium compound or beryllium as the target. The half life of the gamma-ray source should not be too short, so that the rate of neutron emission may remain fairly constant over an appreciable interval of time. Four such sources, namely, Na^{24}, Ga^{72}, Sb^{124} and La^{140}, all artificial radionuclides, satisfy the foregoing requirements. The gamma rays from Na^{24} can be used with either deuterium or beryllium to produce neutrons of different energies in the two cases; those from Ga^{72} are used with deuterium only, in the form of heavy water, while the radiations from Sb^{124} and La^{140} are employed to interact with beryllium, although the yields in the latter case are small.

11.21. A convenient source of neutrons, available from the Isotopes Division of the Atomic Energy Commission, consists of a rod of antimony, containing the 60-day Sb^{124} radioisotope, surrounded by a beryllium metal cup. When newly prepared the system emits neutrons, of approximately uniform (0.03 Mev) energy, at the rate of about eight million per second. After the activity of the Sb^{124} has decayed, it can be regenerated by exposure of the antimony rod to neutrons in a nuclear reactor (Chapter XIV).

11.22. An unusual type of process which has led to the production of neutrons of high energy, around 100 Mev, was discovered in 1947 in the course of experiments with deuterons accelerated to 200 Mev energy in the Berkeley 184-inch synchrocyclotron. The neutrons are formed from the deuterons as a result of a phenomenon called *stripping*, which is believed to occur somewhat in the following manner. As mentioned earlier (§ 10.28), a deuteron behaves as a relatively loosely-bound system consisting of a neutron and a proton which are frequently outside the range of their mutual forces. If a high-energy deuteron strikes a target nucleus in such a way as to graze the edge of the latter, the proton may be stripped off, while the neutron misses and travels on alone. The proton may be captured by the target nucleus, or it may be deflected by the magnetic field of the cyclotron, but the uncharged neutrons continue to move in a straight line, thus permitting their removal as a narrow beam. The energies of the neutrons obtained in this manner range around half the initial deuteron energy, so that, with 200 Mev deuterons, the mean neutron energy is about 100 Mev. Almost any element may be used as the target material in stripping, but the yield of stripped neutrons for a given deuteron intensity varies with the nature of the target.

11.23. In recent years there has become available a source of neutrons so powerful that those described above, important though they may be, are almost insignificant in comparison. This source is a nuclear reactor or "pile," in which uranium is undergoing fission. As indicated in § 10.60, this process is initiated by neutrons, and it is also accompanied by the emission of neutrons. The subjects of fission and of nuclear reactors will be treated in greater detail in Chapters XIII, XIV and XV.

DETECTION OF NEUTRONS

11.24. Since neutrons do not interact appreciably with electrons, they produce very little direct ionization, namely, about one ion-pair per meter of path, compared with something like a million for a proton of approximately the same energy. Direct detection of a neutron in any instrument such as is used for charged particles, or a Wilson cloud chamber, which depends for its action upon ionization due to the entering particle, is thus out of the question. Nevertheless, devices of this type can be adapted to study neutrons by utilizing certain secondary effects.

11.25. Two general principles have been employed in the detection of neutrons: first, use is made of the charged particles produced by the interaction of neutrons with various substances introduced into the counter, and, second, advantage is taken of the recoil of nuclei of light elements after being struck by neutrons. In each case, the secondary particles produce ionization in their paths, so that their presence immediately becomes evident. The choice of procedure depends chiefly on the energy (or speed) of the neutrons to be detected; for slow neutrons, with energies up to a few thousand electron volts, the interaction method is mainly used, but for fast neutrons, having energies of the order of a million (or more) electron volts, the recoil principle is generally employed.

11.26. The most common instruments for the detection of slow neutrons utilize the reaction of these neutrons with the less abundant isotope of boron, B^{10}; thus,

$$_5B^{10} + _0n^1 \rightarrow _3Li^7 + _2He^4 + 2.5 \text{ Mev,}$$

the 2.5 Mev reaction energy being carried off by the resulting lithium nucleus and alpha particle which produce considerable ionization in their tracks. In order to take advantage of this process, a counter containing boron (or a compound of boron) is employed. The chamber may either contain boron trifluoride as part of the filling gas or the walls may be lined with a thin coating of elemental boron or of a solid compound, such as boron carbide. Since it is actually the B^{10} isotope, present to the extent of less than 19 per cent in natural boron, which is involved, better results are obtained if the boron compound is enriched in the B^{10} isotope. By using a chamber of suitable size, every neutron entering can be made to interact with a B^{10} nucleus, so that the number of counts recorded gives the number of neutrons. The counter may be of the ionization chamber type (§ 6.13), although it is more usual to operate it in the proportional region (§ 6.22).

11.27. It was mentioned in § 6.87 that the track of an ionizing particle in a photographic emulsion becomes visible upon development as a line of fine grains of silver. Neutrons do not affect the silver halide in the emulsion directly, but if boron is present in the form of a compound, such as borax, the charged particles produced in the reaction with slow neutrons can be readily detected.

11.28. Another type of neutron reaction, namely fission, has been used in what have been called *fission chambers* to detect slow neutrons. Such neutrons are able to cause uranium-235 to undergo fission, and the fission fragments have considerable ionizing effect. A simple type of fission chamber for observing neutrons thus consists of an ionization chamber of which one electrode is coated with uranium oxide, preferably enriched in the uranium-235 isotope.

11.29. Scintillation counters have also been adapted to the detection and counting of neutrons. The methods used are based on the addition to the scintillator material of an element which interacts with neutrons to yield particles capable of producing scintillations directly. For example, a boron compound may be included in a solid zinc sulfide (silver activated) or a sodium iodide (thallium activated) phosphor. With a liquid organic scintillator, the boron may be included in the form of methyl borate. Since organic phosphors respond readily to gamma rays, an alternative possibility

is to add a cadmium compound, e.g., cadmium octoate. As a result of the capture of slow neutrons by cadmium, the (n,γ) reaction occurs and the gamma-ray photons produce scintillations.

11.30. When fast neutrons are being studied, it is the general practice to make use of the ionization in the track of a light nucleus recoiling after being struck by a high-energy neutron. For this purpose a proportional counter may be filled with hydrogen or deuterium, but a better procedure is to use argon, or one of the heavier inert gases, as the filling gas and to place a thin sheet of a hydrogenous material, such as paraffin, at one end of the chamber. Fast neutrons striking the paraffin cause the ejection of protons; these produce ionization in their paths through the counter, and so can be detected. The recoil effect in a cloud chamber containing hydrogen may also be used to indicate the presence of neutrons, as shown in Fig. 11.2. Alternatively, a bubble chamber, containing liquid hy-

Fig. 11.2. Cloud tracks produced by protons recoiling after collision with neutrons. (From *Phys. Rev.*, 50, 1138 (1936)).

drogen or a hydrogen-containing compound, may be employed. From the maximum length of the paths of the recoiling protons the energy of the neutrons can be estimated. The presence of recoil protons due to neutrons can also be made evident by their effect on photographic film, and from the lengths of the recoil tracks the energy of the neutrons can be calculated. These protons may result from collision of the fast neutrons with hydrogen atoms in the emulsion or in hydrogenous material, such as water, in the vicinity. Fast neutrons can be detected by means of an organic phosphor (solid or liquid) in a scintillation counter, without addition of any other material. The organic compound contains a large proportion of hydrogen so that fast neutrons produce recoil protons which cause scintillations.

11.31. Although uranium-235 undergoes fission with either fast or slow neutrons, only fast neutrons can cause this type of process in the more abundant uranium-238. Hence a fission chamber for the detection of fast neutrons can be designed using a uranium compound which has been depleted in the lighter isotope; such a device will respond to fast, but not to slow, neutrons. Another possibility is to use a fission chamber, without special attention to the particular uranium isotope present, surrounded by cadmium or boron. These materials will absorb the slow neutrons, and so any fission observed in the chamber is due to fast neutrons.

11.32. If it is not required to distinguish between fast and slow neutrons, then the particles may be slowed down by passage through a layer of paraffin or of water a few centimeters in thickness, as explained below. The resulting neutrons can then be observed by any of the forms of slow-neutron counter described above.

11.33. A principle somewhat different from those already considered has been applied to the detection and counting of neutrons of particular energies. Certain metals, such as indium and rhodium, are able to absorb, very strongly, neutrons lying within narrow energy ranges (§ 11.97); then, as a result of a reaction of the (n,γ) type, a radioactive isotope of the original element is formed. The amount of this active material, and hence the number of neutrons absorbed, can be estimated by observing its beta decay in a particle counter. Alternatively, a thin sheet of the metal, indium for example, in contact with a photographic film, may be used to detect neutrons. The radioactivity of the product of neutron interaction with the indium causes a fogging of the film.

SLOWING DOWN OF NEUTRONS

Elastic Scattering

11.34. The simplest type of nuclear reaction in which neutrons are the projectiles is elastic scattering (§ 10.26). There is no formation of a compound nucleus or of an excited state, but the incident neutron is deprived of some of its energy, which appears as kinetic energy, i.e., energy of motion, of the target nucleus. The neutron then recoils with less energy than it had before the impact. The effect is essentially an elastic or "billiard-ball" type of collision of the neutron with the atomic nucleus; the interaction may thus be treated by the ordinary laws of mechanics, based on the principles of conservation of energy and of momentum. In § 11.2, this approach was used in considering a head-on collision in which there is a maximum transfer of energy from a neutron to a struck nucleus, but in the most general case allowance must be made for possible collisions at all angles of impact.

11.35. The calculations are performed by appropriate integration, and the result shows that in each collision a neutron loses, on the average, a definite fraction of the energy it had just prior to the collision. This fraction, as might be expected, is greater the smaller the mass of the nucleus with which the neutron collides. The energy of a neutron, apart from the energy equivalence of its mass, is entirely kinetic in nature, and so it is directly related to its velocity (§ 3.5). It is seen, therefore, that the speed of a neutron is decreased in a collision with an atomic nucleus, the fractional extent of this decrease being greater the lighter the struck nucleus. Thus, in a medium of low atomic weight (or mass number) fewer collisions are required to slow down a neutron over a given energy range than in a medium of higher atomic weight (or mass number).

Thermal Neutrons

11.36. After a number of collisions with nuclei, the speed of a neutron is reduced to such an extent that it has approximately the same average kinetic energy as the atoms (or molecules) of the medium in which the neutron is undergoing elastic scattering. This energy, which is only a small fraction of an electron volt at ordinary temperatures (§ 11.39), is frequently referred to as the *thermal energy*, since it depends upon the temperature. Neutrons whose energies have been reduced to values in this region are designated *thermal neutrons*. The process of reducing the energy of a neutron to the thermal region by elastic scatter-

ing is sometimes called *thermalization* or, more commonly, slowing down. It will be seen in Chapter XIV that the slowing down of fast neutrons by collisions with nuclei plays a significant role in the nuclear fission reactors in which atomic energy is released. The material used for the purpose is then called a *moderator;* a good moderator reduces the speed of neutrons in a small number of elastic collisions, but does not absorb them to any great extent.

11.37. The suggestion that fast neutrons are slowed down by passage through hydrogen-containing substances, such as water or paraffin, until their energies reached thermal values was made by E. Amaldi, O. D'Agostino, E. Fermi, B. Pontecorvo, F. Rasetti and E. Segrè in Italy in 1935, in the course of their important work on the radiative capture of neutrons (§ 11.46). Soon afterward, P. B. Moon and J. R. Tillman in England obtained experimental evidence of this phenomenon by showing that neutrons after passing through paraffin cooled to about −180°C reacted more readily with silver, rhodium and iodine than they did at ordinary temperatures. Slow neutrons are more easily captured by these nuclei than are fast neutrons (§ 11.46). Subsequently, several physicists made direct measurements of neutron velocities, and confirmed the fact that the values were those to be expected for particles with thermal energies.

11.38. It should be emphasized that the property possessed by neutrons, of having their energies reduced from millions of electron volts to thermal values of a fraction of an electron volt, and of still being capable of producing nuclear reactions, is very remarkable. Protons, alpha particles and other charged particles can be slowed down, but they can then no longer interact with nuclei, because they are unable to penetrate the electrostatic energy barriers. In any event, as the positive particles are slowed down they soon pick up electrons, becoming neutral atoms and losing their ability to cause nuclear transformations. Slow neutrons, on the other hand, can enter nearly all atomic nuclei (§ 11.47), and induce fission of certain of the heavier ones (§ 13.71). It is these properties of the neutron, striking and unusual for a nuclear particle, which have made possible the utilization of atomic energy.

11.39. The average thermal (kinetic) energy of any particle is equal to $\frac{3}{2}kT$, where k is called the *Boltzmann constant*,* equal to 1.38×10^{-16} erg, or 8.61×10^{-5} ev, per degree and T is the absolute temperature. The normal value of T is approximately 293° on the absolute scale, that is, 20°C, and so the thermal energy of a particle at ordinary temperatures is about 0.038 ev. In neutron studies the thermal energy is usually taken as kT,† instead of $\frac{3}{2}kT$, so that a thermal neutron is regarded as one with an average energy of 0.025 ev at normal temperatures. It is apparent, of course, that the energy of a thermal neutron will depend on the temperature of the sur-

roundings; thermal neutrons in a nuclear fission reactor will have appreciably larger energies than such neutrons in the atmosphere because the temperature is higher. In any event, even at a specific temperature, not all thermal neutrons will have the same energy (or velocity); just as with molecules of a gas, there is a distribution of energies, usually spoken of as the *Maxwell distribution*.‡ The energies of most thermal neutrons lie close to the mean value, but there is a spread, with small proportions having very low and very high energies. For the purpose of simplicity, the energy distribution will be ignored in the subsequent discussion, as it remains essentially unchanged.

11.40. Since the mean fractional decrease of energy per collision can be determined, as indicated above, it is possible to calculate the number of collisions necessary to reduce the energy of a neutron from a particular value, say 1 Mev, to the thermal energy of 0.025 ev at ordinary temperatures. The results obtained in this manner for a number of the lighter elements are quoted in the accompanying table. It should be noted that, since the fractional energy loss in a given collision depends upon the angle of impact (§ 11.35), the values tabu-

SLOWING DOWN OF 1-MEV NEUTRONS

Element	H	D	He	Be	C	O
Mass number	1	2	4	9	12	16
Fractional energy loss per collision	0.63	0.52	0.35	0.18	0.14	0.11
Collisions for thermalization	18	25	42	90	114	150
Capture cross section (barns)	0.33	0.00046	~ 0	0.009	0.0045	0.0002

* Named for L. Boltzmann, the Austrian mathematical physicist, who made important contributions to the kinetic theory of gases and related subjects.
† This is the energy corresponding to the most probable velocity.
‡ So called after J. C. Maxwell (§§ 2.25, 3.22), who, in 1860, developed the theoretical equation for the distribution of energy (or velocity) among gas molecules.

lated, as well as the numbers of collisions required to thermalize a 1-Mev neutron, are average values based on a large number of collisions between neutrons and the specified nuclei.

11.41. It is seen that a 1-Mev neutron will, on the average, have to make about 18 collisions with hydrogen nuclei before its energy is reduced to thermal values, but approximately 114 collisions will be necessary with carbon nuclei to bring about the same energy decrease.* The number of collisions necessary to thermalize a 1-Mev neutron obviously increases with the mass number of the nucleus with which it collides; hence moderators for slowing down neutrons should consist of the lighter elements. In order that the thermalization process may take place as rapidly as possible, it is desirable to use a solid or liquid as moderator; the nuclei are then packed more closely than in the gaseous state, and collisions with neutrons occur more frequently. Substances like liquid water and paraffin wax, the latter consisting of hydrogen and carbon, are thus cheap and convenient materials for slowing down fast neutrons. But neither of these is altogether satisfactory for use as a moderator, because there is an appreciable probability that the slow-moving neutron will react with, and hence be absorbed by, a hydrogen nucleus. In other words, the hydrogen nucleus has a relatively high cross section (§ 10.73) for the absorption of slow neutrons. This is shown by the approximate capture cross sections for thermal neutrons given in the last line of the table. Nevertheless, for reasons which will be apparent in Chapter XIV, there are several types of nuclear reactor in which water is used as the moderator for slowing down neutrons.

11.42. An ideal moderator, in theory, would be liquid helium, since this element does not absorb neutrons to any detectable extent under any conditions. But, since the temperature would have to be extremely low, use of liquid helium is, obviously, not practical. Of the remaining elements included in the table, deuterium, in the form of deuterium oxide (heavy water), beryllium and carbon offer distinct possibilities, and these materials are actually used as moderators in various nuclear reactors. It will be noted that the light elements lithium and boron have been omitted from consideration; the reason is that their nuclei have such high absorption cross sections for slow neutrons that these substances have no practical value as moderators.

11.43. The speed of a 1-Mev neutron is about 1.4×10^9 cm. per sec., and this is decreased to about 2.2×10^5 cm. per sec., when the energy of the neutron is reduced to that of the thermal region. However, even a "slow," thermal neutron still travels at a rate of appreciably more than a mile per second. After a neutron has been slowed down, a process which takes a very small fraction of a second, it still continues to move about the medium, colliding with nuclei, until it is either captured or it escapes. The motion (or diffusion) of thermal neutrons is of great importance in connection with the design of nuclear reactors. The theoretical treatment of neutron diffusion, which involves mathematics of an advanced character, is somewhat similar to that used by engineers in the study of heat flow.

---

* These collisions do not take into account the possible effect of crystal scattering (§ 11.10), in graphite, for example, and also the increased scattering of slow neutrons by bound hydrogen, as in paraffin. These factors are important, but they do not affect the main arguments.

NEUTRON REACTIONS

RADIATIVE CAPTURE

11.44. The neutron, being electrically neutral, is not subjected to electrostatic repulsion, as are charged particles, when it approaches an atomic nucleus. In fact, as the neutron approaches the nucleus, attractive forces begin to operate and the neutron may be captured with the formation of a compound nucleus. Because of the absence of repulsion, there is no energy barrier preventing the access of the neutron to an atomic nucleus, and so even the slowest neutrons, such as the thermal neutrons described in the preceding section, can be readily captured. For the nuclei of most elements, other than the very lightest, the addition of a neutron results in an increase of energy equal to about 8 Mev (§ 12.7), plus the kinetic energy of the incident neutron. Hence, even when a thermal neutron, with energy a small fraction of an electron volt, is captured the compound nucleus formed will usually be in a high-energy, excited state, which attains relative stability by the ejection of a proton or an alpha particle or by emitting the excess energy as gamma radiation. The residual nucleus is not always completely stable, for it is frequently radioactive.

11.45. The first nuclear transmutations brought about by neutrons were reported in 1932 by N. Feather in England, and by W. D. Harkins, D. M. Gans and H. W. Newson in the United States. Fast neutrons were employed, and (n,α) reactions were observed with nitrogen, oxygen, fluorine and neon nuclei as targets. In 1934, D. E. Lea in England detected gamma rays when hydrogen-containing substances were bombarded with fast neutrons; it was suggested that these represented the energy liberated in the formation of a deuteron from a neutron and a proton, so that the reaction was a simple type of radiative capture, i.e., (n,γ), process.

11.46. The great importance of the radiative capture reaction with neutrons became apparent from the work of E. Fermi and his collaborators in Italy during 1934. At that time the known transmutation reactions involved only the lightest elements, but they found that of some sixty elements bombarded with neutrons, about two thirds, ranging from low to high atomic numbers, were converted into radioactive isotopes of the target material. In the course of these studies, the Italian scientists referred to in § 11.37 noted that if the neutrons were passed through water or paraffin they became much more effective in radiative capture (n,γ) reactions. This extremely significant phenomenon was attributed to the slowing down of the neutrons by the hydrogen-containing material, the slow neutrons being more readily captured by the target nuclei. Subsequently, measurements of absorption cross sections with neutrons of various speeds completely confirmed this suggestion (§ 11.95). The discovery of transmutation by slow neutrons is historically significant, for it led ultimately to the realization of nuclear fission, and consequently to the practical possibility of utilizing nuclear energy.

11.47. The radiative capture reaction with slow neutrons is probably the most common nuclear process, for it takes place with nearly all elements. As stated in § 10.42, the transmutation product is an isotope of the target element with a mass number one unit larger. The energies, i.e., the Q values, of these reactions are always positive, and much of this excess energy is emitted as gamma rays which are sometimes internally converted (§ 7.106). The simplest (n,γ) reaction with slow neutrons occurs with hydrogen as the target nucleus, thus,

$$_1H^1 + _0n^1 \rightarrow _1H^2 + \gamma,$$

the product being deuterium. This is the reaction whereby the absorption of slow neutrons by hydrogen, in water or paraffin, mentioned in § 11.41, takes place. The reaction is seen to be exactly the reverse of that described in § 11.19 for the production of neutrons by the action of gamma rays on deuterium. Since the minimum energy necessary for the latter reaction is known to be 2.225 Mev, it follows that in the (n,γ) reaction with hydrogen, the energy of the gamma radiation will have at least this value. The emission of such radiation, of relatively high energy and penetrating power, has been confirmed experimentally. Cognizance must be taken of this fact when water or other hydrogenous material is used in connection with a nuclear reactor, either as moderator, as a cooling agent, or as a shield to prevent escape of neutrons.

11.48. Since the capture of a neutron, followed by the emission of gamma radiation, must be associated with an increase in the neutron-to-proton ratio, the product of an (n,γ) reaction is likely to be radioactive, especially if the ratio of neutrons to protons in the target nucleus is already near the upper limit of stability for the given atomic number. Consequently, radiative capture reactions have been extensively used for the production of radioisotopes (§ 17.20 *et seq.*). A radionuclide obtained in this manner will emit a negative beta-particle,* for this mode of decay means that the neutron is replaced by a proton, thus bringing the neutron-to-proton ratio back into the range of stability. Over a hundred (n,γ) reactions leading to beta-active isotopes have been reported. Two of these, in which Rh^{103} and In^{115}, respectively, are the target nuclei, i.e.,

$$_{45}Rh^{103} + _0n^1 \rightarrow _{45}Rh^{104} \ (42 \ \text{sec.}) + \gamma$$

$$_{49}In^{115} + _0n^1 \rightarrow _{49}In^{116m} \ (54 \ \text{min.}) + \gamma,$$

are of particular interest since they are used for the detection of neutrons of more or less specific energies, as mentioned in § 11.33.

11.49. Perhaps the most notable of all (n,γ) reactions, to which reference only will be made here, as it will be treated more fully in later chapters, is that undergone by uranium-238; thus,

$$_{92}U^{238} + _0n^1 \rightarrow _{92}U^{239} + \gamma.$$

The product uranium-239 is a negative beta-emitter with a half life of 23.5 min., decaying by the process

$$_{92}U^{239} \rightarrow _{93}Np^{239} + _{-1}e^0,$$

the daughter being an element of atomic number 93, called neptunium (Np), which does not at present exist in nature to any detectable extent. Neptunium-239 is itself beta-active (half life 2.3 days), as follows,

$$_{93}Np^{239} \rightarrow _{94}Pu^{239} + _{-1}e^0,$$

the product being plutonium-239, a relatively long-lived alpha emitter (§ 16.24).

---

* Several instances have been reported of positive beta-active or K-capture products from (n,γ) processes; in each case the neutron-to-proton ratio of the target nucleus is near the lower limit of stability for the particular atomic number (§ 12.41).

EJECTION OF CHARGED PARTICLE

11.50. It has already been stated on several occasions that a charged particle, such as a proton or an alpha particle, is hindered from leaving an atomic nucleus by the electrostatic repulsion barrier. Hence, processes of the (n,p), (n,d) and (n,α) types can take place only when the incident neutron supplies sufficient energy to overcome the force binding the charged particle in the compound nucleus and also to permit it to escape. It is consequently to be expected that these reactions will, in general, require fast neutrons, and this has been found to be true, with some few exceptions which will be considered in due course. Further, since the force of electrostatic repulsion between a nucleus and a charged particle increases with the atomic number, that is, with the positive charge, of the former, the requisite neutron energy becomes greater with increasing atomic number of the target material.

11.51. Nuclear processes of the (n,p) type are usually associated with a negative reaction energy of the order of 1 Mev or more, and so fast neutrons having this amount of energy, at least, are necessary. For a few light nuclides, He^3 and N^{14}, in particular, the energy change for the (n,p) reaction is positive, instead of negative, and, in addition, the potential barrier inhibiting the escape of the proton is relatively low because of the small atomic numbers of the nuclei. In these instances, the (n,p) processes, namely, $He^3(n,p)$ H^3 and $N^{14}(n,p)C^{14}$, respectively, can therefore take place with slow neutrons. The latter reaction is of special interest and importance, for it is used in the preparation of the radioactive C^{14} isotope of carbon. It will be seen in Chapter XVII that this nuclide has proved of exceptional value in the study of processes occurring in living organisms, and appreciable quantities are made by exposing pellets of beryllium nitride to the intense neutron concentration of a nuclear fission reactor. By the action of these neutrons the N^{14} atom is transmuted into one of C^{14}, by the (n,p) reaction mentioned above. After exposure, the material is dissolved in acid and the evolved gases are oxidized by hot copper oxide to yield radiocarbon dioxide. The latter is absorbed in sodium hydroxide solution and, from this, $BaC^{14}O_3$ is precipitated by means of barium hydroxide.

11.52. Because the gain of a neutron and the loss of a proton means an increase in the neutron-to-proton ratio, most of the products of (n,p) reactions are radioactive, decaying with the emission of a negative beta-particle.* It is to be noted that the nuclide resulting from the decay is identical with the original target material, and this fact permits some interesting light to be shed on the energy changes of the (n,p) reactions.

11.53. Consider, for purposes of illustration, the $N^{14}(n,p)C^{14}$ reaction, namely,

$$_7N^{14} + {}_0n^1 \rightarrow {}_6C^{14} + {}_1H^1 + Q,$$

the radioactive C^{14} decaying by the process

$$_6C^{14} \rightarrow {}_7N^{14} + {}_{-1}e^0 + E_{max},$$

so that the final product N^{14} is identical with the initial target nuclide. The reaction energy of the (n,p) process is

---

* A few exceptional cases are known in which the product of an (n,p) reaction is a positive beta-emitter or exhibits K-capture; the neutron-to-proton ratios of the target species are here also, as in the analogous instances in § 11.48, at the lower limit of stability for the particular mass numbers.

is represented by Q, whereas the energy change accompanying the beta decay is equivalent to E_{max} (§ 7.48), the maximum energy of the emitted beta particles.

11.54. The over-all result of the two processes is obtained by adding the two foregoing equations and canceling out such species as appear on both sides; the net effect is seen to be

$$_0n^1 \rightarrow {}_1H^1 + {}_{-1}e^0 + Q + E_{max}.$$

In other words, as a consequence of the (n,p) reaction and the ensuing beta decay, a neutron has been converted into a proton and an electron, together with, of course, a neutrino in the second stage. The energy change of this process is known to be 0.78 Mev (§ 11.7) and so it follows that $Q + E_{max}$ must have this same value.

11.55. The result, derived above by taking a specific example, is completely general for all cases of the type under consideration. The sum of the energy of the (n,p) reaction and the maximum energy of the beta decay which follows must inevitably add up to $+0.78$ Mev, so that the (n,p) reaction energy Q is equal to $0.78 - E_{max}$. In the majority of instances E_{max} is larger than 0.78 Mev, so that the (n,p) reaction energy is negative, as stated above, but it happens that the energies of the beta particles emitted by tritium (H^3), by carbon-14 and by sulfur-35 are exceptionally low, 0.018, 0.156 and 0.167 Mev, respectively. Hence the reactions $He^3(n,p)H^3$, $N^{14}(n,p)C^{14}$ and $Cl^{35}(n,p)S^{35}$, in which these species are formed, are accompanied by positive energy changes, thus making it possible for the reactions to occur with neutrons of low energy.

11.56. As indicated in § 10.43, processes of the (n,d) type should require neutrons of high energy, but such re-actions are somewhat unexpected, in any event, since the emission of a neutron and a proton might be more probable. Nevertheless, (n,d) reactions have been detected as a result of the bombardment of elements of low, medium and high atomic number by 90-Mev neutrons. It appears that the incident neutron moves through the target nucleus so rapidly that it sometimes carries a proton with it, emerging as a deuteron. There is some possibility that an (n,t) reaction takes place in an analogous manner. It should be pointed out, in accordance with the statement in § 10.59, that these reactions with high-energy particles do not involve the formation of a compound nucleus in which there is a redistribution of energy.

11.57. If it were not for the electrostatic potential energy barrier which makes it difficult for an alpha particle to leave the compound nucleus, an (n,α) reaction with a given target material would usually be more probable than the corresponding (n,p) process. The reason is that the removal of an alpha particle from a nucleus generally requires about 4 Mev (§ 10.9), whereas 8 Mev are necessary to detach a proton. Since the entering neutron contributes about 8 Mev, the reaction energies for (n,α) processes usually have positive values. When the target element has a low atomic number, the potential energy barrier tending to hold back the alpha particle is not too high, and hence (n,α) reactions might be expected to take place when such elements are bombarded with slow neutrons. This is actually the case with boron-10, the reaction $B^{10}(n,\alpha)Li^7$ being employed, as stated in § 11.26, for the detection of slow neutrons.

11.58. Another process of the same type has been observed when low-energy neutrons react with the lighter, less common Li^6 isotope of lithium; the (n,α) reaction, with an energy change of about 4.5 Mev, is

$$_3Li^6 + _0n^1 \rightarrow _1H^3 + _2He^4,$$

so that the product is tritium, the hydrogen isotope of mass number 3. The bombardment, by means of neutrons from a nuclear reactor, of ordinary lithium, which contains about 7.5 per cent of lithium-6, is the method used for the production of appreciable amounts of tritium.

11.59. As the atomic number of the target nucleus increases, the height of the potential barrier rises rapidly, and emission of an alpha particle becomes less probable. In order for the (n,α) process to take place, additional energy must be supplied in the form of kinetic energy of the neutron projectile; hence, for elements of higher atomic number the (n,α) reaction is possible only if high-energy, that is, fast, neutrons are available. Processes of the (n,α) type are not common with target materials of atomic number exceeding 40, although mercury, thallium and lead, atomic numbers 80, 81 and 82, respectively, have been reported to react in this manner. As a general rule, when the neutron has sufficient energy to make the (n,α) reaction possible with an element of high atomic number, other processes, such as $(n,2n)$, take place in preference.

11.60. In an (n,α) reaction, one neutron enters the system but two neutrons and two protons leave, in the form of an alpha particle; consequently, the product nucleus has one neutron and two protons less than did the target. That is to say, the neutron-to-proton ratio of the product is greater than that of the bombarded species. It is not surprising therefore that most of the nuclides formed in

(n,α) processes are radioactive, decaying with the emission of a negative beta-particle. Two examples, mentioned in § 10.43, are

$$_9F^{19} + _0n^1 \rightarrow _7N^{16} + _2He^4,$$

followed by the decay, with a 7.36-sec. half life,

$$_7N^{16} \rightarrow _{-1}e^0 + _8O^{16},$$

and

$$_{30}Zn^{68} + _0n^1 \rightarrow _{28}Ni^{65} + _2He^4,$$

followed by the decay, with a 2.56-hour half life,

$$_{28}Ni^{65} \rightarrow _{-1}e^0 + _{29}Cu^{65}.$$

SCATTERING OF NEUTRONS

11.61. For elements of low atomic number, the first excited energy level of the target nucleus is usually about 1 Mev or more higher than the ground state. Consequently, elastic scattering of neutrons, without the formation of an excited state of the target element (§ 11.34), is more probable than inelastic scattering, with the lighter elements, unless the neutron energy exceeds 1 Mev. With increasing atomic number the minimum excitation energy of the nucleus decreases to about 0.1 Mev (§ 11.107), and so neutrons with energy in excess of this amount can exhibit inelastic, as well as elastic, scattering with the heavier elements. In (n,n'), i.e., inelastic scattering, reactions the fast neutron first unites with the target to form a compound nucleus; a neutron of lower energy is then emitted, leaving an excited state of the target nucleus as residue.

11.62. In some cases, the transition of the excited state of the nucleus to the ground state, accompanied by the emission of the excess energy as gamma radiation, takes place within such a short time interval after the ejection of the neutron that the excited state has virtually no independent existence. The expulsion, from the compound nucleus, of the neutron and the gamma ray photon may thus be regarded as taking place almost simultaneously. Of greater interest, however, is the type of inelastic scattering in which the transition from the excited state to the ground state of the target nucleus is "forbidden." The excited state is then a metastable state, i.e., an isomer, of a stable nuclide; it has a fairly long half life, and decays by the emission of gamma rays at a measurable rate (§ 10.120). Four nuclides exhibiting this type of behavior with fast neutrons are Rh^{103}, Ag^{107}, Cd^{111} and In^{115}.

FAST-NEUTRON REACTIONS

11.63. If an incident neutron has about 10 Mev energy, it contributes a total of approximately 18 Mev to the system, since the binding energy of a neutron is usually in the vicinity of 8 Mev, except for the lightest elements. Sufficient energy is consequently available to make it possible for two neutrons to be ejected from the compound nucleus. Hence, with neutrons of 10 Mev energy or more, processes of the $(n,2n)$ type are observed, the probability (or cross section) increasing rapidly with increasing energy of the incident neutron. Such reactions have been detected with a large number of nuclides, ranging from carbon to uranium; two examples are

$$_6C^{12} + _0n^1 \rightarrow _6C^{11} + _0n^1 + _0n^1$$

and

$$_{92}U^{238} + _0n^1 \rightarrow _{92}U^{237} + _0n^1 + _0n^1.$$

the residual nucleus being isotopic with, but one mass unit lighter than, the target in each case.

11.64. About two thirds of the one hundred or so radioisotopes produced in $(n,2n)$ processes decay with the emission of a positive beta-particle, or by the equivalent orbital-electron capture (§ 10.106). This is in harmony with what might be expected, since the reaction is accompanied by a decrease in the neutron-to-proton ratio. The change is rectified by the conversion of a proton into a neutron, resulting from the ejection of a positron or the capture of an orbital electron. Thus, the decay of the 20.4-min. C^{11} occurs by positron emission

$$_6C^{11} \rightarrow _{+1}e^0 + _5B^{11},$$

whereas Hg^{197}, obtained in the Hg^{198} $(n,2n)Hg^{197}$ process, decays by K-capture,

$$_{80}Hg^{197} + _{-1}e^0 \rightarrow _{79}Au^{197},$$

both final products being stable nuclides. With elements of relatively high mass number, the neutron-to-proton ratio is normally considerably in excess of unity (§ 12.38), and the net loss of a neutron in the $(n,2n)$ reaction does not necessarily lead to positive beta-decay. In fact the emission of a negative beta-particle occurs in a number of instances, especially where the neutron-to-proton ratio of the original target nuclide, Ge^{76}, Cd^{116}, Ce^{142} and U^{238} for example, is at the upper limit of the stability range.

11.65. If the energy of the incident neutron approaches 30 Mev, it is evident that the compound nucleus should be able to eject three neutrons or even two neutrons and a proton. There will probably be sufficient energy available to overcome the electrostatic potential barrier which tends to prevent the escape of the proton, in the latter case. Thus, several examples of $(n,3n)$ and $(n,2np)$ reactions have been reported. When neutrons of very high energies, in the region of

100 Mev, are used as projectiles, nuclei of moderate mass number may undergo spallation (§ 10.62), while those of high mass number, notably bismuth and lead, suffer fission.

11.66. Nuclear fission can be induced in certain nuclides, such as uranium-235, by neutrons of almost any energy, but in other cases, fast neutrons are necessary. These processes, which are sometimes represented by the symbol (n,f), will be discussed in some detail in Chapter XIII.

NUCLEAR CROSS SECTIONS FOR
NEUTRON REACTIONS

11.67. The probability (or efficiency) of interaction between a given nucleus and an incident neutron is conveniently represented, as stated in § 10.73, by the nuclear cross section. This quantity may be regarded as the effective size of the target presented by the particular nucleus to the bombarding neutron. A great deal of work has been performed in connection with the determination of nuclear cross sections for neutron reactions, but much still remains to be done, for the subject has considerable practical and theoretical significance. The importance of the cross section in relation to the development of atomic nuclear energy may well be summarized in the words of A. H. Snell of the Oak Ridge National Laboratory. In an essay on *Contemporary Neutron Physics*, published in the journal *Science* in 1948, he said: ". . . a new scale of values of structural materials has sprung up; if a suggestion is made as to a new substance for use as part of a reactor, the first question asked is not 'What is the tensile strength?' or 'What is the cost?', but rather 'What is the cross section?' " But even before 1939, when the release of atomic energy was an uncertain possibility that might be realized in the indefinite future, the study of nuclear cross sections for neutron reactions, referred to briefly as *neutron cross sections*, attracted considerable attention. The reason was that it was thought, with some justification, that the information would contribute to a better understanding of the complexities of nuclear structure.

11.68. When physicists, around 1934, first reported measurements of neutron cross sections, the results appeared to be erratic and conflicting. As further experiments were made it soon became clear that the cross sections for fast and slow neutrons were often very different. However, even this distinction was not entirely sufficient to bring order out of the chaos. It is now realized that a proper understanding of the subject requires a complete study of the cross sections of a given nuclear species for interaction with neutrons of various energies, from the lowest values, which might go down to 0.001 ev, to values as high as 100 Mev or more. Much work has been performed with "slow neutrons" or "thermal neutrons," but the results, although they may have some practical use, are not of fundamental significance. It will be seen shortly that a small difference in the neutron energy may sometimes be accompanied by a very large change in the cross section; consequently, it is often necessary to specify the precise energy for which the cross section is measured. A general description of the neutron energy, such as is implied by the term "thermal neutrons," is then inadequate. Further, most of the measurements made hitherto have been with the elements, usually consisting of a mixture of isotopes, as they occur in nature. Since the cross sections of isotopes of a given element often differ considerably, it will ultimately be necessary to obtain data for each individual nuclide.

11.69. Another factor which must be taken into consideration is that a given nucleus generally has a different cross section for each type of neutron reaction in which it can take part. For example, there is a cross section for elastic scattering, another for inelastic scattering, and still others for radiative capture (n,γ), for proton emission (n,p), for alpha-particle emission (n,α) and so on. With elements of high atomic number, such as thorium, uranium and plutonium, there are also fission cross sections. In due course, the separate cross sections for the different processes to be taken into consideration will be determined, but in the meantime a rough subdivision into *scattering* and *absorption* cross sections may be made. The former is the sum of the cross sections for elastic and inelastic scattering, and the latter is the total cross section for all processes in which a neutron is captured and another particle (or particles) emitted. The sum of the scattering and absorption cross sections is the total neutron cross section for the given nuclide.

11.70. The most direct procedure for determining total cross sections is to make use of the transmission method upon which equation (10.2) is

based. The experimental arrangement is depicted in outline in Fig. 11.3; it consists of a neutron source and a detector, between which can be placed a slab A of the experimental material. If I_0 is the neutron intensity reaching the detector in the absence of the absorbing material, and I is the value when the slab of thickness x, containing N atoms per cc., is present, then it follows, upon taking the logarithm of equation (10.2) and rearranging the result, that

$$\sigma = \frac{2.303}{Nx} \log \frac{I_0}{I}, \qquad (11.6)$$

where the factor 2.303 is used to convert natural to common logarithms. Since all the quantities of the right-hand member of this equation can be determined, the total cross section σ may be calculated.

11.71. If the measurement just described is to give the sum of the scattering and absorption cross sections, it is necessary that the experimental arrangement should satisfy the condition of what is known as "good geometry." In this condition, particles which have deviated even slightly from their original direction of motion, due to scattering, are not detected. The best way of achieving good geometry is to use a neutron shield, as indicated by S in Fig. 11.3, to restrict the neutrons to a narrow, parallel (or collimated) beam. Only those neutrons which have neither been absorbed nor scattered will then reach the detector.

11.72. By deliberately altering the arrangement of source, absorber and detector so as to give "poor geometry" a distinction can be made between scattering and absorption. For example, the collimating shield is removed and the detector is placed at an angle of 90° from the incident beam of neutrons; that is to say, the detector

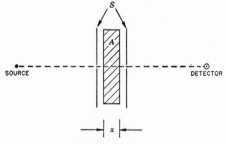

Fig. 11.3. Determination of neutron cross sections.

is in such a position that it can be reached only by neutrons which have been scattered through an angle of 90°. Assuming, as is not always the case, that the neutrons are scattered fairly uniformly over all angles, the total scattering cross section can be calculated from the number scattered at 90°. The difference between the total and scattering cross sections gives the absorption cross section. If a separation into elastic and inelastic scattering is required, it may be borne in mind that the latter probably does not occur with slow neutrons because the nuclear excitation energy is about 0.1 Mev for heavy elements and of the order of 1 Mev for the lighter ones (§ 11.61).

11.73. Ideally, as indicated earlier, it is desirable to determine the cross section of each isotopic constituent of a given element. If the latter consists of two isotopes only, the problem is relatively simple; by making cross section measurements with two samples containing different known proportions of the two nuclides, the contribution of each can be evaluated. There are possibilities even if three isotopes are present, provided a sample which has been considerably enriched in one or more can be obtained.

11.74. Another approach, which is applicable to absorption cross sections, has been opened up by the work, in the United States, of A. J. Dempster, one of the pioneers of the mass spectrometer (§ 8.46). Scattering cross sections, especially with fast neutrons, do not usually vary markedly from one isotope to another, but the absorption cross sections often show striking differences. Hence, it is in the latter connection that data for individual isotopes are desirable; the following procedure may then be employed. The mass spectrogram of the target material is taken before and after exposure to neutrons; from the change in the patterns, the relative amounts of the various isotopes which have taken part in the neutron reactions can be estimated. A method is thus available, at least in principle, for apportioning the observed absorption cross sections among the various constituents. Further reference to this matter will be made later (§ 11.100).

11.75. If a neutron absorption process leads to the formation of a radioactive nuclide which can be distinguished by its activity, it is frequently possible to determine the cross section for that particular process. This is generally referred to as the *activation cross section*. A thin foil of the experimental material is exposed to neutrons of known density, and after a certain time the activity, i.e., the rate of emission of beta particles (or gamma rays), is measured by means of a suitable counter. By using the absorbing material in the form of a thin foil, the target does not absorb sufficient neutrons to cause any appreciable attenuation of the neutron beam. The absorption cross section is then calculated from the measured activity of the foil in the following manner.

11.76. Suppose the neutron source provides a neutron density of n neutrons per cc. moving with a velocity v cm. per sec., in a given direction, then the product nv, expressed in terms of number of neutrons per sq. cm. per sec., is called the *neutron flux*. It is equal to the sum of the distances traveled by all the neutrons in 1 cc. in 1 sec. and is therefore sometimes called the *track length*. Assuming negligible attenuation, this may be regarded as being uniform throughout the whole thickness of the target foil. If the latter contains N target nuclei per cc., and σ sq. cm. is the cross section per nucleus, the quantity $N\sigma$ per cm., called the *macroscopic cross section*, is the total cross section per cc. of the absorber. It gives the probability that a neutron will undergo the particular reaction under consideration while traversing 1 cm. of the foil material. Upon multiplying $N\sigma$, the probability of the reaction per centimeter, by the track length nv, the result $nvN\sigma$ gives the number of neutrons (or nuclei) interacting per cubic centimeter per second. If V cc. is the volume of the foil, the total number of nuclei reacting per second, which is equal to the rate of formation of product nuclei, is then

$$A = nvNV\sigma. \qquad (11.7)$$

11.77. If the product of neutron capture is radioactive, as postulated above, it will commence to decay even while the foil is exposed to neutrons. After a moderate time, the rate of decay will be equal to the rate of formation and an equilibrium condition will be attained. Since the value of A, as given by equation (11.7), is equal to the rate of formation of the radioactive nuclei, this also gives their rate of decay (or activity), as measured. Hence, rewriting equation (11.7) in the form

$$\sigma = \frac{A}{nvNV}, \qquad (11.8)$$

it is seen that the absorption (or activation) cross section can be calculated, provided the product of the neutron density and velocity, i.e., the neutron flux, is known. This is usually determined with one of the counters described earlier.

MONOENERGETIC NEUTRONS

Neutron Velocity Selectors

11.78. In the foregoing paragraphs, the general methods for studying nuclear cross sections were outlined; it is now necessary to consider the devices called *velocity selectors*, whereby neutrons of definite energy (or velocity) may be obtained. As stated in § 11.39, even thermal neutrons at a given temperature have a range of energies, and means must be found for selecting those with known energies. Two main techniques have been developed for making measurements with neutrons having specific, known energies (or velocities). These are the time-of-flight velocity selector and the crystal spectrometer.

11.79. The *time-of-flight* velocity selector owes its origin to the work of L. W. Alvarez of the Radiation Laboratory, Berkeley. It requires a neutron source which can be modulated in such a way that the neutrons are produced in short pulses, lasting only a few millionths of a second, separated by longer intervals. The measurement of cross sections is then made by the transmission method, described in § 11.70, with a detector which is also modulated so that it is sensitive only during certain periods, corresponding to the neutron pulses but delayed by a

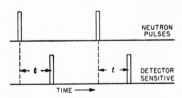

Fig. 11.4. Principle of the time-of-flight velocity selector.

definite interval. The relationship of the neutron pulses to the periods of the detector sensitivity is represented diagrammatically in Fig. 11.4, the latter being always t sec. behind the former. If l cm. is the distance from source to detector, it is apparent that the only neutrons which will register are those having a speed of l/t cm. per sec., for these are the only ones which can reach the detector while it is sensitive.* All other neutrons leaving the source will arrive during the "dead" period of the detector.

11.80. The neutron intensities I and I_0 at the detector are determined with and without the absorber, respectively, and from these the total cross section for the neutrons with velocity l/t cm. per sec. is calculated by means of equation (11.6). By altering either the distance l between source and detector, or the time interval t between the neutron pulse and the sensitive period of the detector, or by changing both, the velocity of the detected neutrons can be changed. Consequently, the cross section measurement can be made for a number of different neutron speeds. Because the distance l cannot be too large, nor the time t too small, there is an upper limit to the speed (and energy) of the neutrons which can be studied by the time-of-flight procedure. The practical range of measurements by this method is from 0.001 to about 10,000 ev.†

11.81. Neutron pulses of short duration, of the type suitable for use with a time-of-flight velocity selector, can be obtained by means of a particle accelerator (see Chapter IX), for these respond very rapidly when switched on and off. The high-energy particles, such as electrons, protons, deuterons and alpha particles, produced in one or other of these devices, are allowed to impinge on a suitable target so as to produce the requisite neutron beam. The neutrons formed in this manner generally have high speeds and they must first be slowed down to some extent since the time-of-flight procedure can be used only with neutrons having moderate or low speeds.

11.82. When a nuclear reactor is used as the source of neutrons, the pulses are obtained by means of a *mechanical velocity selector*, sometimes referred to as a "neutron chopper." A selector for slow neutrons makes use of the fact that cadmium strongly absorbs neutrons with energies less than about 0.3 ev (§ 11.98), but certain other metals, such as aluminum, exhibit little absorption in this region. A cylinder, made up of alternate layers of cadmium and aluminum running parallel to the axis, is rotated before a strong source of slow neutrons, e.g., a nuclear reactor. This device acts as a shutter and only when the laminations are parallel to the neutron direction, as shown in Fig. 11.5, I, can the neutrons get through to the detector. For the time-of-flight technique, the detector must be sensitive for a short period at a definite interval after the neutrons have been transmitted. The timing is achieved by means of a mirror fixed to the rotating cylinder, as shown; when this mirror is in the correct position, as represented in Fig. 11.5, II, light is reflected from it on to a photocell which activates the detector. The time t sec., elapsing between the instant the shutter permits the neutrons to pass

---

* The method gets its name from the fact that t is the time of flight, from source to detector, of the particular neutrons which reach the detector while it is sensitive.

† A 10,000-ev neutron has a speed of approximately 1.4×10^8 cm. per sec., so that it travels 140 cm. in a one-millionth part of a second.

through and that when the detector is sensitive, is determined by the speed of rotation of the cylinder and also by the relative positions of light source and photocell, all of which can be varied. If l cm. is the distance from the source to the detector, the only neutrons which can be detected are those with a speed of l/t cm. per sec. The absorption cross section for these particular neutrons can then be determined, in the manner already de-

can get through, for short pulses at regular intervals, only when the slits in the rotating cylinder are aligned with those in the stationary one. A so-called "fast" chopper of this type can be used with neutrons having energies up to about 5000 ev.

11.84. Owing to the diffraction by crystals of neutrons with energy about 0.02 ev, as stated in § 11.12, there are certain directions in which the reflected neutrons have increased intens-

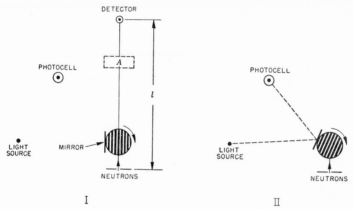

I   II

Fig. 11.5. The mechanical velocity selector for neutrons of low energy.

scribed, by introducing the absorbing material at A, shown in Fig. 11.5, I.

11.83. Since cadmium is not a good absorber of neutrons having energies in excess of about 0.3 ev, the velocity selector described above cannot be used for such neutrons. Another type of mechanical selector, often referred to as a "fast neutron chopper," is therefore employed. In one form, two steel cylinders, about 16 in. long and 4 in. diameter, are mounted horizontally, end to end, in front of the neutron source. Each cylinder has a number of narrow slits on the outside, running parallel to the axis. One cylinder is rotated at high speed, whereas the other is stationary, so that neutrons

ities. The condition for the diffraction maxima may be obtained by combining the Bragg equation (2.13), which is also applicable to neutron diffraction, with the de Broglie equation (3.7) for the neutron wave length, namely $\lambda = h/mv$; the result is

$$\sin \theta = \frac{nh}{2dmv}, \qquad (11.9)$$

or

$$v = \frac{nh}{2dm \sin \theta}, \qquad (11.10)$$

where, as before, m is the mass of the neutron, v its velocity, d is the distance between successive reflecting planes of the crystal, h is the Planck constant, and n is an integer. Since m and h are constants, it follows that, for neutron diffraction by a given crystal, for which d is constant, the glancing angles θ for maximum reflection are directly related to v, the neutron velocities.

11.85. The result just derived forms the basis of the *crystal spectrometer velocity selector*. Slow neutrons from an intense source are allowed to impinge on a crystal, and a detector is placed so that the diffracted beam falls upon it, as shown in Fig. 11.6.

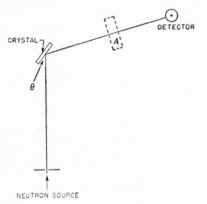

Fig. 11.6.   Crystal spectrometer velocity selector.

Neutrons of various speeds are present in the beam, but for any arbitrarily chosen value θ of the glancing angle, the great majority of the neutrons reaching the detector will have a velocity given by equation (11.10). The crystal spacing d is known, and the only uncertain factor in this equation is the integer n; however, except for large glancing angles, this is almost invariably unity, and so the velocity of the neutrons reflected at the angle θ can be calculated. The intensity measured by the detector, with and without the slab A of absorber, permits the nuclear cross section of the latter, for the neutrons of this partic-

ular velocity for the chosen value of θ, to be determined in the usual manner.

11.86. If the glancing angle θ is changed, neutrons with a different velocity will now reach the detector, so that there will be a range (or spectrum) of neutron velocities corresponding to variations in the angle between the neutron beam and the reflecting surface of the crystal. For this reason the instrument is sometimes referred to as a *neutron spectrometer*. By making transmission measurements, as described above, with different settings of the angle of the spectrometer, it is consequently possible to determine the absorption cross sections for a range of neutron energies. Because the glancing angle diminishes with increasing neutron velocity, the former ultimately becomes too small to be measured with any degree of accuracy. This sets an upper limit to the speed, and energy, of the neutrons which can be studied in the crystal spectrometer. The practical range of usefulness is found to be from about 0.01 to 100 ev.

SOURCES OF MONOENERGETIC NEUTRONS

11.87. As already indicated, the time-of-flight methods can be employed only for neutrons with energies from about 0.001 to 10,000 ev, i.e., up to 0.01 Mev. It happens that this is a particularly interesting energy range, but it is nevertheless desirable to obtain cross sections for neutrons of higher energy. No device analogous to a velocity selector has yet been developed for the study of fast neutrons, but monenergetic neutron beams of certain specific and known energies can be obtained from some of the sources described in § 11.14 *et seq.* The photo-neutron sources, in which gamma rays from artificial radioisotopes produce neutrons from deuterium or beryllium, are particularly useful for this purpose. For example, the decay of the 15.0-hr. Na²⁴ isotope of sodium is accompanied by the emission of 2.75-Mev gamma rays; if these undergo the (γ,n) reaction with beryllium, for which the threshold energy is 1.66 Mev, the energy of the resulting neutrons is about eight-ninths of 2.75 − 1.66, i.e., 0.97 Mev, the remaining 0.12 Mev being recoil energy. Monoenergetic neutron beams, covering a range of energies from about 0.03 to 1 Mev, have been obtained from various photoneutron sources.

11.88. Another source of monoenergetic neutrons is the $Li^7(p,n)Be^7$ reaction, the energy of the incident protons being carefully controlled. As stated in Chapter IX, the Van de Graaff electrostatic generator can yield protons with definite energies up to about 8 Mev, and these may be used to bombard lithium targets. With protons of energy which exceeds the threshold value of 1.88 Mev (§ 11.18) by the least practical amount, it is possible to obtain neutrons of about 0.05 Mev energy. By steadily increasing the energy of the incident protons, monoenergetic neutrons with energies up to 3 Mev can be produced.

11.89. Two sources of approximately monoenergetic neutrons of still higher energies are the reactions $Be^9(d,n)B^{10}$ and $Li^7(d,n)Be^8$, for which the energies are approximately 4 and 15 Mev, respectively. Another procedure for obtaining monoenergetic neutrons of fairly high energy makes use of the (d,n) reaction between accelerated deuterons and tritium absorbed on a zirconium foil target, i.e., $H^3(d,n)He^4$. The reaction energy in this case is 17.6 Mev, to which must be added the energy of the deuteron; four fifths of the total energy released is acquired by the neutron, so that its minimum energy is 14.1 Mev. By the use of accelerated deuterons, preferably from an instrument which yields particles of fairly uniform energy, high-energy neutron beams, up to 20 Mev or more, can be made available for cross section measurements.

11.90. At the other extreme, there is the problem of obtaining neutrons of very low energies. In this connection, an interesting procedure, which makes use of the diffraction of neutrons by crystals, has been devised. Consider a block of material, such as graphite, consisting of a very large number of randomly oriented, small crystals. A beam of thermal neutrons is allowed to enter the graphite, and since the many crystals are arranged at a great variety of angles, neutrons of a considerable range of velocities, as determined by equation (11.10), will suffer diffraction. These neutrons will be reflected from one crystal to another, so that very few will escape from the block of graphite. However, there is a velocity limit below which neutrons will not undergo diffraction in the given material; this limit occurs when the glancing angle θ necessary to produce diffraction is 90°, and sin θ is unity. Upon inserting this value for sin θ in equation (11.10) and taking the integer n to be unity, the corresponding velocity is found to be $h/2dm$, where d is the maximum spacing of the reflecting planes in the graphite crystals, namely, 3.4×10^{-8} cm.

11.91. Neutrons with smaller velocities could be diffracted only if the glancing angle were greater than 90°, which is impossible. Consequently, thermal neutrons with velocities exceeding this limiting value will be diffracted and scattered by the material, but those with smaller velocities will pass right through. The graphite thus acts as a velocity (or energy) filter, which retains nearly all thermal neutrons with velocities greater than $h/6.8 \times 10^{-8}m$ cm. per sec. The corresponding kinetic energy minimum ($\frac{1}{2}mv^2$) can be readily calculated, and this is found to be 0.0018 ev. Thus, by passing a heterogeneous beam of thermal neutrons through a long block of graphite (§ 15.50), only very "cold" neutrons, with energies less than 0.0018 ev, will emerge, corresponding to temperatures below about 20° Absolute or −250°C.

RESONANCE CAPTURE OF NEUTRONS

RESULTS OF CROSS SECTION MEASUREMENTS

11.92. As stated earlier, it would be desirable to determine the neutron cross sections of each individual nuclide for every possible type of nuclear interaction, including scattering, over a large range of neutron energies. The completion of such a program will obviously require a tremendous amount of work, and the investigations so far, extensive as they have been, can be regarded as touching no more than the fringes of the subject. However, from the work already done, certain generalizations of a broad character have appeared and these will be considered here.

11.93. The results of major interest have been obtained in connection with the variation of nuclear reaction cross sections with the energy of the incident neutron. But before these are described, brief reference will be made to scattering cross sections. With the exception of hydrogen, for which the value is fairly large, the elastic scattering cross sections are generally small, e.g., 5 to 10 barns (§ 10.79). This is of the order of magnitude of the actual (or geometrical) cross-sectional area to be expected for atomic nuclei. At high neutron energies, the elastic scattering cross section may decrease somewhat, the limiting value approaching the geometrical area πR^2, where R is the nuclear radius. For the present purpose, the radius may be related to the mass number A by the expression $R = 1.5 \times 10^{-13} A^{1/3}$ cm., so that the nuclear scattering cross section is approximately $0.7 \times 10^{-24} A^{2/3}$ sq. cm. (or $0.7 A^{2/3}$ barn) for neutrons of high energy.

11.94. As seen in § 11.61, for inelastic scattering to occur, the neutron energy must exceed a certain amount, dependent upon the nature of the nucleus. If the energy is less than this threshold value, the cross section is zero; even for higher energies it is small, rarely exceeding a few barns. As a rough guide, it may be assumed that, at high neutron energies, above 10 Mev, the inelastic scattering cross section is equal to the geometrical cross section of the nucleus, i.e., πR^2.

11.95. In considering nuclear absorption (or reaction) cross sections, i.e., for reactions in which the neutron is captured by the target nucleus, and another particle (or a gamma ray) is emitted, the variation with neutron energy is often quite complicated. For the great majority of the lighter elements, i.e., in the mass number range up to about 100, with the exception of helium-3, lithium-6 and boron-10, to which reference will be made shortly, the absorption cross sections are small, ranging from a fraction of a barn (see table in § 11.40) to a few barns for slow (or thermal) neutrons. These cross sections do not vary greatly with energy, although there is generally a decrease at high energies.

11.96. For many elements with mass numbers exceeding 100, the absorption cross sections are small and exhibit the same characteristics as those just described for the lighter elements. However, for a considerable number of nuclides of moderately high (or high) mass numbers, a very different type of behavior has been observed. An examination of the variation of the absorption cross section with the en-

It may be significant that $1/v$ is a measure of the time spent by the neutron within a given distance, such as, for example, the diameter of the nucleus. It would appear, therefore, that in the "$1/v$ region" the probability of interaction between the neutron and the nucleus, as measured by the cross section, is proportional to the time the former spends in the vicinity of the latter.

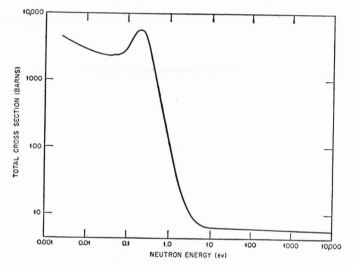

Fig. 11.7. Absorption of neutrons by cadmium, showing the resonance peak at 0.176 ev.

ergy (or speed) of the incident neutron, particularly for radiative capture (n,γ) reactions, reveals the existence of three regions. There is first a low-energy region, which includes the thermal range and often extends beyond, where the cross section decreases steadily with increasing neutron energy. In this region, the absorption cross section, which is often high, is inversely proportional to the velocity. The energy range in which this occurs is frequently spoken of as the "$1/v$ region," because the absorption cross section is proportional to $1/v$, i.e., to the reciprocal of the neutron velocity.

11.97. Following the somewhat indefinite "$1/v$ region," there occurs the "resonance region," in which the cross sections rise sharply to high values, called *resonance peaks,* for neutrons of certain energies, and then fall again (§ 10.70). Some elements, notably cadmium and rhodium, have only one peak, while others, such as, indium, silver, iridium, gold and uranium have two, three or more peaks. These regions of exceptionally high absorption usually occur with neutrons of energy between 0.1 and 100 ev, although the range may extend up to 1000 ev in some cases. Uranium-238, for example, exhibits eight sharp resonance peaks, and several smaller ones, in the neutron energy region from 6.5 to about 200 ev. The peak at 6.5 ev corresponds to an absorption cross section of nearly 7000 barns.

11.98. With neutrons of high energy, in the Mev range, the cross sections are low, being less then 10 barns, compared with possibly hundreds or thousands for the resonance peaks mentioned above. There is usually a gradual decrease with increasing energy, although peaks of a very minor character have been reported between 0.1 and 1 Mev for some elements. The general type of behavior may be illustrated with reference to the neutron cross sections of cadmium, since this is a simple case of practical importance. The variation of total cross section with neutron energy is shown in Fig. 11.7; the results are plotted on logarithmic scales so as to make it possible to include the large ranges of both cross sections and energies. An approximate "$1/v$ region" extends up to about 0.03 ev where the total cross section is about 2500 barns. This is followed by a resonance peak, the cross section reaching a maximum of 7800 barns at 0.176 ev. The cross section then drops sharply, with increasing neutron energy, falling to 5 barns at 5 ev, at which value it remains approximately constant, with a few minor resonance peaks, right up to 10 Mev.

11.99. Incidentally, an examination of Fig. 11.7 shows very clearly the necessity for the use of precisely controlled monoenergetic neutrons in cross section studies, particularly in the region of low energies. For 0.1-ev and 0.25-ev neutrons, the total cross sections of cadmium are 3500 and 2500 barns, respectively, compared with 7800 barns for neutrons of 0.176 ev

energy. It is evident that a slight change in the energy (or velocity) of the neutrons has a considerable influence on the results obtained in this region. In such cases cross sections for "slow neutrons" are virtually meaningless.

11.100. The study of cadmium has proved of interest because it has been established that the exceptionally high cross section is mainly due to the Cd^{113} isotope; the peak value for this nuclide, which is present to the extent of 12.3 per cent in normal cadmium, has been estimated at about 20,000 barns. Striking proof that Cd^{113} absorbs neutrons very strongly was obtained by A. J. Dempster, by the method referred to in § 11.74. Normal cadmium was exposed to slow neutrons, and after some time specimens of the metal from the surface, where the interaction with neutrons had occurred, and from the interior, which had been protected from reaction, were subjected to mass-spectrographic examination, with the result shown in Fig. 11.8. It is seen

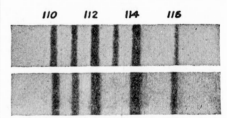

Fig. 11.8. Dempster's identification of cadmium-113 as the strong neutron absorber. (From *Phys. Rev.*, **71**, 829 (1947)).

that the isotope of mass number 113 has essentially disappeared from the surface while the proportion of the 114-isotope has increased. It is apparent, therefore, that the interaction of slow neutrons with cadmium consists largely of an (n,γ) reaction with Cd^{113}, in which the latter is converted into Cd^{114}.

11.101. Other elements which exhibit relatively sharp resonance peaks for slow neutrons, with cross sections attaining thousands of barns, are the following: rhodium (1.3 ev), silver (5.2 ev), indium (1.5 ev), samarium (0.1 ev), europium (0.45 ev), iridium (0.65, 1.25, 5.5 ev) and gold (4.8 ev).

THE BREIT-WIGNER THEORY

11.102. The theory of the absorption of neutrons at, and in the vicinity of, the resonance peaks was worked out by G. Breit and E. P. Wigner in the United States in 1936, and the resulting *Breit-Wigner formula,* as it is called, has formed the basis of the interpretation of neutron cross sections. The fundamental principle involved is similar to that described in § 10.70; if the energy of the neutrons is such that a compound nucleus can be formed at or near one of its energy levels, then the probability of capture of these neutrons will be exceptionally high. The treatment which Breit and Wigner found most successful was similar to that which had previously been employed in connection with the dispersion of light, and so it is sometimes referred to as *dispersion theory.*

11.103. The actual formula obtained from dispersion theory is too complicated to be given here, but some of the general conclusions can be indicated. In the first place, the Breit-Wigner formula leads to the conclusion that, at low neutron energies, the absorption cross sections should be inversely proportional to the neutron speed, as is actually observed in the "$1/v$ region." Further, in the resonance region, the height of a resonance peak, for a given nucleus, is expected to vary approxi-

mately inversely as the square root of the neutron energy at which the peak occurs. This is in agreement with the observation that resonance peaks with large cross sections are found only in regions of low neutron energy. As stated above, such maxima as are observed for high-energy neutrons represent cross sections of a few barns compared with thousands for slow neutrons.

11.104. Another factor which, according to the Breit-Wigner theory, affects the cross section, is a quantity approximately equivalent to the width of the resonance peak. In a general way, if the peak is broad, covering a large energy range, the cross sections are likely to be somewhat decreased, as compared with the case of a sharp and narrow peak. The width of the resonance peak is inversely related to the life of the excited state of the compound nucleus.* Consequently, an excited state of short life, for example, will mean a broad resonance peak, and hence a somewhat lower cross section for that particular energy value.

11.105. It is of interest in this connection to consider the variation with the neutron energy of the cross sections of boron for the (n,α) reaction, in which the B^{10} isotope is mainly concerned. The results are depicted in Fig. 11.9 which is also logarithmic in both directions. Similar behavior is exhibited by the (n,α) reaction with Li^6 and the (n,p) reaction with He^3. It is seen that, although the absorption cross sections are relatively large for neutrons of low energy, there is no resonance peak. In fact, the straight line in Fig. 11.9 shows that the $1/v$ law, which normally breaks down in

---

* It may be noted that this inverse relationship is an aspect of the uncertainty principle mentioned in § 3.45. When the resonance peak for a given energy level is narrow, the energy can be known with some certainty, and hence there will be a large uncertainty in the time factor, that is, in the life of the nucleus in that state, and vice versa.

the resonance region, is obeyed by boron over the considerable energy range from 0.01 to 1000 ev, at least.

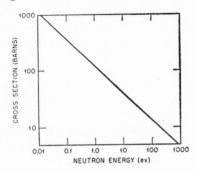

Fig. 11.9. Absorption of neutrons by boron, with no resonance peak.

11.106. It will be noted that the cases under consideration represent reactions in which a charged particle, either an alpha particle or a proton, is emitted. It is known from theoretical considerations that, when an excited compound nucleus has sufficient energy to make emission of a charged particle possible, the process will occur very rapidly. In other words, the excited energy state has a short life; hence the resonance "peak" will be broad. In the present instances, it is so broad as not to be apparent as a peak. The Breit-Wigner theory shows that in these circumstances, the cross section should be inversely proportional to the neutron speed (1/v law), as is actually the case.

11.107. The fact that resonance absorption takes place with slow neutrons, with energy usually less than 100 ev, finds an interpretation along the following lines. According to estimates made by N. Bohr, the energy level separations of a nucleus are approximately of the order shown in Fig. 11.10. Near the ground state the separation of successive levels, for an element of moderately high atomic weight, is about 0.1 Mev. A neutron

with less than this amount of energy undergoes elastic scattering, as mentioned in § 11.61, since it is incapable of raising the nucleus from its lowest (ground) state to an excited state. As the energy of the nucleus is increased, the separation of the energy levels decreases, and in the region of about 8 Mev the successive levels are about 10 ev apart. For still higher energies, the successive levels become so close that they are practically continuous.

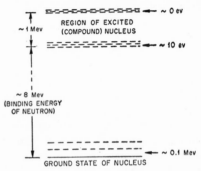

Fig. 11.10. Schematic representation of separation of energy levels near the ground state and in a highly excited nucleus.

11.108. When a neutron of low, virtually zero, energy enters a nucleus of moderate atomic weight, the energy of the compound nucleus formed is about 8 Mev above the ground state value, due to the binding of the additional neutron. The energy levels in the resulting compound nucleus are now usually about 10 ev apart, and hence a small, additional (kinetic) energy of the incident neutron may provide the condition for resonance capture. When several resonance peaks of neutron cross sections are observed, these are separated by energies of the order of 10 ev or so, as is to be expected. Finally, if the neutron has 1 Mev or more of kinetic energy, the nuclear energy levels are now so close that no specific peaks can be observed. In a sense, the absorption of all high-energy neutrons is by resonance, although the cross sections are then very small, in accordance with the requirements of the Breit-Wigner formula.

CROSS SECTIONS AND NUCLEAR DIMENSIONS

11.109. As seen above, many neutrons reactions and scattering cross sections are not very different from the geometrical cross sections of the nuclei, namely, from 2 to 5 barns. If this is the case, then an obvious question may be asked: How is it possible to account for the observed cross sections of several thousand barns? A cross section of 10,000 barns, for example, would mean a nuclear radius close to 10^{-10} cm., instead of the accepted value of approximately 10^{-12} cm. The explanation of these results can be found in the wave-particle duality of matter or in the uncertainty principle, both of which are aspects of the same fundamental law of nature (§ 3.45 *et seq.*).

11.110. According to equation (11.5), the wave length of a 20-Mev neutron is about 0.6×10^{-12} cm., which is of the same order of magnitude as nuclear radii. Interaction between the neutron and a nucleus can then be regarded from the standpoint of classical mechanics, and the scattering cross section is virtually identical with the geometrical nuclear cross section. But with very slow neutrons the conditions become quite different. The wave length associated with a 1-ev neutron is 2.87×10^{-9} cm., and such a neutron can no longer be treated as a point particle colliding with a nucleus, but rather as a wave which can engulf many nuclei. The measured cross section in these circumstances is not strictly that of the nucleus; it is more reasonable to consider it as the area surrounding a nucleus, within which a neutron is likely to be capable of interacting with it.

11.111. The situation may be considered, alternatively, from the standpoint of the uncertainty principle. According to this principle, if the speed of a particle can be estimated with some exactness, its position will be known less definitely. The smaller the speed of a neutron, the more precisely can it be known, and consequently the greater is the uncertainty in its position. Hence, instead of being located at a definite point, the neutron may be regarded as having a large effective area.

11.112. It is of interest to mention that scattering cross sections determined with approximately 100-Mev neutrons, obtained by the "stripping" of 200-Mev deuterons, are appreciably smaller than those for 20-Mev neutrons, especially for the lighter nuclei. For 270 to 280-Mev neutrons, produced by 350-Mev protons on beryllium, the cross sections are smaller still. At these high energies, the neutron wave length is 0.2 to 0.3×10^{-12} cm., which means that the neutron behaves as such an extremely small particle that there is a distinct probability it will pass right through an atomic nucleus, without being affected. The nuclear cross section thus appears to be smaller than would be the case for ordinary scattering. The striking variation in nuclear cross sections for interaction with neutrons serves to emphasize the point that classical ideas of size do not have real significance when applied to the lightest particles of matter.

MODIFICATION OF COMPOUND NUCLEUS MODEL

11.113. Although the compound nucleus model, as described in Chapter

X, has proved very useful in providing a qualitative understanding of nuclear reactions, measurements of neutron cross sections have shown that it requires some modification. The resonance phenomena observed at low neutron energies, e.g., less than 1000 ev, represent special circumstances, dependent upon the energy levels in the excited nucleus. But, in the range of neutron energies from about 0.05 to 3 Mev, some anomalies exist which cannot be explained in terms of the simple compound nucleus model.

11.114. If the total cross sections, including the contributions of both neutron scattering and absorption, are averaged over individual fluctuations and minor resonances, certain variations are observed. According to the compound nucleus theory, these cross sections, for a given element, should decrease steadily with increasing neutron energy. In some instances, this is certainly the case, but in others it is not so. For example, for elements having mass numbers near to 40 and also around 100 and 120, the total cross sections exhibit a broad minimum for energies of about 1.5 Mev. On the other hand, for mass numbers in the vicinity of 50 and 150, there are broad maxima in the variation of the total cross section with neutron energy.

11.115. In order to account for these results, it has been necessary to discard part of the original compound nucleus theory, namely, that the captured particle very rapidly shares its energy among the nucleons in the compound nucleus (§ 10.11). Instead, it is postulated that the sharing of energy is a relatively slow process, involving collision of the entering particle with a single nucleon, followed by further collisions between the latter and other nucleons. Because of the slowness of the energy sharing process, there is a strong probability that a neutron, for example, after entering a target nucleus will be subsequently expelled and move off in a different direction, having suffered little or no energy loss. The consequences of this behavior can best be understood by considering the neutron as a wave, rather than as a particle.

11.116. According to the neutron wave picture, the rapid sharing of energy among the nucleons in the compound nucleus is equivalent to a light wave striking a "black" sphere. All the energy of the light is absorbed and none is emitted. In the modification suggested above, the nucleus behaves like a translucent (or semitransparent) glass sphere, in which some of the light is absorbed and some is refracted (or bent), so that, after passage through the sphere, it emerges in a different direction. For obvious reasons, this model is referred to colloquially as the *cloudy crystal ball*. It is also known as the *optical model*, because the interaction of neutrons with nuclear matter is treated in a manner similar to light passing through a group of semitransparent glass balls.

11.117. The total neutron cross section of a given nuclear species depends on the proportion of the neutron wave which is absorbed by the (cloudy crystal ball) compound nucleus, and this is determined by the relationship between the neutron wave length and the diameter of the nucleus. If the diameter is such that the neutron wave reflected in the nucleus is in phase with the incoming wave (§ 3.10), so that they enhance one another, the neutron will dissipate all its energy in the nucleus. In these circumstances, the cross section will be high. On the other hand, when the two waves are out of phase, so that interference occurs, there is a high probability that the neutron will emerge from the nucleus, and the cross section will be small.

11.118. Suppose that, at a certain atomic weight (or mass number), the total cross section exhibits a definite minimum at a particular neutron energy. Then, according to the theory, the incoming and reflected neutron waves are largely out of phase in this nucleus. As the mass number A, increases, the nuclear radius (or diameter) also increases, in proportion to $A^{1/3}$ (§ 11.93). Consequently, the phase difference becomes less and less marked. In due course, a mass number (and nuclear diameter) is attained at which the neutron waves are in phase. The neutron cross section will then have a definite maximum value at a particular neutron energy. With further increase in atomic weight, the neutron waves become increasingly out of phase, leading to a steady decrease in the maximum cross section, and eventually to a minimum once again, and so on.

11.119. It will be apparent from this discussion that the optical model provides a qualitative interpretation of the occurrence of atomic weight (or mass number) ranges in which the cross sections for neutron interaction exhibit alternate maxima and minima. In addition, H. Feshbach, C. E. Porter and V. F. Weisskopf, who developed the consequences of the cloudy crystal ball nucleus in the United States in 1954, have shown that it can reproduce with fair accuracy the quantitative variation of total cross section with neutron energy, as a function of increasing atomic weight.

11.120. The optical picture of the nucleus is not yet complete, and will undoubtedly be improved in the future. Nevertheless, it does seem to have established that an incoming particle in a nuclear reaction does not share its energy rapidly among the nucleons present in the compound nucleus. This is, incidentally, what would be expected on the basis of the model of nuclear structure, to be described in Chapter XII, which is widely accepted at the present time. One of the consequences of the cloudy crystal ball concept is that the behavior of a compound nucleus may not be entirely independent of its method of formation, as was originally postulated (§ 10.17).

Nuclear Forces and Nuclear Structure

Chapter XII

NUCLEAR FORCES

THE PACKING FRACTION

12.1. From time to time in the course of the preceding chapters it has been indicated that one of the prime purposes of atomic studies is to obtain information which will make it possible to understand the fundamental basis of nuclear structure. Such an understanding is imperative if full use is to be made of the potentialities of the atomic nucleus, either as a source of energy or as a means for providing knowledge that will contribute to the enrichment of human life in various ways. In the present chapter an attempt will be made to gather together certain facts, some of which have been mentioned in earlier portions of this book, and to see what conclusions may be drawn from them regarding the forces determining nuclear stability.

12.2. It was recorded in § 8.60 that, although isotopic weights, as determined by the mass spectrograph, and by other methods (§ 9.33), are close to whole numbers, they almost invariably differ from integers by small amounts. When F. W. Aston, in 1927, showed this to be the case, he expressed the deviations in the form of a *packing fraction* for each isotope, defined by

$$\text{Packing Fraction} = \frac{\text{Isotopic Weight} - \text{Mass Number}}{\text{Mass Number}} \times 10{,}000, \qquad (12.1)$$

where the isotopic weight is the actual mass of the isotope (or nuclide) on the physical atomic weight scale (§ 8.61), and the mass number is the nearest integer. The difference between the isotopic weight and the mass number is frequently called the *mass defect*, although it is not a satisfactory name, as will be seen below. This difference divided by the mass number gives the first term on the right-hand side of equation (12.1), and some writers refer to this quantity as the packing fraction. However, since it is so small, Aston multiplied the result by 10,000, so as to obtain figures which were easier to record.[*]

12.3. When plotted against the cor-

---

[*] In 1915, when the subject of isotopes was in the early stages of development, W. D. Harkins and E. D. Wilson, in the United States, defined a quantity, which they called the "packing effect," representing the percentage deviation of atomic weights from whole numbers, particularly applicable to cases where it appeared that the element occurred as a single species.

responding mass numbers, the packing fractions of nearly all the stable nuclides studied, with the exception of He⁴, C¹² and O¹⁶, fall on or near to a curve of the form shown in Fig. 12.1. There are certain deviations from this curve, but they are of a relatively minor character which may be ignored for the present. It is seen that the packing fraction is high for elements of low mass number, apart from the helium, carbon and oxygen isotopes

the particular nucleus. Since this same amount of energy would have to be supplied in order to break up the nucleus, it appears that a negative packing fraction implies exceptional nuclear stability. On the other hand, a positive packing fraction suggests that the nucleus is somewhat less stable. With these conclusions in mind, an examination of Fig. 12.1, in a qualitative rather than a quantitative sense, indicates that the nuclides He⁴, C¹² and O¹⁶ are

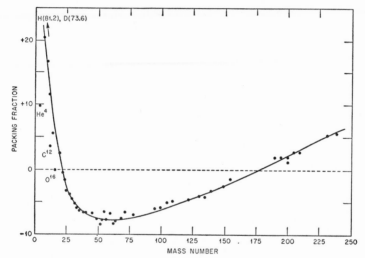

Fɪɢ. 12.1. Aston's packing fraction curve for stable nuclides.

mentioned above, but it decreases rapidly with increasing mass number. Then, after passing through a comparatively flat minimum, the packing fraction commences to increase slowly but steadily.

12.4. It will be shown in the next section that packing fractions do not have a precise theoretical significance; nevertheless, they do give an indication of a fundamental nuclear property. A negative packing fraction means that the isotopic weight is less than the nearest whole number, and this suggests there has been a conversion of mass into energy in the formation of

very stable, as compared with other species in the same mass number region. In the intermediate range of mass numbers, the packing fractions are negative, showing that the nuclei are stable, but the steady change leading to positive fractions for elements of high mass number, is in harmony with the observed instability of such elements, as is manifested by their radioactivity.

Dᴇᴛᴇʀᴍɪɴᴀᴛɪᴏɴ ᴏꜰ
Bɪɴᴅɪɴɢ Eɴᴇʀɢɪᴇs

12.5. With the discovery of the neutron and the development of the theory that nuclei consist of neutrons and protons, it has become clear that the packing fraction, as defined by equation (12.1), is merely a way of stating certain experimental facts, namely, the deviations of isotopic weights from integral values. As a result, the relationship between the packing fraction and nuclear stability outlined above, can be regarded as more or less satisfactory from a qualitative point of view only. A more exact treatment is to consider the difference between the isotopic weight and the total weight of the individual electrons, protons and neu-

This quantity may be regarded as the loss of mass or, more correctly, the mass which would be converted into energy, if a particular atom were to be assembled from the requisite numbers of electrons, protons and neutrons. The same amount of energy would be required to break up the atom into its constituent particles, and hence the energy equivalent of the true mass defect is taken as a measure of the *binding energy*. Thus, if m_H, m_n and M are expressed, as usual, in physical atomic weight units (a. m. u.), the binding energy in Mev is given by

$$\text{Binding energy in Mev} = 931\,[Zm_H + (A - Z)m_n - M], \qquad (12.3)$$

trons which make up the atom; it is this quantity which is the true mass defect.

12.6. If, as in previous chapters, the atomic number of an element is represented by Z and its mass number by A, then the nucleus, according to accepted views, consists of Z protons and $A - Z$ neutrons. In addition there are Z extranuclear, or orbital, electrons, to balance the charge of the Z protons. The constituents of the atom are consequently Z protons and Z electrons, which are equivalent in mass to Z hydrogen atoms,* and $A - Z$ neutrons, and the total mass is $Zm_H + (A - Z)m_n$, where m_H and m_n represent the masses of the hydrogen atom

according to equation (3.17). The binding energy of the electrons to the nucleus may be neglected or it may be regarded as included in the Zm_H term, so that equation (12.3) is a measure of the binding energy of the constituent particles in the nucleus of the given atom.†

12.7. The nature of the results obtained may be illustrated by reference to two specific examples. The masses of the hydrogen atom and of the neutron are 1.008145 and 1.008986, respectively, on the physical atomic weight scale, and hence for the $_{10}Ne^{20}$ isotope of neon, whose isotopic weight is 19.99877, and for which A is 20 and Z is 10, the binding energy is

$$931[(10 \times 1.008145) + (10 \times 1.008986) - 19.99877] = 160 \text{ Mev.}$$

and of the neutron, respectively. If the experimentally determined isotopic weight is M, then the true mass defect is defined by

For bismuth, with atomic number 83 and mass number 209, the isotopic weight is 209.0458, and hence the bind-

$$\text{True mass defect} = Zm_H + (A - Z)m_n - M. \qquad (12.2)$$

---

* The very minute change in mass which may conceivably accompany the formation of a hydrogen atom from a proton and an electron is neglected.

† It will be recalled that an essentially similar method was used in § 4.40 to calculate the binding energy of the alpha particle. The reverse procedure, utilizing the binding energy of the deuteron determined experimentally, is employed to derive the mass of the neutron (§ 11.5).

ing energy, expressed to three significant figures, is

$$931[(83 \times 1.008145) + (126 \times 1.008986) - 209.0458] = 1640 \text{ Mev.}$$

The binding energy of the neon (Ne^{20}) nucleus is thus 160 Mev, and that of the bismuth (Bi^{209}) nucleus is 1640 Mev. It is of particular interest to note that if these energies are divided by the appropriate mass numbers, 20 and 209, the results are 8.0 and 7.8 Mev, respectively. The mass number is equal to the number of nucleons, i.e., the total number of protons and neutrons, and hence the quantities just determined against the respective mass numbers. With the exception of He^4, C^{12} and O^{16}, the values fall on or in proximity to a single curve. The binding energies of some of the lighter nuclides, such as H^2 and He^3, are very low, but over a very considerable range of mass numbers, the binding energy per nucleon is close to 8 Mev. This is the figure used in earlier chapters for the average energy associated with the attachment to, or removal from, a nucleus of a neutron or proton.

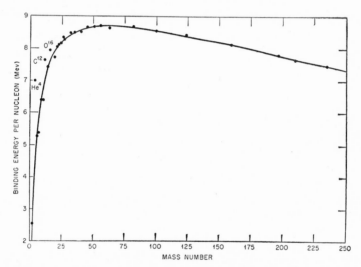

Fig. 12.2. Binding energy per nucleon as a function of the mass number of stable nuclides.

represent the *binding energy per nucleon* in each case. These are seen to be approximately equal, in spite of the fact that the two nuclides lie almost at the extremes of the mass number (or atomic weight) scale.

12.8. An examination of the values for the binding energy per nucleon in the stable nuclides, for which the necessary data are available, has revealed a striking regularity shown in Fig. 12.2, where the results are plotted

12.9. A closer study of the curve in Fig. 12.2 reveals that the binding energy has a broad maximum close to 8.5 Mev per nucleon, in the mass number range from about 40 to 120. For higher mass numbers the value decreases and has fallen to 7.6 Mev per nucleon for uranium. It is this diminution in binding energy which is the fundamental cause of the release of energy in the fission of nuclei of high mass number, as will be shown in

Chapter XIII. It is seen that nuclear binding energies are in the range of millions of electron volts, compared with a few electron volts for the binding energies of electrons involved in chemical reactions. Consequently, the energy released in nuclear processes, such as fission, may be a million times as great as that obtained from the same quantity of material taking part in a chemical change, such as combustion.

12.10. It may be remarked that, although Fig. 12.2 is important and useful, it does not give a complete picture of the variation in binding energy. The values plotted are the *average* binding energy per nucleon for all the protons and neutrons present in the particular nucleus. But it is evident from the shape of the curve that the actual binding energy is not the same for each nucleon. As the maximum of the curve is passed, almost every successive proton or neutron is bound less tightly than those already present, so that the over-all average decreases steadily. What is desirable, but is as yet only partly available from isotopic weights, is the binding energy of every stable, and even unstable, nuclide, so that the binding energy of each added proton or neutron could be determined throughout the whole mass range. A reasonably good estimate of these quantities can, however, be made by calculation, and some of the information obtained in this manner will be discussed later.

12.11. A matter to which attention may be called here is the problem of radioactive decay by alpha-particle emission. Although both light and heavy radioelements exhibit beta activity, the emission of alpha particles is a rare occurrence among the lighter

elements (§ 10.102). This fact can be correlated with the binding energies derived from isotopic weights. The formation of an alpha particle from two protons and two neutrons would release 28.2 Mev of energy, as seen in § 4.40; hence, if the energy required to detach two protons and two neutrons from a nucleus were less than this amount, radioactive decay by the expulsion of an alpha particle should be theoretically possible. However, if the decay is to take place at an observable rate, at least from a nucleus of high atomic number, the alpha particle must have about 5 Mev energy, so that it has an appreciable probability of penetrating the electrostatic potential barrier (§ 7.31). Hence, for alpha-particle emission to be detected, the detachment from the nucleus of two protons and two neutrons should require no more than approximately $28 - 5 = 23$ Mev.

12.12. The total binding energy of bismuth (Bi^{209}), as seen above, is 1640 Mev, and that of uranium (U^{238}) is 1800, so that in this range of mass numbers, the mean binding energy per *additional* nucleon is $1800 - 1640 = 160$ Mev, divided by $238 - 209 = 29$, i.e., 5.5 Mev. The energy necessary to detach two protons and two neutrons from an atomic nucleus would thus be about 22 Mev, which is less than the maximum for alpha-particle emission. It can be understood, therefore, why this type of radioactivity is common among elements with mass numbers exceeding 210.* If the same calculations are made for elements with atomic numbers somewhat less than that of bismuth, it will be seen that the mean binding energy per nucleon is greater than 6 Mev, and consequently radio-

* The occurrence of the stable system of 126 neutrons in this vicinity is probably a contributory factor (§ 12.109).

active decay by the expulsion of alpha particles is not generally observed.

12.13. It was stated in § 10.102 that a few alpha-emitters with mass numbers in the region of 150 have been detected. In these neutron-deficient nuclides the number of protons, compared to that of neutrons, is definitely higher than for stable species of similar mass number. It will be seen later (§§ 12.39, 12.82) that this will result in a considerable decrease in the binding energy, so that the removal of an alpha particle evidently becomes possible. Another factor, which will be mentioned in § 12.110, undoubtedly facilitates this type of decay in the cases under consideration.

NUCLEON-NUCLEON FORCES

12.14. The next matter to consider is the nature of the forces which bind together the protons and neutrons in atomic nuclei. One thing is certain: these forces are essentially different from the more familiar gravitational and electrostatic forces of attraction. The small size of the nucleus and its great stability show that the nuclear forces are what are known as *short-range forces,* operating over very short distances only. This distinguishes them from the forces associated with gravitational and electrostatic fields, which can act over relatively long distances. Further, if long-range forces were operative, so that there were interactions between distant nucleons, as well as those in close proximity, the total binding energy would increase roughly as the square of the number of particles in the nucleus. Actually, as stated in the preceding section, the binding energy is approximately proportional to the number of constituent nucleons. This is attributed to the *saturation character* of the forces between nucleons; they are, in some respects, similar to the chemical forces binding together the atoms in a molecule. In the latter case, each atom is firmly bound to a limited number of other atoms in its immediate vicinity, by the so-called valence bonds, while the force between nonadjacent atoms is relatively small. Thus, chemical binding is a type of saturation force. An analogous situation probably exists within the nucleus, each neutron and proton being strongly held by a limited number of other nucleons adjacent to it. Since the binding energy per nucleon is greater in the alpha particle than in other light nuclei, it appears that two protons and two neutrons form a saturated system.

12.15. The existence of proton-neutron $(p\text{-}n)$, proton-proton $(p\text{-}p)$ and neutron-neutron $(n\text{-}n)$ forces of attraction can be readily proved by consideration of a few simple nuclei. The relative stability of the deuteron made up of one proton and one neutron, shows that the $(p\text{-}n)$ force has appreciable magnitude. Further, the addition of an extra neutron, to form a tritium (H^3) nucleus, or of an extra proton, to yield the helium (He^3) nucleus, is accompanied by a marked increase of binding energy, partly due to $(n\text{-}n)$ and $(p\text{-}p)$ forces, respectively. Since the nucleus of tritium contains a proton and two neutrons, it may be assumed that there are two $(p\text{-}n)$ and one $(n\text{-}n)$ forces; on the other hand, the He^3 nucleus consists of two protons and a neutron, so that there are two $(p\text{-}n)$ and one $(p\text{-}p)$ forces. The binding energy of the former, as calculated from its isotopic weight, is 8.48 Mev, and that of the latter is 7.72 Mev, both being appreciably greater than the binding energy of the deuteron (2.225 Mev).

12.16. It would appear from the binding energies that the $(n\text{-}n)$ force in tritium exceeds the $(p\text{-}p)$ force in He^3 by $8.48 - 7.72$, i.e., 0.76 Mev. However, from a variety of considerations, the conclusion is drawn that the attractive $(n\text{-}n)$ and $(p\text{-}p)$ forces are virtually equal, but that the latter is decreased to some extent by electrostatic repulsion between the protons. This view finds some support in the remarkable constancy of nuclear densities. As stated in § 4.19, the radius of any nucleus is approximately proportional to $A^{1/3}$, and so the volume varies directly as A, the mass number. The nuclear density, which is determined by the mass divided by the volume, is thus very nearly the same for all nuclei, irrespective of the number of protons and neutrons they contain. Such a result indicates an approximate equality of the attractive forces operating between the individual nucleons.

12.17. It is generally accepted at the present time that $(p\text{-}p)$, $(p\text{-}n)$ and $(n\text{-}n)$ forces are essentially equal; this is referred to as the *charge independence* of nucleon forces. The best evidence for the equality of $(p\text{-}p)$ and $(p\text{-}n)$ forces has been obtained from studies of the scattering (or deflection) of protons by protons and of protons by neutrons, respectively. After allowing for Coulomb interaction in the former case, the similarity in behavior is quite marked.

12.18. As regards the magnitude of $(n\text{-}n)$ forces, evidence could be obtained, in principle, from neutron-neutron scattering measurements, but the experiments do not appear to be practical. However, the information can be secured from a detailed comparison of the binding energies of the mirror nuclei (§ 7.82). The members of each pair contain the same total numbers of nucleons, but they differ by unity in the number of protons (and neutrons). If allowance is made for the difference in the electrostatic (or Coulomb) repulsion of the protons, as mentioned in § 12.16, the binding energies are found to be the same for each pair. In other words, the nucleon attractive energy in these cases depends only on the total number of nucleons and not on their nature. Hence, the $(n\text{-}n)$ force must be equal to the $(p\text{-}p)$ and $(p\text{-}n)$ forces. It is also of interest to note that, apart from minor differences attributable to electrostatic effects, the energies of the first few excited states are almost identical in each pair of mirror nuclei. This suggests that the replacement of a proton by a neutron has little effect on the nuclear forces in these instances.

THE DINEUTRON AND DIPROTON

12.19. In view of the probable equality of $(p\text{-}p)$, $(p\text{-}n)$ and $(n\text{-}n)$ forces and the existence of the stable deuterium nucleus (or deuteron), consisting of a proton and a neutron, it is reasonable to consider the possibility of the occurrence of a stable combination of two neutrons (or dineutron) and of two protons (diproton). Since 1946, a number of provisional claims have been made to the identification of the dineutron, but none has been substantiated. Further, experiments designed to detect this particle in the high neutron density of a nuclear reactor have led to negative results. As far as the diproton, which would be a helium nucleus of mass number 2, i.e., He^2, is concerned, there has been no indication that it might exist as a stable entity.

12.20. A clue to the solution of the problem of the stability of the deuteron, on the one hand, and the instability of the dineutron and diproton, on the other hand, is to be found from an examination of the resultant nuclear spins. The spin of the deuteron is known to be one unit, and since both the proton and the neutron each have ½ unit of spin, it is evident that in the deuteron the proton and neutron spin in the same direction, i.e., the spins are parallel. In the dineutron and diproton, this situation is prohibited by the Pauli exclusion principle, described in § 4.64 in connection with the grouping of the extranuclear electrons. As applied to nucleons, this principle implies that two protons can exist in the same energy state only if they have oppositely directed (or antiparallel) spins. Consequently, assuming the two neutrons (or two protons) in the dineutron (or diproton) to be in the same energy state, the spins must be antiparallel, so that the net spin is zero.

12.21. Experiments and calculations on proton-neutron scattering show that the only bound (or stable) state is that of the deuteron with a spin of unity. The state with zero spin is unbound and consequently unstable. It is to be expected, therefore, that the dineutron and diproton will be unstable. The only possibility is for the two nucleons to have different spatial coordinates (or quantum numbers); that is to say, there is a difference in one (or more) of the quantum numbers other than that of spin. If this were the case, the two neutrons (or two protons) could have parallel spins, so that a net spin of unity would be permissible. However, it is known that a system of this kind, with the nucleons having different spatial coordinates, is less stable than when they have the same spatial coordinates. The conclusion to be drawn, therefore, is that the occurrence of the dineutron and the diproton as stable particles is not to be expected. It will be apparent from this discussion that the equality and charge independence of the forces between pairs of nucleons applies only if the spatial and spin coordinates (or quantum numbers) are the same in each case.

MESON THEORY OF NUCLEON FORCES

12.22. An attempt to account for the characteristics of nucleon forces was made by H. Yukawa (see § 10.106) in 1935, based on an analogy with electromagnetic forces. The application of quantum mechanics to the electromagnetic field surrounding a charged particle leads to the conclusion that the electrical force is exerted by the transfer of a photon (§ 3.35) from one charged body to another. It is certain that forces of this kind do not account for the attraction between pairs of nucleons. Nevertheless, Yukawa thought that nucleon forces might be due to a field similar to an electromagnetic field, but involving the transfer of a particle of an entirely different character.

12.23. In order to determine the mass of this postulated field particle, use was made of the fact that the effective range of the forces should be roughly equal to $h/2\pi mc$, referred to as the *Compton wave length* of the particle, where h is the Planck quantum theory constant (§ 3.30), m is the mass of the particle, c is the velocity of light and π has its usual significance. Taking the effective range of nucleon forces as 2×10^{-13} cm., the mass m of the hypothetical field particle was calculated to be about 200 times the mass of an electron. Such a particle would thus be intermediate in mass between an electron (or positron) and a proton. It was estimated by Yukawa, in 1938, that the life of the nucleon field particle should be about a millionth of a second, but this was based on what now appear to be questionable grounds.

12.24. As was stated toward the end of Chapter II, a particle called a meson, which seemed to satisfy the requirements of the Yukawa theory, was discovered in cosmic rays about 1936. Further study showed that this particle could not account for nucleon forces, but in 1947 the pi-meson, with a mass about 270 times that of an electron, was identified. Its properties were found to be in harmony with those to be expected for a nucleon field particle. It is generally accepted at the present time, therefore, that every nucleon is surrounded by a *meson field,* through which it interacts with other nucleons, just as a charged body interacts with other charged bodies through an electromagnetic field. The pi-meson then serves the same function in the meson field as the photon does in the electromagnetic field.

12.25. It must be admitted at the outset that the meson theory of nucleon forces has not been conspicuously successful in its quantitative predictions. In fact, in spite of the lapse of more than twenty years since the theory was first proposed, it is still not possible to calculate theoretically the binding energy of such a simple combination as the deuteron. One of the major problems associated with the development of the meson field theory arises from the use of the equations employed in the mathematical treatment known as *quantum electrodynamics,* which has proved so successful when applied to electromagnetic fields. The general solution of these equations is based on the use of a series involving increasing powers, e.g., x, x^2, x^3, x^4, etc., of an interaction (or coupling) constant which measures the interaction of an electron (or other particle) with its own field.

12.26. In the case of the electromagnetic field, this coupling constant is equal to $2\pi e^2/hc$, where e is the electronic charge and the other quantities have their usual significance. Upon inserting the values for π, e, h and c, the coupling constant is found to be $1/137$, i.e., 7.3×10^{-3}. This is so small, that all terms in the power series beyond the first can be neglected, since $(1/137)^2$ is 5.3×10^{-5}, and succeeding powers are still smaller. When these terms are neglected, the results obtained by calculation are in excellent agreement with experiment. However, in the case of a nucleon in a meson field, the forces at short range are so much greater than for an electron that the coupling constant is also much larger, namely, at least 1 and possibly as large as 10. The neglect of the higher terms in the power series is then not permissible and the equations cannot be solved.

12.27. In default of any other plausible approach to the problem of nucleon forces, numerous attempts have been made to find methods for solving the equations of electrodynamics as applied to the meson field. So far, these efforts have not been very promising and further progress must await some new development. What this will be it is impossible to predict. It may be a modification of the electrodynamic equations, the discovery of new mathematical methods for solving the equations, or some new theoretical approach based on the highly complex observations on mesons and other "strange" particles (see Chapter XVIII). Writing in 1947, H. A. Bethe, in the United States, remarked that meson theory has "so far not given any results in quantitative agreement with empirical facts on nuclear forces." Some eight years later, in a contribution to the *Essays Dedicated to Niels Bohr on the Occasion of his 70th Birthday,* the eminent Russian theoretical physicist L. D. Landau could do no more than express the opinion that "meson theories cannot be constructed without deep changes in the basic principles of modern physics."

12.28. In spite of the failure of the quantitative aspects of the meson field theory, the essential ideas have proved useful in understanding many nuclear phenomena. In physical terms, the theory implies that a neutron or a proton is continuously emitting and absorbing positive, negative and neutral pi-mesons. These mesons remain free for such a short time that they are undetectable and are consequently referred to as *virtual mesons*. The situation can best be explained with the aid of the uncertainty principle (§ 3.46).

12.29. It follows from the Einstein mass-energy relationship that the creation of a pi-meson, with a mass of about 270 m_e, where m_e is the electron mass, requires about 139 Mev of energy, i.e., 2.22×10^{-4} erg. The uncertainty in the energy of a nucleon is permissible if its product with the time interval in which it occurs does not exceed $h/2\pi$, where h is 6.62×10^{-27} erg sec. (§ 3.32). The time interval, during which a virtual meson can exist without being detected, is thus about 5×10^{-24} sec. The maximum speed of the meson is that of light, 3×10^{10} cm. per sec., and so the maximum distance the meson can travel and yet remain undetected is $5 \times 10^{-24} \times 3 \times 10^{10}$, i.e., 1.5×10^{-13} cm. This distance is close to the known range of nucleon forces, so that the concept of the virtual emission of mesons appears justified.*

12.30. A nucleon may thus be thought of as being surrounded by a "cloud" of virtual pi-mesons, which constitutes the nucleon force field. When two nucleons are close enough, i.e., within 1.5×10^{-13} cm., for a pi-meson to pass from one to the other, then a force of attraction is exerted between them. Attraction between two protons or between two neutrons requires the transfer of a neutral meson. On the other hand, the attraction between a proton and a neutron is achieved by the transfer of a positive meson from the former to the latter, or of a negative meson in the reverse direction. Since the spin quantum number of both the proton and the neutron is $\frac{1}{2}$, the conservation of spin momentum in the transfer of a meson would require the pi-meson to have a spin of either 1 or, preferably, zero. It is of interest, therefore, to record that the experimentally observed spin is zero.

Nucleon Exchange Forces

12.31. It was seen in § 12.14 that an important feature of forces between nucleons is their saturation character. Forces which are purely attractive cannot account for this property, and it is necessary in some manner to introduce the possibility of repulsion into the nucleon forces for distances of close approach between the nucleons. One way in which this can be done is to postulate that these forces are, at least partially, of an "exchange" nature. The possibility that nuclear forces might be *exchange forces* was suggested by W. Heisenberg in 1932, soon after he put forward

---

* It may be noted that the calculation given above is really the reverse of that presented in § 12.23 for the calculation of the mass of the field particle from the assumed range $(2 \times 10^{-13}$ cm.) of nuclear forces.

the idea that atomic nuclei contained only protons and neutrons (§ 4.35). The concept of exchange forces, which has been used successfully in such diverse respects as the optical spectrum of helium and the stability of the hydrogen molecule, is a direct consequence of wave mechanics and has no equivalent in classical (or Newtonian) mechanics.

12.32. As applied to the problem of the interaction between nucleons, the origin of the exchange forces may be described somewhat along the following lines. Consider, first, the interaction of a proton and a neutron; these two particles are indicated at I, below, each being surrounded by a

virtual meson cloud. Suppose that one of the positive pi-mesons from the cloud surrounding the proton is transferred to the neutron. An intermediate stage is shown in II, where it is seen that the removal of the positive pi-meson from the proton leaves a neutron. Finally, when the transfer is complete, as in III, the original neutron has been converted to a proton. The net result of the transfer (or exchange) is that, although there has been a change in the identity of the individual nucleons, the final state III, like the initial state I, consists of a proton and a neutron, and hence it has the same energy.

12.33. The exchange described above may be represented in symbolic form as follows.

$$p + n \to n' + \pi^+ + n \to n' + p',$$

where a prime is used to indicate a change in a particle. Using the same method of presentation, it can be seen that the same state of affairs, i.e., a

change of identity without an over-all energy change, can arise by the transfer of a negative pi-meson from a neutron to a proton; thus,

$$n + p \to p' + \pi^- + p \to p' + n'.$$

Similarly, a neutral meson may be transferred from one nucleon to another of the same kind; thus,

$$p + p \to p' + \pi^0 + p \to p' + p'$$

and

$$n + n \to n' + \pi^0 + n \to n' + n',$$

leaving the energy unchanged.

12.34. One of the consequences of wave mechanics is that when a system can be represented by two (or more) states with the same energy, then two actual combined states of the system are possible. One of these states is more stable, representing an attraction between the nucleons, and the other is less stable, implying a repulsion, depending on certain symmetry characteristics of the nucleons. By making a proper combination of the attractive and repulsive states to represent the actual situation in the nucleus, the conditions for the saturation character of the nuclear forces can be satisfied. These forces are then attractive at distances of the order of the nucleon radius, but become repulsive at shorter distances.

12.35. There are other ways whereby the saturation of nuclear forces can be explained. One, which follows from certain aspects of meson theory, is that a nucleon behaves as if it had a small repulsive core. Some indication for the existence of such a core has been obtained from experiments on the scattering of protons by protons at high energies. However, there is also experimental evidence for the occurrence of neutron-proton exchange, from some remarkable observations reported in 1947 from the Radiation Laboratory in Berkeley, California. When neutrons of 100 Mev energy, obtained by the bombardment of beryllium by deuterons from the 184-inch synchrocyclotron, were allowed to impinge on paraffin, protons were ejected from the latter. This is, of course, not unexpected (§ 11.30); the surprising fact was that many of these protons had the same energy as the incident 100-Mev neutrons. A similar effect was observed upon the passage of the high-energy neutrons through hydrogen gas contained in a Wilson cloud chamber (§ 6.68).

12.36. The only satisfactory interpretation of the results appears to be that the neutrons have exchanged identity with the protons. As the high-energy neutron approaches a proton, a positive pi-meson from the proton's virtual meson cloud may be captured by the neutron, which is thereby converted into a proton. There is thus a possibility that the original 100-Mev neutron, after its encounter with a proton, will proceed as a 100-Mev proton, while the original proton remains as a neutron.*

NUCLEAR STABILITY

Neutron-Proton Ratios in Stable Nuclei

12.37. A review of the nuclear compositions and masses of various nuclides has revealed a number of general rules concerning the stability (or instability) of atomic nuclei. Consider, first, the variation with increasing mass number of the ratio of neutrons to protons in the stable nuclides. The experimental results are plotted in Fig. 12.3, with the numbers of protons (Z) as abscissae and the numbers of neutrons ($A - Z$) as ordinates. A line is drawn at an angle of 45°, so that points lying on this line represent nuclei containing equal numbers of protons and neutrons. It will be observed that for elements of low mass number, the neutron-to-proton ratio for the stable species is close to unity.† In fact, of the eighteen nuclides with mass numbers through 20,

there are equal numbers of neutrons and protons in eight and a difference of only one in nine others. This approximate (or exact) equality is what might be expected, on general grounds, from the similarity between (p-p), (n-n) and (n-p) forces.

12.38. A further examination of Fig. 12.3 shows that, when the number of protons (or neutrons) in the nucleus is greater than 20, the ratio of neutrons to protons in stable nuclides is always larger than unity. In other words, in order to maintain stability the number of neutrons must exceed the number of protons, the neutron excess increasing with increasing atomic number or mass number. For the heaviest stable nuclides, such as $_{82}Pb^{208}$ and $_{83}Bi^{209}$, the ratio of neutrons to protons is slightly greater than 1.5.

12.39. The explanation of this fact

---

* If a projectile particle has sufficient energy, it may cause a virtual pi-meson to become a real (or free) meson, i.e., at a distance greater than 1.5×10^{-13} cm. from the nucleon. Such a free pi-meson can then be detected before it is either captured by another nucleon or decays into a mu-meson (§ 2.126). This is the manner in which free pi-mesons are produced and detected (see Chapter XVIII).

† For such elements the number of protons, and hence the nuclear charge, is approximately half the mass number (or atomic weight), as stated in § 4.22.

is not far to seek. As indicated above, the electrostatic forces between protons do not exhibit the saturation property of the attractive nuclear forces, so that each proton repels, and is repelled by, all the others present in the nucleus. As a result, the electrostatic repulsive force grows rapidly as the atomic number increases. The total electrostatic repulsion in a nucleus is roughly proportional to Z^2/R, where Z is the number of protons, i.e., the atomic number, and R is the radius of the nucleus. The latter varies as $A^{1/3}$, where A is the mass number, so that the electrostatic repulsion is determined by the quantity $Z^2/A^{1/3}$. It is

a matter of simple arithmetic to show that the repulsion energy of the protons in $_{82}Bi^{209}$ is about ten times as great as that in $_{20}Ca^{40}$, which is the heaviest stable nuclide with a neutron-to-proton ratio of unity.

12.40. In order to overcome the increasing repulsion of the protons and maintain stability in the heaviest elements, the nuclei must contain a larger proportion of neutrons. The additional $(n\text{-}n)$ and $(n\text{-}p)$ attractive forces then partly compensate for the growing proton-proton repulsion. Nevertheless, beyond a certain point, around $Z = 30$, the electrostatic repulsion has increased to such an ex-

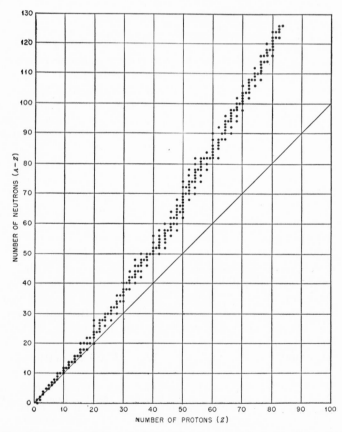

Fig. 12.3. Plot of the numbers of neutrons and protons in stable nuclei.

tent that the binding energy per nucleon decreases steadily with increasing mass number, as seen in Fig. 12.2; this matter will be considered more fully in § 12.80 *et seq.*

12.41. In Chapter X frequent reference was made to the stability range for the ratio of neutrons to protons; that such a more or less definite range exists for each atomic number (or mass number) is evident from Fig. 12.3. The most abundant isotopes of any given element, which are presumably the most stable, are usually found near the middle of the stability range. It is true, for reasons which will become apparent later, that a few nuclides lying within the range are unstable, but those outside the range are inevitably radioactive. They decay by the emission of either negative or positive beta-particles, or by electron capture, so as to bring the neutron-to-proton ratio within the stability range for the particular mass number.

Odd-Even Rules of Nuclear Stability

12.42. A survey of the even or odd nature of the numbers of protons and neutrons in the naturally occurring, stable nuclides, tabulated in § 8.47, has brought to light some interesting regularities. In the first place, it is found that nuclei containing even numbers of both protons and neutrons are much more common than any others; nuclei with an odd number of protons and an even number of neutrons, and vice versa, are equally common, while those containing odd numbers of both protons and neutrons are rare. The numbers of the various types of definitely stable nuclides are given in the preceding column. From these data it may be concluded that nuclei containing even numbers of both protons and neutrons are the most stable, whereas those with odd numbers of both are very unstable. Incidentally, the six nuclides O^{16}, Mg^{24}, Si^{28}, Ca^{40}, Ti^{48} and Fe^{56}, which are in the former category, constitute about 80 per cent of the earth's crust.

12.43. The preferential stability of even-even nuclei may be correlated with the requirement of the Pauli exclusion principle. For a given set of spatial quantum numbers (or coordinates), there can be only two neutrons and two protons, the spins being oppositely directed in each case. Thus, a pair of neutrons and of protons may be regarded as constituting a kind of complete sub-shell, leading to greater stability than would be the case for an incomplete sub-shell, i.e., with odd numbers of nucleons. According to the arguments in § 12.21, the greatest stability is to be expected when the neutrons and protons have the same spatial coordinates. This is the case in even-even nuclei containing equal numbers of neutrons and protons, i.e., nuclei with mass numbers that are multiples of four and neutron-to-proton ratios of unity. It is noteworthy that five of the more abundant naturally occurring species, namely, $_2He^4$, $_8O^{16}$, $_{12}Mg^{24}$, $_{14}Si^{28}$ and $_{20}Ca^{40}$, fall into this category.

12.44. Attention may also be drawn to the nuclei $_2He^4$ (alpha particle), $_6C^{12}$ and $_8O^{16}$, which are even-even nuclei with equal numbers of neutrons and protons. It may be seen from Fig. 12.2 that the binding energies per nucleon for these species lie above the curve so that they are relatively more

		Number of Protons	
		Even	Odd
Number of	Even	164	50
Neutrons	Odd	55	4

stable than other nuclei of low mass number. It may appear surprising that the $_4Be^8$ nucleus, which satisfies the same requirements as those mentioned above, does not exist in nature. Actually, Be^8 is relatively stable, but He^4 is so much more stable that the Be^8 nucleus splits up immediately it is formed into two He^4 nuclei. The great stability of the He^4 nucleus, i.e., the alpha particle, is well known. It is significant in this connection that He^5 and Li^5, which contain one neutron and one proton, respectively, more than He^4, almost instantaneously expel the extra nucleon. On the other hand, Be^9, C^{13} and O^{17}, with one excess neutron, are stable nuclides, although B^9, N^{13} and F^{17}, with an excess proton, are not.

12.45. According to the tabulation given at the beginning of this section, there are only four stable nuclear species of the odd-odd type, that is, with odd numbers of both protons and neutrons. These are $_1H^2$, $_3Li^6$, $_5B^{10}$ and $_7N^{14}$, and no definitely stable odd-odd nuclide of mass number exceeding 14 is known; it appears, therefore, that such isotopes are unstable.* The stability of the H^2 nucleus, i.e., of the deuteron, has been attributed to the attraction of a neutron and a proton, having the same spatial coordinates and parallel spins (§ 12.21). In the other three stable odd-odd nuclides, the numbers of neutrons and protons are equal, so that the extra, unpaired neutron and proton probably have the same spatial coordinates. Further, the observed spins of the nuclei indicate that the neutron and proton spins are parallel, as in the deuteron. The stability of Li^6, B^{10} and N^{14} is thus not surprising. The next member of this

odd-odd series should be $_9F^{18}$, but this and subsequent members are unstable because the mutual electrostatic repulsion of the protons requires the presence of an additional neutron (or neutrons) for stability. The stable nuclides are thus $_9F^{19}$, $_{11}Na^{23}$, $_{13}Al^{27}$, etc.

12.46. In odd-odd nuclei which do not have equal numbers of neutrons and protons, the odd (unpaired) nucleons must have different spatial coordinates. The odd neutron and proton thus contribute little, if anything, to the stability of the nucleus. If the extra neutron were converted into a proton, and an electron emitted, or the proton were replaced by a neutron, accompanied by the emission of a positron or the capture of an orbital electron, depending on the circumstances, the resulting nucleus would be of the even-even type and consequently likely to be stable. Hence odd-odd nuclei of mass number greater than 14 are radioactive, exhibiting beta decay; whether this is positive or negative will depend on the neutron-to-proton ratio required for stability in the product.

12.47. Certain corollaries to the foregoing even-odd generalizations will be mentioned briefly. Elements of even atomic number frequently have several stable isotopes of even mass number, since the number of neutrons is then also even. On the other hand, stable isotopes of elements of even atomic number and odd mass number, that is, with an odd number of neutrons, are not common. A few elements of this type have two isotopes, but tin is the only element of even atomic number (50) with three stable isotopes of odd mass number

---

* The odd-odd nuclides K^{40}, La^{138}, Lu^{176} and Ta^{180}, which occur in nature, are radioactive, and hence are not stable; V^{50} is probably also radioactive but with a very long half life (§ 12.51).

(115, 117 and 119). As will be seen later (§ 12.107), there appear to be special circumstances in this case, associated with the 50 protons present in the nucleus.

12.48. For elements of even atomic number, the mass range of isotopes of even mass number is considerably greater than it is for those of odd mass number. This fact may be illustrated by reference to the nine stable isotopes of xenon, atomic number 54, which are as follows:

and this fact has an interesting bearing on the subject of radioactivity by beta decay. For any odd value of the mass number, there is, in general, only one stable nuclide, so that no stable isobars exist. There are two possible exceptions to this rule, for mass numbers 113 and 123, which will shortly be considered in detail. Among the species which occur in nature, the pairs Rb^{87}-Sr^{87}, In^{115}-Sn^{115} and Re^{187}-Os^{187} represent isobars of odd mass number, but the first member of each

Even mass number....	124	126	128	130	132	134	136
Odd mass number.................				129	131		

It is evident from these figures that there is a relatively narrow range of neutron-to-proton ratio in which the nuclides of even atomic number and odd mass number, that is, with an odd number of neutrons, are stable.

12.49. If the atomic number is odd, the element has few stable isotopes, never more than two, and provided the atomic number is greater than 7, the mass numbers are always odd, since the number of neutrons will then be even.* In general, irrespective of its atomic number, no element, with the exception of tin, has more than two stable isotopes of odd mass number; these numbers invariably differ by two units.

Isobars and Beta Activity

12.50. Isobars, as defined in § 8.15, are nuclides having the same mass number, that is, the same total number of protons and neutrons. Apart from isomeric nuclei (§ 10.114), which will not be considered here, isobars have different atomic numbers. The number of possible stable isobars for a given mass number is very limited,

pair is radioactive and is consequently not a stable nuclide.

12.51. When the mass number is even, there may be two stable isobars; if they do exist, their atomic numbers are also even and differ by two units. In four cases, with mass numbers of 96, 124, 130 and 136, three apparently stable isobars of even atomic number are known. In four other instances of naturally occurring triple isobars of even mass number, viz., A^{40}-K^{40}-Ca^{40}, Ce^{138}-La^{138}-Ba^{138}, Yb^{176}-Lu^{176}-Hf^{176} and Hf^{180}-Ta^{180}-W^{180}, the successive atomic numbers differ by unity. However, the middle nuclide of each set is radioactive. The triplet Ti^{50}-V^{50}-Cr^{50} also exists in nature, but the middle (odd-odd) member, i.e., V^{50}, occurs in very small proportions and is probably radioactive. The fact that V^{50} apparently has a nuclear spin of 6 units, whereas the possible decay products, Ti^{50} and Cr^{50}, have zero spin in their ground states, suggests that both positive and negative beta decay of V^{50} are highly forbidden (§ 7.81). Taking into consideration the accompanying energy change, it is estimated that the

* Potassium, atomic number 19, has three naturally occurring isotopes of mass numbers 39, 40 and 41; the 40-isotope, however, is radioactive, decaying with the emission of a negative beta-particle.

half life would be at least 10^{14} years, and so the radioactive decay would be very difficult to detect.

12.52. Since stable isobars, where they exist, differ by two units of atomic number, there should be no stable isobars of elements adjacent to one another in the periodic system, for the atomic numbers would then differ by unity.* Actually, the two apparent exceptions to the rule that there are no stable isobars of odd mass number are also exceptional in this respect. If two adjacent elements have isobaric nuclides, then one or the other may be expected to be unstable, decaying by beta activity or by orbital-electron capture.

12.53. In general, a nucleus will be unstable if its isotopic weight is greater than the combined masses of two or more particles into which it may be subdivided. Such a nucleus should disintegrate spontaneously into these particles, the extra mass appearing in the form of energy. As seen in Chapter X, negative beta-decay and orbital-electron capture are not restricted by any mass (or energy) difference, except that the mass of the parent nucleus must be at least equal to that of the daughter. For positive beta-activity, however, the mass of the parent must exceed that of the product by two electron masses, that is, by about 0.0011 atomic mass unit. In each of these three types of radioactive decay the product has the same mass number as, and hence is isobaric with, the parent nuclide, but the atomic number differs by one unit.

12.54. It can be seen, therefore, that if there are two isobars of adjacent elements, with isotopic weights which differ by a small amount, the one with the larger mass will tend to disinte-grate by beta decay or by electron capture, forming the nuclide with the smaller mass. The mass difference may be quite small, as is the case, for example, with the isobars H^3 (tritium) and He^3. The isotopic weights are 3.017005 and 3.016986, respectively, so that the mass difference is only 0.00002 atomic mass unit, equivalent to about 0.018 Mev. Nevertheless, tritium is radioactive, since it has the higher isotopic weight, decaying to form helium-3, with the emission of a negative beta-particle having a maximum energy of only 0.018 Mev.

12.55. These arguments account for the virtual nonexistence of stable isobars of elements differing by unity in atomic number. Of course, numerous instances are known of pairs of isobars of adjacent elements where either one is stable and the other is an artificial radionuclide, or both are such radioactive species. But, in addition, there are the two examples, referred to above, of apparently stable isobaric pairs of elements differing by unity in atomic number; these are Cd^{113}-In^{113} and Sb^{123}-Te^{123}. Unless the isotopic weights of the isobars are essentially identical, one member of each pair must be intrinsically unstable with respect to the other.

12.56. The reason why these pairs appear to be stable is probably that the beta transitions are highly forbidden because of the large difference in the nuclear spins, combined with small energy changes. For example, the nuclear spin of Cd^{113} in its ground state is $\frac{1}{2}$, whereas that of In^{113} is $\frac{9}{2}$, and the energy difference is very small. It may be noted, however, that the negative beta decay of a meta-stable (isomeric) state of Cd^{113}, with an estimated nuclear spin of $\frac{7}{2}$, has

* This is a form of what is known as *Mattauch's rule*, discussed by the Austrian physicist J. Mattauch in 1934.

been observed to the ground state of In^{113}. It would appear, therefore, that Cd^{113} is beta-active, but the half life is so long that the radioactivity has not been detected. A somewhat similar situation apparently exists in connection with the Sb^{123}-Te^{123} pair; in this case, it is believed that the Te^{123} exhibits a positive beta activity of very long half life.

PROPERTIES OF NUCLEI

NUCLEAR RADII

12.57. The procedures used for determining nuclear radii are of two general types, namely, nuclear interaction methods and electrostatic methods. Some of those in the first category have been indicated earlier and they will be reviewed here. It was seen in § 7.25 *et seq.* that the decay of an alpha-particle emitter depends on penetration of a hypothetical potential barrier. For a given alpha-particle energy, the thickness of the barrier, and hence the rate of penetration, is related to the maximum height of the barrier which is inversely proportional to the effective nuclear radius. Thus, from the known radioactive half lives of alpha-particle emitters and the energies of the alpha particles, it is possible to calculate the respective nuclear radii.

12.58. A rough method for determining the order of magnitude of nuclear radii, based on the scattering of alpha particles, was described in § 4.18. A somewhat more accurate, although still approximate procedure, makes use of the anomalous scattering observed with nuclei of low mass when the alpha particle exceeds a certain energy. For energies below this value, the scattering is in agreement with Coulomb's law (§ 4.16), but at higher alpha-particle energies, the law is not obeyed, and the scattering is said to be anomalous. The radius of the scattering nucleus can then be evaluated from the minimum energy at which this anomalous scattering commences.

12.59. Total neutron cross sections, i.e., for both absorption and scattering, exhibit somewhat irregular behavior at moderate and very high energies. For neutron energies of about 20 Mev, however, theory indicates that the total cross section should be equal to $2\pi R^2$, where R is the nuclear radius. Hence, the radii can be determined from the measured cross sections. A related method is based on the reaction cross sections for charged particles, e.g., protons. These would also be equal to $2\pi R^2$ were it not for the fact that the charged particles must penetrate the potential barrier opposing their entry into the target nucleus. Allowance for this penetration can be made by a method similar to that used for alpha-particle emission, and then the radius of the nucleus can be estimated from the measured reaction cross section.

12.60. In all the foregoing procedures, the quantity calculated is the distance from the center of the nucleus at which an approaching (or emitted) particle "feels" the full effect of nuclear interaction. It may thus be regarded as the effective radius for nuclear interaction. The results obtained in all cases may be represented, to a fair approximation, by the relationship

$$R = 1.5 \times 10^{-13} \, A^{1/3} \text{ cm.,}$$

where R is the nuclear radius and A

is the mass number of the particular species.

12.61. The methods described below for obtaining nuclear radii do not involve the approach or emission of particles with which the nucleus interacts. They depend, rather, on electrical forces of one kind or another. One method makes use of the energy difference, as measured by the radioactive decay energy, between mirror nuclei (§ 12.18). This energy difference may be attributed entirely to the electrostatic (Coulomb) repulsion of the extra proton in one member of each pair, and this can be related to the nuclear radius. The electrostatic energy estimated by classical methods must, however, be adjusted for certain wave mechanical effects in order to give the correct results.

12.62. Mu-mesons interact to a negligible extent with nuclei by specifically nuclear forces, and the only significant interaction that does occur is purely electrostatic in nature. It was seen in § 4.77 that a negative mu-meson may be trapped for an appreciable time by a nucleus, and mesonic X-rays are then emitted as a result of transitions of the meson from one energy level to another. Because of its relatively high mass, compared with that of an electron, the mu-meson spends much of its time close to (or actually within) the nucleus. Consequently, the nucleus does not behave as a point-charge, but as a positive charge distribution of finite size, equal to the size of the nucleus. From the difference in the observed energies of the mesonic X-rays and those calculated on the basis of a point nuclear charge, the dimensions of the nucleus may be determined. A somewhat similar effect occurs with the normal characteristic X-rays of an element (§ 4.71). Although the magnitude is much less than for mesonic X-rays, the results can also be used to estimate nuclear radii.

12.63. An interesting method, having definite possibilities, for investigating nuclear dimensions makes use of the scattering of electrons of high energy, e.g., 100 Mev or more. As with mu-mesons, the only interaction between electrons and an atomic nucleus is by electrostatic forces. From the extent of the electron scattering in different directions, it is possible to obtain information concerning the distribution of the positive charge, i.e., of protons, in the nucleus.

12.64. As may be expected, the electrostatic methods for obtaining nuclear radii give values somewhat smaller than those recorded above; the results may be expressed by

$$R = 1.2 \times 10^{-13} A^{1/3} \text{ cm.}$$

This means that the nuclear forces extend over a greater distance than does the positive charge distribution in the nucleus. Incidentally, although some of the procedures described above are based on the assumption that the positive electrical charge is uniform throughout the nucleus, the electron scattering measurements indicate that this may not be so. It appears that most of the positive charge is concentrated near the center of the nucleus, and there is a more or less gradual tapering off toward the outside. If this is the case, the exact significance of the term "nuclear radius" is somewhat in doubt, although the results recorded above do give some indication of nuclear size.

NUCLEAR MAGNETIC MOMENTS

12.65. Because it has a direct bearing on the problems of nuclear structure, some mention must be made here of the subject of nuclear magnetic moments. An electrically charged particle possessing angular momentum, that is to say, undergoing rotation of some kind, will act like a small magnet and will possess a *magnetic moment,** the value of which can be expressed in terms of a unit called a *magneton,* equal to $eh/4\pi mc$, where e is the magnitude of the charge, h is the Planck constant, m is the rest mass of the charged particle, c is the velocity of light and π has its usual meaning. If the charged particle is an electron, the unit is known as the *Bohr magneton,* but if m is taken as the mass of a proton, the resulting quantity is referred to as a *nuclear magneton.*

12.66. The measured magnetic moment of a fundamental particle, such as an electron or a proton, should be equal to $2s$ magnetons, where s is the spin quantum number. Since the electron and proton each have a spin of ½ unit, the magnetic moment should be exactly 1 Bohr magneton or 1 nuclear magneton, respectively. As will be seen shortly, the magnetic moment of the proton is considerably larger than this theoretical value, but for the electron the agreement is good. Nevertheless, precise measurements of quite different types, reported in 1947 by W. E. Lamb and by P. Kusch in the United States, indicated that the magnetic moment of the electron was actually 1.0016 Bohr magnetons. This discrepancy, although small, had considerable theoretical significance, and H. A. Bethe in 1947 and J. S. Schwinger in 1948 showed that it could be accounted for by the interaction of the electron with its own electromagnetic field. The correction was calculated to be $1/2\pi$ times the coupling factor of $1/137$ mentioned in § 12.26, i.e., 0.00161, in excellent agreement with the observed value.

12.67. Rough measurements of the magnetic moments of the proton and deuteron were made in 1933 and 1934 by the German-born physicists O. Stern and I. Estermann, but the most important developments in the field of nuclear moments are due mainly to the work of I. I. Rabi and his collaborators, performed in the United States since 1933. In this connection, the *radiofrequency spectrum* method, described in 1939, has proved to be of particular significance. Because of its magnetic properties, a nucleus, when placed in a strong magnetic field, is capable of existing in one of a number of different energy levels. These are actually sublevels of the main nuclear energy levels, which are involved in gamma-ray transitions, and are much more closely spaced. The spacing depends on the magnetic moment of the nucleus and its spin.

12.68. Suppose a beam of atoms is passed through a strong, uniform magnetic field, and upon this is superimposed a weak field, oscillating with a known frequency. This oscillating field is equivalent to a radiation field, and when its frequency has the proper value, energy can be taken up from it by the atomic nuclei, so that they undergo transitions from lower to higher magnetic sublevels. When this happens there is a change in the orientation of the nuclear magnets in the uniform magnetic field, which can be detected by measurement of the atomic beam impinging upon a detector placed in a suitable position. Thus, by steadily varying the frequency of the magnetic field and observing the corresponding beam strengths, the resonance frequency, at which the nuclei absorb energy from the field, can be determined.

---

* The moment of a magnet is equal to the distance between the poles multiplied by the pole strength.

12.69. Assuming there are no complicating factors, or that allowance has been made for them, the nuclear magnetic moment μ is related to the resonance frequency ν by the expression

$$\mu = \frac{\nu I h}{H}, \qquad (12.4)$$

where I is the nuclear spin quantum number (§ 4.86), h is the Planck constant, and H is the strength of the uniform magnetic field. In order to evaluate the magnetic moment it is necessary to know the spin of the given nucleus; this can be determined either from magnetic measurements, related to those just described or, in many cases, more simply from a study of optical or microwave spectra.

12.70. The procedure for determining the nuclear magnetic resonance frequency described above utilizes the material in the form of a gaseous beam of atoms (or molecules), and so it is often referred to as the molecular beam resonance method. In 1946, however, F. Bloch and E. M. Purcell and their respective collaborators, working independently in the United States, developed methods for obtaining the magnetic moments of nuclei utilizing matter in bulk, i.e., liquid or solid. The basic idea was originally enunciated by C. J. Gorter in Holland in 1936, but he was unsuccessful in his attempts to put it into practice because of experimental difficulties.

12.71. In the molecular (or atomic) beam method, the occurrence of resonance is observed by the effect on the beam itself of the nuclear magnetic transitions. In the magnetic resonance absorption (Purcell) and resonance induction (Bloch) methods, however, the resonance is detected either by the absorption of energy or by the electromotive force resulting from a change

in orientation of the nuclear magnets. The material under investigation, surrounded by a coil of wire, is placed in a strong uniform magnetic field. A high-frequency, alternating current is passed through the coil, to produce a weak, oscillating field of known frequency. For the magnetic resonance absorption technique, the resonance frequency is indicated by the absorption of energy by the nuclear magnets, as indicated by a sharp drop in the voltage of the high-frequency circuit. In the resonance induction procedure, the occurrence of resonance is detected by an electromotive force induced in a coil placed at right angles to the one carrying the high-frequency current. From a knowledge of the resonance frequency and the magnetic field strength, the nuclear magnetic moment can be obtained with the aid of equation (12.4).

12.72. The spin quantum numbers I and the magnetic moments μ of a number of simple nuclei, and of the neutron, are given in the accompanying table; the moments are expressed in terms of the nuclear magneton defined above. A positive sign means

NUCLEAR SPINS AND MAGNETIC MOMENTS

Nucleus	I	μ
$_0n^1$	$\frac{1}{2}$	-1.9131
$_1H^1$	$\frac{1}{2}$	2.7927
$_1H^2$	1	0.8574
$_1H^3$	$\frac{1}{2}$	2.9788
$_2He^3$	$\frac{1}{2}$	-2.1275
$_5B^{10}$	3	1.8008
$_5B^{11}$	$\frac{3}{2}$	2.6885
$_9F^{19}$	$\frac{1}{2}$	2.6285
$_{21}Sc^{45}$	$\frac{7}{2}$	4.7563
$_{32}Ge^{73}$	$\frac{9}{2}$	-0.8791
$_{48}Cd^{113}$	$\frac{1}{2}$	-0.6224
$_{49}In^{113}$	$\frac{9}{2}$	5.523
$_{54}Xe^{129}$	$\frac{1}{2}$	-0.7766
$_{54}Xe^{131}$	$\frac{3}{2}$	0.70
$_{62}Sm^{147}$	$\frac{5}{2}$	-0.80
$_{83}Bi^{209}$	$\frac{9}{2}$	4.080

that the direction of the magnetic moment is the same as that produced by a rotating (or spinning) positive charge, whereas a negative sign means that it is equivalent to a rotating negative charge.

12.73. Nuclei with even numbers of protons and neutrons have not been included in the tabulation, since they all have zero spins. As I is zero, the magnetic moments are presumably zero, according to equation (12.4). The pairing of the oppositely directed spins of both the protons and the neutrons results in a net nuclear spin of zero. As might be anticipated, odd-odd nuclei have integral spins, whereas for odd-even and even-odd species the resultant spin is half integral. If the number of protons is odd and the neutrons even, the magnetic moment is generally large and positive, presumably due to the effect of the odd proton. On the other hand, in nuclei with an odd number of neutrons and an even number of protons, the magnetic moment is frequently smaller and, like that of the free neutron, has a negative sign.

12.74. The bearing of nuclear spin and magnetic moment information on the problems of nuclear structure will be considered later (§ 12.117). Reference will be made here, however, to some of the results given above. It will be noted, in the first place, that the proton, unlike the electron, does not behave as a simple charged particle. If the latter were true, the magnetic moment would be 1 nuclear magneton (§ 12.66), but the actual value is much larger. The discrepancy has been interpreted qualitatively as being due to interaction of the protons with the positive meson field resulting from the emission and absorption of virtual mesons. This explanation is analogous to that used successfully to account for the small discrepancy in the magnetic moment of the electron. But, as

seen in § 12.26, the coupling of a nucleon with the meson field is very much stronger than is the case for an electron with its field. Hence, the large difference between the observed magnetic moment of the proton and the theoretical value of 1 magneton is not surprising.

12.75. The neutron, although an electrically neutral particle, has a fairly large negative magnetic moment, so that it is equivalent to a spinning negative charge. It would appear, therefore, that there is a separation of charges in the neutron, and a possible way to account for this is in terms of a negatively charged cloud of virtual mesons surrounding the neutron.

12.76. Since the deuteron is believed to consist, mainly at least, of a proton and a neutron with parallel spins, the magnetic moment should, as a first approximation, be equal to the sum of the separate nucleon moments, i.e., $2.79294 + (-1.91314) = 0.8796$, compared with the actual value of 0.8574 magnetons. Although the two values are in general agreement, there is a difference. This has been explained by postulating that, as is also indicated by other measurements, the deuteron spends part of its time in a state of higher orbital momentum, in which its magnetic moment would be definitely less than the ground state. However, it should be pointed out that some of the discrepancy may be due to a difference in the magnetic moments of the nucleons in the free and combined conditions.

12.77. This point may be brought out by a consideration of the magnetic moments of H^3 and He^3. In the H^3 nucleus, consisting of a proton and two neutrons, it is to be expected that the neutron spins will be oppositely directed. The magnetic moment of the H^3 nucleus should thus be approximately equal to that of the proton; actually, it is about 0.185 magneton larger. Similarly, the magnetic moment of the He³ nucleus, containing two protons with opposite spins and a neutron, is found to be 0.214 magneton more negative than that of the free neutron. The fact that the differences are approximately equal and of opposite sign is attributed to a moment arising from the exchange of mesons in the interaction of the nucleons. In other words, the magnetic moment contributed to the nucleus as a whole by each nucleon is different from the moment of the nucleon (neutron or proton) in the free state.

MAGNETIC QUADRUPOLE MOMENTS

12.78. The moments considered above are magnetic *dipole moments,* similar to those produced by a simple magnet with two poles. From studies of the behavior of nuclei in magnetic

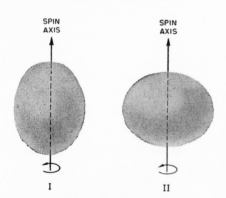

FIG. 12.4. Representation of nucleus with positive (I) and negative (II) quadrupole moment.

fields, and also from the fine structure of optical and microwave spectra, it appears that many nuclei also possess *quadrupole moments,* equivalent to a system of four magnetic poles. If the

positive charge on a nucleus were distributed in a completely symmetrical, spherical manner, the quadrupole moment would be zero; the fact that it is frequently not zero means that there is an unsymmetrical (or distorted) charge distribution. A positive quadrupole moment means that the charge distribution, instead of being spherical, is drawn out (or elongated) in the direction of the spin axis in the form of a prolate spheriod (Fig. 12.4, I), sometimes referred to as "cigar shaped." On the other hand, a negative quadrupole moment implies that there is a flattening of the spherical distribution about the spin axis, leading to an oblate (or flattened) spheroid (Fig. 12.4, II). These distortions from a true sphere, in the shape of the nucleus, are not large, rarely exceeding 10 per cent of the radius in extent.

12.79. Negative quadrupole moments are usually small and are not common; they generally occur with nuclei in certain mass number regions, as will be seen below. Positive values, on the other hand, are found more frequently and are sometimes quite large. Of special interest is the appreciable positive quadrupole moment of the deuteron, so that this nucleus is elongated in the direction about which the neutron and the proton are spinning. The presence of the quadrupole moment in the deuteron implies that, in addition to what are called *central forces,* determined only by the distance between the neutron and proton, there is also a small contribution from *tensor forces.* The latter depend, in addition, on the angle between the spins of the nucleus and the line joining their centers. The inference is that a state of higher orbital momentum exists in the deuteron, as mentioned in § 12.76.

NUCLEAR STRUCTURE

THE LIQUID-DROP MODEL

12.80. Because of the difficulty in explaining quantitatively the forces between nucleons, another approach to the problem of the atomic nucleus is to set up a model which will, it is hoped, account for the properties of the nucleus as a whole. Three such models have attracted special attention. The liquid-drop model will be discussed first and then the nuclear-shell model, representing a diametrically opposed point of view. Finally, mention will be made of the collective model which combines certain features of the other two models.

12.81. Because the binding energies and volumes of atomic nuclei are approximately proportional to the number of constituent nucleons, indicating saturation character of the nucleon forces, the nucleus has been compared in its behavior to a drop of liquid. This analogy appears to have been suggested by G. Gamow (see § 7.30) in 1930, but it was not until 1936 that the concept was developed by N. Bohr, as the basis of the compound nucleus theory (§ 10.11). According to the *liquid-drop model*, the nucleons in a nucleus interact very strongly with each other, just as do the molecules in a drop of liquid. Hence, any excess energy associated with an individual nucleon would be very rapidly shared among the other nucleons. The energy levels of the nucleus are thus regarded as quantum states of the nucleus (or liquid drop) as a whole, rather than of a single nucleon. An important application of the liquid-drop model is in connection with nuclear fission, as will be seen in Chapter XIII. Other achievements of the model, related to

nuclear binding energies and the properties of isobars, will be considered here.

CALCULATION OF NUCLEAR BINDING ENERGIES

12.82. The net binding energy of a nucleus may be regarded as being made up of a number of factors, some of which depend upon the similarity of the nucleus to a drop of liquid and others upon forces that are concerned with the constituent nucleons. Since nuclear forces are of a short-range character, with saturation properties (§ 12.14), each nucleon will be strongly held by those in its immediate vicinity, but will be unaffected by the others. As a result, to a first approximation, there will be an *attractive* (or *volume*) *energy*, proportional to the number of nucleons in the nucleus; in other words, this energy term will vary approximately as the mass number A, so that it can be represented by the term $a_1 A$, where a_1 is a proportionality constant.

12.83. The value just derived for the energy of attraction is probably reasonably correct when the number of protons in the nucleus is equal to the number of neutrons. But, since most nuclei contain an excess of neutrons, the result is somewhat of an overestimate. These extra neutrons are inevitably in higher quantum states than the other nucleons, and so they contribute a smaller amount (per neutron) to the total binding energy. Statistical calculations, which are too difficult to explain here, lead to the conclusion that allowance for this *composition* (or *asymmetry*) *effect*, as it may be called, can be made by including in the binding energy the term $-a_2(A - 2Z)^2/A$, where $A - 2Z$ is the neutron excess and a_2 is a constant.*

12.84. As seen in § 12.39, the long-range electrostatic forces due to *repulsion of the protons* decrease the binding energy by a quantity proportional to $Z^2/A^{1/3}$; hence the contribution of these forces can be expressed by $-a_3 Z^2/A^{1/3}$, where a_3 is the proportionality constant.

12.85. In addition, a term must be included here which was omitted from the earlier qualitative discussion because it is related directly to the mass number and consequently is the same for a series of isobaric nuclei. In stating that the binding energy is proportional to the mass number, it is tacitly assumed that every nucleon has the same access to other nucleons. Actually, those at the surface of the nucleus will be less tightly bound than those in the interior, so that the binding energy is reduced by an amount which varies as the surface area of the nucleus. Since the nuclear radius is proportional to $A^{1/3}$, its area is related to $A^{2/3}$, and the *surface effect* is given by a term $-a_4 A^{2/3}$, where a_4 is the proportionality constant in this case.

12.86. Finally, in calculating the nuclear binding energy, consideration must be given to the influence of the odd or even character of the numbers of protons and neutrons. When these numbers are both even, the nuclei are exceptionally stable, and when they are both odd the system is particularly unstable. This may be attributed to the pairing, or otherwise, of nucleon

spins; if all the spins are paired, as they would be in an even-even nucleus, there is an additional contribution to the binding energy, but if both a proton and a neutron with unpaired spins are present, as in an odd-odd nucleus, there is a corresponding negative or repulsive effect. This may be called the *spin* (or *pairing*) *effect*. Although there is no theoretical basis, it appears that the influence on the binding energies of even-even or odd-odd nuclei can be represented with sufficient accuracy by a term $\pm a_5/A$, where the positive sign, implying an increase in the binding energy, applies to the former type, and the negative sign, which results in a decrease of this energy, is applicable to the latter type. Nuclei containing either an even number of protons and an odd number of neutrons, or the reverse, have intermediate stability and the spin contribution is taken as zero.

12.87. Upon adding the five terms derived above, it is seen that within the limitations of the foregoing treatment which, it must be acknowledged, is probably oversimplified in spite of its apparent complexity, the binding energy (B.E.) of a nuclide of mass number A and atomic number Z is given by

$$\text{B.E.} = a_1 A - a_2 \frac{(A - 2Z)^2}{A} - a_3 \frac{Z^2}{A^{1/3}} - a_4 A^{2/3} \pm \frac{a_5}{A}. \quad (12.5)\dagger$$

12.88. In order to utilize this expression to calculate binding energies, the values of the five constants must be known; of these, a_3 can be derived from electrical theory, but the other four are empirical and must be obtained from experimental data. By differentiating equation (12.5) with

---

* The excess number of neutrons, equal to $(A - Z) - Z$, i.e., to $A - 2Z$, is sometimes called the *isotopic number,* a name introduced by W. D. Harkins in 1921. However, the appellation "isotopic" does not convey the real significance of the number.

† An equation of this type was derived by C. F. von Weizsäcker in Germany in 1935.

respect to Z, with the mass number A maintained constant, and setting the result equal to zero, the condition is obtained for the maximum value of the binding energy, and hence for the atomic number (Z), of the most stable nuclide for a given mass number. In the differentiation the terms involving a_1, a_4 and a_5 disappear because A is constant, and since a_3 is known, it is possible to determine the value of a_2 giving the best fit of a mean curve for which the atomic numbers of the stable isotopes are plotted against their mass numbers. Since a_5 is zero for an odd-even or an even-odd nucleus, the two remaining constants a_1 and a_4 can be calculated from the known binding energies of any two nuclides of this type, as determined from their isotopic weights (§ 12.7). The spin-effect constant a_5 is obtained empirically from the binding energies of even-even nuclei. Upon inserting the constants derived in this manner, the binding energy in Mev can be represented by the expression

are given in the table; the estimated binding energies are seen to be 342, 1004 and 1796 Mev, compared with the values 342, 1020 and 1800 Mev, respectively, derived from the isotopic weights. Since the data, in either case, are probably not reliable to more than three significant figures, the agreement between the observed binding energies and those obtained from equation (12.6) is very satisfactory.

12.90. Upon examining the various energy terms it will be noted that the decreased binding energy per nucleon for elements of high atomic number, discussed in § 12.9, is due mainly to the marked increase in the electrostatic repulsion of the protons. It is, consequently, also the factor largely responsible for the possibility of alpha-particle emission, since this depends on the decrease in binding energy of the nucleons, as explained earlier, and also for the considerable liberation of energy accompanying nuclear fission, to which reference will be made in § 13.23.

$$\text{B.E. (Mev)} = 14.0A - 19.3\frac{(A - 2Z)^2}{A} - 0.585\frac{Z^2}{A^{1/3}} - 13.05A^{2/3} \pm \frac{130}{A}. \quad (12.6)$$

12.89. The relative effects of the various factors on the net binding energy can best be seen by performing the calculations for nuclides of low, medium and high mass number. The results for $_{20}Ca^{40}$, $_{50}Sn^{120}$ and $_{92}U^{238}$

PROPERTIES OF ISOBARS

12.91. Although isobars have the same mass number, they contain different numbers of protons and neutrons, so that the total binding en-

CALCULATION OF BINDING ENERGIES (MEV)

	$_{20}Ca^{40}$	$_{50}Sn^{120}$	$_{92}U^{238}$
Attraction of Nucleons	+560	+1680	+3332
Composition Effect	0	−64.3	−236
Repulsion of Protons	−68.4	−296	−799
Surface Effect	−153	−317	−501
Spin (Odd-Even) Effect	+3.2	+1.1	+0.5
Resultant Binding Energy	342	1004	1796
Binding Energy per Nucleon	8.52	8.37	7.54

ergies will, in general, be different. The individual values could be determined from equation (12.6), but for the present purpose this is not necessary. An examination of the equation shows that, for a set of isobaric nuclides, i.e., having the same value of A, the second, third and fifth terms on the right of equation (12.6) will vary, the other two terms remaining unchanged. As the atomic number Z

effect is zero throughout. Of the other two energy contributions, one decreases whereas the other increases, in magnitude, with increasing atomic number. It follows, therefore, that the total binding energies for a series of nuclides of constant (odd) mass number must fall on a parabola-like curve, such as is depicted in Fig. 12.5. For the sake of reality, the mass number is taken as 73, and the atomic numbers

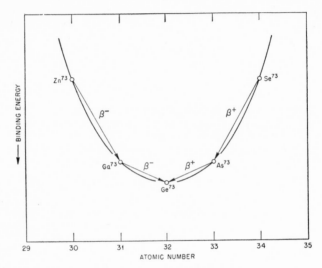

Fig. 12.5. Properties of isobaric nuclides of odd mass number.

increases, the second term, due to the excess nucleons, becomes smaller numerically, so that the binding energy will increase. The third term, arising from electrostatic repulsion of the protons, increases with Z, so that its effect is in the opposite direction. Finally, the last (odd-even or spin) term is positive in an even-even nucleus, negative in an odd-odd nucleus and zero in all others, i.e., for nuclei of odd mass number.

12.92. Consider, in the first place, the variation with atomic number of the binding energies of isobars of odd mass number. The odd-even (or spin)

range from 30(Zn) to 34(Se); the corresponding binding energies are, however, only qualitatively correct. It should be noted that it is the common practice to plot the binding energies so that the bottom of the curve represents the most stable nuclide of the series, with the largest binding energy.

12.93. It can be seen that, in general, there will be one isobar for which the energy is at, or nearest, the bottom of the curve; this will be the only stable member of the isobaric series, in accordance with the established fact that for any given odd mass number there is but one stable species. It may happen, in certain circumstances, that the binding energies of the nuclides are such that a pair of adjacent isobars with closely similar binding energies lie near the bottom of the curve. In this event both might appear stable, although one is really unstable unless the binding energies are identical.

than that of the parent in each case. For the isobars of mass number 73, for example, two stages of beta decay are known; thus,

$$_{30}Zn^{73} \xrightarrow{\beta^-} {}_{31}Ga^{73} \xrightarrow{\beta^-} {}_{32}Ge^{73} \text{ (stable)}.$$

12.95. Isobars which appear to the right of the lowest point of the binding-energy curve (Fig. 12.5) contain more protons than the stable species.

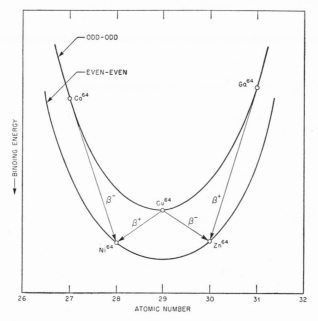

Fɪɢ. 12.6. Properties of isobaric nuclides of even mass number.

12.94. All isobaric nuclides, whose binding energies are less than that of the stable one, will lie on the two arms of the parabolic curve in Fig. 12.5. They will be unstable, and will decay by the emission of a negative or positive beta-particle or by orbital-electron capture. Those to the left of the stable species have lower atomic numbers and, hence, fewer protons; they will consequently exhibit negative beta-activity, and the atomic number of the product will be one unit larger

Hence, these nuclides decay by the emission of a positive beta-particle or by K-electron capture (or both), and the product has an atomic number one unit smaller than that of the parent. A chain of disintegrations may occur until finally the stable isobar is formed; thus,

$$_{34}Se^{73} \xrightarrow{\beta^+} {}_{33}As^{73} \xrightarrow{\beta^+(K)} {}_{32}Ge^{73} \text{ (stable)}.$$

12.96. For isobars of even mass number the results are somewhat different because of the inclusion of the odd-even effect. The general parabola-like shape of the binding energy curve with increasing atomic number, due to the repulsive proton and excess neutron forces, is the same as for isobars of odd mass number. However, all nuclides with even numbers of protons and neutrons have an additional binding energy, while for those with odd numbers of protons and neutrons the energies are correspondingly diminished. The result is that the points representing the former are lowered, while those indicating the latter are raised, so that two parabolic curves are obtained, as shown in Fig. 12.6.

12.97. A number of interesting conclusions, which are in agreement with the established facts, may be drawn from these curves. Since the isobars with odd numbers of protons and neutrons lie on the upper curve, they will be unstable with respect to those with even numbers. Hence, no stable odd-odd nuclide should exist.* As regards the even-even species, it is seen that there are two isobars near the bottom of the lower curve whose atomic numbers differ by two units. These constitute the stable isobaric pairs, of which several are known, containing even numbers of protons and neutrons. Since radioactive transitions involving the simultaneous emission of two beta particles do not occur,† both nuclides are stable, although one may have a greater binding energy than the other, and hence be the more stable of the pair.

12.98. As is the case in Fig. 12.5, nuclides to the left of the stable species decay by negative beta-emission, while those to the right either eject a positive beta-particle or capture an orbital electron. The isobar at the bottom of the upper curve is in the unique position of being between two stable nuclei;‡ hence, it should be capable of exhibiting both positive and negative beta-decay. It was stated in § 10.100 that a few artificial radionuclides are known which decay in this dual manner; they invariably contain odd numbers of protons and neutrons, and lie between two stable isobars, each of which is of the even-even type. But in several instances these intermediate odd-odd species emit either positive or negative beta-particles, but not both. Evidently, one type of decay takes place preferentially either because this leads to the more stable of the two possible products, or because the other transition is "forbidden."

12.99. Although specific elements have been indicated in Figs. 12.5 and 12.6, the foregoing discussion applies quite generally, with a few exceptions, to all isobaric series other than those of the lowest and highest mass numbers. In some cases, several members of a series have been identified, while in others only a few are yet known. It is consequently possible to predict the properties of hitherto undiscovered radionuclides. In this connection, a simple relationship between the half life of a particular species and its position on the binding-energy curve is of special interest. For isobars of odd mass number, the instability is greater, and hence the half life should be shorter, the larger the difference of binding energy between the given nuclide and the stable member of the series. In a chain of beta disintegrations, the half life should increase more or less regularly as stability is

---

* The only definite exceptions are H^2, Li^6, B^{10} and N^{14}, mentioned in § 12.45, which contain equal numbers of protons and neutrons.

† Some evidence for double-beta decay has been reported, but the results are not conclusive. The half lives appear to be of the order of 10^{20} years (§ 7.67).

‡ Species of this kind are referred to as *shielded nuclides* (§ 13.94) or *shielded nuclei*.

approached, as may be illustrated by the following example:

$$_{51}Sb^{133} \xrightarrow{\text{4.1 min.}} {}_{52}Te^{133} \xrightarrow{\text{2 min.}} {}_{53}I^{133} \xrightarrow{\text{20.8 hr.}} {}_{54}Xe^{133} \xrightarrow{\text{5.3 day}} {}_{55}Cs^{133} \text{ (stable).}$$

Another possible member of this series, preceding Sb^{133}, is Sn^{133}; it is described as a beta emitter of "very short" half life, but its existence is not completely certain.

12.100. An analogous effect occurs with isobars of even mass number, but the regularity is observed only if the even-even and odd-odd members are taken separately; thus,

$$_{54}Xe^{140} \xrightarrow{\text{16 sec.}} {}_{55}Cs^{140} \xrightarrow[\text{66 sec.}]{} {}_{56}Ba^{140} \xrightarrow{\text{12.8 d.}} {}_{57}La^{140} \xrightarrow[\text{40.0 hr.}]{} {}_{58}Ce^{140} \text{ (stable).}$$

Since this is a series of even mass number, two stable isobars might be expected, the second, differing from $_{58}Ce^{140}$ by two units of atomic number, being $_{60}Nd^{140}$. However, the latter is unstable, presumably because its neutron-to-proton ratio lies just outside the stability range.

12.101. While considering the subject of the life periods of beta-emitting radionuclides, reference may be made, in passing, to the mirror nuclei mentioned earlier. Each of these species contains one proton in excess of the number of neutrons, and the instability can be accounted for by the electrostatic repulsion of the protons (§ 12.18). With increasing atomic number this repulsion increases, so that there is an increasing degree of instability reflected in the progressively greater energies of the emitted positive beta particles and the shorter half lives (§ 7.83).

MISSING ELEMENTS

12.102. During the past two or three decades, chemists have been interested in the problem of the occurrence in nature of the elements of atomic numbers 43 and 61. Claims have been made from time to time to the discovery of these elements on earth, but none of these claims has been definitely substantiated.* The situation is, then, that while it is not possible to state categorically that there are stable forms of these elements, it equally cannot be affirmed that they do not exist. Nevertheless, some significant conclusions may be reached on this problem in the light of the discussion of the preceding paragraphs. Since element-43 has an odd atomic number, it can have, at most, two stable isotopic forms. The neighboring elements of the same type, namely, niobium and rhodium, exist naturally only as the single stable species $_{41}Nb^{93}$ and $_{45}Rh^{103}$, respectively. It would appear, therefore, that 97 and 99 are the only reasonable mass numbers for possible stable forms of element-43. The same conclusion can be reached by means of detailed calculations of the binding energies using equation (12.6).

12.103. An examination of the table of isotopes (§ 8.47) shows that the elements molybdenum and ruthenium exist in the stable forms $_{42}Mo^{97}$ and $_{44}Ru^{99}$. Since adjacent elements rarely have stable isobars, it is very improbable that element-43 can have stable nuclides with these mass numbers. As a matter of fact, both of these isotopes have been obtained artificially in various ways and have

---

* As stated in § 10.86, radioactive forms of both these elements are now known (see Chapter XVI). It has been reported that element-43, called technetium (§ 16.77), is present to an appreciable extent in certain stars.

been found to be radioactive; the ground state of the form with mass number 99, however, has a half life of about 210,000 years. Minute amounts of the latter may thus conceivably exist on earth, although it is unstable. The half life of the isotope of mass number 97 is 93 days, and this undoubtedly does not occur naturally.

12.104. A consideration of the stable forms of praseodymium (atomic number 59) and of europium (atomic number 63), or a calculation of the binding energies, suggests that the most stable nuclides of element-61 should be those with mass numbers 145 and 147. The existence of the stable isobars $_{60}Nd^{145}$ and $_{62}Sm^{147}$ of the adjacent elements neodymium and samarium,* respectively, shows that these forms of element-61 may be expected to be unstable. The isotope of mass number 145 has a half life of about 30 years and that of mass number 147 is stated to be 2.52 years. Several other isotopes of this element, ranging in mass numbers from 141 to 153, are known, but they all have even shorter half lives. It is safe to predict, therefore, that element-61 will not be detected on earth.

THE NUCLEAR-SHELL MODEL: MAGIC NUMBERS

12.105. The *nuclear-shell model* differs basically from the liquid-drop model in the respect that the former postulates a weak interaction between the nucleons in the atomic nucleus. For this reason, this model is sometimes referred to as the *independent-particle model*. It is based on the realization that there are specific numbers of protons and neutrons, generally referred to as *magic numbers* or *shell numbers*†, for which the nuclei exhibit exceptional stability, just as do atoms containing certain numbers of closed shells of electrons (§ 4.67). In 1932, soon after the discovery of the neutron and the suggestion that nuclei were made up of neutrons and protons, the American physicist T. H. Bartlett indicated the possibility that the nucleons might occupy quantum groups or shells, just as do the extranuclear electrons in atoms. This idea was developed by W. Elsasser in France and by K. Guggenheimer in Germany during 1933 and 1934. Subsequently, in 1937, the German scientists T. Schmidt and H. Schüler, independently, showed that the concept of nuclear shells could be fairly well correlated in a simple manner with the known magnetic moments of nuclei.

12.106. With the success of Bohr's concept of the compound nucleus, and of the liquid-drop model to which it was related, the nuclear-shell picture was generally neglected. Apart from its persistent advocacy by W. D. Harkins, the model attracted little interest until 1948, when (Mrs.) M. G. Mayer, in the United States, brought together a considerable amount of convincing evidence showing the reality of the so-called magic numbers of nucleons, namely, 2, 8, 20, 50, 82, and 126, which apparently represent closed shells in the nucleus. Some of the main aspects of this evidence will be reviewed here.

12.107. It will be seen from Fig. 12.3 that the elements having the largest numbers of stable isotopes are

---

* The nuclide Sm^{147}, which occurs in nature, is not strictly stable since it is an alpha-emitter of very long half life.

† The term "magic numbers" appears to have been used first by O. Haxel, J. H. D. Jensen and H. E. Suess in 1949; later, J. H. D. Jensen used the expression "shell numbers."

those containing 20 and 50 protons or 20, 50 and 82 neutrons. For example, tin, with an atomic number of 50 has ten isotopes; this element is also unique in the respect that it has three stable isotopes of odd mass number, i.e., 115, 117 and 119. It is noteworthy, too, that the nuclides which are more abundant in the universe than others in the same mass number regions are $_8O^{16}$, $_{20}Ca^{40}$, $_{38}Sr^{88}$, $_{39}Y^{89}$, $_{40}Zr^{90}$, $_{50}Sn^{118}$, $_{56}Ba^{138}$, $_{57}La,^{139}$, $_{58}Ce^{140}$ and $_{82}Pb^{208}$. These nuclei all contain magic numbers of either neutrons or protons (or both).

12.108. The stability of nuclides containing magic numbers of neutrons is shown by their small cross sections for neutron capture. For 1-Mev neutrons, the cross sections are much lower than the average values in the same region, when the neutron numbers are 50, 82 or 126. Similarly, for thermal neutrons, exceptionally low cross sections for the (n,γ) reaction are observed when the nuclei contain 20, 50, 82 or 126 neutrons. Another aspect of this reluctance to increase the number of neutrons above the magic numbers is the unusual property of the emission of neutrons by the slightly excited nuclides $_8O^{17}$, $_{36}Kr^{87}$ and $_{54}Xe^{137}$ (§ 10.131, *et seq.*). Each of these species has one neutron in excess of a magic number.

12.109. In the emission of alpha particles by radioactive decay of the heaviest nuclides, it is found that the energy change, as indicated by the alpha-particle energy, is exceptionally large when the decay product (or daughter nuclide) is in the magic number category. A corollary to this is the fact that the alpha-particle energies are exceptionally low when the parent is a magic number nuclide. It is significant, too, that the end-products of the four radioactive series

described in Chapter V are $_{82}Pb^{206}$, $_{82}Pb^{207}$, $_{82}Pb^{208}$ and $_{83}Bi^{209}$.

12.110. Among other phenomena which can be correlated with the special stability of magic number nuclides are the following: the high binding energy of the last neutron in such nuclides; the departure of the total binding energy determined from the isotopic mass from that calculated by equation (12.6), which makes no allowance for the special stability of closed shells; the occurrence of alpha-particle emission among the isotopes of certain elements of medium atomic weight (§ 10.102); the nonexistence of stable isotopes of elements-43 and -61; and the variation of quadrupole moment with the numbers of neutrons and protons.

12.111. It will be apparent from the foregoing statements that the behavior of atomic nuclei is frequently determined by the excess or deficiency of nucleons with respect to closed shells of magic numbers, just as the chemical and spectral properties of atoms are dependent upon an excess or deficiency of electrons. In accounting for the arrangement of the extra-nuclear electrons in an atom, it is assumed that each electron moves in an electrostatic (or Coulomb) potential field due to the nucleus and to all the other electrons. In the nuclear shell (or independent-particle) model, it is postulated, in an analogous manner, that each nucleon in a nucleus moves independently of the others in a potential field representing the average effect of the interactions of all the other nucleons. Every nucleon is thus treated as an independent particle, except in the respect that the Pauli principle requires two nucleons with the same spatial coordinates (or quantum numbers) to have opposite spins. It may be mentioned, incidentally, that the independent-particle concept, which does not require strong interaction among the nucleons, is in better agreement with the cloudy crystal ball model (§ 11.116) than is the liquid-drop nucleus.

12.112. One reason why the independent-particle model received little attention was the difficulty in accounting for the closed-shell numbers, particularly 50, 82 and 126. A method for doing so, which has proved to be remarkably successful, was proposed independently in 1949 by (Mrs.) M. G. Mayer in the United States and by O. Haxel, J. H. D. Jensen and H. E. Suess in Germany. There are two ways in which the approach differs from that used in connection with the extranuclear electrons. The first, which has been accepted for several years, is that the potential (or force) field in which a nucleon moves is quite different from the electrostatic field to which an electron is subjected. The second, for which there is as yet no adequate explanation except that it gives correct results, is concerned with the interaction (or coupling) of the orbital and spin motions of the nucleons.

12.113. Two types of potential, in particular, have been tried in connection with nuclear forces. One is the so-called "square well" form, represented schematically by the full lines in Fig. 12.7, I for a neutron and Fig. 12.7, II for a proton. The barrier in the latter case, like that in Fig. 7.4, arises from the electrostatic repulsion between a proton and the remainder of the nucleus. In the square-well potential, a nucleon experiences no attraction by the other nucleons until it reaches a certain distance R, equal to the nuclear radius, from the center of the nucleus; then the full attractive force is suddenly exerted. This

potential has been found to be not completely satisfactory and it requires modification by a certain amount of a *harmonic oscillator potential*, representing a more gradual onset of the nuclear force, as shown by the dotted curves in Figs. 12.7, I and II. The horizontal lines in the

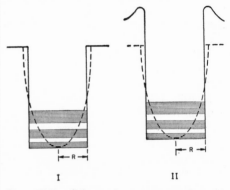

Fig. 12.7. Schematic representation of neutron (I) and proton (II) energy levels in a nucleus.

figures are an attempt to indicate the groups of quantum levels in the nucleus which can be occupied by the nucleons.

12.114. The next matter to consider is the coupling of the orbital angular momentum and the spin. In accounting for the arrangement of the extranuclear (orbital) electrons, it is postulated that the orbital momentum quantum numbers of all the electrons couple together, as also do the spin quantum numbers, independently. This type of coupling, however, cannot account for the magic numbers in nuclei. The important contribution made by the scientists mentioned in § 12.112 was to show that the observed results could be explained by assuming strong coupling between the orbital momentum and the spin of each individual nucleon; this is referred to as *spin-orbit coupling*.

12.115. As a result of this coupling, the nucleon energy level for a given value l of the orbital quantum number (except $l = 0$) is split into two sublevels, characterized by total angular quantum numbers j equal to $l + \frac{1}{2}$ and $l - \frac{1}{2}$, corresponding to spins of $+ \frac{1}{2}$ and $- \frac{1}{2}$, respectively. This situation is illustrated in Fig. $+ \frac{1}{2}$ or $l - \frac{1}{2}$. The total number $(2j + 1)$ of neutrons or protons for each j value is indicated by a superscript. The horizontal lines show places where there is a marked change in the binding energy, so that completed nuclear shells are implied. The fourth column then gives the total numbers of neutrons or protons required to

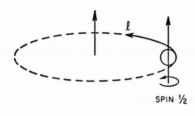
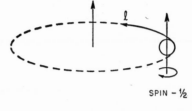

SPIN ½   SPIN − ½

$j = l + \frac{1}{2}$ $j = l - \frac{1}{2}$

FIG. 12.8. Coupling of orbital angular momentum and spin of electron.

12.8. Each of these sublevels can accommodate $2j + 1$ neutrons and $2j + 1$ protons. As the levels are gradually filled, the $l + \frac{1}{2}$ levels are first occupied and then the $l - \frac{1}{2}$ levels. It appears that the energy difference between the $l + \frac{1}{2}$ and $l - \frac{1}{2}$ levels, for a given value of l, is quite large and increases with l. Consequently, when l is 4 or more, the energy separation is so great that nucleons occupying the $l - \frac{1}{2}$ level are actually in a different shell from those in the $l + \frac{1}{2}$ level, as will be seen below.

12.116. The results of applying the spin-orbit coupling procedure are shown in the accompanying table. The first column gives the *radial quantum number,* which may be regarded as the equivalent in the square well potential of the principal quantum number in the electrostatic potential field (§ 4.51). The orbital quantum numbers l are in the next column, and this is followed by one giving the corresponding total angular momentum quantum numbers $j = l$

complete the shells; these are seen to coincide with the magic numbers.

FILLING OF NUCLEON SHELLS

Radial Quantum Number	Orbital Quantum Number (l)	Total Angular Momentum (j)	Total Number (Neutrons or Protons)
1	0	$(\frac{1}{2})^2$	2
1	1	$(\frac{3}{2})^4, (\frac{1}{2})^2$	8
1	2	$(\frac{5}{2})^6$	
2	0	$(\frac{1}{2})^2$	
1	2	$(\frac{3}{2})^4$	20
1	3	$(\frac{7}{2})^8$	
2	1	$(\frac{3}{2})^4$	
1	3	$(\frac{5}{2})^6$	
2	1	$(\frac{1}{2})^2$	
1	4	$(\frac{9}{2})^{10}$	50
1	4	$(\frac{7}{2})^8$	
2	2	$(\frac{5}{2})^6, (\frac{3}{2})^4$	
3	0	$(\frac{1}{2})^2$	
1	5	$(\frac{11}{2})^{12}$	82
1	5	$(\frac{9}{2})^{10}$	
2	3	$(\frac{7}{2})^8, (\frac{5}{2})^6$	
3	1	$(\frac{3}{2})^4, (\frac{1}{2})^2$	
1	6	$(\frac{13}{2})^{14}$	126

12.117. One of the significant achievements of the shell model of the nucleus is the ability to correlate the spins of nuclei containing odd numbers of either protons or neutrons. Provided the spin is equal to or less than $\frac{9}{2}$ in the ground state, it is equal to the j value of the odd nucleon or to that of the vacant sublevel (or hole) near the completion of a shell. As an example, consider the nuclide $_{49}\mathrm{In}^{113}$; the nuclear spin is found to be $\frac{9}{2}$, which is the j value for the hole that would be occupied by the 50th proton. The isotope $_{49}\mathrm{In}^{115}$ has the same spin, as also does $_{38}\mathrm{Sr}^{87}$, which has 49 neutrons. The nuclide $_{51}\mathrm{Sb}^{123}$ has one proton beyond the closed shell of 50, and its spin is $\frac{7}{2}$, as expected, and the same is true for $_{40}\mathrm{Zr}^{91}$ with 51 neutrons. However, in $_{51}\mathrm{Sb}^{131}$ the odd proton prefers the next sublevel for which j is $\frac{5}{2}$, for this is the observed spin.

12.118. There are a number of other instances, wherein the sublevels are not filled exactly in the order indicated in the table. But this is not unexpected, as there are various factors which affect the energies, just as is the case with electrons. When j is greater than $\frac{9}{2}$, such a spin does not appear in the ground state of the nucleus. Thus, when spins of $11\frac{1}{2}$ or $13\frac{1}{2}$ (and sometimes $\frac{9}{2}$) are expected, the values are generally $\frac{1}{2}$ or $\frac{3}{2}$, indicating an inversion of the normal order of filling the nucleon sublevels. However, there is invariably an excited state in which the higher spins appear. An interesting case in point is that of the seven odd-mass-number isotopes of tellurium with 69, 71, 73, 75, 77, 79 and 81 neutrons, respectively. For the last six of these, at least, a nuclear spin of $11\frac{1}{2}$ is to be expected, but the observed values are $\frac{1}{2}$ and $\frac{3}{2}$. How-

ever, in all cases, there is an excited state with a nuclear spin of $11\frac{1}{2}$.

12.119. It is just this kind of situation which accounts for the three islands of isomerism referred to in § 10.129. These occur when the numbers of neutrons or protons are somewhat less than the closed shell values of 50, 82 and 126. In the first of these instances, the nuclear spin in the ground states should be $\frac{9}{2}$, and either $\frac{1}{2}$ or $\frac{3}{2}$ in the first excited states (or the reverse). In the other two cases, the ground state spins are $\frac{1}{2}$ or $\frac{3}{2}$, and in the excited state $11\frac{1}{2}$ or $13\frac{1}{2}$. There is in all these nuclides a difference of at least three units of spin between ground and excited states, so that nuclear isomerism is to be expected.

12.120. The shell model also provides a qualitative, but not quantitative, interpretation of the observed nuclear magnetic moments, by relating this property to the j value of the odd proton. A point of special interest, in harmony with the model, is that certain groups of two or three isotopes of odd atomic number and odd mass number have identical spins and closely similar magnetic moments, e.g., Ag^{107} and Ag^{109}; In^{113} and In^{115}; Cs^{133}, Cs^{135} and Cs^{137}; and Tl^{203} and Tl^{205}. It is evident that the two additional neutrons do not affect the behavior of the odd proton, which is responsible for the spin and the magnetic moment. This is regarded as a strong argument for the independent-particle model of nuclear structure.

12.121. Although there are several other aspects of the nuclear-shell model which are of interest, mention will be made of only one more, namely, the relationship between magic numbers and quadrupole moments. The observations show that most cases of quadrupole moments which differ from zero occur with nuclides having an odd number of protons. There are a few with odd numbers of neutrons, but the moments are usually small. The values are found to be very small or zero when the number of nucleons corresponds to a closed shell, but they are larger in between.

12.122. According to the nuclear-shell model, the distortion of the spherical distribution of nucleons (§ 12.78), which an appreciable quadrupole moment implies, should be due to the odd (unpaired) proton. If the proton subshell is more than half filled, the quadrupole moment should be positive, but if it is less than half filled, a negative value is to be expected. This is in general agreement with the experimental results, but in several instances quadrupole moments calculated on the basis of the model are very much smaller than the observed values. This failure to account in even an approximately quantitative manner for quadrupole moments represents the main weakness of the independent-particle model of the nucleus.

The Collective Model

12.123. The calculation of quadrupole moments on the basis of the shell model involved the assumption that the so-called nuclear "core," consisting of all the nucleons other than the odd one, was spherical. It was pointed out by the American physicist J. Rainwater, in 1950, that it is probable that the odd nucleon would distort the core, and this would make an additional contribution to the quadrupole moment. Further, such distortion could be due to an odd neutron as well as to an odd proton, so that appreciable quadrupole moments would be expected in

nuclides of both types, as is actually the case.

12.124. The idea of the nonspherical (or deformed) nuclear core which, incidentally, had been previously proposed in an entirely different connection, has been developed since 1951 by A. Bohr, son of the famous Niels Bohr, in collaboration with B. Mottelson, in Denmark, and by others, into the *collective* (or *unified*) *model* of the nucleus. This model retains the essential features of the independent-particle (or nuclear-shell) picture while, at the same time, bringing out the analogy between the nucleus and a liquid drop. However, as will be seen shortly, the collective model is more than merely a satisfactory compromise between two opposing nuclear models.

12.125. The fundamental postulate of the model is that, owing to the collective action of the nucleons, the surface of the nucleus behaves like that of a liquid drop. Thus, the deformations move over the surface of the nuclear core in the form of waves which are equivalent to surface oscillations and rotations. These motions are regarded as occurring with nuclei of all kinds, with both odd and even mass numbers, that is to say, whether they have odd nucleons or not.

12.126. By taking into consideration the mutual interactions of the distorted nuclear core and the odd nucleon, in nuclei of odd mass number, it is possible to improve the calculation of quadrupole moments. Near closed shells, where the deformation is relatively small, the results are not very different from those given by the individual-particle model. But, when the shells are partially filled and the latter model fails, the collective model can account for the high observed quadrupole moments. Further, the collective model gives much better agreement than does the shell model with experimental values of the nuclear magnetic moments.

12.127. The main achievement, however, of the collective model lies in another connection. It appears that, in many nuclei of moderate and high (odd or even) mass number, the excited states of low energy, e.g., a few tenths of an Mev, are not due to excitation of an individual nucleon, as required by the simple shell theory, but rather of the nucleus as a whole. According to the collective model, certain motions of the nuclear surface are like the rotation, at a definite rate, of a tidal (surface) wave about the nucleus. Although the nucleus as a whole does not rotate, the effect is similar to a nuclear rotation. The problem can then be treated by quantum-theory methods long used in the study of the rotation of certain molecules. As a result, it is possible to calculate the energies corresponding to various values of the rotational quantum number. The agreement with the observed excitation energies in the cases mentioned above is very striking.

12.128. The consequences of the collective model have not yet been fully explored, and various minor modifications are already indicated. Nevertheless, it is certain that the model has contributed greatly to the understanding of the behavior of atomic nuclei. Among other things, it accounts for the fact that such diverse points of view, as the liquid-drop and independent-particle models, can be applied to the study of the nucleus. The conclusions drawn earlier in this chapter from the liquid-drop model can thus be justified, although equation (12.6) for the nuclear binding energy must inevitably fail, to some extent, at or near closed nucleon shells, since the derivation ignores the special stability associated with such shells.

Nuclear Fission

Chapter XIII

THE PHENOMENA OF FISSION

THE DISCOVERY OF NUCLEAR FISSION

13.1. In their public statements made prior to 1939, atomic scientists, both in America and in Europe, had not been too sanguine concerning the prospects for the practical utilization of atomic energy within the foreseeable future. Then came the discovery of nuclear fission (§ 10.60), a process attended with the liberation of large amounts of energy, and the picture changed almost overnight. It should be clearly understood, however, that fission alone, although of considerable scientific interest, would not have provided an adequate solution to the problem of the release of nuclear energy. The important point to remember is that fission, which is initiated by neutrons, is also accompanied by the emission of neutrons. Consequently, it is possible for the process, like a fire, to be self-sustaining, and for energy to be generated continuously, while the fuel is accessible.

13.2. In the course of their systematic investigation of the nuclear reactions produced by neutrons, E. Fermi and his associates (§ 11.46) reported in 1934 that when uranium was bombarded with slow neutrons, at least four different beta activities, distinguished by their half lives, could be

detected. One of these was presumably due to the $_{92}U^{239}$ isotope of uranium, which does not occur naturally, produced by the (n,γ) reaction with the common isotope $_{92}U^{238}$. As a result of its beta decay, $_{92}U^{239}$ should yield a new element of atomic number 93 and mass number 239; this could also well be a beta emitter, decaying to give an element of atomic number 94. It thus appeared that the several activities resulted from a series of unstable elements, with atomic numbers 93, 94 and possibly higher, which were referred to by the general name of *transuranium elements*.

13.3. The prospect of identifying these new elements, lying beyond uranium in the periodic system, naturally attracted the interest of many scientists, among them being such highly experienced radiochemists as O. Hahn and (Frl.) L. Meitner in Berlin, and (Mme.) I. Joliot-Curie in Paris, together with various collaborators. The general procedure employed in their investigations was based on the carrier technique (§ 5.29), the object of which was to separate the invisible amounts of each new element together with a stable element whose chemical properties were well known. There is little purpose in describing in detail the confusing and perplexing results obtained, as their first interpretation has proved erroneous. Nevertheless, certain aspects are of special interest, for they led ultimately to the correct explanation of the bewildering observations.

13.4. In 1938, O. Hahn and F. Strassmann described experiments made with barium as a carrier, and found that three different activities— later a fourth was added—resulting from the bombardment of uranium by neutrons, were precipitated with the barium. In view of the similarity of this element to radium (§ 5.7), it was concluded that the activities were due to new isotopes of radium, although the formation of radium, atomic number 88, from uranium would require the simultaneous emission of two alpha particles, for which there was no evidence. Apparent confirmation of this view came from the fact that after the so-called radium isotopes were permitted to decay, by the emission of beta particles, the products were carried down by lanthanum, acting as a carrier, as would be expected for isotopes of actinium, atomic number 89.

13.5. About the same time, Mme. Joliot-Curie and P. Savitch were making a detailed examination of a particular product, with a 3.5-hr. half life, which they referred to as R 3.5 hr., obtained by the action of neutrons on uranium. Hahn considered this to be an isotope of actinium, because it could be separated with lanthanum, but Curie and Savitch found that in the fractional precipitation of the oxalates from a nitric acid solution containing the R 3.5 hr., the latter concentrated with the lanthanum rather than with the actinium. Obviously, the substance could not be an isotope of actinium, and Curie and Savitch concluded that "on the whole the properties of R 3.5 hr. are those of

lanthanum." However, owing to the presence of an impurity, they were misled into thinking that the activity could be separated from lanthanum, whereas later events were to prove that no such separation is possible.

13.6. Nevertheless, the proof that the 3.5-hr. activity was not due to an isotope of actinium completely upset the Hahn and Strassmann scheme. The Canadian radiochemist L. G. Cook, who was in Berlin in September 1938, when the report of the work of Curie and Savitch was published, describes the events of the time in the following words: "You can readily imagine Hahn's astonishment. I well recall the day he received the paper. His reaction was that it just could not be, and that Curie and Savitch were very muddled up. However, he drew the obvious conclusion that if the so-called actinium turned out to be lanthanum, then its mother, [the] so-called radium, must be really barium."

13.7. Consequently, Hahn, in conjunction with Strassmann, set out to see if the activity which had been ascribed to a radium isotope was actually due to such an isotope or whether it could be attributed to a form of barium. To their surprise they found that the active species was inseparable from barium, although it could be separated from radiothorium, a known isotope of radium. Reporting on their work, early in January 1939, Hahn and Strassmann wrote: "We have come to this conclusion: our 'radium isotopes' have the properties of barium . . . [and] we must really state that in the new substances we are not dealing with radium but with barium." But, because of the unexpected nature of this result they were reluctant to commit themselves definitely. "As chemists," they said, "we should replace the symbols Ra, Ac and Th . . . in [our] scheme . . . by Ba, La and Ce . . . [although] as nuclear chemists, closely associated with physics, we cannot decide to take this step in contradiction to all previous experience in nuclear physics."

13.8. It appears, however, that Hahn and Strassmann were preparing their minds for the final plunge. They had previously found that one of the supposed transuranium elements was similar to rhenium, and they assumed it to be a higher homologue. But when their supposed radium proved, apparently, to be barium, it seemed possible that the product related to rhenium might be a lower homologue, the element of atomic number 43, which was at one time called masurium, symbol Ma. Hahn and Strassmann pointed out that "the sum of the mass numbers Ba + Ma, thus, for example, 138 + 101, gives 239," which is the sum of the masses of a uranium-238 atom and a neutron. It would appear, therefore, that they were on the point of suggesting that the neutron caused the uranium nucleus to break up into two portions of somewhat similar mass, a type of nuclear reaction not previously encountered.

13.9. As a matter of fact, this possibility had been considered some five years earlier, but Hahn was either not aware of it, or else he, like others, did not take it seriously. Soon after the publication in 1934 of the claim by Fermi and his associates to have identified the transuranium elements, (Frau) Ida (Tacke) Noddack, a German woman chemist, who, some ten years earlier, had collaborated with her husband in the discovery of the element rhenium, wrote a paper entitled *On the Element 93* in which she criticized the conclusions of the Italian

scientists. It is not intended to refer to these criticisms here, but it is of interest to quote from Ida Noddack's general discussion of the unusual reaction of neutrons with uranium. "One may equally well accept," she said, "that in this new type of nuclear disintegration brought about by neutrons, important nuclear reactions take place other than those hitherto observed by the action of protons and alpha rays on atomic nuclei. It is conceivable that in the bombardment of heavy nuclei with neutrons, these nuclei break up into several large fragments which are actually isotopes of known elements, but are not neighbors of the irradiated elements."

13.10. It was left to (Frl.) L. Meitner, who had formerly worked with Hahn in Berlin, in association with O. R. Frisch, to suggest what has proved to be the correct interpretation of the results described above, and thus to provide the explanation of the complex phenomena associated with the interaction between neutrons and uranium. In a letter dated January 16, 1939, and published in the English scientific magazine *Nature*, Meitner and Frisch wrote: "At first sight, this result [obtained by Hahn and Strassmann] seems very hard to understand. The formation of elements much below uranium has been considered before but always rejected by physical reasons, so long as the chemical evidence was not entirely clear cut. The emission, within a short time, of a large number of charged particles may be regarded as excluded by the small penetrability of the Coulomb barrier. . . . On the basis, however, of present ideas about the behaviour of heavy nuclei, an entirely different and essentially classical picture of these new disintegration processes suggests itself. . . . It seems possible that the uranium nucleus has only small stability of form, and may after neutron capture, divide itself into two nuclei of roughly equal size."

13.11. This process of division of a heavy nucleus into two approximately equal parts was called *fission*. Consequently, if a uranium nucleus suffered fission as a result of interaction with a neutron, the presence of lighter elements, such as barium and lanthanum, among the products could be explained. Further, Meitner and Frisch indicated that, because of their exceptionally high neutron-to-proton ratio,

ity. Such energetic particles should be capable of producing considerable ionization in their paths. Within a few days of the conception of the nuclear fission theory, Frisch was successful in proving, with the aid of an ionization chamber and amplifier (§ 6.13), that the bombardment of uranium by neutrons released particles with exceptional ionizing power, as required by the theory.

CONFIRMATION OF NUCLEAR FISSION

13.13. In the meantime, the Danish physicist N. Bohr, whom Frisch, then

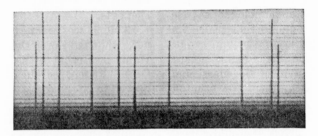

FIG. 13.1.   Oscillographic record, obtained at Columbia University, of ionization bursts due to fission.

the fission fragments should be unstable, undergoing a chain of beta disintegrations. It was the half-life periods of the members of these decay chains that had been erroneously attributed to transuranium elements.

13.12. The evidence which led to the concept of nuclear fission was essentially chemical, being based on the supposed identity of one of the products with barium. In view of the novel character of the process it was, of course, desirable to obtain confirmatory evidence in other ways, if possible. It will be seen shortly (§ 13.20) that fission is accompanied by the liberation of large amounts of energy, as Meitner and Frisch predicted, and hence the fission fragments would be expected to fly apart with high veloc-

in Copenhagen, had told of the conjectures concerning the fission of uranium, was on a visit to the United States; through him information of the idea spread, partly by word of mouth and partly as a result of a report he made at a conference on theoretical physics held in Washington, D. C., on January 26, 1939. Immediately, physicists in various laboratories devised experiments to detect the intense ionization expected from the products of fission, and by the middle of February, when the results secured by Frisch, referred to above, were published, confirmation had been reported from Columbia University, Johns Hopkins University, The Carnegie Institution of Washington, and the University of California. A striking oscillographic record, obtained at Columbia University, of the ionization bursts produced by the particles accompanying fission is seen in Fig. 13.1; the dark background at the bottom of the photograph is due to alpha particles from uranium, which obviously have much less energy than do the fission fragments.

13.14. In addition to the evidence for fission derived from ionization and cloud-chamber effects, F. Joliot, in Paris, found that the fission fragments were ejected with such high velocity from a thin layer of uranium that they could be deposited on a surface placed a short distance away. Similar results were obtained in Denmark by Meitner and Frisch, using a water surface to collect the recoil products, and by E. M. McMillan, in the United States, who showed that the fission particles had a range of up to about 2.2 cm. in air. The nuclei which were ejected from the uranium were found to possess the radioactive properties which had at one time been ascribed to the transuranium elements.

13.15. Finally, in reviewing the discovery of nuclear fission, brief mention may be made of the identification of the products, perhaps the most convincing argument of all for the splitting of the uranium nucleus by neutrons. Apart from lanthanum and barium, mentioned earlier, which provided the original clues, I. Joliot-Curie and P. Savitch in France, N. Feather and E. Bretscher in England, P. Abelson in the United States, O. Hahn and his collaborators in Germany, and F. A. Heyn, A. H. W. Aten and C. J. Bakker in Holland adduced arguments for the formation, either as fission fragments or as products of their radioactive decay,* of several elements of medium atomic number, including bromine, krypton, strontium, molybdenum, rubidium, antimony, tellurium, iodine, xenon and cesium. Most of the work described had been completed within three months of the original announcement of the theory of nuclear fission, so that in this short period of time the revolutionary new concept had become widely accepted.

TYPES OF FISSION REACTIONS

13.16. The foregoing description has referred, in particular, to the fission of uranium by slow neutrons. This was actually the first and, as later events were to prove, the most important type of nuclear fission. But it was soon realized that the nuclei of other elements of high atomic number could be made to undergo fission, and that other particles, besides neutrons, could be effective in this respect. Uranium can be split by either thermal neutrons of about 0.03 ev, or by fast neutrons with energy exceeding 1 Mev; it will be seen later (§ 13.63) that the U^{238} isotope suffers fission only in the latter case, but neutrons of all energies are effective for uranium-235. Two other nuclides, which do not occur in nature, but which have proved to be fissionable by neutrons of all energies, are uranium-233 (atomic number 92) and plutonium-239 (atomic number 94). As with other neutron reactions, fission cross sections are generally high for slow neutrons, but, apart from an intermediate resonance region, they decrease as the speed (or energy) of the incident neutron increases (§ 11.96).

13.17. The fission of thorium re-

---

* It is frequently desirable to make a distinction between the direct or primary fission particles, and the numerous products of their radioactive decay. The former will be referred to as *fission fragments* or as direct or primary fission products. The general term *fission products,* without qualification, will apply to all the products of fission, including the primary or direct fragments as well as the nuclides formed by their decay.

quires fast (about 1 Mev) neutrons, as also does protactinium. That 9-Mev deuterons could produce fission in both uranium and thorium was reported by D. H. T. Grant in England in 1939, and by I. C. Jacobsen and N. O. Lassen in the United States in the following year; and in 1941, American workers showed that 32-Mev alpha particles (E. Fermi and E. Segrè), 7-Mev protons (G. Dessauer and E. M. Hafner), and 6.3-Mev gamma rays (R. O. Haxby, W. E. Shoupp, W. E. Stephens and W. H. Wells) were also effective. The procedure in the latter case is often called *photofission* since it is caused by radiation.

13.18. Until 1947, fission had not been observed in any element of atomic number less than 90, but in that year successful fission of bismuth, lead, thallium, mercury, gold, platinum and tantalum was achieved in the Radiation Laboratory, Berkeley, by means of alpha particles, deuterons or neutrons of very high energy, 100-Mev or more, as stated in § 10.61. With bismuth, atomic number 83, fission was detected with 50-Mev deuterons, but tantalum, atomic number 73, required alpha particles of 400 Mev energy. Fission of uranium (and other elements) has also been brought about by the capture of negative pi-mesons or of high-energy carbon ions.

13.19. It is of theoretical interest (§ 13.62) that the uranium nucleus suffers spontaneous fission, as found in 1940 by the Russian physicists G. N. Flerov and K. A. Petrjak. The half life of uranium-238 for spontaneous fission is nearly 10^{16} years, so that in one gram of ordinary uranium about 25 nuclei, on the average, undergo spontaneous fission every hour. The rate of radioactive decay of uranium-238 by alpha-particle emission is about two million times as great. Other heavy nuclei exhibit the phenomenon of spontaneous fission, the half life showing a general decrease with increasing atomic number. It is noteworthy that, although uranium-235 is more readily fissionable than uranium-238 by neutrons, its rate of spontaneous fission is less.

ENERGY LIBERATION IN FISSION

13.20. Aside from the fact that fission represents a new and unexpected type of nuclear transformation, the process is remarkable because it is accompanied by the liberation of such large amounts of energy. Before 1939, the largest known nuclear reaction energy was 22.2 Mev, associated with the $Li^6(d,\alpha)He^4$ process, but the early estimates made by Meitner and Frisch, and by others, as well as experimental determinations, showed that in the fission of uranium nearly ten times this amount of energy, namely, about 200 Mev, is released. As in other nuclear reactions, the energy produced in fission is equivalent to the difference in mass between the interacting particles and the final products. It happens in this instance that, for reasons which will be explained below, the "loss" of mass accompanying the reaction is exceptionally large, and hence there is a correspondingly large liberation of energy.

13.21. The most direct method for calculating the total fission energy is to determine the amount whereby the masses of the original uranium nucleus and the neutron with which it interacts exceed those of the final stable products of the reaction. The isotopic weight of uranium-235 is 235.118 and the mass of a neutron is 1.009, making a total of 236.127 atomic mass units, for the mass of the reacting particles. It will be seen in § 13.33 that, when it undergoes fission, a uranium nucleus splits in many different ways, but the products which are obtained in greatest yield have mass numbers of 95 and 139. These numbers add up to 234, instead of 236, because some neutrons, pound nucleus U^{236} from its constituent nucleons, that is, its total binding energy, would be approximately 236×7.6 Mev, whereas for the fission products the corresponding energy release would be 236×8.5 Mev; thus

$$92\,p + 144\,n \rightarrow U^{236} \text{ (compound nucleus)} + 236 \times 7.6 \text{ Mev}$$

$$92\,p + 144\,n \rightarrow \text{Fission product nuclei} + 236 \times 8.5 \text{ Mev}.$$

assumed to be two in this case, are always liberated in the fission process (§ 13.37). The isotopic weights of the stable nuclides Mo^{95} and La^{139} are 94.936 and 138.950, respectively; these, together with 2×1.009 for the masses of the two neutrons, add up to a total mass of 235.904. The excess mass which is converted into energy in fission is therefore represented by

Mass converted into energy
$$= 236.127 - 235.904$$
$$= 0.223 \text{ atomic mass unit.}$$

If this is multiplied by 931 the result will give the energy equivalent of this mass, that is, the energy released in fission, expressed in Mev units. The fission energy is thus found to be $0.223 \times 931 = 208$ Mev.

13.22. A procedure equivalent to the above is to utilize the known or calculated binding energies. The binding energy per nucleon in uranium-238 is 7.6 Mev, and the value is approximately the same for the U^{235} isotope. The stable fission products, on the other hand, lie toward the center of the mass-number scale, where the binding energy is about 8.5 Mev per nucleon, as may be seen from Fig. 12.2. In other words, the energy released in the hypothetical formation of the com-

Upon subtracting the first of these expressions from the second and rearranging, it is seen that the formation of the fission products from uranium will be accompanied by the liberation of roughly $236 \times (8.5 - 7.6)$, i.e., 236×0.9 Mev, which is, again, in the vicinity of 200 Mev.*

13.23. It will be apparent that the liberation of energy in fission is accounted for by the fact that the binding energy per nucleon in the heavy element uranium is lower than it is in nuclei of moderate mass number. As stated in § 12.90, this decrease is mainly due to the rapid growth of the force of electrostatic repulsion in the nucleus with increasing atomic number. The smaller the binding energy per nucleon, the smaller the mass defect and hence the larger the mass per nucleon; the greater mass of the uranium nucleus as compared with that of nuclei into which it may be split is thus also to be attributed to the effect of electrostatic repulsion of the protons. The actual process of fission is probably accounted for by the large value of this repulsive force in heavy nuclei (§ 13.54), and so it is responsible both for fission and for the release of energy accompanying this nuclear reaction.

---

* There may be some difficulty, at first sight, in understanding why the formation from a uranium nucleus of fission product nuclei, in which the binding energy per nucleon is larger, should lead to a liberation of energy. The reason is that the binding energy is not energy possessed by the nucleus, but the energy which would be liberated in its formation from neutrons and protons. It is consequently numerically equal to the energy which would have to be supplied in order to break up the nucleus into its constituent nucleons (§ 12.6).

13.24. Incidentally, the energy of electrostatic repulsion when the fission fragments are in actual contact, that is, at the instant the nucleus is split, gives a good approximation to the energy released in fission. If the atomic numbers of the product nuclei are Z_1 and Z_2, the electrostatic energy is given by

$$E = \frac{Z_1 Z_2 e^2}{(R_1 + R_2)}, \qquad (13.1)$$

where R_1 and R_2 are the respective nuclear radii, and e is the unit (electronic) charge. If the products are assumed, as above, to have the mass numbers 95 and 139 and if, further, it is supposed that the 92 protons available from the uranium nucleus are divided between the fragments in the same proportion as the neutrons, the values of Z_1 and Z_2 will be about 38 and 54, respectively. For the present purpose, the nuclear radii may be taken as the interaction values, i.e., $1.5 \times 10^{-13} A^{1/3}$ cm., where A is the mass number (§ 12.60), and hence taking the electronic charge as 4.8×10^{-10} e.s.u. (§ 2.41), the electrostatic energy in ergs, according to equation (13.1), is

$$E = \frac{38 \times 54 \,(4.8 \times 10^{-10})^2}{1.5 \times 10^{-13} \,(95^{1/3} + 139^{1/3})}$$

$$= 3.2 \times 10^{-4} \text{ erg.}$$

Upon dividing by 1.6×10^{-6}, to convert ergs into Mev (§ 3.33), the result, which is a rough measure of the fission energy, is seen to be 200 Mev.

13.25. The foregoing calculations are all somewhat approximate, chiefly because of the uncertainty concerning the nuclei formed in fission. Actually, there are at least forty, and possibly more, different modes of fission, and the mass difference, and energy release, is not exactly the same in every

case. However, it can be shown that the variation is not large, and so it is usually accepted that the fission energy of uranium-235 is close to 200 Mev.

13.26. The first attempts to measure the energy of uranium fission directly were made in 1939 by W. Jentschke and F. Prankl in Germany, and by E. T. Booth, J. R. Dunning and F. G. Slack in the United States; the energy of the fission particles was estimated from the extent of the ionization they produced. The results showed that the energy distribution is not uniform, but consists of two distinct groups, with approximately equal numbers of particles in each; that this is the case may be seen from the oscillogram in Fig. 13.1. The values of the mean energies in each group were found to be about 70 and 100 Mev, making a total of 170 Mev, although more recent work suggests a result of about 168 Mev. It is now known that there is a more or less continuous distribution of energy among the fission products, from 40 to 150 Mev, with definite maxima, representing preferred energies, near 62 and 93 Mev, respectively.

13.27. A direct calorimetric measurement of the energy liberated in the form of heat when uranium was subjected to the action of neutrons, made in 1939 by M. C. Henderson in the United States, gave a value of 175 Mev. The result, although admittedly approximate, is larger than that obtained by the ionization method, while both are considerably less than the calculated fission energy of 200 Mev. Actually, these differences are just what might have been expected. The energy of the fission fragments as determined from the ionization they produce is merely their kinetic energy, whereas the heat liberated also includes part, at least, of the kinetic energy of the neutrons produced in fission (§ 13.37), as well as of the beta particles emitted during the course of the measurement by the radioactive fission products. According to the latest estimates the total amount of energy released by the fission products when they have decayed completely is about 23 Mev, including the energies carried off by beta particles, gamma rays and neutrinos. Since some of these products have fairly long lives, only a portion of the energy liberated in this manner is included in the calorimetric determination. This accounts for the observed difference between the two types of energy measurement.

13.28. As just indicated, the energy released in the fission process appears in several different forms. The major part occurs as kinetic energy of the fission fragments, and a substantial portion as radioactive energy of the fission products. In addition, neutrons and gamma rays liberated at the instant of fission carry appreciable amounts of energy. An indication of the manner in which the fission energy is distributed is given in the table.

APPROXIMATE DISTRIBUTION OF
FISSION ENERGY

	Mev
Kinetic energy of fission fragments	168
Energy of fission neutrons	5
Instantaneous gamma-ray energy	5
Beta particles from fission products	7
Gamma rays from fission products	6
Neutrinos from fission products	10
Total fission energy	201

The total fission energy, as determined experimentally, is thus close to 200 Mev, in agreement with the calculated value. The neutrons, beta particles and gamma rays are absorbed, either immediately or over a period of time, and the energy they carry ultimately

appears as heat. Because the neutrinos are not easily absorbed (§ 7.59), their energy is presumably dissipated very slowly over a large area. Their energy has been estimated from the beta-decay energy.

MASS DISTRIBUTION OF FISSION PRODUCTS

13.29. It was mentioned above that the kinetic energies of the fission particles fall into two groups; this was interpreted as indicating that uranium fission takes place in an unsymmetrical manner, the two nuclear fragments having different masses. If these masses are represented by m_1 and m_2, and the respective velocities, with which they are ejected in opposite directions, are v_1 and v_2, then the principle of conservation of momentum requires m_1v_1 to be equal to m_2v_2. The kinetic energies E_1 and E_2 are $\frac{1}{2} m_1v_1^2$ and $\frac{1}{2} m_2v_2^2$, respectively, so that

$$\frac{E_1}{E_2} = \frac{m_1v_1^2}{m_2v_2^2} = \frac{m_2}{m_1}. \qquad (13.2)$$

The ratio of the energies should thus be inversely proportional to the ratio of the masses or mass numbers. The ratio of the energies was found to be about 1.45, and this was in general agreement with the fact, already apparent in 1939, that the known fission fragments fall into two groups, one around krypton, mass number about 90, and the other around xenon, mass number 140.

13.30. Because it was necessary to have precise information concerning the products of nuclear fission, in connection with the development of atomic energy (Chapter XIV), a great deal of work has been done with the purpose of identifying these products. Some of the details of these difficult investigations will be considered later, but for the present it will be sufficient to outline the general nature of the results; these are represented by the data for the fission of uranium-235 by thermal neutrons plotted in Fig. 13.2.

venience. Incidentally, the reason why mass numbers, rather than atomic numbers, are plotted is that the fission fragments are probably all radioactive, decaying by the loss of a nega-

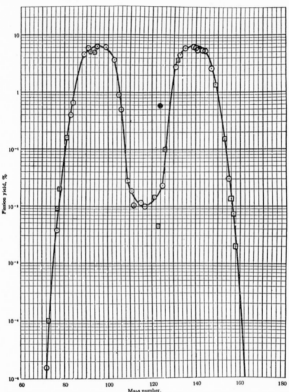

FIG. 13.2.   Fission-yield curve for uranium-235 and slow neutrons. (From *J. Amer. Chem. Soc.*, **68**, 2437 (1946)).

The mass number of the product is plotted against its *fission yield,* this being the proportion of nuclear fissions yielding that particular product, usually expressed as a percentage of the total.* Since the observed fission yields cover such a large range, from about 10^{-5} to 6 per cent, they are plotted on a logarithmic scale for con-

tive beta-particle. The atomic numbers consequently change with time but the mass numbers are unaffected in the beta decay.

13.31. An examination of the fission yield curve shows immediately that, in accordance with the conclusions drawn from the particle energies, the products fall into two broad mass-

---

* It should be noted that since two nuclei result from each act of fission, the total fission yield adds up to 200 per cent. In about 0.3 per cent of thermal-neutron fissions, three nuclei are produced; this *ternary fission,* as it is called, is mainly of theoretical interest.

number groups. The range of mass numbers detected experimentally is from 72, probably an isotope of zinc (atomic number 30), to 160, believed to be an isotope of gadolinium (atomic number 64). Of the thirty-five different elements covered by this range of atomic numbers, there is evidence that all but nine are produced directly in fission; even these gaps may be filled, in due course, as the experimental methods are improved. The difficulty of the work may be realized when it is stated that in the fission of uranium-235 something like 200 different nuclides, including fission fragments and products of their radio-active decay, have been detected (§ 13.75).

13.32. About 97 per cent of the uranium-235 nuclei undergoing fission yield products which fall into two groups, a "light" group, with mass numbers from 85 to 104, and a "heavy" group, with mass numbers from 130 to 149. The most probable type of fission, representing nearly 6.4 per cent of the total, gives products with mass numbers 95 and 139. It is apparent from these results that the thermal-neutron fission of uranium-235 is far from symmetrical. If the compound nucleus split into two equal fragments, the mass of each would be 117 or 118; only 0.01 per cent of the nuclei suffering fission break up in this manner.

13.33. Since there are 89 possible mass numbers in the range from 72 through 160, it is conceivable that this may represent the total number of different nuclides formed as direct fission fragments. In this case, the uranium nucleus should be capable of splitting in over forty different ways. The loss of mass, and hence the energy

liberated, will not be exactly identical for every mode of fission, although the variations are not large, as stated above. It is, in fact, because the mass or energy differences are nearly the same in all cases that the several fission modes take place simultaneously.

13.34. It is useful to note that the fission yield curve in Fig. 13.2 is symmetrical about the line passing through the ordinate for mass number 117, the two parts being mirror images. This means that the products represented by points on the left-hand (outer) limb of the "light" group will correspond to those of the same yield on the right-hand (outer) limb of the "heavy" group; similarly, products on the right-hand (inner) limb of the "light" group will be paired with those on the left-hand (inner) limb of the "heavy" group. For example, the fission fragment of mass number 81 is formed at the same time as 153, the yield being about 0.15 per cent; similarly, nuclides of mass number 103 and 131 are produced simultaneously in about 3.5 per cent of the fissions.[*]

13.35. The yields of products of various mass numbers have also been determined for the thermal-neutron fission of uranium-233 and plutonium-239. The general shape of the fission-yield curve is very similar to that obtained for uranium-235, shown in Fig. 13.2. However, since the masses of the nuclei undergoing fission are somewhat different, there is a slight shift in the position of the curve with reference to the mass-number axis. In all three instances, symmetrical fission takes place to the extent of 0.01 to 0.02 per cent only, all other fissions being unsymmetrical.

13.36. The results recorded above apply in particular to fission by ther-

---

[*] These results are strictly correct only for fissions in which two neutrons are liberated, so that the sum of the mass numbers of the fission fragments is 234.

mal neutrons; there is evidence that with neutrons of a few Mev energy the fission yields are not the same. It is found that symmetrical fission is more probable than when slow neutrons are employed. With particles of much higher energy, such as the 100-Mev neutrons, 200-Mev deuterons, 380-Mev alpha particles and 100-Mev carbon ions, the fission product distributions are quite different from those accompanying thermal-neutron fission. The general nature of the products indicates that the process occurring is a combination of fission and spallation (§ 10.64). It appears that the excitation energy of the compound nucleus formed when the high-energy projectile enters the nucleus is so large that ten or more neutrons are expelled immediately; the residual nucleus then splits in an approximately symmetrical manner. One of the consequences of the ejection of the neutrons is that some of the products are apparently stable nuclei, although there is no evidence that such nuclides are formed in fission by slow neutrons.

EMISSION OF NEUTRONS IN FISSION

13.37. It was stated at the beginning of this chapter that one of the notable features of nuclear fission is the liberation of neutrons by which it is accompanied. That such simultaneous neutron emission was to be expected was suggested, and also verified, by H. von Halban, F. Joliot and L. Kowarski in France,* soon after the announcement of the theory of nuclear fission. Within a few days, independ-

ent confirmatory evidence was reported by H. L. Anderson, E. Fermi and H. B. Hanstein, and by L. Szilard and W. H. Zinn in the United States. In view of the large amount of energy carried by the fission products, there should be ample available to cause the expulsion of one or more nucleons; that these will probably be neutrons may be readily seen from the following considerations.

13.38. Suppose, in order to simplify the argument, that a uranium-235 nucleus upon fission by a neutron were to split into two nuclei of mass numbers 95 and 139; suppose further that, as in § 13.24, the atomic numbers are in the same proportion, so that these will be 38 and 54, respectively. The instantaneous products of fission may consequently be taken to be $_{38}Sr^{95}$ and $_{54}Xe^{139}$, whereas the highest mass numbers of stable forms of these elements are 88 and 136, respectively. It is evident that the highly energetic, primary nuclei formed in fission contain several more neutrons than is permissible for stability, and hence the expulsion of neutrons is not surprising.

13.39. The same conclusion may be reached in a more general manner by recalling, from § 12.38, that the ratio of neutrons to protons in stable, naturally occurring nuclei increases with increasing mass number. At the upper end of the periodic system, the ratio is greater than 1.5, but in the middle, where the fission products lie, the neutron-to-proton ratio for stability ranges from 1.28 to 1.4. It follows, therefore, that if a nucleus of high mass number is split into two smaller

---

* H. D. Smyth, in his report on *Atomic Energy for Military Purposes,* states: "At the meeting [held in Washington, D. C., January 26-28, 1939] Bohr and Fermi discussed the problem of fission, and in particular Fermi mentioned the possibility that neutrons might be emitted during the process." This conversation must have taken place some time before the publication of the paper by von Halban, *et al.* Further, according to O. R. Frisch, both (Frl.) L. Meitner and C. Møller (in Copenhagen) had pointed out to him the possibility of neutron emission accompanying fission.

nuclei, the ratio of neutrons to protons for at least one of the latter must be considerably greater than is compatible with stability.

13.40. In order to test the possibility of neutron release in fission, von Halban and his associates placed a neutron source at the center of a large vessel, with detectors at various distances from it to determine the neutron density in the vessel. This was filled first with uranyl nitrate solution, and then with ammonium nitrate solution for comparison. In spite of the absorption of neutrons by the uranium, the mean density of neutrons in the vessel was found to be larger in the former case, indicating that more neutrons were formed in fission than were used up in the process. From the results it was estimated that, for each atom of uranium undergoing fission, between three and four neutrons were emitted, on the average. The release of neutrons in fission was confirmed by scientists in the United States, as well as in France and Germany. The number of neutrons released undoubtedly depends upon the mode of fission; some modes may be accompanied by one, others by two, three or possibly more neutrons, so that the over-all average is not an integer. The average values for the numbers of neutrons produced in the fission of uranium-235, plutonium-239 and uranium-233 by thermal neutrons are recorded below.

NEUTRONS PRODUCED IN
THERMAL-NEUTRON FISSION

Uranium-235	2.47
Plutonium-239	2.91
Uranium-233	2.55

13.41. In accordance with theoretical expectation, the distribution of the neutrons accompanying nuclear fission indicates that they are ejected from the fission fragments, and not from the compound nucleus.[*] In other words, the latter first breaks up into two parts, each of which, as seen above, probably has too many neutrons for stability, as well as sufficient energy to make neutron emission possible. Each excited, unstable nucleus consequently expels one or more neutrons, probably within 10^{-12} sec., in an attempt to attain or approach stability. The instantaneous gamma rays accompanying fission are probably emitted at the same time. As is common with particles produced in nuclear reactions, the fission neutrons have high energies, of the order of 1 to 2 Mev, on the average.

13.42. Over 99 per cent of the neutrons produced in fission are released within an extremely short interval of time; these are referred to as *prompt neutrons*. But, in addition, about 0.75 per cent of the neutrons accompanying the slow-neutron fission of uranium-235 are *delayed neutrons*, the emission of which continues for some time after the nuclear fission process. The delayed neutrons can be detected for several minutes, the intensity falling off in a manner analogous to that for a mixture of radioactive nuclides of different half lives. It will be seen in § 14.60 that the emission of the delayed neutrons is an important factor in the control of nuclear fission reactors.

13.43. Early in 1939, apparently before the simultaneous expulsion of neutrons in fission had been reported, R. B. Roberts, L. R. Hafstad, N. C. Meyer and P. Wang, in the United

[*] The ten or more neutrons expelled in fission by very high-energy particles, mentioned in § 13.36, probably are ejected directly from the compound nucleus. The same is true for the small number of 16-Mev alpha particles which accompany slow-neutron fission of uranium-235 (one in 250 fissions) and of plutonium-239 (one in 500 fissions).

States, noted that uranium and thorium continued to emit neutrons for a short time after the bombardment by neutrons had ceased. These were the delayed neutrons accompanying nuclear fission. An analysis of the rate of decrease of the neutron density by the American physicists E. T. Booth, J. R. Dunning and F. G. Slack in 1939, and later in the same year by K. J. Bro-strøm, J. Koch and T. Lauritsen, in Denmark, revealed the presence of four decay periods. More recent work has shown that the delayed neutrons from the slow-neutron fission of uranium-235 fall into five, possibly six, groups (§ 10.131). The rate of decay of the neutron density in each group is exponential in nature, as it is for radioactive decay in general, and the half lives range from a fraction of a second to nearly a minute.

13.44. The study of the delayed-neutron emitters of short life is facilitated by the use of a device referred to colloquially as a "rabbit"; by this means a sample of fissionable material, after exposure to a high density of neutrons, usually in a nuclear fission reactor, is rapidly transferred to a counter where the emission of the delayed neutrons is registered automatically. The characteristic properties of the various delayed neutrons, and the percentage which each constitutes of the total, prompt and delayed, neutron emission are given in the table for the fission of uranium-235 by thermal neutrons. Similar results have been found in connection with the fission of plutonium-239 and uranium-233; neutrons, emitted with

the same half-life periods, have been observed, but the respective yields are different. For the thermal-neutron fission of plutonium-239, about 0.36 per cent of the neutrons are delayed and for uranium-233, about 0.26 per cent.

DELAYED NEUTRONS IN FISSION OF
URANIUM-235 BY THERMAL NEUTRONS

Half Life (sec.)	Yield (%)	Energy (Mev)
55.6	0.025	0.25
22.5	0.17	0.56
4.51	0.21	0.43
1.52	0.24	0.62
0.43	0.08	0.42
0.15 (?)	0.025 (?)	—

13.45. The explanation of the delayed neutron emission has been given in § 10.132. The 55.6 sec. and 22.5 sec. periods are apparently due to the negative beta-emitters Br^{87} and I^{137}, respectively, called *delayed-neutron precursors*. These are believed to be direct fission fragments, and their decay products, Kr^{87} and Xe^{137}, are formed with sufficient excitation energy to permit them to expel a neutron instantaneously, yielding Kr^{86} and Xe^{136}, respectively. Both of the latter are stable, naturally occurring nuclides. It will be noted from the table given above that the energies of the delayed neutrons are not very high; these energies are equal to the energy of the excited nucleus, such as Kr^{87} and Xe^{137}, minus the binding energy of the neutron in each case, and so it is unlikely that they will be large. There has been some speculation concerning the origins of the other delayed neutrons, but the results are not conclusive.

THEORY OF NUCLEAR FISSION

MECHANISM OF NUCLEAR FISSION

13.46. It was stated in § 12.53 that if any nucleus has a mass greater than

the sum of the masses of the particles into which it may be subdivided, it will tend to be unstable, because the subdivision process would be accompanied by a decrease of mass and a consequent liberation of energy. The mass of a uranium nucleus is certainly greater than the combined masses of any pair of fission fragments, as seen above. It is consequently pertinent to inquire: Why do not uranium nuclei all suffer spontaneous fission? There is a certain amount of spontaneous fission, it is true, but the extent of this process is extremely small. The question of why uranium does not break up spontaneously is, however, only part of the problem. The gradual decrease, with increasing mass number, of the binding energy per nucleon for elements of mass number exceeding about 70 (Fig. 12.2), means that all elements of high mass number, especially if they are greater than 140, should be theoretically capable of undergoing spontaneous fission with the consequent liberation of energy. Actually, tantalum, with a mass number of 181, is the lightest element known to be capable of fission, but this was made possible only by bombardment with particles of very high energy.

13.47. Although the situation appears to be contradictory, it is really not very different from that with which chemists have long been familiar. A mixture of hydrogen and oxygen gases at ordinary temperatures and pressures, for example, is known to be very unstable with respect to liquid water, because the total free energy of the latter is much less than that of the former. Nevertheless, mixed hydrogen and oxygen gases could probably be kept in a glass vessel for millions of years without any appreciable formation of water. The reason why the reaction does not occur is that the reacting substances must acquire a certain critical amount of energy, called the *energy of activation,* before

they can combine. Under normal conditions, this energy is available to a negligible number of molecules, and so no interaction is observed. Upon raising the temperature sufficiently, or by passing an electric spark through the gas mixture, the reaction can proceed.

13.48. Somewhat similar factors are operative in essentially all chemical reactions. Fuels, such as wood, and other carbohydrates, and hydrocarbon oils together with oxygen are really unstable with respect to the products of combustion. Explosives are also unstable, but they can be kept safely, under proper conditions, for long periods of time. In each case, an activation energy is necessary to make the reaction take place. It will be shown below that a nucleus which, on account of mass-energy considerations, is potentially unstable with respect to two smaller nuclei, can undergo fission only if sufficient energy, equivalent to an energy of activation, is supplied.

13.49. A useful approach to understanding the mechanism of fission is by means of the liquid-drop model of the nucleus, the general picture being largely unchanged by the more complete collective model described in Chapter XII. It is postulated that, just as the surface tension forces tend to maintain a liquid drop in a stable form which resists distortion, so the nuclear forces serve to keep the nucleus in a stable state. For a drop of liquid to be broken up into two smaller drops, or for a nucleus to undergo fission, there must be considerable distortion which will be possible only if additional energy is available. This is the basis of the interpretation of fission indicated by Meitner and Frisch in their original publication (§ 13.10); it was developed in 1939 by N. Bohr, while visiting the United States, first in a qualitative manner and later quantitatively in conjunction with J. A. Wheeler.

13.50. The general ideal of the proposed mechanism for fission may be understood by considering a drop of liquid which is made to break up into two smaller droplets, by the application of a suitable force. The system passes through a series of stages, some of which are represented in Fig. 13.3.

nucleus could, if sufficient energy were available, expel one or more nucleons. But there is a distinct probability that, because of the excess energy, the compound nucleus, like a liquid drop to which energy is supplied, will undergo a variety of strong oscillations; and in the course of these oscillations it will pass through a phase similar to B in Fig. 13.3. If the gain in energy accompanying the ab-

Fig. 13.3.   Liquid-drop model of an atomic nucleus undergoing fission.

The drop is at first spherical, as shown at A; it is then elongated into an ellipsoid, as at B. If insufficient energy is available to overcome the force of surface tension, the drop will return to its original spherical shape. But, if the deforming force is sufficiently large, the liquid acquires a shape similar to a dumbbell, as at C in Fig. 13.3. Once it has reached this stage, it is unlikely to return to the spherical form, but it will rather split into two droplets. These will, at first, be somewhat deformed, with protuberances corresponding to the constriction of the dumbbell, but finally they will become spherical, as indicated at D.

13.51. The situation in nuclear fission is believed to be quite analogous to that just considered for a liquid drop, even though the nuclei are not necessarily spherical. A target nucleus combines with a neutron to form a compound nucleus; the energy gained by the latter is then equal to the binding energy of the additional neutron plus any kinetic energy the incident neutron may have possessed. The excitation energy may then be emitted as gamma radiation or the compound

sorption of the neutron is insufficient to cause further deformation beyond B, the intranuclear forces will compel the nucleus to return to its original spherical form; the excess energy will then be removed, usually by the expulsion of a particle of some kind.

13.52. However, if the nucleus has obtained enough energy to permit it to form the dumbbell shape C, the restoration of the initial state A becomes very improbable. The reason is that the electrostatic repulsion between the positive charges on the two ends of C can now overcome the relatively small portion of the nuclear binding force operative in the constricted region. Consequently, from C the system passes rapidly to D, representing fission into two separate nuclei, which are propelled in opposite directions. It will be understood, of course, that the series of changes just described can occur only if it is accompanied by a net decrease of mass, that is, by an emission of energy; the state D, consisting of two separate nuclei, is then more stable than the initial state A.

13.53. One of the outstanding problems in the theory of nuclear fission is to account for the highly unsymmetrical nature of the process, at least when initiated by thermal neutrons. Many ideas on the subject have been put forward from time to time, but none has proved to be completely satisfactory. A promising hypothesis is based on the assumption that the nucleus consists of a number of layers of nucleons, in general agreement with the shell or unified models of the nucleus. It is suggested that once the critical deformation of the nuclear surface is attained, the outer nuclear shells begin to break up in a symmetrical manner, as might reasonably be expected. The tightly bound inner core, however, does not break up and it ultimately moves off with half of the nucleons from the outer shell (or shells). The net result is, therefore, to produce two fission fragments with different masses. Some of the consequences of this theory have been developed and appear to be in agreement with the experimental facts.

The Critical Energy for Fission

13.54. The critical energy (or activation energy) requisite for fission to occur is the energy which must be supplied to the original nucleus in order to deform it to the state C, where the electrostatic repulsion overcomes the binding force still holding the two parts of the nucleus together. The repulsive force depends on the product of the positive charges on these two portions, and, as a fair approximation, this may be taken as proportional to Z^2, where Z is the positive charge, i.e., the atomic number, of the original nucleus. The binding force, on the other hand, is dependent on the number of nucleons, i.e., on the mass number A. Since an increase in the electrostatic

repulsion favors fission, whereas an increase of the binding energy opposes fission, it can be seen, in a general way, that the ease of fission will be related to Z^2/A.* The larger Z^2/A for a given nucleus, the smaller the energy which must be supplied in order to make it suffer fission; in other words, the larger the value of Z^2/A, the more easily will the nucleus undergo fission.

13.55. By means of detailed computations, based on the liquid-drop analogy, Bohr and Wheeler concluded that if Z^2/A exceeded 45, no additional energy would be necessary to cause fission of the nucleus to take place. The electrostatic repulsion would then be so great that the slightest deformation of the nucleus from the spherical shape would immediately result in its splitting into two parts. Since Z^2/A might be expected to have a value of 45 for an element having an atomic number of about 115, this would represent a definite upper limit of nuclear stability, even of temporary stability. The calculations are not exact enough to permit this maximum atomic number to be estimated with any degree of accuracy, but the general conclusion is undoubtedly correct: there is evidently a more or less definite limit of atomic number or mass number beyond which elements would be too unstable to exist for longer than about 10^{-12} sec., if they can exist at all.

13.56. For plutonium-239, the value of Z^2/A is 37.0, for uranium-233 it is 36.4, and for uranium-235 it is 36.0; these are fairly high, but they are sufficiently less than the limiting value of 45 to require appreciable activation (or deformation) energies for fission. The critical energy for uranium-235 has been calculated to be 6.1 Mev. Tantalum is the lightest element for

* The same conclusion can be reached by a more rigorous, but more complicated, treatment based on the liquid-drop model.

which fission has been observed, although 400-Mev alpha particles are necessary; for this element Z^2/A is about 29, and the critical (activation) energy is consequently large.

13.57. It will now be understood why fission does not occur with lighter elements, although it should, theoretically, lead to a more stable state. The amount of energy that would have to be supplied to the nucleus to reach the critical deformation state (Fig. 13.3, C) is very large. But even if this energy were supplied, by the use of a suitably accelerated particle, it is not certain that fission would occur, for the highly excited compound nucleus can break up in other ways, by spallation, for example. This probably accounts for the fact, mentioned in § 13.36, that fissions brought about by particles of very high energy differ from those due to neutrons of low or moderate energies.

FISSION POTENTIAL ENERGY BARRIER

13.58. An alternative point of view concerning the conditions for nuclear fission, which has some interesting aspects, makes use of a potential energy diagram, such as that in Fig. 13.4, in which the energy of the fission fragments is plotted as a function of their distance apart. The exact shape of the curve depends on the nature of the target nucleus, but the general form is as shown in the figure. At the extreme left of the diagram the fission fragments are supposed to be brought together, so that A represents the energy of the target nucleus and an incident neutron.* At the extreme right, the fission fragments are at a consider-

able distance apart, so that at D their interaction is small, approaching zero.

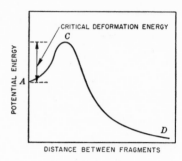

Fig. 13.4. Potential energy curve for fission, showing the critical deformation energy.

13.59. Between A and D lies a hypothetical barrier, somewhat similar to that which prevents an alpha particle, or other positively charged particle, from leaving the nucleus (§ 7.28). The top of the barrier, indicated by the point C, corresponds to the state of critical deformation of the nucleus. The curve from C to D represents the electrostatic repulsion of the nuclei produced in fission, the energy decreasing as the fragments move further apart. If the mass (or energy) conditions are such that fission is theoretically possible, that is to say, if the mass of the target nucleus plus that of the incident neutron exceeds the sum of the masses of the fission fragments, then A will lie above D, as in Fig. 13.4; the potential energy of the system at A exceeds that of the separate fission fragments at D. If the energy at A is such that it lies below D, then fission would be virtually impossible.

13.60. Suppose fission is possible, as in Fig. 13.4; then, if it is to take place,

---

* Apart from the fact that A in Fig. 13.3 represents the compound nucleus already formed, whereas in Fig. 13.4 it applies to the target nucleus and the incident neutron *before they combine*, i.e., without the binding energy of the neutron, the letters in the two figures correspond to the same conditions.

the system must pass from A to D. The obvious way for it to do so is for the incident neutron, or other particle, to supply enough energy to bring that of the resulting compound nucleus to a point lying above C. This occurs when a U^{235} nucleus takes up a slow neutron, as will be shown in the next section. If the energy gained by the entry of the incident particle is insufficient to raise the energy from A to C, as is the case, for example, with uranium-238 and a thermal neutron, then fission will not occur. However, by using neutrons of 1 Mev energy, the energy of the system is increased so that it now lies above the point C, and fission takes place.

13.61. The energy difference from A to C is the critical deformation energy, equivalent to the activation energy of a chemical reaction, and this must be supplied if fission is to occur at a measurable rate. In accordance with the discussion presented earlier, the critical energy depends on the quantity Z^2/A for the given nuclide. The larger the value of Z^2/A, the more closely will the energy at A approach that of C. If Z^2/A is sufficiently large, then the energy of the nucleus, even before taking up an incident particle, may already lie above C; if this particular nucleus were formed in some manner, it would undergo instantaneous fission.

13.62. It will be recalled that although an electrostatic potential barrier would appear to make it impossible for an alpha particle with insufficient energy to leave the nucleus of a radioactive element, there is nevertheless a certain probability that such particles, which are unable to surmount the barrier, will be expelled (§ 7.30). Somewhat similar conditions must be operative in the case of nuclear fission. Even though the nucleus

in its normal state does not have enough energy to permit it to pass through the critical deformation stage, the principles of wave mechanics require that there should be a definite probability that fission will take place. This is believed to be the cause of spontaneous fission of uranium mentioned in § 13.19. In general, the rate of spontaneous fission becomes greater as Z^2/A increases, indicating a greater probability of penetration of the potential barrier, as is to be expected.

NEUTRON ENERGY AND FISSION

13.63. According to the Bohr-Wheeler treatment, the critical deformation energy for neutron fission of uranium-238 is 7.0 Mev, compared with 6.1 Mev, as stated above, for the rarer U^{235} isotope. The difference of 0.9 Mev in favor of the latter would make this isotope more fissionable, but it alone would not account for the fact that thermal neutrons, with energy of a fraction of an electron volt, can cause fission of uranium-235, as compared with at least a million electron volts required for uranium-238. Even before any of the foregoing quantitative estimates were made, or any experimental information concerning the respective isotopes suffering fission by slow or fast neutrons was available, Bohr had predicted, in February 1939, that it was the lighter isotope, U^{235}, which was split by thermal neutrons.

13.64. The basis of his argument was that since uranium-235 has an even number of protons and an odd number of neutrons, whereas the compound nucleus formed by taking up a neutron has even numbers of both kinds of nucleons, more energy is gained by this isotope than by uranium-238, an even-even nucleus which changes into one of the even-odd type when it takes up a neutron (§ 12.82 *et seq.*). The compound nucleus formed by U^{235} and a neutron will thus be in a more energetic state than that resulting from the combination of U^{238} with a neutron; hence, Bohr argued, it is the uranium-235 isotope which is more likely to undergo fission when the nucleus takes up a slow neutron.

13.65. Actually, when the detailed calculations were made by Bohr in conjunction with Wheeler, it turned out that both the critical deformation energy and the energy gained upon the entry of the neutron were important in determining the ease of fission. The latter quantity is numerically equal to the increase in binding energy resulting from the addition of an extra neutron to the target nucleus, U^{235} or U^{238} in the cases under consideration, and hence it can be readily obtained with the aid of equation (12.6). First, the total binding energy is calculated for U^{235}, for which A is 235 and Z is 92; then, the corresponding quantity is determined for the compound nucleus formed by the addition of a neutron, which is an excited state of U^{236}, having A equal to 236 and Z to 92. The difference between these two binding energies represents the energy gained when a neutron of zero kinetic energy is taken up by a U^{235} nucleus; using equation (12.6) the result is found to be

$$\text{B.E.}(U^{236}) - \text{B.E.}(U^{235}) = 6.5 \text{ Mev.}$$

Upon repeating the calculations for U^{238}, for which A is 238 and Z is 92, and the corresponding compound nucleus (U^{239}), with A equal to 239 and Z to 92, the energy acquired when a neutron is added to the U^{238} nucleus is given by

$$\text{B.E.}(U^{239}) - \text{B.E.}(U^{238}) = 5.5 \text{ Mev.*}$$

13.66. The considerable difference between these two values is mainly due, in accordance with expectation, to the effect of the last term, that is, the spin (or odd-even) term, in equation (12.6). In the first of the foregoing cases, the term makes a positive contribution of about 0.55 Mev to the binding energy of U^{236}, but it is zero for U^{235}; in the second case, on the other hand, the contribution is zero for U^{239} but it is about 0.55 Mev positive for the U^{238} nucleus. The odd-even (or spin) effect alone is thus responsible for approximately 1.1 Mev of the difference in the energies gained by the two uranium isotopes upon the addition of a neutron.

13.67. In reviewing the results, it is seen that for the U^{238} nucleus a critical deformation energy of 7.0 Mev is necessary for fission, but it acquires only 5.5 Mev when it takes up a neutron of zero kinetic energy. Fission by thermal neutrons, with 0.03 ev energy, is thus highly improbable. It would appear that the incident neutrons would need to have at least $7.0 - 5.5 = 1.5$ Mev of additional kinetic energy to make fission of uranium-238 possible. Experiments indicate that neutrons of about 1 Mev energy are required. The discrepancy between the observed (1 Mev) and calculated (1.5 Mev) energies is, no doubt, due partly to the inexact nature of the calculations.

13.68. With uranium-235, the situation is quite different. Here the critical deformation energy for fission is 6.1 Mev, but somewhat more energy, namely, about 6.5 Mev, is made available by the capture of a slow neutron. It is evident that in this instance thermal neutrons should be capable of causing fission of the U^{235} nucleus.

---

* Slightly different results from those quoted here will be found in the literature, due to the use of somewhat different values for the empirical constants in equation (12.6).

Definite proof that it was the less common isotope of uranium, of mass number 235, which was split by slow neutrons, was obtained early in 1940 by E. T. Booth, J. R. Dunning and A. V. Grosse at Columbia University. Small samples of the separate 235 and 238 isotopes were secured, first by A. O. Nier and shortly after by K. H. Kingdon and H. C. Pollock, by the electromagnetic method, as mentioned in § 8.92. These were subjected to bombardment by slow neutrons; the uranium-235 isotope definitely suffered fission, but the heavier isotope, of mass number 238, did not.* The latter, however, could be split by fast neutrons. The establishment of these facts was of great significance in connection with the design of fission reactors for the release of nuclear energy (Chapter XIV).

13.69. Estimates made for uranium-233 and plutonium-239 show that the critical deformation energies for fission, as described above, are about 6.0 and 5.0 Mev respectively. In both cases the target nuclei contain an even number of protons and an odd number of neutrons, while the compound nucleus formed by the capture of a neutron has even numbers of both. The energy made available by the taking up of a slow neutron, as calculated by means of equation (12.6), is about 6.6 Mev in each case. Hence, thermal neutrons should be able to cause fission, as indeed they do, in both uranium-233 and plutonium-239.

13.70. Similar considerations explain the necessity for the use of high-energy neutrons to induce fission of thorium-232 ($_{90}Th^{232}$), protactinium-231 ($_{91}Pa^{231}$) and neptunium-237

($_{93}Np^{237}$). The $_{90}Th^{232}$ is an even-even nucleus, and changes to an even-odd nucleus upon taking up a neutron; the energy released in the capture of a slow neutron is thus about 5.4 Mev, as in the analogous case of uranium-238, compared with about 7 Mev for the critical deformation energy. The nuclei $_{91}Pa^{231}$ and $_{93}Np^{237}$ contain an odd number of protons and an even number of neutrons, and the addition of another neutron converts them into odd-odd nuclei, which are known to have relatively low binding energies (§ 12.96). The energy liberated in the absorption of a thermal neutron is thus 5.0 to 5.5 Mev, which is less than the minimum necessary to cause fission. In these three cases neutrons of about 1 Mev energy must be captured to produce the critical deformation leading to fission.

13.71. A general consideration of the change in various types of nuclei resulting from the addition of a neutron shows that the liberation of energy is greater if the original nucleus contains an even number of protons and an odd number of neutrons or an odd number of both, than is the case for nuclei, in the same mass region, of the odd-even or even-even types. It is to be expected that nuclei of the former group are likely to undergo fission with slow neutrons, whereas fast neutrons would be required for the latter. Thus, uranium-233, uranium-235 and plutonium-239 contain even numbers of protons and odd numbers of neutrons and are fissionable by slow neutrons. So also are the odd-odd nuclei protactinium-232, neptunium-236 and -238 and americium-242. On the other hand, for neptunium-237, with an odd

---

* Ordinary uranium contains about 0.005 per cent of a third isotope, mass number 234, which is uranium-II of the uranium disintegration series (Chapter V). This isotope will not undergo slow-neutron fission, and because of its small abundance its presence can be ignored here.

number of protons and an even number of neutrons, and for thorium-232 and uranium-238, which are of the even-even type, fast neutrons are necessary to induce fission.

PRODUCTS OF NUCLEAR FISSION

PROPERTIES OF FISSION PRODUCTS

13.72. A knowledge of the physical properties and the chemical nature of the products is important in connection with the utilization of nuclear fission as a source of energy. These subjects have consequently been given careful study. Since the primary fragments carry off most of the fission energy as kinetic energy, they have high initial velocities, in the vicinity of 10^9 cm. per sec. The actual speed of a given fragment depends on its mass, the value being somewhat greater than 10^9 cm. per sec. for the lightest nuclei and somewhat less for the heavier ones. In accordance with their high speed, the particles have appreciable penetrating power, in spite of their relatively large mass, the ranges in air varying from 1.9 cm. for the heaviest to 2.5 cm. for the lightest. The neutrons and gamma rays formed in fission, and the beta particles resulting from subsequent radioactive decay of the fission fragments have, of course, much greater penetrating power.

13.73. Another point of interest concerning the fission fragments relates to the charges they carry. Hitherto, the orbital electrons have been completely ignored, since fission is a nuclear process. The uranium atom, however, has 92 electrons, and when fission takes place it appears that about 40 of them are stripped off. Consequently, each fragment has approximately twenty electrons less than the normal atom, and hence is, effectively, an ion carrying this number of positive electric charges. Such charged particles will naturally have considerable ionizing power, as is exemplified by the use of fission chambers for the detection of neutrons (§ 11.28). As already noted, the earliest confirmation of the reality of fission came from a study of the ionization produced by the fission particles.

13.74. Since the direct fission fragments invariably have too large a proportion of neutrons for stability, they exhibit negative beta-activity. Each fragment thus initiates a short radioactive series, involving the successive emission of beta particles. Each *fission decay chain*[*] consists of three stages, on the average, although shorter and longer chains occur frequently. Referring to the possible fission fragments $_{38}Sr^{95}$ and $_{54}Xe^{139}$, indicated in § 13.24, the stable nuclides with the same mass numbers, which will ultimately be formed in a series of beta decays, are $_{42}Mo^{95}$ and $_{57}La^{139}$, respectively. In the former case four, and in the latter three, beta particles would be expelled, making a total of seven. The mean value for a number of cases is found to be just over six, so that there will be an average of about three stages per decay chain. Some examples of fission decay chains will be given below.

13.75. As seen in § 13.33, there are

---

[*] Although the term *fission chain*, without qualification, is often used to describe these radioactive series produced in fission, it is likely to cause confusion with the fission chain reaction to be considered in Chapter XIV. It is desirable, therefore, to specify that a decay chain is meant here.

more than 80 possible fission fragments, and if each initiated a chain with three stages, the fission products might include a total of something like 250 radionuclides. Hence, it is evident that the process of fission yields mixtures of very great complexity, especially as isomeric nuclei and stable end-products have not been included in the foregoing estimate. It can be seen that the problem of determining the masses and atomic numbers of the fission fragments, as well as of identifying the members of the many decay chains, is one of great difficulty. Nevertheless, as the result of persistent and painstaking work, much of which was carried out in connection with the wartime atomic energy project in the United States, more than 60 chains have been established, and over 200 different radionuclides, as well as a number of isomers, have been assigned to them.

IDENTIFICATION OF FISSION PRODUCTS

13.76. In the study of the fission products, the first step was the isolation of the different elements. For this purpose, use was made of some of the previously known methods for dealing with minute amounts of radioactive material (§ 5.29 *et seq.*), and in addition some new procedures were devised. Precipitation in the presence of a carrier was frequently employed, the latter being either a stable isotope of the desired material or a compound of an element with similar chemical properties. Because some precipitates have a marked tendency to adsorb, or to carry down with them in other ways, substances which are normally soluble, *hold-back carriers* were often added. Traces of the latter, rather than one of the fission products, were carried down by the precipitate. Extraction by means of an organic solvent and volatilization found application in certain instances. The inert gases krypton and xenon occur among the fission products, and their removal is, of course, relatively simple. Electroplating and displacement of one metal from solution by another, were also employed for separation purposes.

13.77. One of the most difficult tasks was the separation and identification of the rare-earth elements (§ 1.48), of which eight occur among the fission products. On account of the similarity of their properties, chemical separation methods are almost unknown and the tedious fractional crystallization methods, which had previously been applied to achieve a partial separation of these elements, requiring large amounts of material and long periods of time, were useless. A remarkably simple and ingenious solution to this problem was finally worked out; the procedure has had a significant influence in the study of the rare-earth elements, and also in other fields of chemistry.

13.78. It has long been known that certain minerals behave like salts of an insoluble negative (acidic) anion, which constitutes the main framework of the mineral, and a soluble positive (basic) cation. When such a mineral is in contact with a solution containing a soluble salt, the positive cation of the latter is able to exchange places with the corresponding ion in the mineral until an equilibrium is established. The phenomenon of "base exchange," familiar to soil scientists for over one hundred years, is an illustration of this behavior.

13.79. During the present century the principle of *ion exchange* has found considerable application in connection with the softening of hard waters on the large scale. The substances used for this purpose were either natural minerals, known as *zeolites* or, more commonly, artificial products resembling zeolites in composition and, in particular, in their cation exchange properties. The soluble ions in the solid zeolite are normally positive sodium ions, and if a hard water, containing calcium and magnesium salts, is passed through a column of the zeolite, an equilibrium is set up between the various cations. As a result, the sodium ions from the zeolite pass into the water while the calcium and magnesium ions are substituted in the solid. Thus, the salts of calcium and magnesium, responsible for hardness in the water, are replaced by the corresponding sodium salts which are harmless. After a time, when most of the sodium ions in the zeolite have been removed, the mineral can be regenerated by passing through it a concentrated solution of sodium chloride. Because of the high proportion of sodium ions in the solution, the establishment of equilibrium now requires these ions to enter the zeolite, replacing the calcium and magnesium ions in the spent material.

13.80. An important advance in the subject was made, during the 1930s, when it was found that certain synthetic organic resins containing acidic groups, such as a carboxyl (—COOH), a phenolic (—OH) or a sulphonic acid (—SO₃H) group, exhibit cation-exchange properties.* Such resins, notably of the Amberlite and Dowex types, are manufactured in the United States and have found various applications in industry, for the purification of water and for other purposes requiring the removal of ions from solution.

13.81. Starting in 1942, largely due to the suggestions of G. E. Boyd and W. E. Cohn and their respective associates, working in connection with the wartime nuclear fission project (Chapter XIV), a procedure was developed for the separation and purification of the rare-earth elements, in particular, by means of ion-exchange resins. The method, which is based on certain principles used in the chromatographic adsorption process of separating complex organic compounds, is somewhat as follows.

13.82. A solution containing the salts of the elements to be studied, obtained by a preliminary precipitation from the fission product mixture, is passed through a column packed with small particles of the solid resin. As a result the rare-earth ions are almost entirely removed from the solution, being taken up by the top layers of the resin. A solution containing a substance capable of forming complexes of varying stability with the several ions to be separated, commonly known as a *complexing agent*, is then allowed to flow slowly down the column of resin. Most of the data reported so far for separation of the rare-earth ions are based on the use of a solution of ammonium citrate adjusted to a suitable acidity, that is, to the optimum pH value, by means of citric acid. Solutions of oxalic acid have also been employed, particularly to separate zirconium and niobium, which are not rare earths.

13.83. As the complexing agent percolates through the column, there is a competition between the solid resin and the citrate ions in solution for the rare-earth ions. The ionic species forming the most stable complexes with the citrate is extracted (or eluted) preferentially, so that this is found, to the virtual exclusion of the

---

* Synthetic anion-exchange resins are also known, and have useful properties; they need not, however, be considered here.

other ions, in the first solution to leave the column. As the procedure continues, and the first ion is removed almost completely, another ion is eluted, and so on, the order in which the rare-earth ions are extracted being the reverse of their atomic numbers. In fact, it has been claimed that in a mixture of radioisotopes of the rare-earth ions the atomic number of a specific ion can be determined from a curve giving the elution yield, ascertained from the radioactivity, against the volume of the solution emerging from the column. The fundamental principles of the extraction process are quite complicated, but the actual technique is remarkably simple, especially in view of the striking results obtained.*

13.84. No matter what procedure is used in the separation of the fission products, two tests of purity are invariably employed. One is to study the rate of beta decay by means of a nuclear-particle counter, to see if it follows the familiar logarithmic equation (§ 5.35). If the decay is not simple, the presence of an impurity, which may possibly be the daughter element, is indicated. An analysis of the decay curve, especially after further purification, often provides useful information. The second test for the effectiveness of the separation is to examine the absorption of the beta particles by aluminum foils (§ 7.5); from the shape of the absorption curve certain conclusions can be drawn concerning the number of components present.

13.85. Once a product has been identified, from the fact that its char-

acteristic radioactivity follows the chemistry of a known element with which it is isotopic, a search is made for a possible radioactive parent, for this will be an element with an atomic number one unit less. In the course of time, too, a daughter element, with an atomic number one unit higher, will accumulate. In this way evidence is gradually collected which makes possible the establishment of a decay chain starting with a direct fission fragment and ending with a known stable nuclide. A check on the correctness of the results is often provided by the half lives which must fall into a more or less definite order, as explained in § 12.99 *et seq.*, according as the mass numbers are odd or even.

13.86. Since all the members of a given beta-decay chain are isobaric with one another, each chain has a definite mass number. The assignment of the proper mass number is a matter of some importance, and often of difficulty. One possibility is to show that a particular product is the same as a radioactive nuclide which has been obtained in an unequivocal manner, in one of the ways described in Chapter X. A good illustration is provided by the chain of which one of the members is a 40-hr. radioisotope of lanthanum. There is probably only one stable form of this element, of mass number 139, which is known to undergo an (n,γ) reaction to yield a 40-hr. isotope; the mass number of the latter must be 140, and so this is also the mass number of the chain under consideration.

13.87. Some use has also been made of the mass spectrograph to assign

---

* A significant development of the ion-exchange method for the separation of the rare-earth elements, due to F. H. Spedding and his associates at Iowa State College, is the production of gram, and sometimes even of kilogram, quantities of these elements with a high degree of purity. One of the consequences is the availability for research of compounds of lanthanum, cerium, praseodymium, neodymium, samarium, gadolinium, ytterbium and yttrium in amounts, and of a purity, that had previously been inconceivable.

mass numbers. The procedure for recognizing the stable end-products is quite straightforward, especially if these are gaseous, such as krypton and xenon. An ingenious modification of the method has been devised for the study of radioactive substances by A. J. Dempster and his associates at the University of Chicago. A mass-spectrograph record is obtained on a plate, in the ordinary way, and this is placed in contact with an undeveloped photographic film. The beta particles emitted by the active product affects the latter, and so the mass position can be readily located in the presence of other substances. If two or more active species should happen to be present, they can be identified by the rate of decay of the activities deposited on the plate of the mass spectrograph.

13.88. As seen in Fig. 13.2, the plot of the fission yield against the mass number is a continuous smooth curve,* and, consequently, the mass number of a particular product can be determined from the fission yield, especially in regions where the fission yield curve has a steep slope. The rate at which a given quantity of material undergoes fission can be readily ascertained by counting the fission fragments in an ionization chamber; suppose this is found to be f nuclei per second. After fission has taken place continuously for a period that is long in comparison with the half life of a given product or of any of its precursors, the amount of the product will have reached an equilibrium or steady state value, when the rate of decay is equal to the rate of its formation (§ 5.42).

13.89. If, for a particular mass number, y is the fission yield, expressed as a fraction of the total number of fissions, the rate of formation of the product is fy nuclei per second, and the rate of decay, as measured by the steady state activity, or *saturation activity*, will consequently have the same value. The saturation activity can be measured by means of a suitable counter, and since the fission rate f is known, the yield y can be calculated. This result can then be utilized to confirm or to assign the mass number.

FISSION DECAY CHAINS

13.90. By piecing together evidence obtained in various ways, it has been possible to draw definite conclusions concerning the identities of the fission fragments and the products of their radioactive decay. Some of the results obtained have already been described, and a few others of special interest will be mentioned here. As stated above, there are, on the average, three stages of beta emission in each fission decay chain, although most chains are either longer or shorter. The shortest chains, involving one or two stages, generally occur at the beginning and end of both light and heavy groups; the longest chains are found around the middle of each group, where the fission yields are high (Fig. 13.2). One of the longest series of disintegrations among the lighter fission products is that of mass number 97; thus,

$$_{36}Kr^{97} \xrightarrow{\text{short}} {}_{37}Rb^{97} \xrightarrow{\text{short}} {}_{38}Sr^{97} \xrightarrow{\text{short}} {}_{39}Y^{97} \xrightarrow{\text{short}}$$

$$_{40}Zr^{97} \xrightarrow{17 \text{ h.}} {}_{41}Cb^{97} \xrightarrow{74 \text{ m.}} {}_{42}Mo^{97} \text{ (stable)}.$$

* The fission yields of certain (magic number) nuclei with closed nucleon shells (§ 12.106) apparently do not fall on the curve, but lie above it.

13.91. A long chain in the heavy group is the one of mass number 143; thus,

$$_{54}Xe^{143} \xrightarrow{1 \text{ s.}} {}_{55}Cs^{143} \xrightarrow{\text{short}} {}_{56}Ba^{143} \xrightarrow{\text{short}} {}_{57}La^{143} \xrightarrow{19 \text{ m.}}$$

$$_{58}Ce^{143} \xrightarrow{32 \text{ h.}} {}_{59}Pr^{143} \xrightarrow{13.7 \text{ d.}} {}_{60}Nd^{143} \text{ (stable)}.$$

13.92. One other chain worthy of mention is that of mass number 140, namely,

$$_{54}Xe^{140} \xrightarrow{16 \text{ s.}} {}_{55}Cs^{140} \xrightarrow{66 \text{ s.}} {}_{56}Ba^{140} \xrightarrow{12.8 \text{ d.}} {}_{57}La^{140} \xrightarrow{40 \text{ h.}} {}_{58}Ce^{140} \text{ (stable)},$$

because the 12.8-day Ba^{140} was the product, resulting from the action of neutrons on uranium, which Hahn and Strassmann originally called "radium," and which they later found to be separable from radium but inseparable from barium (§ 13.7).

13.93. The chains of mass number 99 and 147 are of particular interest because they have as members fairly long-lived isotopes of the elements of atomic numbers 43 and 61, respectively, whose existence in nature is doubtful (§ 12.102 *et seq.*). The chain of mass number 99 is

$$_{42}Mo^{99} \xrightarrow{67 \text{ h.}} 43^{99} \xrightarrow{2 \times 10^5 \text{ y.}} {}_{44}Ru^{99} \text{ (stable)},$$

in which the nuclide of atomic number 43 has a half life of about 200,000 years. This, incidentally, happens to be the active species of longest life that has thus far been found as a product of uranium fission. The mass-number 99 isotope of element-43 is at present available in appreciable quantities and in almost pure form. The element of atomic number 61 is obtained in the decay chain.

$$_{60}Nd^{147} \xrightarrow{11 \text{ d.}} 61^{147} \xrightarrow{2.5 \text{ y.}} {}_{62}Sm^{147}.$$

This 2.5-yr. nuclide of mass number 147 is one of the longest-lived isotopes of element-61. Further consideration will be given to these elements in Chapter XVI.

13.94. Among the fission products, there have been detected small amounts of the nuclides $_{35}Br^{82}$, $_{37}Rb^{86}$ and $_{55}Cs^{136}$; these are of interest because they are examples of shielded nuclides (§ 12.98 footnote). Each of these species has two stable isobars with atomic numbers higher and lower by one unit, respectively; thus $_{35}Br^{82}$, for example, is "shielded" by the stable nuclides $_{34}Se^{82}$ and $_{36}Kr^{82}$. The significance of this situation is that Br^{82} and the other shielded nuclides cannot be the products of beta decay, either positive or negative, for the positions which would have to be occupied by the radioactive parents are already filled by stable species. It follows, therefore, that the shielded nuclides observed among the fission products are either primary fission fragments, or else they result from the expulsion of prompt neutrons by highly excited nuclei formed as a result of the splitting of the uranium nucleus (§ 13.41).

13.95. In conclusion, it may be pointed out that the fission of uranium has made available a large number of radioactive nuclides which could not be obtained by the ordinary bombardment procedures. The neutron-to-proton ratios of the products formed in the latter manner are not very different from those of the stable elements. Because of the high neutron-to-proton ratio in uranium, however, the products of fission have much higher values of this ratio than could be obtained in any other known way, at least in anything like the quantities at present available. Certain of these nuclides may prove to have practical value, but in any event, by extending the range of information available they are helping to solve some of the outstanding problems of nuclear structure.

The Utilization of Nuclear Energy

Chapter XIV

ENERGY FROM NUCLEAR FISSION

THE CONCEPT OF ATOMIC ENERGY

14.1. The conception of the atom as a possible source of energy developed at the turn of the century, mainly as a result of the discovery of radioactivity. The fact that certain atoms could spontaneously eject electrically charged particles capable of producing ionization and affecting a photographic plate meant that energy was being liberated. The question then was: What is the source of this energy? Two different points of view were evidently being given consideration, for in a somewhat noncommittal paper published in 1902, Pierre and Marie Curie wrote: "Each atom of a radioactive substance functions as a constant source of energy.* . . . In seeking to specify the origin of the energy of radioactivity, various suppositions can be made which group themselves into two general hypotheses: first, each radioactive atom possesses in a state of potential (internal) energy the energy which it releases;

second, the radioactive atom is a mechanism which continuously derives from outside itself the energy which it gives off."

14.2. The possibility that a radio-element might have the property of extracting energy from its surroundings or from external radiation, and that this energy was utilized to eject alpha and beta particles, received support, notably from W. Crookes and from Lord Kelvin, in spite of the fact that it appeared to contradict the second law of thermodynamics. But it was the alternative suggestion, that radioactive energy represented internal energy of the atom itself, which was favored by H. Becquerel and, especially, by E. Rutherford and F. Soddy, and this view met with general approval.

14.3. Incidentally, it was in the course of a discussion of the energy of radioactive change that Rutherford and Soddy made the suggestion that all atoms, and not only radioactive

---

* The Curies were misled into thinking the source of energy remained constant because, as they said, "experiments of several years show that for uranium, thorium, radium and probably also for actinium . . . the activity does not vary with time." The elements mentioned have, of course, relatively long half lives, so that no variation in activity was observed during the course of a few years.

413

atoms, possess large amounts of energy. Writing in 1903, they said: "All these considerations point to the conclusion that the energy latent in the [radioactive] atom must be enormous compared with that rendered free in ordinary chemical change. Now the radioelements differ in no way from other elements in their chemical and physical behaviour. . . . Hence there is no reason to assume that this enormous store of energy is possessed by the radio-elements alone. It seems probable that atomic energy in general is of a similar, high order of magnitude, although the absence of [radioactive] change prevents its existence being manifested."

14.4. In 1904, the famous English mathematical physicist and astronomer, J. H. Jeans, suggested an explanation of radioactive energy which was later proved to have a germ of truth, although it was based on the erroneous idea that all mass is electromagnetic in origin. "The mutual annihilation of two ether strains [electrical charges] of opposite kinds, i.e., the coalescence of a positive and a negative ion," he wrote, "would . . . result in the disappearance of a certain amount of mass . . . [and] the process of radioactivity would consist in an increase of material energy at the expense of the destruction of a certain amount of matter." In other words, Jeans thought the energy associated with radioactivity resulted from the mutual annihilation of positive and negative charges in the atom. It is now accepted that such annihilation would certainly produce energy (§ 3.84), but it is very doubtful that radioactive energy arises in this manner.

14.5. An explanation of the energy of radioactivity and, in fact, of atomic energy in general, can be given in terms of the Einstein relationship concerning the equivalence of mass and energy (§ 3.72). The energy accompanying radioactive change is equivalent to the difference between the mass of the parent atom, on the one hand, and that of the daughter element plus the emitted particle (or particles) on the other hand. It is of interest to mention that although Einstein did not consider radioactive energy in detail, he did indicate in 1905 that a possible test of the mass-energy equation might be found in the study of radioactivity. A similar suggestion was made eight years later by R. Swinne, in Germany, who thought that the Einstein equation might be verified by accurate determinations of the atomic weights of radioelements. However, the effects to be expected would be quite small, and consequently difficult to detect, especially when working with radioactive materials.

14.6. In spite of the absence, at the time, of any direct verification of the mass-energy relationship, it seems to have influenced scientific thought on the subject of the origin of atomic energy. It was apparently realized that the energy of the atom was related to the mass changes resulting from the packing of its constituent units. In his book on *The Electron*, R. A. Millikan says: "Not long after 1905 [when the Einstein equation was published] packing fractions were discussed in many physical laboratories as a source of energy; for, although Aston's curve [Fig. 12.1] did not appear until the early twenties, the basic facts of 'atomic packing-fraction' energy were widely discussed and even quantitatively worked out for some atoms . . . long before that date."

14.7. A particular case in point is the detailed consideration of the subject by W. D. Harkins and E. D. Wilson (§ 12.2 footnote) in the United States in 1915. Basing their arguments on the postulate, which is not completely correct, that all atoms are built up from hydrogen, that is, from equal numbers of protons and electrons, they associated the stability with the accompanying loss of mass and release of the equivalent amount of energy. The energy released in the formation of a gram atom, i.e., 4.00 grams, of helium from four gram atoms of hydrogen was calculated to be nearly 10^{12} calories, compared with values of the order of 10^3 to 10^6 calories for normal chemical reactions. "Energy involved in our ordinary chemical reactions," wrote Harkins and Wilson, "is extremely small in comparison with that involved in the formation of the elements."

14.8. It may be mentioned in the same connection that in his Presidential Address to the Mathematical and Physical Sciences Section of the British Association in 1920, A. S. Eddington, the renowned astronomer and mathematician, said: "A star is drawing on some vast reservoir of energy. . . . This reservoir can scarcely be other than the sub-atomic energy which, it is known, exists abundantly in all matter; we sometimes dream that man will one day learn how to release it and use it for his service." He then went on to suggest that the energy is liberated in the stars as a result of the combination of hydrogen atoms to form the atoms of more complex elements, helium, in particular.

14.9. The publication of Aston's packing fraction curve (§ 12.3) in 1927 revived interest in the problem of atomic energy, but the discussion remained somewhat academic until the early 1930s when the development of various methods for accelerating charged particles (Chapter IX) led to the discovery of nuclear reactions accompanied by the release of large amounts of energy. These processes differed from radioactivity in the respect that they could be deliberately controlled, and were not restricted to elements of high mass number.

14.10. Nevertheless, they offered little prospect for the practical utilization of atomic energy. The reason may be given in the words of Rutherford, as expressed in his lectures on *The Newer Alchemy*, published in 1937: "The energy release in the transformation of an atom of lithium by deuterons [in the $Li^6(d,\alpha)He^4$ reaction] is 22.5 million [electron] volts, nearly twice as great as the energy emitted during the disintegration of any radioactive atom. Since transformation can be produced by a deuteron of energy 20,000 volts, it is clear that there is a large gain of energy in the individual process. On the other hand, only about one deuteron in 10^8 is effective, so that on the whole far more energy is supplied than is emitted as a result of the transformation. . . . [Consequently,] the outlook for gaining useful energy by artificial processes of transformation does not look promising."

14.11. In his Sigma Xi lectures on *Atoms, New and Old*, delivered in 1938, E. O. Lawrence (see § 9.53) expressed his views on the prospect of utilizing atomic energy as follows: "Whether it will be possible to release subatomic energy on a practical and profitable basis . . . [is a question] . . . of interest to everyone, and accordingly this has been a subject for much popular discussion and speculation. The fact is, at this time, that although we now know that matter can be converted into energy, we are aware of no greater prospect of destroying nuclear matter for power purposes than of cooling the ocean . . . and extracting the heat for profitable work. . . . The establishment of the great principle of mass-energy equivalence is, however, a keystone in the development of physical theory."

NUCLEAR FISSION AS A SOURCE OF ENERGY

14.12. Early in 1939, the outlook concerning the possibility of converting mass into energy was suddenly changed by the discovery of nuclear fission (Chapter XIII). In the fission of uranium a thermal neutron, with energy of about 0.03 ev, releases about 200 Mev, so that several billion times as much energy is produced as is carried by the incident particle. But, the importance of nuclear fission does not lie in this fact alone. The essential point is that the process is accompanied by the liberation of neutrons which are capable of causing fission of other uranium nuclei (§ 13.37); these can produce more neutrons which cause further fission and so on. Thus, in principle, a single neutron could start off a branching chain of fissions, the number of nuclei involved increasing at a tremendous rate.

14.13. Suppose, for simplicity, that for each nucleus suffering fission two neutrons are liberated; if each of these causes fission, with the release of two neutrons in each case, there will be four neutrons available. These could induce fission in four more uranium nuclei, accompanied by the emission of eight neutrons, the chain continuing, in theory, until no more fissionable nuclei remain.

14.14. The fission process would thus differ from other nuclear reactions in a highly significant respect: whereas, in the latter cases each incident particle causes the transmutation of a single nucleus only, in the former, one neutron could, conceivably, lead to the fission of all the uranium in the target. The original neutron would thus act like a match applied to combustible material; the heat of the match flame causes part of the material to burn, and the resulting heat induces combustion of other portions, until the whole is consumed and its energy liberated. Combustion is thus a thermal (or heat) chain process. In fission, however, the chain is maintained by neutrons.

14.15. Before proceeding further with a discussion of the possibilities of nuclear fission, it is of interest to calculate the amount of energy involved in terms of units more familiar to the engineer than are those of the physicist. It was seen in § 3.33 that 1 Mev is equivalent to 1.60×10^{-6} erg, so that the approximately 200 Mev liberated in a single fission is equal to 3.20×10^{-4} erg, which is 3.20×10^{-11} watt-sec.* It consequently requires 3.1×10^{10} fissions to release 1 watt-sec. of energy; in other words, fissions at the rate of 3.1×10^{10} per sec. produce 1 watt of power.

14.16. If the energy released per fission is multiplied by the Avogadro number, 6.02×10^{23} (§ 1.60), the result, $6.02 \times 10^{23} \times 3.20 \times 10^{-4} = 1.93 \times 10^{20}$ ergs, or 1.93×10^{13} watt-sec., is the energy liberated in the fission of 1 gram atom,† i.e., of 235 grams of uranium-235, 233 grams of uranium-

---

* The *watt* is a unit of power, i.e., a rate of production or expenditure of energy, equal to 10^7 ergs per sec.; a kilowatt is 1000 watts. Other practical units frequently used are the horse-power, which is 746 watts, and the British Thermal Unit (B.T.U.) of energy, which is 0.293 watt-hours.

† One gram atom, i.e., the atomic weight in grams, contains 6.02×10^{23} individual atoms (or nuclei), this being the Avogadro number.

233 or 239 grams of plutonium-239. Neglecting the small mass difference between the three fissionable species, it follows that the complete fission of 1 gram releases 8.2×10^{17} ergs, which is 8.2×10^{10} watt-sec. or 8.2×10^7 kilowatt-sec.; this is equivalent to $8.2 \times 10^7/3600 = 2.3 \times 10^4$ kilowatt-hours, or $2.3 \times 10^4/24 = 0.96 \times 10^3$ kilowatt-days. The power production corresponding to the fission of 1 gram of uranium or plutonium per day would thus be 0.96×10^3 kilowatts or roughly 1000 kilowatts, i.e., 1 million watts or 1 megawatt. To obtain the same amount of heat by combustion would require more than 3 tons of coal or nearly 700 gallons of fuel oil. This comparison shows the much larger order of magnitude of nuclear energy as compared with chemical energy (§ 12.9).

The Nuclear Chain Reaction

14.17. The possibility of a *nuclear chain reaction* accompanying the fission of uranium by neutrons was considered in March 1939 by H. von Halban, F. Joliot and L. Kowarski in France, by E. Fermi in the United States, and undoubtedly by other physicists both in Europe and America. If such a chain reaction could be actually realized, then there was some prospect that the release of atomic energy or, more correctly, nuclear energy,* might become a practical and economic possibility. Naturally, the subject attracted widespread and enthusiastic interest in the world of science, but there was one aspect which was the subject of serious consideration. If the fission energy were liberated in a short time interval, as it might well be, since nuclear processes are rapid, the chain reaction might lead to a catastrophic explosion.†

14.18. If, as suggested above, the number of neutrons, and hence of nuclei undergoing fission, is doubled in each generation, then starting with a single neutron the numbers would increase steadily, thus, 1, 2, 4, 8, 16, 32, 64, . . . In eighty generations there would be 10^{24} neutrons present in the system, sufficient to cause the fission of every uranium nucleus in more than a gram atom, i.e., in about 240 grams, of uranium. The total energy released would then be equivalent to about 5 million kilowatt-hours—triggered by a single neutron with a negligible amount of energy!

14.19. The time required for the actual fission process is very small, and so the interval between successive generations would be determined by the time taken for a free neutron to be captured by a uranium nucleus. Supposing this to be about 10^{-8} sec. for a fast neutron, then, the eightieth generation, in which 10^{24} neutrons were formed, would be attained in less than

---

* Since the energy of fission is actually due to a decrease of nuclear mass, resulting from a rearrangement of protons and neutrons, it should strictly be called *nuclear energy*. Nevertheless, the general, historical name "atomic energy," which is widely used, although not quite so precise, is justifiable because the nucleus is part of the atom.

† As far back as 1934, the Hungarian-born physicist, L. Szilard, then resident in England, conceived the idea of a neutron chain based on the reaction $Be^9(n, 2n) Be^8$ (or $2He^4$), in which one neutron is captured and two are released, accompanied by the liberation of energy. In the following year, a patent application was filed in England, part being classified as secret and assigned to the British Government. The reason for the secrecy was Szilard's conviction that, if a nuclear chain reaction were possible, it could be used to produce violent explosions. Although the general ideas were correct, it is now known that a neutron chain reaction with beryllium is not possible. The reason is that neutrons of high energy are required for the $(n, 2n)$ reaction, but the neutrons liberated have relatively low energies, so that a chain could not be maintained.

a millionth part of a second. The release of an enormous amount of energy in such a short interval of time would result in a tremendous explosion. It should be borne in mind, however, that this energy calculation has been based on the postulate that every neutron liberated in the fission of each uranium nucleus goes on to produce fission in other nuclei. Actually, as will be explained below, a proportion of the neutrons are absorbed in non-fission capture processes, while others escape from the system altogether. The situation is, therefore, not as simple as has been implied; nevertheless, provided the loss of neutrons is not too great, the possibility of a chain reaction and of an explosion still exists.

14.20. In general, during the early months of 1939, scientists were divided into two camps: those who doubted the feasibility of a nuclear chain reaction, on the one hand, and those, on the other hand, who considered a fission chain possible, although it would not necessarily lead to an explosion. It was thought that if a uranium salt were dissolved in water, the fast neutrons which are formed in fission would be slowed down so that the rate of the propagation of the nuclear fission chain would be diminished; thus the chance of an explosion would be lessened. Further, it was suggested by F. Adler and H. von Halban and, independently, by F. Perrin in France that the introduction into the uranium-water system of a substance like cadmium, which is a strong absorber of slow neutrons (§ 11.98), would permit the chain reaction to be controlled. The removal of sufficient neutrons would obviously interfere with the propagation of the chain and could even stop it completely.

Possibility of an Atom Bomb

14.21. The foregoing ideas were largely based on speculation; it was clear that further experimental data were necessary before any definite conclusions could be reached. It appeared reasonably certain that while a devastating explosion could be avoided, by the use of water or other material to slow down the neutrons, and by including in the system a substance with a high cross section for absorption of slow neutrons, it could not be stated definitely that the conditions for fission chain propagation could be established. However, by the middle of 1940, sufficient information had been accumulated that made it seem not unlikely that under appropriate conditions the chain reaction could be controlled, by the use of slow neutrons. Alternatively, a fast-neutron fission chain might be made to take place with extreme rapidity thus making possible an atomic energy bomb, generally referred to as an *atomic bomb*, of tremendous power.[*]

14.22. In view of this prospect, it was decided, in the interest of national security, to withhold the publication of any discoveries relating to nuclear fission. As seen in Chapter XIII, it was then generally known that uranium-235, the isotope present to the extent of only 0.72 per cent, i.e., one part in 139, in ordinary uranium, is fissionable by slow (thermal) neutrons, and to a lesser extent by fast neutrons, the fission cross section of the neutrons decreasing as their speed or energy increases. The most abundant uranium isotope, of mass num-

---

[*] The detailed history of the project which led to the production of such bombs is given by H. D. Smyth in his report on *Atomic Energy for Military Purposes* (see § 8.83 footnote). The report covers the material in § 14.12 through § 14.84 of this chapter.

ber 238, however, does not undergo fission with slow neutrons, but does so when subjected to the action of fast neutrons. It was also known in 1939 that, for each uranium-235 nucleus suffering fission by slow neutrons there are expelled between two and three neutrons of high energy; the largest proportion of these are the prompt neutrons emitted virtually simultaneously with the fission process, but a small fraction, about 0.75 per cent, are delayed neutrons.

14.23. These facts all had a bearing on the practicability of the nuclear chain reaction; in addition, by the end of 1940 or early 1941, other information of considerable significance came to light. The uranium-238 nucleus was known to have an appreciable cross section for the resonance capture of slow neutrons of 5 to 100 ev energy, leading to the formation, by the (n,γ) process, of uranium-239 (§ 11.49). Consequently, although uranium-238 would not suffer fission when exposed to slow neutrons, it could capture some of the neutrons in the system and thus interfere with the propagation of the fission chain of uranium-235. It is probable that slow neutrons would produce fission in uranium-239, but this artificial isotope has a half life of only 23.5 minutes, decaying with the emission of a negative beta-particle to form neptunium-239. The latter is also beta-active, its half life being 2.3 days, yielding as product the highly important, long-lived, artificial nuclide, plutonium-239; as seen in Chapter XIII, this substance undergoes fission with slow, and hence also with fast, neutrons.[*]

14.24. Although uranium-238 is fissionable by fast neutrons, it did not seem probable that a fast-neutron fission chain could be maintained either in this material or in natural uranium. In addition to the nonfission capture of neutrons by uranium-238, there is another, more important, reason for this situation. As a result of inelastic collisions with uranium (§ 11.61), the energy of the fission neutrons is very rapidly reduced to below 1 Mev, when they are no longer able to cause appreciable fission in uranium-238. On the other hand, uranium-235 is fissionable by neutrons of all energies; even if the fast neutrons accompanying fission are slowed down to some extent, the fission chain can still be maintained. Hence, uranium considerably enriched in the isotope of mass number 235 might be used in the so-called atomic bomb. Since there is a loss of neutrons by escape from the exterior surface, the relative importance of which decreases with increasing size, it appeared that a certain minimum quantity of fissionable material would be necessary if the chain propagation, leading to an explosion, was to be maintained (§ 14.79). Preliminary estimates indicated that this minimum might be somewhere between 1 and 100 kilograms of pure uranium-235.

14.25. According to the calculations in § 14.16, the energy liberated by the complete fission of 1 kilogram, i.e., 2.2 pounds, of uranium-235 would be approximately 8.2×10^{20} ergs (or 2×10^{10} kilocalories), which is roughly equivalent to the energy developed in the explosion of 20,000 tons of T.N.T. In view of the tremendous potentialities of an atomic (nuclear energy) bomb, even if only a few per cent of its energy could be released explosively, it appeared desirable, in spite of the obvious difficulties of the task,

[*] The properties of neptunium, plutonium and other true transuranium elements will be described in more detail in Chapter XVI.

to consider the prospects for the large-scale separation of uranium-235 from ordinary uranium. An investigation of the problem was initiated in the summer of 1940; several methods were tried out, as mentioned in Chapter VIII, of which the gaseous diffusion procedure with uranium hexafluoride proved to be the most successful.

14.26. Simultaneously with the interest in the separation of uranium-235, a study was made of plutonium-239 which was obtained as a result of the action of neutrons on the abundant uranium-238 isotope, as stated above. Since plutonium was believed to be fissionable by both slow and fast neutrons, it was realized that it might provide an alternative to uranium-235 for use in an atomic bomb. Hence, consideration was given to the feasibility of producing plutonium in appreciable amounts. This matter is connected with the problem of the operation of a controlled chain reacting system, and so it will be examined more fully in § 14.63 *et seq.*

THE NUCLEAR CHAIN-REACTING SYSTEM

CONDITIONS FOR CONTROLLED CHAIN REACTION

14.27. In order to ascertain whether a controlled slow-neutron chain reaction was feasible, it was first necessary to decide upon a suitable substance to reduce the speed of the neutrons, that is, to act as a moderator (§ 11.36). From preliminary experiments, made by H. von Halban and his associates in France, it appeared that a chain reaction might be maintained with slow neutrons and a solution of a uranium salt in ordinary water. It was soon realized, however, that the relatively large cross section for the absorption of slow neutrons by hydrogen rules out the use of water as a moderator, at least with uranium containing the usual proportions of the isotope of mass number 235.

14.28. Of the other substances mentioned in Chapter XI as possible moderators, heavy water (deuterium oxide) and carbon appeared to offer the best prospects. Beryllium would have been suitable, but there seemed little hope of obtaining adequate amounts in pure form. The French workers evidently decided to experiment with heavy water,* but in the United States, at the suggestion of E. Fermi and L. Szilard, efforts were concentrated on carbon, in the form of graphite, as a moderator, because of its availability. At the same time steps were taken, in conjunction with Canadian scientists, to speed the large-scale production of heavy water (§ 8.117). However, because of the successful results obtained with graphite, and also because of the convenience of using a solid moderator, heavy water played a relatively minor role in the wartime atomic energy project. Since it has many advantages as a moderator, it has been extensively employed in later years.

14.29. During the war, German scientists, directed by W. Heisenberg

---

*In June 1940, when France fell, von Halban and Kowarski escaped to England with about 160 liters of heavy water which had been obtained from Norway. This was insufficient for a chain reaction to be realized, but apparently enough data were obtained with it by the end of 1940 to indicate that a uranium-heavy water system would maintain a fission chain. However, even before any reliable information was available, the National Center for Scientific Research, an agency of the French Government, filed an application on May 1, 1939 for a Swiss patent on a nuclear reactor using heavy water as moderator.

(see § 3.46), tried a system consisting of a large number of uranium metal cubes, total weight 1.5 tons, suspended in a tank containing 1.5 tons of heavy water, with a graphite reflector. According to Heisenberg, this was still too small to maintain a fission chain. But, before any increase in the amount of uranium was possible, the village of Haigerloch, where the later experiments were being conducted in a cellar cut out of solid rock, was occupied by U. S. troops on April 22, 1945.

14.30. For the maintenance of a chain reaction it is not necessary that every neutron produced in fission should be able to initiate another fission. The minimum condition is that for each nucleus undergoing fission there shall be produced, on the average, at least one neutron which causes fission of another nucleus. This condition is conveniently expressed in terms of a *multiplication factor* or *reproduction factor* of the system, defined as the ratio of the number of neutrons of any one generation to the number in the immediately preceding generation. If the multiplication factor, represented by k, is exactly equal to, or somewhat greater than, unity a chain reaction will be possible, but if k is less than unity, even by a very small amount, the chain cannot be maintained. Suppose, for example, a particular generation starts with 100 neutrons; if the multiplication factor is unity, there will be 100 neutrons at the beginning of the second generation, 100 at the third, and so on. Once it has started, the fission will continue at the same rate as at the commencement.

14.31. If k is greater than unity, say, 1.05, it would be possible to start with 100 neutrons, which would produce 100×1.05, i.e., 105 at the commencement of the second generation;

105 × 1.05 at the third; and, in general, $100 \times (1.05)^{n-1}$ at the nth generation. This would mean, with n equal to 100, for example, that the hundredth generation would start with about 13,000 neutrons. A few neutrons could thus initiate a rapidly growing chain of fissions; to prevent such a chain from going out of control, a neutron absorber could be introduced into the system. On the other hand, if the multiplication factor were less than unity, 0.95 for instance, the number of neutrons would be reduced from 100 at the beginning to 95 at the commencement of the second generation, 95×0.95 at the third, and so on. At the start of the hundredth generation there would be, on the average, less than one neutron available for fission. It is obvious, therefore, that the chain cannot be propagated under these conditions.

14.32. The value of the multiplication factor in any system consisting of uranium and a moderator depends on the relative extents to which the neutrons take part in four main processes. These are: (a) complete loss of neutrons by escaping from the system; (b) nonfission capture, as a result of the (n,γ) reaction with uranium-238, the abundant isotope; (c) nonfission capture, often referred to as *parasitic capture*, by the moderator and by various extraneous substances, such as impurities in the uranium and in the moderator, and by fission products; and, finally, (d) fission capture of slow neutrons by uranium-235, or of fast neutrons by both uranium-238 and uranium-235. In all four of these processes neutrons are removed from the system, but other neutrons are generated in the fourth process, i.e., the fission reaction, to replace them. Hence, if the number of neutrons produced in the latter process exceeds the total number lost by escape and by fission and nonfission capture, there will be a net gain of neutrons in each generation. The multiplication factor will then exceed unity and a chain reaction should be possible, at least in principle.

14.33. Several procedures have been suggested for calculating the multiplication factor for a given uranium-moderator system. The most straightforward of these is the one proposed by E. Fermi and developed by himself, and by E. P. Wigner and others associated with the wartime atomic energy project in the United States. It is not possible here to do more than outline the general approach to the problem.

THE INFINITE MEDIUM MULTIPLICATION FACTOR

14.34. Of the four neutron processes mentioned in § 14.32, the last three, namely, (b), (c) and (d), are dependent only upon the composition of the chain-reacting system, i.e., upon the nature of the materials present, their relative amounts and their arrangement. The first process, that is, the escape of neutrons, frequently referred to as *neutron leakage*, is influenced, however, by the geometry, i.e., by the size and shape of the system. It is convenient, therefore, to divide the multiplication factor into two parts, one of which is a property of the materials and the other of the geometry. The former is called the *infinite medium multiplication factor* and is represented by the symbol k_∞. It is defined as the ratio of the number of neutrons of any one generation to the number in the immediately preceding generation in a system of infinite size. Hence, in view of the definition of the multiplaction factor k in § 14.30, it is seen that k_∞ is the value

in a system so large that there is no loss of neutrons by leakage. It is then possible to write

$$k = k_\infty P,$$

where P, called the *nonleakage probability*, depends upon the geometry; it is the probability that fission neutrons will remain in the system of finite size and not escape before being absorbed. In order to distinguish the two factors k and k_∞, the former is generally known as the *effective* multiplication factor.

14.35. A convenient way of expressing the infinite medium multiplication factor, in terms of measurable or calculable quantities, is to consider the fate of any particular generation of neutrons. Suppose that n fast neutrons are present in the system at the beginning of this generation, in a system consisting of natural uranium and a moderator, such as graphite. Before their velocity is decreased appreciably, a few of these neutrons will cause fission of uranium-238 nuclei, and also, in view of their smaller proportion, of a negligible number of uranium-235 nuclei. Since more than one fast neutron is liberated in each act of fission, this will result in a slight increase in the number of available neutrons. Allowance for the effect may be made by multiplying n by a quantity ϵ, which is called the *fast fission factor*, having a value slightly in excess of unity, frequently about 1.03.

14.36. As the $n\epsilon$ neutrons move through the uranium-moderator system, they will undergo many elastic collisions with nuclei of the moderator (graphite), and inelastic collisions with uranium nuclei, as a result of which their energy, and speed, is rapidly decreased. While they are slowing down through the resonance region of uranium-238, which extends from about 6 to 200 ev, there is a chance that some neutrons will be captured. Allowance for this can be made by means of a factor p, named the *resonance escape probability*. It is always less than unity, and is a measure of the probability that any fast neutron will reach the thermal region without suffering nonfission capture. Consequently, $n\epsilon p$ is the number of fast neutrons, compared with the n originally entering the system, which survive thermalization by the moderator. The value of p, as will be seen below, depends largely on the relative proportions of the graphite and uranium in the system, as well as upon their arrangement. When the energy of the neutrons has been reduced to the thermal region, they will diffuse in the moderator, the distribution of energy remaining essentially constant (§ 11.39), until they are ultimately absorbed either by the uranium, by the graphite or by any impurities or other substances which may be present. If f, referred to as the *thermal utilization factor*, is the fraction of the thermal neutrons taken up by uranium nuclei, some of which undergo fission, it follows that $n\epsilon pf$ represents the number of neutrons involved in this process. The thermal utilization factor, like the resonance escape probability, is governed by the composition of the uranium-graphite mixture, and also by its arrangement.

14.37. Finally, let η be the average number of *fast* neutrons produced by fission for each thermal neutron absorbed by the uranium, then $n\epsilon pf\eta$ is the number of fast neutrons produced as the result of the admission of the n original neutrons to the system. The n fast neutrons of the first generation have thus produced $n\epsilon pf\eta$ similar neutrons of the second generation, so that the infinite medium multiplication fac-

tor k_∞ is, according to its definition, given by

$$k_\infty = \frac{n\epsilon pf\eta}{n} = \epsilon pf\eta. \quad (14.1)$$

In the design of a self-sustaining, chain reacting system it is necessary, as seen above, to make it practical for this quantity to be somewhat greater than unity.

14.38. In order to make sure that the nuclear reaction chain will propagate itself, once it has been initiated, both p and f should be as large as possible, although they are, of course, always less than unity. It is an unfortunate circumstance that such changes in the relative proportions of uranium and the moderator as cause one of these factors to increase, result in a decrease of the other. If the system contains a large amount of moderator as compared with the uranium, the resonance escape probability p will be increased, since there is a greater chance that the neutrons will reach the thermal region without suffering nonfission capture by uranium-238. Conversely, a smaller proportion of uranium, and hence of U^{235} nuclei, in the system means that the thermal utilization factor f will be diminished. Similarly, it can be readily seen that if the ratio of moderator to uranium is decreased, the value of p will also decrease, but f will increase at the same time. In actual practice, therefore, it is necessary to find the particular composition of the system which gives the maximum value for the product pf, if the chain reaction is to be maintained.

14.39. One fairly obvious way in which the difficulty concerning the oppositely directed changes in p and f could be overcome would be to use "enriched" uranium, that is, uranium containing a greater abundance than normal of the isotope of mass number 235. This would have the effect of increasing both p and f for a given proportion of moderator, since the chances of escaping resonance capture by U^{238} and of causing thermal fission of U^{235} would both be greater. By employing enriched uranium it is therefore possible to decrease the amount of moderator and still have a controllable chain reaction. Reference to the use of enriched, chain reacting systems of this kind will be made in Chapter XV.

HOMOGENEOUS AND HETEROGENEOUS SYSTEMS

14.40. In the foregoing discussion, it has been mentioned that the values of both p and f are dependent upon the arrangement of the uranium and moderator. The simplest arrangement would be a uniform mixture of the graphite and uranium, either as metal or a compound. This is referred to as a *homogeneous system*. But calculations, based on measured neutron absorption and scattering cross sections at various energies, showed that the maximum possible value for k_∞ in a homogeneous system of natural uranium and graphite is 0.80. Consequently, the maintenance of a chain reaction would be impossible. Fortunately, however, Fermi and Szilard realized that, for a given uranium-graphite composition, the infinite medium multiplication factor might be increased by building a *heterogeneous system*, that is, a lattice consisting of fairly large lumps of uranium (or uranium oxide) imbedded in a mass of graphite.

14.41. Upon entering a lump of uranium, neutrons with energies in the resonance region, where the cross sections are very high, are essentially all captured in the outer layers. As a result, the material in the interior is shielded from resonance neutrons; the resonance absorption of neutrons by uranium nuclei in a lump is consequently appreciably less than if the uranium was dispersed in the form of single atoms or as very small particles. Hence, the use of a lattice consisting of lumps of uranium increases the value of p, the resonance escape probability. It is true that there is an accompanying decrease in the thermal utilization factor f, but this is relatively small. Theoretical calculations, which have been confirmed by experimental measurements, show that, at least with lumps up to a certain size, the gain in p more than offsets the decrease in f, so that the product pf is increased by using relatively large pieces of uranium. The maximum value for k_∞, with the optimum arrangement of uranium in the graphite lattice, was estimated to be 1.07, so that a heterogeneous chain reacting system should be possible with these materials.

CRITICAL SIZE OF A CHAIN-REACTING SYSTEM

14.42. The requirement for the maintenance of a fission chain is that the effective multiplication factor k must be at least equal to unity (§ 14.30). Since, in the case considered above, k_∞ has a maximum value of 1.07, it follows that the nonleakage probability P must not exceed 0.93; that is to say, the rate of loss of neutrons by leakage must be kept below about 7 per cent of the rate of formation in the fission process. The proportion of neutrons lost by leakage, relative to those which cause fission, and so produce more neutrons, can be diminished by increasing the size of the system. The escape of neutrons occurs at the exterior, but fission takes place in the interior of the uranium-moderator lattice. The number of neutrons lost by escape thus depends on the external surface area, whereas the number of fission neutrons released is determined by the volume. To minimize the loss of neutrons by escape it is necessary, therefore, to decrease the ratio of area to volume; this can be done by having the system as large as convenient, preferably in the form of a sphere.*

14.43. *The critical size* of a system containing fissionable material is defined as the size for which the number of neutrons produced in the fission process just balances those lost by leakage and by capture. The critical size is not a constant, but depends on the isotopic composition of the uranium, the proportion of moderator, the shape and arrangement of the materials and the presence of various substances causing parasitic capture of neutrons. If a system is smaller than the critical size, i.e., *subcritical*, neutrons are lost at a greater rate than they are replenished by fission, and so a self-sustaining, chain reaction will be impossible. It is essential, therefore, that the size of the uranium-moderator lattice should be equal to or larger than the critical value, i.e., *supercritical*, if the fission chain is to be maintained. Some attempts were made in 1939, by F. Perrin in France and by S. Flügge in Germany, to calculate the critical size for a chain reacting system, but the results were of little value, partly because the details of

the fission process were not clearly understood at the time, and partly because of the lack of the necessary data concerning cross sections and other nuclear constants. "In principle it was possible in 1940," according to the Smyth *Report*, "to calculate the critical size, but in practice the uncertainty of the constants involved was so great that the various estimates differed widely." Consequently, a comprehensive series of investigations were undertaken in order to provide the data which would make reliable calculations possible.†

14.44. By the middle of 1941 sufficient information had been accumulated as to make desirable experimental measurements with a small uranium-graphite lattice, estimated to be from one fifth to one quarter of the critical size. It was realized that such a system would not be chain reacting, but by means of calculations based on diffusion theory it would be possible to ascertain the multiplication factor for an infinite lattice of the same type. With k_∞ known, the maximum value of the nonleakage probability could be estimated and, hence, the critical size calculated for a given shape.

14.45. In addition to the factors mentioned above which affect the critical size, it was suggested that neutron loss could be minimized, and hence the critical size of the system reduced, by surrounding the latter with a *neutron reflector*. Any substance which is suitable as a moderator, such as carbon or beryllium (or its oxide), can be used as a reflector, for it can slow

---

* For a given volume, a sphere has the smallest possible area. If r is the radius, the area is $4\pi r^2$ and the volume $4\pi r^3/3$, so that the ratio area/volume is $3/r$, which decreases as the radius, and hence the size, is increased.

† This work was done in the United States in connection with the project for the use of atomic energy for military purposes. The details are given in the Smyth *Report*, which states that "the attainment of a slow neutron chain reaction seemed a necessary preliminary step in the development of our knowledge and became the first objective of the group interested in the problem [of a uranium fission bomb]."

down fast neutrons, which might otherwise escape, without absorbing them to any appreciable extent. Many of the slowed down neutrons, as well as slow neutrons which have escaped from the chain-reacting system itself, called the *core*, are then scattered back by collisions with the nuclei of the reflector material.

14.46. The first experimental lattice structure of uranium and graphite was erected about July 1941, at Columbia University, under the supervision of Fermi. It was a cube of graphite, with an 8-foot edge, containing about 7 tons of uranium oxide in iron vessels distributed at equal distances throughout the cube. A radium-beryllium source of neutrons (§ 11.14) was placed near the bottom of the uranium-graphite lattice, and the number of neutrons measured at various points throughout the structure. From the data so secured, the value of the infinite medium multiplication factor was calculated, as mentioned above.

14.47. The results obtained with the first lattice are not recorded, but a second, similar, but larger, structure, set up at Columbia University in September 1941, gave a k_∞ value of 0.87. In view of the fact that the uranium oxide contained from 2 to 5 per cent of impurities, including boron which has a high cross section for capture of both slow and moderately fast neutrons (Fig. 11.9), the result, although less than unity, was not decisive. Efforts were consequently made to obtain materials of greater purity, and, by May 1942, uranium dioxide with total impurities under 1 per cent was available; this gave an infinite medium multiplication factor of 0.98 with a graphite moderator, so that the goal of unity was being rapidly approached.

THE CHICAGO CHAIN-REACTING PILE

14.48. Definite indication that a chain reaction was possible in a uranium oxide-graphite lattice was obtained in July 1942, when a value of 1.07 was calculated for the infinite medium multiplication factor. It should be understood that no actual chain was propagated in this system, because it was below the critical size, but the results indicated that a sufficiently large structure, of the same general type, would maintain a nuclear fission chain. Since the oxygen in the uranium oxide captures neutrons to some extent, it was to be expected that an infinite medium multiplication factor appreciably greater than unity could be achieved by using uranium metal in place of the oxide.

14.49. To insure the propagation of the chain it was desirable to secure large quantities, of the order of several tons, of both uranium and graphite, containing no more than a few parts per million of impurities. "When it is recalled," says Smyth, "that up to 1940 the total amount of uranium metal produced in this country was not more than a few grams and even this was of doubtful purity . . . it is clear that the problem of producing and purifying materials was a major one." So little was, in fact, known about metallic uranium that its melting point was recorded as 1850°C, whereas the actual value has been found to be 1133°C. The problem of obtaining graphite was not so formidable, as this was already being manufactured in large amounts, although the purity was not quite up to the standard desirable. The presence, for example, of one part of boron in 500,000 of the graphite would normally have escaped notice, but in a neutron moderator this small amount of impurity assumed considerable significance.

14.50. By the use of an ether extraction method, uranyl nitrate was obtained in a pure form. Upon heating, the nitrate is converted into the oxide UO_3, and this can be reduced to UO_2 with hydrogen gas. "It was a remarkable achievement," in the words of the Smyth *Report*, "to have developed and put into production [by July 1942] on the scale of the order of one ton per day a process for transforming grossly impure commercial oxide to oxide of a degree of purity seldom achieved even on a laboratory scale." But the problem still remained of converting the oxide into pure metal. The commercial processes in use at the time gave unsatisfactory products, and it is largely due to the efforts of F. H. Spedding and his associates at Iowa State College that a suitable method was developed toward the end of 1942.* This involved conversion of uranium dioxide to the tetrafluoride by means of hydrogen fluoride, followed by reduction to metallic uranium, by means of calcium or magnesium.

14.51. The production of pure graphite proved to be less difficult than of uranium. The process used was essentially that already employed on a large scale for the manufacture of graphite electrodes, except that special precautions were taken to eliminate impurities.

14.52. Toward the end of 1942 sufficient pure materials were available to justify an attempt to construct, at the University of Chicago,† an actual

chain-reacting system which, exceeding the critical size, would be self-sustaining. The plan was to build a cubic lattice of lumps of uranium and uranium oxide within a sphere of graphite, the amount of pure metal available, namely, 12,400 pounds, being insufficient to fill all the lattice points. The graphite was cut in bricks and built up in layers, alternate ones containing lumps of uranium or oxide. Since the structure was made by piling one layer upon another, it was called a *pile*. The name was very convenient and useful at the time, because it did not reveal the purpose of the structure. During the construction of the pile, cadmium strips, acting as neutron absorbers, were inserted as a safety measure, for it was anticipated that neutrons produced by spontaneous fission (§ 13.19) or derived from cosmic rays (Chapter XVIII), might otherwise set off the reaction chain at the instant the critical size was reached. This was a necessary precaution since the multiplication factor increased more rapidly than had been anticipated, and the critical state was attained sooner than expected. Consequently, the completed pile, instead of being spherical as planned, was an oblate spheroid flattened at the top, shaped somewhat like a doorknob (Fig. 14.1). It contained a total of 40 tons of uranium and 385 tons of graphite.

14.53. By cautiously withdrawing the cadmium strips, and measuring the neutron intensity within the pile, by means of counters containing boron trifluoride (§ 11.26), the approach to the critical size could be observed.

---

* A striking achievement among the many associated with the wartime atomic energy project in the United States was the production of many tons of pure uranium by a group consisting of faculty and students working in a disused building on the campus of the Iowa State College at Ames.

† The construction was carried out in a squash court under the West Stands of Stagg Field.

When the neutron count commenced to rise rapidly, while the size of the pile was being increased, the multiplication factor was approaching unity. On the afternoon of December 2, 1942, upon withdrawal of the neutron absorbing rods, the sharp increase in neutron intensity within the pile, de-

the chain reaction possible. The pile was initially operated at the low power of 0.5 watt but on December 12, 1942, it was raised to 200 watts; it could have been increased still further but it was decided not to do so, because of the possible harmful effects to personnel of the radiations emitted.

FIG. 14.1. Artist's conception of the first chain-reacting pile built under the West Stands of Stagg Field, University of Chicago.

picted in the historic record reproduced in Fig. 14.2, showed that a fission chain was actually being propagated. In the words of Smyth: "So far as we know, this was the first time that human beings ever initiated a self maintaining nuclear chain reaction." *

14.54. The actual multiplication factor of the system was about 1.0006 with all the neutron absorbers removed; this was sufficient to make

For this reason, the first chain-reacting pile was dismantled in the spring of 1943 and reconstructed at Palos Park, outside Chicago. The original materials, together with some additional uranium metal and graphite, were used, but the rebuilt pile, in the form of a cube, had adequate radiation shielding and improved safety devices. The normal power was about 2 kilowatts, although it was sometimes operated for periods of an hour or

---

* The qualification "so far as we know" was presumably made because it was not known definitely at the time whether scientists in other countries, Germany, in particular, might have had prior success in this connection. However, as stated earlier, it has now been established that such was not the case.

more up to about 100 kilowatts. From the data given in § 14.16, it can be calculated that when running continuously at 2 kilowatts the pile consumed only about 0.002 gram of uranium-235 per day.

POWER OF NUCLEAR REACTOR

14.55. Brief mention may be made of the method for determining the power of a pile, or *nuclear reactor*, as it is now preferably called. By

of fissionable (uranium-235) nuclei per cc., σ is the cross section for fission, and V is the volume of the reactor. It was seen in § 14.15 that 3.1×10^{10} fissions per sec. produce 1 watt of power; hence, the power P of a nuclear reactor in watts is obtained upon dividing the fission rate A, as given by equation (14.2), by 3.1×10^{10}, that is,

$$P = \frac{nvN\sigma V}{3.1 \times 10^{10}} \text{ watts.} \quad (14.3)$$

TIME ⟶

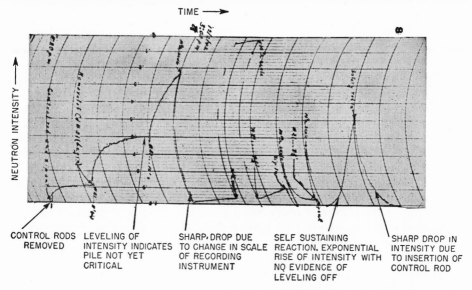

CONTROL RODS REMOVED — LEVELING OF INTENSITY INDICATES PILE NOT YET CRITICAL — SHARP DROP DUE TO CHANGE IN SCALE OF RECORDING INSTRUMENT — SELF SUSTAINING REACTION. EXPONENTIAL RISE OF INTENSITY WITH NO EVIDENCE OF LEVELING OFF — SHARP DROP IN INTENSITY DUE TO INSERTION OF CONTROL ROD

FIG. 14.2. Record of neutron intensity obtained with the first chain-reacting system on December 2, 1942.

means of arguments similar to those in § 11.76, it can be seen that the total number of nuclei A undergoing fission per second in the reactor is given by an expression identical with the equation (11.7); thus,

$$A = nvN\sigma V, \quad (14.2)$$

where n is the average neutron density, i.e., the number per cc., v is the average speed, so that nv is the average neutron flux; N is now the number

14.56. The product NV is equal to the total number of fissionable nuclei in the reactor and this is related to the mass g grams by $g = 235NV/(6.02 \times 10^{23})$, where 235 is the atomic weight of the fissionable material, assumed to be uranium-235 and 6.02×10^{23} is the Avogadro number (§ 1.60). The fission cross section σ of uranium-235 for thermal neutrons is 590×10^{-24} sq. cm., and upon inserting these values in equation (14.3), it is found that

$$P = 5.6 \times 10^{-11} \; gnv$$
$$= 2.5 \times 10^{-8} \; wnv \quad \text{watts,} \quad (14.4)$$

where w is now the weight of uranium-235 in pounds. It is seen from this expression that the power output of a given reactor, containing a definite amount of fissionable material, is proportional to the neutron flux, nv. Hence, reactor power is generally determined by measuring the appropriate, e.g., thermal, neutron flux by means of a suitably calibrated instrument of the type described in § 11.24, *et seq.*

CONTROL OF NUCLEAR REACTOR

14.57. An important aspect of nuclear reactor construction is the nature of the controls required to bring the reactor up to its normal operating level, to maintain it at that level, and to shut it down when required. Controls are also necessary to prevent the chain reaction from becoming too violent. If the effective multiplication factor were always exactly unity, the number of neutrons present would not increase from one generation to the next. In this event, there would be no flexibility in the operation of the reactor. The system must be capable of having an effective multiplication factor exceeding unity, even by a small amount, so as to permit an increase in the number of neutrons in successive generations. However, unless the growth is checked at some point, the system might disintegrate as a result of the too rapid liberation of energy.

14.58. It may be mentioned that there is little likelihood that a reactor consisting of ordinary uranium and a moderator would actually explode. If the rate of nuclear fission became too great, and the heat generated became excessive, the system would probably break apart. Since each piece would then be subcritical, that is, less than the critical size, chain propagation would cease, and there would be no further risk of explosion. The danger due to radiations would, however, be very considerable.

14.59. In order to maintain the effective multiplication factor at unity, and the neutron density (or flux) constant, once the desired energy level has been reached, control rods of cadmium or of boron steel are used; both boron and cadmium have large capture cross section for slow neutrons. These rods are inserted in the reactor to such a depth as will permit them to absorb all excess neutrons. In other words, when the reactor has reached a predetermined power level, the control rods serve to keep the effective multiplication factor at exactly unity. If it is required to increase the power, the controls are partially removed; the multiplication factor then exceeds unity, and the neutron density rises. When this attains the desired value, the controls are inserted to the extent necessary to keep the output (or power level) constant. When shutting down the reactor, the cadmium or boron-steel rods are inserted to a considerable depth; they then can capture so many neutrons that the effective multiplication factor becomes less than unity. The neutron density thus decreases and the nuclear reaction chain is no longer maintained. To start up the reactor, all that is necessary is carefully to withdraw a control rod, and then readjust it when the required output is attained.*

---

* In the preliminary experiments, described above, with systems below the critical size, a constant neutron source was employed so that satisfactory measurements could be made. In a system exceeding the critical size the fission chain may be initiated by extraneous neutrons produced in spontaneous fission or present in cosmic rays. However, many reactors have built-in neutron sources in order to facilitate the start-up operation.

14.60. Since fission is a virtually instantaneous process, it might be thought that the neutron density and the energy output would increase with extreme rapidity, so that mechanical control, even if automatic, might not be sufficiently rapid. Fortunately, the liberation of the delayed neutrons in fission, amounting to about 0.75 per cent of the total (§ 13.42), has helped to overcome this difficulty. Suppose that, in general, β is the fraction of the fission neutrons which are delayed, so that $1 - \beta$ represents the fraction of prompt neutrons. Of the total number η of fast neutrons produced for each thermal neutron absorbed, $(1 - \beta)\eta$ are emitted instantaneously, and $\beta\eta$ are delayed and expelled gradually over several minutes. It follows, therefore, that the multiplication factor may be regarded as consisting of two parts: one, equal to $k(1 - \beta)$, representing the prompt neutron multiplication factor, and the other, equal to $k\beta$, due to the delayed neutrons, where k is the effective multiplication factor.

14.61. If, in the start-up of a reactor, the quantity $k(1 - \beta)$ is adjusted so as to be just less than, or equal to, unity, then the rate of increase in the number of neutrons from one generation to the next will be determined essentially by the rate of emission of the delayed neutrons. Since β is actually 0.75 per cent, or a fraction 0.0075 of the total, for the fission of uranium-235, this condition can be realized by having k somewhat less than 1.0075, but, of course, greater than unity. In these circumstances, the neutron density and the power output increase fairly slowly, and control by means of neutron absorbers is a relatively simple matter. The condi- tion in which $k(1 - \beta)$ is equal to unity, so that k is 1.0075, with uranium-235 as the fissionable material, is referred to as *prompt critical*. The reactor can then become critical on the prompt neutrons alone. Hence, in the start-up of a reactor, or in any circumstances involving an increase in the neutron flux, it is necessary that the effective multiplication factor be kept fairly well below the prompt critical value.*

14.62. In the construction of a nuclear reactor several different controls are used. Broadly, these fall into three categories. There are the coarse (or shim) controls for reactor start-up and shut-down and fine (or regulating) controls for maintaining a steady operating level. Then, there are safety (or scram) controls for shutting the reactor down rapidly in the event of an emergency. Frequently, the same control rods of cadmium or boron steel are used for coarse control and for safety purposes. These rods are held up by electromagnets and so they can be dropped quickly by switching off the magnetizing current. In the earliest reactors, control rods were moved by hand (see Fig. 14.1), but electric motors are now invariably used. For some purposes, the motion of the rods is determined by a human operator, but for others it may be done automatically.

Production of Plutonium

14.63. When it was originally planned, the purpose of studying the uranium-graphite system was mainly to determine whether it was possible to realize a nuclear chain reaction. However, while the work was in the course of development, the nuclear

* In some reactors, e.g., those based on natural uranium and graphite, the maximum value of the effective multiplication factor is about 1.007, so that they can never become prompt critical.

chain reactor acquired an additional interest of the greatest significance. As already stated, it was known, by early 1941, that uranium-238 absorbs slow neutrons with the formation of the short-lived uranium-239 which is ultimately transformed into plutonium-239. Since the formation of the tions were confirmed (§ 16.4). The new element plutonium thus offered prospects for use in a nuclear fission (atomic) bomb. In a report submitted in July 1941, E. O. Lawrence wrote: "An extremely important new possibility has been opened for the exploitation of the chain reaction with

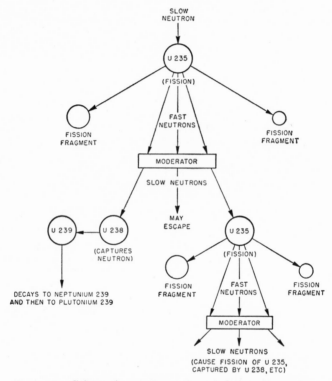

SLOW NEUTRON

U 235

(FISSION)

FISSION FRAGMENT

FAST NEUTRONS

FISSION FRAGMENT

MODERATOR

SLOW NEUTRONS

U 239 ← U 238

(CAPTURES NEUTRON)

MAY ESCAPE

U 235

(FISSION)

DECAYS TO NEPTUNIUM 239 AND THEN TO PLUTONIUM 239

FISSION FRAGMENT

FAST NEUTRONS

FISSION FRAGMENT

MODERATOR

SLOW NEUTRONS

(CAUSE FISSION OF U 235, CAPTURED BY U 238, ETC)

Fig. 14.3. Schematic representation of fission of uranium-235 and capture of neutrons by uranium-238 in a nuclear reactor.

latter element follows two stages of beta decay, it appeared that it might be an alpha emitter of relatively long life, and its even-odd nuclear composition indicated that it would probably be fissionable by slow neutrons (§ 13.69).

14.64. In experiments carried out at the Radiation Laboratory in Berkeley, during 1941, both of these expecta-

unseparated isotopes of uranium. . . . It appears that, if a chain reaction . . . is achieved, it may be allowed to proceed . . . for a period of time for the express purpose of manufacturing element 94 [plutonium]. . . . If large amounts . . . were available it is likely that a chain reaction with fast neutrons could be produced. In such a reaction the energy would be released at an explosive rate which might be described as [a] 'super bomb.' "

14.65. If plutonium could be produced in a chain-reacting system with ordinary uranium, it meant that the neutrons which suffered nonfission capture by uranium-238 would not be wasted, for the resulting uranium-239 would, in a relatively short time, be changed into fissionable plutonium-239. In a properly designed nuclear reactor, containing uranium isotopes of mass numbers 235 and 238, the nuclei of the former would undergo fission; some of the neutrons produced would then serve to carry on the chain, while others would be captured by nuclei of uranium-238, which would ultimately change into plutonium. An oversimplified schematic diagram of the behavior in such a system is given in Fig. 14.3. For purposes of representation, it is assumed that three neutrons are produced in fission, and that of these one carries on the fission chain with uranium-235, another is captured by a uranium-238 nucleus, whereas the third is lost, either in other forms of nonfission capture or by escape from the system.

14.66. Since the atomic number of plutonium is two units greater than that of uranium, it would seem probable that the two elements could be separated by a suitable chemical procedure and the plutonium utilized in the construction of an atomic bomb. In view of the uncertainty of success in the attempts which were then being considered to separate uranium-235, for the same purpose, plans were made in 1942 to investigate the possibility of extracting appreciable quantities of plutonium from a chain-reacting system containing ordinary uranium and a moderator.

14.67. The original Chicago (pile) reactor was not suited to the production of plutonium, for two reasons: first, since it had no cooling system, its maximum safe operating level was so low that only the merest traces of plutonium would be formed; and, second, the use of lumps of uranium and of uranium oxide built into the graphite would necessitate dismantling the reactor in order to obtain the plutonium. As can be seen from the data in § 14.16, the fission of 1 kilogram of uranium-235 per day releases about a million kilowatts of power, most of which appears in the form of heat. Suppose, for the sake of the present argument, that, for every uranium-235 nucleus undergoing fission, one of the emitted neutrons suffers nonfission capture by uranium-238, and so is ultimately converted into plutonium-239, as indicated in Fig. 14.3. Then the fission of 1 kilogram of uranium-235 per day will result in the formation of approximately 1 kilogram of plutonium-239 and the liberation of about a million kilowatts of power. Hence, a reactor designed for the production of 1 kilogram of plutonium per day, would release energy, mostly as heat, at the enormous rate of a million kilowatts.* The problem of cooling such a reactor is therefore considerable.

OAK RIDGE AND HANFORD REACTORS

14.68. The early plans, made in 1942, called for the eventual use of helium gas in order to cool the production reactors, and consequently the decision was made to build at Oak Ridge, Tenn., an experimental air-cooled plant of 1000-kilowatts capacity. This was intended partly to act as a pilot plant for large-scale pro-

---

* An average modern coal-burning unit employed in the production of electricity has a heat power output of around 500,000 kilowatts, i.e., 500 megawatts.

duction units, and partly to provide some plutonium which was badly needed for experimental purposes. Because of the difficulties associated with a gas as coolant in a large reactor, the designs for the latter were changed so as to use water for cooling. But the construction of the intermediate air-cooled Oak Ridge reactor* was continued so as to permit the testing of

nels, represented diagrammatically in Fig. 14.4. The metallic uranium is in the form of cylinders or slugs enclosed in gas-tight aluminum casings; these are slid into the channels in the graphite, which are somewhat wider than the slugs, thus providing space for the flow of air for cooling purposes. When the uranium slugs are ready for proc-

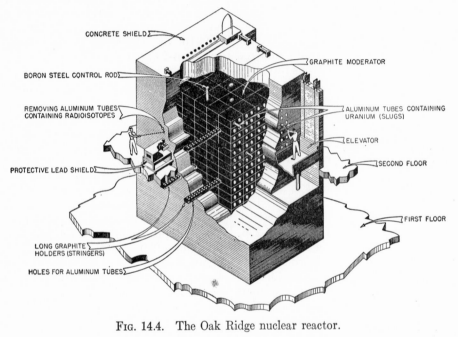

CONCRETE SHIELD

BORON STEEL CONTROL ROD

REMOVING ALUMINUM TUBES CONTAINING RADIOISOTOPES

PROTECTIVE LEAD SHIELD

LONG GRAPHITE HOLDERS (STRINGERS)

HOLES FOR ALUMINUM TUBES

GRAPHITE MODERATOR

ALUMINUM TUBES CONTAINING URANIUM (SLUGS)

ELEVATOR

SECOND FLOOR

FIRST FLOOR

FIG. 14.4.   The Oak Ridge nuclear reactor.

tinued so as to permit the testing of possible methods for the chemical separation of plutonium from the unchanged uranium and the numerous fission products (§ 16.32).

14.69. In order to make it possible to remove the uranium without dismantling the reactor, the latter was redesigned, with some small loss of efficiency. The Oak Ridge reactor was thus built as a cube of graphite containing a number of horizontal chan-

essing, they are pushed out at the back of the reactor, while new ones are fed in at the front. Control of the neutron density is achieved by means of boron-steel rods, and there is heavy shielding to protect operating personnel from the harmful effects of penetrating neutrons and gamma radiations (Chapter XIX).

14.70. It might be imagined that the uranium slugs could be left in the reactor until all the uranium-235 had

* This was originally known as the "Clinton pile," after the town of Clinton, Tenn., in the vicinity.

suffered fission, accompanied by the production of a more or less equivalent amount of plutonium. This is, however, far from being the case. In the first place, many of the fission products which accumulate with time have large cross sections for neutron capture. The replacement of the uranium-235 by products capable of absorbing neutrons means a steady decrease in the multiplication factor; this may ultimately fall below unity, when the chain reaction would stop. Further, as the fissionable plutonium accumulates, it competes with uranium-235 for thermal neutrons, so that in the course of time the plutonium would be lost by fission just as fast as it was formed. The point at which the uranium slugs were removed for processing represented a compromise between the desire to attain a maximum plutonium concentration in a given time and the necessity for maintaining the chain reaction.*

14.71. When the "spent" uranium slugs are pushed out of the back of the reactor they fall into tanks of water where they stay for some days; this allows the uranium-239 to be converted into neptunium-239 which changes into plutonium, and also permits the shorter-lived, and hence most highly radioactive, fission products to decay. The slugs are then dissolved in acid and the solution is made to undergo a series of reactions leading to the separation of the small proportion of plutonium from the mixture of fission products and unchanged uranium.† The chemical processes are straightforward, but, owing to the intense beta and gamma activity of the material, they must be carried out by remote control in concrete chambers most of which are underground.

14.72. The Oak Ridge reactor started operating on November 4, 1943, and it soon reached a power level of 800 kilowatts, the surface temperature of the uranium being 150°C. By rearranging the slugs, so that there were fewer in the center, where the neutron flux was greatest, the over-all power level was increased to 1800 kilowatts, without the temperature becoming too high at any point. After the cooling was improved, by the installation of better fans, in June 1944, the power output of the Oak Ridge reactor was increased still further, so that it now operates at a power of nearly 4000 kilowatts. The first batch of spent slugs entered the separation plant on December 20, 1943, and by the end of February, 1944, plutonium was being produced at the rate of several grams per month.

14.73. Even before the first self-sustaining, nuclear chain reaction had been achieved, and certainly long before any plutonium had been obtained from the Oak Ridge reactor, plans were being made for the production of plutonium on a large scale. As mentioned in § 14.68, the reactor for this purpose was to be water-cooled, a fact which introduced complications because of parasitic capture of neutrons by the water and by the containing pipes. The water cooling, and the jacketing (or "canning") of the uranium to protect it from corrosion, presented tremendous problems which can be no more than mentioned here, but they were ultimately solved with conspicuous success.

14.74. Early in 1943, a site at Han-

---

* Since the Oak Ridge (graphite) reactor is no longer used for plutonium production, the discharge of uranium slugs is determined by other factors.

† Some reference to the chemistry of plutonium and its separation will be made in Chapter XVI.

ford, Washington, sufficiently remote for safety, and with ample accessible water for cooling purposes from the Columbia River, was chosen. Work on the first Hanford production reactor was started on June 7, 1943, and operation began in September, 1944; a second and a third reactor were completed toward the end of 1944 and early in 1945, respectively. Subsequently, a number of other reactors of

not only unknown in 1939, but which did not even exist on the earth except perhaps in the merest, virtually undetectable, traces (§ 16.26).

14.76. It is remarkable that the only previous experience with chain-reacting systems when the production reactors were designed was obtained with the low-powered experimental Chicago pile, operating at a maximum of 200 watts, little more than the

Fig. 14.5. Portion of the plutonium plant at Hanford, Wash., showing cooling equipment which handles tens of thousands of gallons of water per minute.

the same type were constructed at the Hanford site.

14.75. The Hanford reactors, each as high as a five-story building (Fig. 14.5), with their attendant remotely controlled plants (Fig. 14.6) for the extraction of grams of plutonium from tons of material, including uranium and the numerous fission products, represent, like the Oak Ridge gaseous diffusion plant described in § 8.88, a monumental and spectacular achievement of science and technology. At Hanford there was produced, for the first time, a new element, which was

power of an average electric-light bulb! Equally, or even more, remarkable was the fact that the plant for the separation of plutonium was based on chemical studies made with a total of only half a milligram, i.e., one two-thousandth part of a gram, of plutonium—about the size of a head of a pin!—produced by the bombardment of uranyl nitrate with neutrons obtained with the aid of cyclotrons (§ 16.30).

14.77. It has been estimated that a factor of 10^{10} was involved in the scale-up from the laboratory studies to the actual plant. "The proposed extrapolations [necessary for the design of the large-scale plant from the available data] both as to chain-reacting piles and as to separation processes," says the Smyth *Report*, "were staggering. In peace-time no engineer or scientist in his right mind would consider making such a magnification in a single stage, and even in wartime

the release of the fission energy is a gradual and controlled process, but in the bomb the energy produced by the fission of an appreciable quantity of either uranium-235 or plutonium-239 is liberated rapidly and in an uncontrolled manner. A brief outline of the principles of the nuclear fission (atomic) bomb will be given here; the characteristics of different types of

FIG. 14.6. Remotely controlled plants for extraction of plutonium from material discharged from reactor; waste gases are discharged through the 200-ft. stack.

only the possibility of achieving tremendously important results could justify it."

THE NUCLEAR FISSION (ATOMIC) BOMB

14.78. A chain-reacting system, that is, a nuclear reactor, can take various forms, depending upon its construction, its composition, and the purpose for which it is required. The ultimate objective of the Hanford reactors was the production of plutonium for use in an atomic bomb which itself is, strictly, a nuclear reactor. In the piles

controlled nuclear reactors will be described in the next chapter.

14.79. When a large amount of energy is released, within a very short time interval, in a small space the result is an explosion (§ 3.4). In order to achieve such a state of affairs by utilizing fissionable material, there are two main requirements. First, it is necessary to have a mass of relatively pure uranium-235 or plutonium-239,* whose dimensions exceed the critical size, so that the chain reaction can be sustained; and second, fission must be due, as far as possible, to fast neu-

* Uranium-233 (§ 15.11) might presumably also be used for this purpose.

trons, so that the process takes place with extreme rapidity. In spite of the fact that the fission cross sections for thermal neutrons are large, and in spite, also, of their high speeds—2.2 × 10^5 cm. per sec.—referred to normal standards, the rate of liberation of energy in thermal-neutron fission would be too slow to produce an effective explosion. Such a system would behave like a reactor that had gone out of control, as described in § 14.58; it would heat up and then break apart into pieces of subcritical size, when the chain reaction would cease. If this occurred in an enclosed space, there would be a minor explosion, at most.

14.80. In an atomic bomb the chain reaction must be maintained by fast neutrons, so that the use of a moderator, or of any material capable of slowing down the neutrons, must be avoided. Further, by minimizing the possibilities of nonfission capture, virtually all the neutrons produced in fission will cause further fission; thus, the multiplication factor will exceed unity and the rate of energy release will increase with great rapidity.

14.81. The presence of stray neutrons in the atmosphere makes it impossible to prevent a chain reaction in a supercritical mass, that is, in a quantity exceeding the critical size, of fissionable material. It is consequently necessary that before detonation the bomb should not contain any fissionable material that is as large as the critical mass for the given conditions. In order to cause an explosion, the material must then be made supercritical within a very short interval of time. Extreme rapidity is necessary, because if the chain reaction were to be initiated by stray neutrons before the fissionable material had reached the most compact form, a relatively weak explosion would occur. Two general methods have been described for bringing about an atomic (or nuclear) explosion by quickly converting a subcritical system of fissionable material into a critical one.

14.82. In the first method, two or more pieces of fissionable material, each less than a critical mass, are brought together very rapidly in order to form one piece that exceeds the critical size. This may be achieved in some kind of gun-barrel device, in which a high-explosive charge is used to blow one subcritical mass of fissionable material from the breech end of the gun into another subcritical mass firmly held at the nozzle end. "The obvious method of very rapidly assembling an atomic bomb," says the Smyth *Report,* "was to shoot one part as a projectile in a gun against a second part as a target." If the two parts, which are not necessarily of the same size, are each subcritical, there is no danger of explosion, but if a supercritical mass is formed when they are brought together in an extremely small fraction of a second, the desired explosion will occur.

14.83. The second method of causing a mass of fissionable material to explode makes use of the fact that when a subcritical quantity of the material is compressed it can become supercritical. The reason is that by decreasing the size and, hence, the surface area of a given quantity of fissionable material by compression, the rate of neutron loss by leakage is decreased relative to the rate of production of neutrons by fission. The previously subcritical mass may thus become supercritical under the new conditions. The required compression may be achieved by means of a spherical arrangement of specially fabricated shapes of ordinary high explosive. In a hole in the center of the system is then placed a subcritical sphere of fissionable material. When the high explosive is set off, by means of a number of detonators on the outside, an inwardly directed *implosion wave* is produced. The force of this wave causes the sphere of fissionable material to be rapidly compressed so that it becomes supercritical and explodes.

14.84. It was mentioned in § 14.45 that the escape of neutrons, and hence the critical size of a chain-reacting system, can be reduced by the use of a suitable reflector; the same is true, to some extent, of an atomic bomb. But in the latter case, the nature of the reflector is different, and it also serves an additional, more important, purpose. Elements of high density, and high atomic weight, do not absorb fast neutrons to any great extent, neither do they slow them down appreciably; such elements are thus suitable to act as reflectors in a fast-neutron chain reactor. Further, the high density provides inertia which delays expansion of the exploding material, so that it acts like the familiar *tamper* in blasting operations. Thus, according to the Smyth *Report*, "use of a tamper . . . makes for a longer lasting, more energetic, and more efficient explosion."

14.85. Since a nuclear fission bomb must exceed a certain minimum size, a "small atomic bomb," that could be used as an experimental model for the purpose of designing a larger weapon, is not practical. Hence, the first atomic bomb, which was exploded with such tremendous effect at Alamogordo, New Mexico, on July 16, 1945, was planned, constructed and detonated on the basis of theoretical calculations, without benefit of a preliminary test. To appreciate the stupendous and unprecedented nature of this achievement requires a complete understanding of the magnitude of the problems involved. Subsequently, as is well known, nuclear fission bombs, with an energy release equivalent to 20,000 tons of T.N.T. (§ 14.25), were exploded over Hiroshima and Nagasaki, Japan, in the early days of August, 1945. Since that time, the design of atomic weapons has been improved to such an extent that fission bombs with twenty-five times this energy yield have been produced. As will be seen below (§ 14.104), weapons of even higher explosive energy have been made possible by the use of thermonuclear reactions.

14.86. The temperature accompanying the explosion of an atomic bomb is believed to be about 10 million degrees Centigrade, not very different from that of the interior of the sun. Consequently, the fission products, as well as any unchanged uranium or plutonium, are converted into gases at very high pressure. The sudden expansion of these extremely hot, compressed gases is responsible for much of the damage and destruction resulting from the explosion. Some of the fission energy appears as biologically harmful gamma radiation, and some as beta and gamma radioactivity of the products. In addition, the high temperatures attained result in the emission of thermal radiation capable of causing skin burns and initiating fires at considerable distances from the explosion.*

* For a full account of the phenomena and consequences of nuclear explosions, see *The Effects of Nuclear Weapons*, U. S. Government Printing Office, Washington, D. C., 1957.

ENERGY FROM NUCLEAR FUSION

FUSION OF LIGHT NUCLEI

14.87. If, before 1939, nuclear physicists had been urged to express an opinion as to the probable direction in which the successful release of atomic energy might be realized, it is extremely doubtful if they would have thought it to be by fission. The general feeling was that it would prove more practical to obtain energy by the combination (or fusion) of light nuclei than by fission of heavy nuclei. It is evident from § 13.22 that the liberation of energy in fission is due, essentially, to the binding energy per nucleon being less in the heavy elements than it is in those of intermediate mass number formed in fission. An examination of the binding energy curve in Fig. 12.2 will show that precisely equivalent circumstances arise at the low mass number end of the system of elements. The binding energy per nucleon in the lightest nuclei is, like that in the heaviest, less than for nuclei of intermediate mass number. In other words, the sum of the masses of the individual light nuclei is more than would be the mass of the nucleus formed by their fusion. The combination of two or more of the lightest nuclei, by a process of fusion, should thus, like fission, result in a liberation of energy.

14.88. Many reactions between nuclei of low mass number can be brought about by accelerating one or other of the nuclei in a suitable manner, as described in Chapter IX. These are often nuclear fusion processes accompanied by the release of energy. However, as indicated in § 14.10, reactions involving artificially accelerated particles cannot be regarded as of any significance for the utilization of atomic energy. To have practical value, fusion reactions must occur in such a manner as to make them self-sustaining; that is to say, more energy must be released than is consumed in initiating the reaction.

14.89. Some indication of how this might be achieved can be obtained by considering the source of the enormous amounts of energy produced continuously in the stars, including the sun. The earliest scientific theory concerning the source of the sun's energy was proposed by H. von Helmholtz in 1853; making use of the principle of the conservation of energy (§ 3.75), he suggested that the sun's energy was released in the process of contraction. In other words, according to Helmholtz, gravitational work was being converted into heat in the sun. The inadequacy of this theory was shown by the fact that it led to an estimate of the age of the sun which was undoubtedly much too short.

14.90. With the discovery of radioactivity at the end of the nineteenth century, it appeared possible that what was vaguely called "atomic energy" might be contributing to the sun's energy. Thus, T. C. Chamberlin of the University of Chicago pointed out in 1899 that "the Helmholtz theory takes no cognizance of latent and occluded energies of an atomic or ultra-atomic nature." During the first two decades of the present century, due largely to its exposition by A. S. Eddington, the view was widely held that the energy of the sun resulted from the mutual annihilation of positive and negative charges. It will be recalled (§ 14.4) that this theory of energy release was put forward in 1904 by J. H. Jeans to account for the energy of radioactivity.

14.91. As mentioned earlier, Eddington, in 1920, considered the alternative possibility that stellar energy was liberated in the formation of helium from hydrogen. A similar suggestion was made by the French scientist J. Perrin, who thought that the sun's energy was produced in the process of building up complex atoms from protons and electrons. Because of the large amounts of hydrogen and helium known to exist in the sun, Eddington's theory received wide support, although there was no satisfactory mechanism to account for the formation of helium from hydrogen.

Sources of Stellar Energy

14.92. In 1929, R. d'E. Atkinson and F. G. Houtermans, in Germany, considered the possibility that energy might be liberated in the stars as a result of nuclear fusion reactions occurring at the very high stellar temperatures, from 15 to 30 million degrees Centigrade. Such processes are called *thermonuclear reactions* and there are reasons for believing that they can take place at rates sufficient to account for the release of large amounts of stellar energy.

14.93. The arguments may be presented in the following manner. In order for two nuclei to interact, they must have enough kinetic energy to permit them to overcome (or penetrate) the electrostatic repulsion barrier which tends to keep them apart (§ 9.18, *et seq.*). Simple calculations show that for nuclei of the lowest atomic number, e.g., the isotopes of hydrogen, the energy required to make the nuclear reactions occur at a detectable rate is about 0.1 Mev. Experiments with accelerators confirm that

energies of this order are, in fact, necessary to cause interaction among the nuclei of low atomic number; larger amounts are required for nuclei of higher atomic number to overcome the greater repulsive force. The energy acquired by a charged particle in an accelerator is kinetic in nature, and the same energy could, in principle, result from a sufficient increase in temperature. However, the temperature would have to be as high as about 1000 million degrees Centigrade, if the *average* energy of the particles is to be 0.1 Mev. Such temperatures are considerably higher than those existing in stars.

14.94. It was noted in § 11.39 that, at any given temperature, there is a distribution of energies among the molecules of a gas. At temperatures of millions of degrees a gas does not consist of molecules, but rather of a completely ionized system of positively charged nuclei and electrons, often referred to as a *plasma*. Nevertheless, it appears that the concept of the distribution of energies should still apply. As a consequence, it can be stated that, whereas most nuclei will have energies close to the average value for the existing temperature, there will always be a certain proportion with energies greatly exceeding the average. Thus, at a temperature of 20 million degrees, for example, where the average kinetic energy is only 0.002 Mev, there are an appreciable number of nuclei with energies of 0.1 Mev or more. These have sufficient energy to permit them to take part in thermonuclear fusion reactions resulting in the release of energy.

14.95. The foregoing discussion has tacitly assumed, for simplicity, a threshold energy below which the nuclear reaction does not occur. Actually this is not the case, for there is a certain probability (or cross section) that reaction will take place at any energy, although, for the isotopes of hydrogen it increases sharply as the energy approaches something of the order of 0.1 Mev. The rate at which the thermonuclear reaction occurs depends on the product of the number of nuclei having a certain energy and the reaction probability at that energy. The general nature of the variation of these quantities at a given temperature is shown in Fig. 14.7. It is seen that

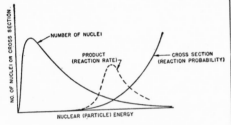

FIG. 14.7. Dependence of rate of nuclear reaction on particle energy at a given temperature.

most of the reactions are due to nuclei with energies in excess of the average.

14.96. At the time the theory of nuclear reactions at high temperatures was proposed, there were insufficient data to permit of its development. Since 1938, largely due to the suggestions of H. A. Bethe in the United States, two sets of nuclear reactions have been found to account for the energies of what are called "main sequence" stars. The first is known as the *carbon cycle*, in which carbon acts as a sort of catalyst in facilitating the combination of four protons to form a helium nucleus.* The second is referred to as the *proton-proton chain*, since the first step involves the combination of two protons. Other nuclear reactions accompanied by the release of energy undoubtedly occur in many

stars, but those given below appear to be the most important sources of stellar energy.

14.97. In the carbon cycle, a proton (hydrogen nucleus) first interacts with a C^{12} nucleus, with a release of (fusion) energy; thus,

$$_6C^{12} + {}_1H^1 = {}_7N^{13} + \text{energy}.$$

The product N^{13} is known to be radioactive, emitting a positron, with a half life of 10.1 min.; consequently, it decays in a very short time, according to the equation

$$_7N^{13} = {}_6C^{13} + {}_{+1}e^0.$$

The stable C^{13} nucleus then reacts with another proton, more energy being liberated by the process

$$_6C^{13} + {}_1H^1 = {}_7N^{14} + \text{energy},$$

which is followed by combination of the stable N^{14} nucleus with a third proton; thus,

$$_7N^{14} + {}_1H^1 = {}_8O^{15} + \text{energy}.$$

The O^{15} is a positive beta-emitter, with a half life of 2.05 min., which decays by the process

$$_8O^{15} = {}_7N^{15} + {}_{+1}e^0,$$

and, finally, the resulting N^{15} interacts with a fourth proton,

$$_7N^{15} + {}_1H^1 = {}_6C^{12} + {}_2He^4,$$

so that the C^{12} nucleus is regenerated.

14.98. Upon adding the six foregoing equations, it is seen that the over-all reaction is

$$4_1H^1 = {}_2He^4 + 2_{+1}e^0 + \text{energy},$$

the carbon nucleus having acted much like a catalyst in a series of chemical reactions. Since the four protons are associated with four electrons, to maintain electrical neutrality, whereas

* A similar scheme was proposed independently by C. F. von Weizsäcker in Germany.

only two are required for the helium nucleus, two electrons will be available to combine with the two positrons, so that the net result is equivalent to the conversion of four hydrogen atoms into a helium atom, plus energy, amounting to a total of about 26.7 Mev.

14.99. In the proton-proton chain, two protons first fuse to produce a deuterium nucleus and a positron; thus,

$$_1H^1 + _1H^1 = _1D^2 + _{+1}e^0 + \text{energy.}$$

The deuteron then combines with another proton to yield helium-3, i.e.,

$$_1D^2 + _1H^1 = _2He^3 + \text{energy,}$$

and then two helium-3 nuclei interact; thus,

$$_2He^3 + _2He^3 = _2He^4 + 2_1H^1 + \text{energy.}$$

To obtain the two helium-3 nuclei each of the first two stages must occur twice, and upon adding the various equations, the net result is found to be the same as that given in § 14.98, namely, the formation of a helium-4 nucleus (and two positrons) from four protons. The energy released is the same as in the carbon cycle, namely, 26.7 Mev for each helium nucleus (or atom) produced.

14.100. The relative probabilities of the carbon cycle and the proton-proton chain depend on the temperature. At low (stellar) temperatures, the proton-proton chain predominates, but as the temperature is raised the carbon cycle rapidly becomes of increasing significance. In the sun and similar stars, with interior temperatures of the order of 20 million degrees, the two processes take place at

about the same rate. In the larger (and hotter) stars of the main sequence, it is probable that nearly all the energy comes from the carbon cycle, but in the smaller (and cooler) stars, the proton-proton chain is the main source of energy.

14.101. Calculations show that, even at the temperature of the sun, it would take several million years to convert a single gram of hydrogen into helium. Yet, because of its large mass, this is adequate to account for the enormous amount of energy liberated by the sun. Further, there is sufficient hydrogen available to permit the energy release to continue at this rate for another 30 billion years.[*]

THERMONUCLEAR REACTIONS ON EARTH

14.102. The possibility of bringing about thermonuclear (fusion) reactions on earth, to serve as a source of energy, has naturally attracted much attention. Bearing in mind the masses of material available on earth, it is certain that the reactions of the carbon cycle and the proton-proton chain would occur too slowly to be of any practical value. It is necessary, therefore, to seek for other nuclear reactions involving light nuclei, and the only ones which appear to offer any prospects for success are three reactions among the nuclei of the hydrogen isotopes, deuterium and tritium; they are

$$_1D^2 + _1D^2 = _2He^3 + _0n^1 + 3.2 \text{ Mev}$$

$$_1D^2 + _1D^2 = _1T^3 + _1H^1 + 4.0 \text{ Mev,}$$

which take place at approximately the same rate at a given temperature, and

---

[*] The chief terrestrial sources of energy, namely, coal, oil, natural gas and water power, are actually stores of energy originally derived from the sun. Consequently, although it is not generally appreciated, nuclear energy is indirectly supplying the world's power requirements.

$_1T^3 + _1D^2 = _2He^4 + _0n^1 + 17.6$ Mev,

the rate of which, at equivalent concentrations, is about a hundred times as great.*

14.103. If these reactions could be made to occur at a reasonable rate, the deuterium present to the extent of about 0.015 (atomic) per cent in all natural waters would represent an almost inexhaustible source of energy. The total amount of deuterium in the oceans is estimated to be about 10^{17} pounds. Allowing for the fact that probably not all of the energy of the reactions given above would be available for use, it nevertheless seems reasonable to state that the energy that could be released from this quantity of deuterium is 3×10^{27} British Thermal Units (B.T.U.), compared with an estimate of 6×10^{20} B.T.U. from fission sources (§ 15.120).†

14.104. One way in which temperatures of the order of millions of degrees can be obtained on earth is by means of a nuclear fission bomb. By combining a quantity of deuterium or tritium (or a mixture) with an atomic bomb, it has been possible to bring about tremendously powerful explosions due to the very rapid release of large amounts of energy in the thermonuclear reactions occurring among the isotopes of hydrogen. This is the basis of the hydrogen (or thermonuclear) bomb. In the explosion of such devices, the energy is released in an uncontrolled manner and cannot be applied to any constructive use.

14.105. Extensive investigations are proceeding in the United States, in Great Britain, in the U.S.S.R. and probably in other countries with the object of finding how thermonuclear fusion reactions involving the isotopes of hydrogen could be brought about in a controlled manner. In order to provide useful energy, the process must be self-sustaining, like a fire; in other words, once enough heat has been supplied to raise the temperature to the point at which nuclear fusion occurs at an appreciable rate, the energy released must be sufficient, at least, to maintain that temperature. In estimating the minimum temperature at which a particular thermonuclear reaction will be self-sustaining, a balance must be struck between the energy released in the reaction and the amount lost in various ways. Both of these quantities increase as the temperature is raised, but the energy release goes up more rapidly, so that at a certain temperature the process will become self-sustaining.

14.106. As far as the amount of energy released is concerned, it appears that only that part of the energy carried by the charged particles, H, He^3, T and He^4 in the reactions given in § 14.102, will be deposited locally, i.e., will be available to the reacting system. Owing to their high speed and relatively long range, most of the energy carried by the neutrons, which is one fourth of the total in the D-D reactions and four fifths in the T-D reaction, will be deposited elsewhere. The energy will not necessarily be lost, since the neutrons can be slowed down and captured, but it will not help in maintaining the temperature of the plasma in which reaction occurs.

14.107. The energy loss—although it is not strictly a loss since there are ways in which it might be absorbed

---

* There are some subsidiary reactions involving He^3, T, etc., but these may be ignored for the present purpose.

† In 1957, the price at which the U. S. Atomic Energy Commission was selling heavy water (deuterium oxide) was $28 per pound. The energy obtainable from it by fusion reactions would be equivalent to that from about 2500 tons of coal.

outside the reacting system—is due largely to energy leaving the system as radiation. If the plasma behaved like a black body (§ 3.27), the radiation losses would be extremely large at temperatures of the order of millions of degrees. Because of the relatively small volume of the reacting system, it is probable, however, that the radiation consists almost entirely

foregoing considerations indicate that the minimum temperature for maintenance of the D-D reactions is about 350 million degrees and that for the T-D reaction is roughly 45 million degrees Centigrade.

14.108. High as these temperatures are, there appears to be a possibility that they may be attained by electrical methods, but before any attempt

Fig. 14.8. Pinch effect produced in argon gas by electrical discharge in a straight tube. (Los Alamos Scientific Laboratory.)

of bremsstrahlung (or X-rays) accompanying the deflection of the rapidly moving electrons in the plasma by the electrostatic fields of the positively charged nuclei (§ 4.75). The escape of energy as bremsstrahlung is greatly increased if nuclei of moderate or high charge (or atomic number) are present. Such nuclei must therefore be rigorously excluded from the reaction system. Calculations based on the

is made to realize them there is an important question to be answered: How is the plasma to be contained at temperatures of millions of degrees, when all matter is not only vaporized but completely ionized? Since the plasma consists entirely of electrically charged particles, i.e., electrons and nuclei, it appears that containment might be achieved by the use of electric and magnetic fields.

14.109. One containment procedure, which has attracted interest, is based on what is called the *pinch effect*. This was considered theoretically by the American physicist W. H. Bennett in 1934 and later (in 1937) by L. Tonks, who gave the phenomenon its familiar name. The first experimental observations of the effect to be reported were apparently made in England by A. A. Ware in 1951. The basic idea of the pinch effect is that, if a number of electrically charged particles, such as exist in a plasma, are moving in such a way as to represent an electric current flowing in one direction, a magnetic field is produced which tends to confine the particles by self-constriction (or pinching) of the plasma.

14.110. The motion of the charged particles can result from an electrical discharge passed between electrodes in the plasma or by inducing a current within the plasma from an external discharge (Fig. 14.8). If the pinch effect is to be used to contain plasma at very high temperatures, the latter procedure must be used; that is to say, there must be no electrodes within the plasma, in order to avoid loss of heat due to contact with any solid material. For the same reason, it would be necessary to induce the current within the plasma in a doughnut-shaped (or toroidal) closed tube, i.e., one without ends.

14.111. Although the pinch effect appears to offer a promising approach to the confinement of ionized plasma at high temperatures, there is a fundamental difficulty. The pinched plasma is extremely unstable and breaks up within a few millionths of a second or so. It seems doubtful whether sufficient nuclear fusion energy can be released within such a short time to make the process self-sustaining. If a method can be developed for maintaining the plasma in the pinched condition for an appreciable period of time, the situation would be different. In this event, there is a possibility that much of the energy released in the thermonuclear fusion reactions could be converted directly into electricity. Since the plasma can be compressed by its own magnetic field, it appears that the process might be reversible. That is to say, if the energy produced by fusion caused the plasma to expand against an applied magnetic field, electricity could be produced in an external circuit.

14.112. In addition to offering the prospect of the efficient conversion of nuclear energy into electrical power, without the necessity of producing steam or a hot gas to drive a turbine (§ 15.3), fusion would have an advantage over fission as a source of power in the respect that there are no radioactive wastes for disposal. Shielding of the thermonuclear reactor would be necessary, as with a nuclear fission reactor, and some effort would have to be made to utilize the energy of the neutrons and radiations leaving the reacting system. However, this does not present any great difficulties. The problems still to be solved are mainly those relating to the heating and stable confinement of the plasma for a reasonable length of time. Several ideas, other than the pinch effect, are being pursued, but it is as yet impossible to predict the outcome. Physicists are confident that controlled thermonuclear power, for which the fuel will be the almost inexhaustible supply of deuterium in the oceans, will one day be a reality. But whether it will take one, ten or a hundred years, no one can say.

CATALYZED FUSION REACTIONS

14.113. Toward the end of 1956, L. W. Alvarez and a group of collaborators at the University of California Radiation Laboratory, Berkeley, reported a novel type of reaction in which nuclear fusion occurred. In the course of observations of the tracks made in a 10-inch liquid hydrogen bubble chamber (§ 6.81) by negative mu-mesons, obtained from the Bevatron, gaps were occasionally observed. Such gaps must be due to the forma-

tion of neutral particles incapable of causing ionization and, hence, bubble formation. This is apparently followed by the re-emission of a mu-meson, since the track is subsequently continued, although in a different direction (Fig. 14.9).

14.114. The explanation offered for this remarkable behavior is that, toward the end of its path, the mu-meson is captured by a deuterium nucleus present in the liquid hydrogen to form a mesonic atom (§ 4.77). Inci-

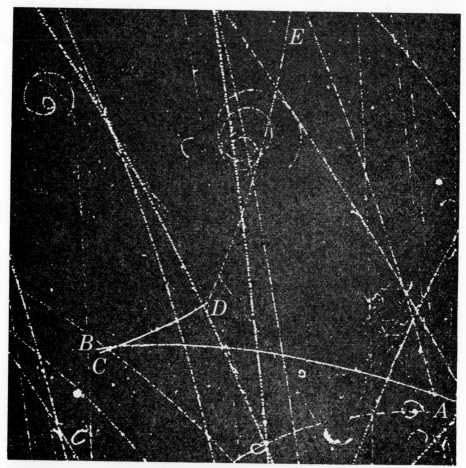

FIG. 14.9.   Hydrogen bubble chamber photograph of catalyzed nuclear fusion reaction.
(University of California Radiation Laboratory.)

dentally, capture of the mu-meson by a deuterium nucleus (or deuteron) occurs more readily than capture by an ordinary hydrogen nucleus (or proton). Immediately the neutral mesonic deuterium atom is formed, the bubble track ceases, and there is a gap. In a short time, however, this mesonic deuterium attaches to itself a proton; the mu-meson is apparently capable of overcoming (or counteracting) the electrostatic propulsion of the two nuclei, so that they approach sufficiently closely to fuse together to form a helium-3 nucleus. The mu-meson is then set free and carries off most of the 5.4 Mev of energy accompanying the nuclear reaction. The released energetic mu-meson is capable of causing ionization and the track in the bubble chamber reappears. Addition of extra deuterium to the liquid hydrogen in the bubble chamber increases the frequency of these events.*

14.115. In most instances, the mu-meson, after re-emission, decays in the normal way into an electron (§ 2.126), but in a few cases a second gap was observed, indicating the combination of another pair of nuclei.

Thus, the mu-meson acts as a sort of catalyst in facilitating the fusion, at low temperatures and low energies, of one, and sometimes two, deuteron-proton pairs. This process has therefore been called a *catalyzed nuclear reaction*.

14.116. Because of the short life of the mu-meson, about 2×10^{-6} sec., it seems unlikely that combination of more than two (or so) proton-deuteron pairs can be realized. The energy liberated is thus only a small fraction of that expended in the production of the mu-meson. Consequently, nuclear reaction catalyzed by mu-mesons does not appear to be a promising approach to the release of energy by fusion. However, it has been suggested that if there were a particle with similar properties having a much longer life, able to catalyze the fusion of many deuteron-proton (or other) pairs, the situation might be different. The Russian physicist, A. I. Alikhanian has reported the discovery of a long-lived meson, but the claim has not yet been confirmed. In any event, it is not known whether such a meson would act as a nuclear reaction catalyst.

* In Fig. 14.9, the negative mu-meson, entering at A, moves along the path AB; at B it is captured by a deuteron to form a neutral mesonic deuterium atom which travels to C, the path BC being invisible. At C the mesonic deuterium fuses with a proton, liberating the mu-meson. This follows the path CD, coming to rest at D, where it decays and emits an electron of high energy which travels along the path DE.

Nuclear Reactors

Chapter XV

GENERAL ASPECTS OF REACTOR DESIGN

INTRODUCTION

15.1. The discussion of nuclear reactors in the preceding chapter has referred primarily to the historical development during World War II, when the prime objective was the production of plutonium for weapons. In recent years, the nuclear reactor field has grown enormously and the basic interests have changed, so that the main emphasis is now on peaceful applications. Numerous reactors of many different designs, intended for a variety of purposes, have been constructed (or are under construction) in all parts of the world. Whereas in 1950 it was possible to describe all the known reactors in the course of a few pages, the task would now require a whole book. All that can be done, within a reasonable space, is to describe the main reactor types and to illustrate the descriptions by reference to a limited number of specific cases.

15.2. In spite of numerous possible variations in the design and components of nuclear reactor systems, there are, nevertheless, a number of general features which all reactors possess in common, to a greater or lesser extent. In outline, a reactor consists of an active core in which the fission chain is sustained and in which most of the energy of fission is released as heat. The core contains the fissionable material in a suitable form, i.e., the reactor fuel, and also a moderator if it is required to slow down the neutrons. The relative amounts and nature of the fuel and moderator determine the energy of the neutrons causing most of the fissions. The core is surrounded by a reflector of a material which is largely dependent on this neutron energy. The combination of core and reflector, together with other components present, e.g., coolant and structure, must be capable of maintaining a fission chain.

15.3. Control, including start-up, operation at any desired power level and shut-down, is achieved either by rods containing a strong neutron absorber (§ 14.59) or by moving parts of the core or reflector so as to permit (or prevent) the escape of neutrons. The operation of the reactor at appreciable power levels depends on the ability to remove the heat produced by fission as fast as it is liberated. This involves the use of a coolant which must circulate throughout the reactor in such a manner as to maintain a temperature distribution that is as uniform as possible. If the energy generated in the reactor is to be

449

converted into electrical power, then the heat must be transferred from the coolant to a working fluid, to produce steam or a hot gas. The resulting vapor or gas can then be used to generate power in a conventional manner, e.g., by means of a turbine (Fig. 15.1).

15.4. In the design of a nuclear reactor for a particular purpose, which may be research, production of fissionable material or the conversion of nuclear energy into useful power, the first decision to be made concerns the neutron energy region in which most of the fissions are to occur. The next step is to choose the basic reactor components, namely, the fuel material, the moderator (if any), the reflector and, finally, the coolant for removing the heat generated by fission. As an aspect of the latter, the particular method of heat removal to be used must be selected. The various factors which must be taken into consideration in making a choice among the different possibilities will be outlined in the succeeding paragraphs.

THERMAL, FAST AND INTERMEDIATE
REACTORS

15.5. Reactors are classified as "thermal," "fast" or "intermediate" according to the neutron energy region in which the majority of the nuclear fissions occur. With the exception of the atomic bomb, which is not strictly a reactor in the sense used here, since the fission rate cannot be controlled, all the reactors mentioned in Chapter XIV are *thermal reactors* in which most of fissions are (or were) due to the absorption of slow neutrons. In order to slow down the fast neutrons released in fission, a sufficient amount

of moderator must be included in the core of the reactor, as already seen (§ 14.27).

15.6. Thermal reactors have the great advantage of flexibility in size, which can be attained by varying the nature and properties of the fuel (containing the fissionable material) and the moderator, in particular. For example, a reactor with natural uranium as fuel and graphite as moderator is roughly 20 feet across, at least. At the other extreme, with a fuel material highly enriched (about 90 per cent) in uranium-235* and ordinary water as moderator, a thermal reactor may have linear dimensions of no more than one or two feet. The main drawback to thermal reactors is the loss of neutrons due to parasitic capture by constructional and other materials, as well as by fission products. The choice of such materials is therefore largely determined by their cross sections for neutron capture (§ 11.67).

15.7. In a *fast reactor*, the majority of fissions occur by interaction of the fissionable material with neutrons of high energy, i.e., neutrons which have suffered relatively little slowing down from the initial fission neutron energy. The use of a moderator, or of any material of low mass number, which might slow down the neutrons, must consequently be avoided. Because absorption cross sections for fast neutrons are generally small, parasitic capture is a minor problem in fast reactors. The choice of materials is thus greater than for a thermal reactor. On the other hand, there is some restriction in the possible fuel materials. By proper choice of moderator, etc., a thermal reactor can function on anything from natural to highly en-

---

* In addition to natural uranium metal, with 0.70 per cent by weight of uranium-235, authorized users can purchase from the U. S. Atomic Energy Commission uranium (as hexafluoride) containing 0.72 to 90 weight per cent of the fissionable isotope. This enriched material is produced in the gaseous diffusion method of isotope separation (§ 8.78 *et seq.*),

riched uranium or plutonium. But a fast reactor requires an enriched fuel containing about 25 per cent, at least, of fissionable material, e.g., uranium-233, uranium-235 or plutonium-239.

15.8. A disadvantage of a fast reactor is the larger amount of fissionable material necessary to attain criticality. However, because there is

tron density and heat generation increase at a tremendous rate.

15.10. An *intermediate reactor* is one in which fissions are caused mainly by neutrons slowed down into a broad energy range between fast and thermal energies, preferably above the resonance region (§ 11.97). Some moderation is necessary, but not as much

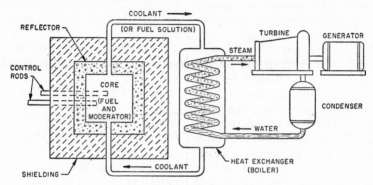

Fig. 15.1. Schematic representation of a nuclear reactor system for generating electric power.

no moderator, the critical size may be quite small, e.g., a foot or less across, so that heat removal is difficult when the operating power is high. The outstanding aspect of certain fast reactors, as will be seen below, is their ability to "breed" fissionable material, plutonium-239, in particular. It is mainly for this reason that such reactors are attracting interest.

15.9. It might appear, upon first consideration, that a fast reactor would be difficult to control, since it is like an atomic bomb in the respect that fissions are mainly due to fast neutrons. This is, however, not the case. As long as the effective multiplication factor is kept below the prompt critical value for the existing conditions (§ 14.61), a fast reactor is just as controllable as a thermal reactor. In a fission bomb, the design is such as to make the multiplication factor as large as possible, so that the neu-

as in a thermal reactor. In a sense, an intermediate reactor represents a compromise between thermal and fast reactors. The parasitic capture of neutrons can be less than in a thermal reactor and the fuel inventory is smaller than in a fast reactor, although the total size of the core is greater. An intermediate reactor also offers the possibility of breeding plutonium-239, but not as efficiently as a fast reactor. Only one intermediate reactor has been constructed (§ 15.100) and further interest in systems of this type appears to be small.

REACTOR FUEL MATERIALS

15.11. The material containing the fissionable isotope is called the *reactor* (or *nuclear*) *fuel*. Its composition may range from natural uranium to material highly enriched in uranium-235, plutonium-239 or uranium-233. The basic source materials for nuclear fuels are the elements uranium and thorium. Only the uranium-235, present to the extent of about 0.7 per cent in ordinary uranium, is fissionable; hence, this is the only natural material that can be used to produce nuclear energy directly. However, there are prospects that the 99.3 per cent of uranium-238 and the thorium-232, which constitutes nearly 100 per cent of natural thorium, can be converted, partly at least, into fissionable material.

15.12. The transformation of uranium-238 into plutonium-239 by the capture of neutrons followed by two stages of beta decay has already been described in Chapter XIV. Thorium-232 may be converted into fissionable thorium-233 in an exactly similar manner, by means of neutrons available in a reactor. By the (n,γ) capture of a slow neutron, the thorium-232 is converted into thorium-233, which is a negative beta-emitter with a half life of 23.5 min., the product being protactinium-233; this is also beta active with a half life of 27.4 days. The reaction and disintegration scheme is thus,

for the reasons given in § 14.24. Thus, uranium-238 and thorium-232 are not fissionable materials in the sense in which the term is generally used. The only fissionable materials are uranium-233, uranium-235 and plutonium-239, since they can suffer fission as a result of capture of neutrons of all energies. However, since both uranium-238 and thorium-232 can be converted into fissionable species, they are referred to as *fertile materials*. The extent to which such conversion is possible will be considered later (§ 15.39).

15.14. The form in which a fuel is used in a reactor depends upon various circumstances. In many reactors solid *fuel elements* are used; they may consist of uranium metal or an alloy of uranium and aluminum (or zirconium), or the uranium may be present as the dioxide (UO_2). The fuel material is usually clad with (or contained in) another metal to protect it from chemical reaction with air, water or other material used as coolant. The cladding also serves the purpose of preventing the escape of fission prod-

$$_{90}\text{Th}^{232} + n \rightarrow {}_{90}\text{Th}^{233} \xrightarrow[\text{23.5 m.}]{\beta^-} {}_{91}\text{Pa}^{233} \xrightarrow[\text{27.4 d.}]{\beta^-} {}_{92}\text{U}^{233},$$

the uranium-233 being a long-lived alpha emitter of 1.63×10^5 years half life. Hence, upon exposure to neutrons, thorium-232 would, after the lapse of some days to permit decay of the protactinium, be converted into uranium-233. This nuclide is fissionable by slow neutrons and is consequently a possible fuel material for sustaining a chain reaction.*

15.13. Although both uranium-238 and thorium-232 will undergo fission by fast neutrons with energy greater than 1 Mev, it is not possible to sustain a chain reaction in these isotopes,

ucts. Several reactors have been designed which make use of fluid fuels, e.g., a solution of a uranium salt in water or a solution (or suspension) of uranium in a liquid metal, e.g., bismuth.

15.15. Two main types of solid fuel elements have been used in reactor design, namely, the cylindrical (or rod) type and the plate type. In several of the early reactors, such as the natural uranium-graphite reactors at Oak Ridge and elsewhere, cylindrical fuel elements, about an inch in diameter, were used. The dimensions were

---

* The discovery of uranium-233 is described in § 16.92.

determined by the conditions required to optimize the infinite medium multiplication factor. Because of their relatively small area for the removal of the heat liberated in fission, these fuel elements are not suitable for reactors operating at fairly high power levels.

15.16. A great improvement in this respect has been achieved by using rods of smaller diameter or by going over to a plate-type of fuel element. These generally require enriched uranium as the fuel material, since there is some sacrifice in the multiplication factor which can be compensated for by the higher proportion of uranium-235. The plate type of fuel element consists of a number of long, flat (or curved) "sandwich" plates held in a box-like frame. The center of the sandwich contains a relatively low proportion of enriched uranium, either as metal or dioxide, dispersed in a matrix of aluminum, zirconium or stainless steel. The outer cladding layers of the sandwich are of the same material as the matrix in the center layer.

15.17. Although thin rods or plate-type fuel elements provide a relatively large area for heat removal, there is a corresponding increase in the amount of cladding material. This results in an increase in the loss of neutrons by parasitic capture. In addition to being resistant to corrosion and able to withstand the high temperatures that may be experienced in a reactor without loss of strength, the cladding material, particularly in a thermal reactor, must also have a small cross section for neutron capture. Only three materials, available at reasonable cost, satisfy these requirements in most cases. They are the ones mentioned above,

namely, aluminum, zirconium and stainless steel.* Zirconium, in the form of a corrosion-resistant alloy, is undoubtedly best for thermal reactors using ordinary or heavy water as moderator or coolant. But it is expensive and so stainless steel, which is cheaper, is an alternative possibility, although it is more wasteful of neutrons. In fast reactors, stainless steel is a suitable cladding and containing material, since parasitic neutron capture is then unimportant.

15.18. Apart from purely mechanical failures, the life (or "burn-up") of a fuel element in a nuclear reactor is limited by a number of factors. Because of the high cost of recovering the fissionable and fertile materials that still remain, a significant objective of reactor design is to increase the length of time in which fuel elements will operate satisfactorily. One of the limiting factors is that referred to by the general name of *radiation damage*. It was predicted by E. P. Wigner in 1942, while working on the wartime atomic energy project, that when solid materials are subjected to the action of high-energy particles, such as neutrons, the atoms would become displaced from their normal positions in the crystal lattice. As a result of this disruption of the internal structure, the properties of the material might be expected to change. Various changes due to radiation have, in fact, been observed. The effects of radiation damage are most marked in fuel elements due to the action of the fission fragments, which have large energies (§ 13.28), as well as to neutrons and gamma rays.

15.19. From the standpoint of reactor operation, the detrimental effects of radiation on fuel elements are

---

* For certain applications, not involving contact with air or water, magnesium and beryllium are also possibilities.

dimensional changes and, sometimes, loss of mechanical strength. In many reactors, especially those intended for operation at high power levels, the dimensions of the fuel elements and their spacing must be kept within very close tolerances. In these circumstances, a relatively small dimensional disturbance may make it necessary to shut the reactor down and replace the damaged fuel element. Since radiation damage is essentially a new phenomenon, it is being extensively studied. One purpose is to use the information to design fuel elements that will not be seriously affected during operation of the reactor.

15.20. In addition to the limitation set by radiation damage, there is another factor which restricts the life of fuel elements. This is the decrease in the amount of fissionable material as the reactor operates and the simultaneous increase in the parasitic neutron capture by fission products. The latter aspect is referred to as *fission product poisoning*. For reasons of safety and economy, the amount of fissionable material in a reactor must not greatly exceed that required for criticality. As the extra quantity is used up, in the course of reactor operation, the effective multiplication factor of the system steadily decreases until a point may be reached when satisfactory operation is no longer possible. This limitation in the operating life (or burn-up) may be partially overcome in some reactors by including fertile material in the fuel element. As a result of neutron capture, this is converted into fissionable material to replace, to some extent, that which has been consumed. Even if this replacement were complete, however, the accumulation of fission products would sooner or later make it necessary to shut down the reactor for recharging with fresh fuel.

15.21. A possible way of overcoming the problems arising from radiation damage and fission product poisoning in solid fuel elements is to use the fuel material in solution. Thus, certain (homogeneous) reactors employ a solution of an enriched uranium salt, e.g., uranyl sulfate, in ordinary water as the fuel. The water is decomposed to some extent by radiations, i.e., fission products, neutrons and gamma rays, into hydrogen and oxygen gases, but this is not too serious a drawback. Otherwise, there is no radiation damage. The effects of depletion in fissionable material and accumulation of fission products can be overcome by withdrawing some of the fuel solution, without shutting the reactor down. This is treated so as to remove the fission products having the largest neutron absorption cross sections; new fissionable material can then be added and the solution returned to the reactor.

REACTOR MODERATORS AND REFLECTORS

15.22. For thermal reactors, the moderator and reflector have essentially the same characteristics and so they will be considered together. The basic requirements of a moderator are that it should consist solely of elements of low mass number (or atomic weight) and that it should not capture neutrons to any appreciable extent. The only practical materials for use as moderators (and reflectors) are, consequently, ordinary water, heavy water, beryllium and its oxide, graphite (carbon) and, possibly, certain organic compounds.

15.23. Ordinary water is attractive as a moderator because of its low cost, even allowing for the high degree of purity desirable for reactor use, and also for its ability to slow down neutrons. However, neutron capture by hydrogen is so appreciable that enriched uranium, with at least 1 per cent of uranium-235, must be used as the fuel material. Because of the particular neutronic properties of the hydrogen in water, e.g., large scattering cross section, it is possible to design water-moderated reactors of relatively small size. The fact that water can be used as both moderator and coolant, as well as reflector, is an advantage. The chief drawback to the employment of water as moderator-coolant is encountered in reactors which must operate at high temperatures. Since water boils at 100°C at atmospheric pressure, high operating pressures, e.g., 2000 pounds per square inch, are thus required. Expensive pressure vessels and piping are consequently necessary.

15.24. Regarded purely as a neutron moderator, heavy water is the best material available. It has excellent slowing down properties and the cross section for neutron capture is very small (see table in § 11.40). It does not require enriched uranium as fuel to attain criticality, although the use of such fuel material makes the design more flexible. Like ordinary water, heavy water can be used as a coolant, but it suffers from the same drawback, namely, low boiling point and consequent need for pressurization. The cost of heavy water is high, even though it has been considerably reduced in recent years (§ 14.103, footnote). Nevertheless, it is possible that, in some reactor designs, the advantages of heavy water as a moderator (or moderator-coolant) may outweigh its high cost.

15.25. Both beryllium and its oxide are good moderators. The oxide can withstand very high temperatures, although its strength decreases. In spite of many technical advances, beryllium is still an expensive metal. Until recent years, the products available were very brittle, difficult to fabricate and susceptible to attack by both air and water at high temperatures. With new developments in powder metallurgy, beryllium metal, having improved properties with regard to ease of fabrication, mechanical strength and corrosion resistance, has been produced. Nevertheless, the material is still somewhat brittle, as compared with other metals, and is attacked by air and water at high temperatures and pressures. Beryllium is consequently used as a moderator or reflector in special cases only.

15.26. Carbon, in the form of graphite, has been employed as moderator or reflector, in a number of reactors. Although it is not quite as good as beryllium for these purposes, "reactor grade" graphite, of high purity, can be made at a relatively low cost. It can be machined easily into desired shapes and has sufficient strength to be used, to some extent, as a structural material, as it was in the original Chicago pile. The chief drawbacks of graphite are the relative ease with which it breaks when struck, and the possibility of interaction with oxygen (in air) and carbon dioxide at high temperatures. It was thought at one time that, in a reactor, radiation damage to graphite might be serious, but this now appears to be unimportant, provided the temperature is above about 250°C.

15.27. The moderating properties of certain organic compounds of carbon and hydrogen (hydrocarbons) should be almost as good as that of water since, like water, they contain a large proportion of hydrogen. For some time, consideration has been given to the use of a hydrocarbon of high boiling point as moderator (and coolant) for thermal reactors. Such a material would be relatively inexpensive and could be used in a reactor operating at fairly high temperatures without the need for pressurization, as is necessary with water. This development has been held back by the extensive decomposition suffered by most organic compounds when exposed to nuclear radiations. It appears now, however, that certain compounds known as polyphenyls (or their derivatives) may prove satisfactory as moderator-coolants. There is some decomposition by radiation but this is not too serious. The impurities formed in this manner are continuously removed by distillation.

15.28. The materials mentioned above are not satisfactory for use as the reflector for a fast reactor, because the neutrons returned to the core would be slowed down. To avoid this situation, the reflector must obviously be a material of fairly high mass number. Iron (or steel) is a possibility in this connection, although, for reasons which will be apparent shortly, fast reactors employ natural uranium as reflector, at least in the region immediately surrounding the core.

REACTOR COOLANTS

15.29. Just as no ideal moderator exists, so there is no ideal or perfect coolant for removing the heat produced in a reactor. The materials proposed for coolants may be divided into four general categories, namely,

ordinary and heavy water, liquid metals, organic liquids (hydrocarbons) and gases. Each type has its advantages and disadvantages, as will soon be evident. The actual choice thus represents what appears to be the best compromise in the circumstances.

15.30. Both ordinary and heavy water are good coolants for thermal reactors, in so far as their heat removal properties are concerned. They have, in addition, the advantage of serving as moderators, as well as coolants. But, as indicated above, for reactors operating at high temperatures, high pressures are required to raise the boiling point of the liquid. Further, water is very corrosive at high temperatures, so that special materials, such as zirconium alloys or stainless steel, may be necessary.

15.31. For use at temperatures higher than those that are practical with water, liquid metals have been proposed as coolants.* Probably the best of these is sodium; it is an excellent material for removing heat and does not require pressurization even at very high temperatures. It attacks zirconium and stainless steel to a small extent, but the rate of corrosion is regarded as acceptable. On the other hand, sodium is very reactive with oxygen (in air) and water, and the liquid sets to a solid well above ordinary temperatures. Further, when passed through a reactor, sodium becomes radioactive, due to the capture of neutrons and the formation of sodium-24, half life 15 hours, which decays with the emission of beta particles and gamma rays. Since this radiation is a potential hazard to operating personnel, special shielding of the sodium system outside the reactor

---

*The use of liquid metals (among other fluids) for removing heat generated by fission was proposed in a French patent application, filed by C. Chilowsky on July 28, 1939, more than 2 years before the first nuclear fission chain was realized.

is necessary. For heat removal in fast reactors, sodium is almost the only coolant that is at all satisfactory.

15.32. As a compromise between water, which requires the use of high pressures, and liquid sodium, which is so chemically active and hazardous, attention is being given to certain organic compounds, e.g., polyphenyls, mentioned above. They do not require pressurization, do not become appreciably radioactive due to neutron capture, are not corrosive and are fairly stable to the action of heat and radiation. However, the heat removal properties of these hydrocarbons are definitely inferior to those of water or liquid sodium.

15.33. Cooling by means of a gas, namely air, was used in several of the earliest reactors. It could be forced through the reactor with fans and vented to the atmosphere, without the necessity for using a closed coolant circuit. This procedure, although relatively costly, was simple and particularly suited to large natural uranium-graphite reactors used for research, and operating at relatively low powers. For high power levels, and the accompanying high temperatures, air is not satisfactory as a coolant because it reacts chemically with so many materials, e.g., graphite, aluminum, beryllium, zirconium, etc. The best gaseous coolant, from the standpoint of heat removal, is hydrogen, but this would represent a hazard, since it forms an explosive mixture with air. In addition, it causes many metals to become brittle. The next choice is helium, which is a nonreactive gas having a negligibly small cross section for neutron capture. It is, however, not available in sufficient amounts and is probably too expensive for general reactor use.

15.34. The gases which appear to be most practical as coolants are nitrogen and carbon dioxide. Nitrogen has somewhat better heat removal properties than carbon dioxide and is less chemically active, but it absorbs neutrons more readily. Nevertheless, both of these gases are being (or have been) used as reactor coolants. A gas-cooled reactor is probably less potentially dangerous than one using either sodium or pressurized water. The main drawback is that, unless the gas is under a fairly high pressure, e.g., a few hundred pounds per square inch, the cost of pumping is considerable. This is an important aspect of the economics of electric power production through the use of nuclear reactors.

METHODS OF HEAT REMOVAL

15.35. One of the possible variables in reactor design is the method of heat removal. Suppose that, as would be the case for a reactor intended for power production, use is made of the heat generated to operate a turbine. Three general methods may then be utilized to convert the heat into the vapor (steam) or gas at high temperature required for this purpose. In the first method the coolant, which may be water, liquid sodium, an organic liquid or a gas, is pumped through the reactor core so that it takes up heat from the fuel elements. The coolant then passes through an external heat exchanger, where the heat is transferred to water for the production of steam, and returns to the reactor in a closed cycle (see Fig. 15.1).

15.36. The second method is applicable when the fuel is in the form of a solution or suspension in a liquid, e.g., a solution of a uranium salt in ordinary or heavy water (§ 15.21), or one of uranium metal in liquid bismuth. The fuel-bearing liquid, in which heat is generated by fission, is pumped continuously through the external heat exchanger and then back to the reactor core. Steam is produced in the heat exchanger, as in the case described above.

15.37. A third system for heat removal, when either ordinary or heavy water is the moderator-coolant, is to permit the liquid to boil in the core, thus producing steam. In these circumstances, no external heat exchanger is required. The condensed steam from the turbine is returned to the reactor to keep the volume of liquid constant. This method of heat removal could be used, in principle, with either solid fuel elements or with a solution of the fuel material in water. However, so far, it has been applied only to the former situation.

15.38. A combination of the first and third methods just outlined, which is still in a state of development, offers interesting possibilities. It makes use of a gas at high pressure as coolant. This is heated to a high temperature in the reactor and then proceeds directly to operate a gas turbine. After leaving the turbine, the gas is re-compressed and returns to the reactor core in a closed cycle.

REGENERATION AND BREEDING OF FISSIONABLE MATERIAL

15.39. One of the remarkable aspects of nuclear reactors is that they can be designed so as to produce their own fuel, by conversion of fertile into fissionable material. Such reactors are called *regenerative reactors* or *converters*. As seen in Chapter XIV, the Hanford reactors fall in this category. In these reactors, uranium-235 serves to maintain the fission chain, but some of the neutrons are captured by the fertile uranium-238 with the ulti-

mate formation of plutonium-239. It is seen, therefore, that the uranium-235 consumed by fission (and in other ways) is replaced, to some extent at least, by another fissionable species, plutonium-239. At the same time energy is released in the fission of the uranium-235. In the Hanford (and other) reactors, this heat is wasted, but, in principle, a regenerative reactor can produce useful energy while converting fertile material into new fissionable material to replace that consumed. Although the fertile species has been assumed in the foregoing to be uranium-238, the general argument applies equally to thorium-232 (§ 15.12).

15.40. Because uranium-235 is the only fissionable material in nature, it is inevitable that, in the early stages of reactor development, such as those existing at present, this must be used to maintain the fission chain in nuclear reactors. There is no known method for regenerating uranium-235 and so, unless there is some unforeseen discovery, this material will eventually be consumed completely. At this stage, it may be supposed that a roughly equivalent amount of plutonium-239 (or uranium-233) has been produced by conversion of fertile material. Since natural uranium contains about 140 times as much uranium-238 as it does uranium-235, it is evident that considerable quantities of the former as well as of thorium-232, will still remain. The long-range future of the nuclear energy industry must therefore depend on the efficiency of converter reactors in which plutonium-239 (or uranium-233) is consumed and is, at the same time, regenerated from uranium-238 (or thorium-232). Three general cases will be considered.

15.41. First, suppose that for every

fissionable nucleus consumed less than one neutron is available for capture by the fertile material. The quantity of fissionable material regenerated will then be less than that of the same species consumed. In this event, the stockpile of fissionable material will steadily decrease, and in due course the operation of reactors will no longer be possible, although large quantities of fertile materials may be available. If this were the situation, there would be no real future for fission energy as a source of power.

15.42. The second possibility is that exactly one fissionable nucleus is regenerated for every one consumed in the reactor. The stockpile of fissionable material will then remain constant. The maximum rate of energy production will be determined by the available fissionable material and no increase will be possible. It is true that, in due course, essentially all the available fertile material would be converted into fissionable species, but there could be no expansion of the nuclear power industry.

15.43. Suppose, however, that it were possible to design a reactor in which more fissionable material, e.g., plutonium-239, was formed, by conversion of uranium-238 than was used up in its operation. This would be possible, in principle, if for every plutonium-239 nucleus undergoing fission, more than one neutron, on the average, were captured by uranium-238 to regenerate plutonium-239. A reactor of this type is called a *breeder* and the regeneration process is referred to as *breeding*. By the use of the breeding process, the stockpile of fissionable material could be steadily increased, instead of remaining constant as would be the case for the one-to-one conversion considered above. Thus, not only would all the fertile material be convertible into fissionable material, but the amount of the latter available, and hence the rate of power production, could be steadily increased. This would not go on indefinitely, of course, because a time would be reached in the ultimate future when all the fertile material was consumed, just as coal and oil fuels might eventually be used up.

15.44. The situation with regard to breeding may be compared with the availability of a certain amount of capital (plutonium-239) to a bank. The bank will use the capital for various purposes (production of power) and replace it with profits (fissionable material). If the capital cannot be replaced as fast as it is used up, the bank will eventually fail, even though there are still outlets (fertile material) for capital. This is equivalent to incomplete regeneration in a nuclear fission reactor. On the other hand, the capital may be replaced just as fast as it is drawn upon; then the amount of capital remains constant, and the bank will survive, although no expansion will be possible.

15.45. Finally, the profits may be large enough to replace the capital and also pay interest on it; if the interest is not withdrawn, but goes to increase the capital, then compound interest will accrue. This situation is analogous to breeding in a nuclear reactor. If the interest, that is, the rate of increase of capital (plutonium-239) is only 5 per cent per annum, the amount will be doubled in less than 15 years, quadrupled in 30 years, and so on. This can, in theory, continue until there are no further outlets (fertile material) for capital. The same general arguments apply to the breeding of uranium-233 from thorium-232.

15.46. The prospects for realizing breeding depend upon the number of fission neutrons liberated for each neutron absorbed by the fissionable material.* One neutron is required to carry on the fission chain and, in addition, more than one is needed, on the average, to make breeding possible. Hence, apart from neutrons lost by leakage or parasitic capture, somewhat more than two fission neutrons must be available for each neutron absorbed. From the known facts, it can be concluded immediately that breeding of plutonium-239 in a thermal reactor is impossible. However, thermal breeding of uranium-233 from thorium-232 would appear to be feasible.

15.47. Since the accessible supplies of uranium-238 are more abundant than those of thorium-232, the problem of breeding plutonium-239 is of greater importance. It is fortunate therefore that, owing to the smaller proportion of nonfission capture of fast neutrons, breeding of plutonium-239 from uranium-238 should be possible in a fast reactor. This expectation has been confirmed by experiments both in the United States and in Great Britain. It may be concluded, therefore, that fast breeder reactors, using plutonium-239 as fuel and uranium-238 as fertile material, will play an important role in the development of nuclear power. Until sufficient plutonium-239 is available for the purpose, uranium-235 will generally be used as the fissionable material. In a fast reactor of this type, more plutonium-239 is regenerated than the uranium-235 consumed, but the gain is less than if plutonium-239 were the fuel.†

15.48. There are various ways in which fertile material may be located with respect to the core of a breeder reactor. The one commonly favored is to surround the core with a *blanket* of fertile material, so that neutrons escaping from the core will be captured in the blanket. One significant advantage of this arrangement is that the spent fuel in the core can be replaced and reprocessed, as required, independently of the blanket.

REACTOR TYPES

RESEARCH REACTORS

15.49. Having outlined above the general considerations upon which the choice of a reactor system must be based, some descriptions will now be given of a number of reactors of specific types. In this connection, it is convenient to classify reactors according to the main purpose for which they are intended, although, as will soon be apparent, some reactors have more than one application. The types to be examined here are (*a*) research reactors, (*b*) production reactors and (*c*) power reactors and reactor experiments.

15.50. A research reactor is one of low or moderate power intended primarily as a strong source of neutrons, in particular, and of gamma rays for research purposes. Materials may be subjected to the action of neutrons

---

* The values given in the table in § 13.40 refer to the number of fission neutrons *per* (*thermal*) *fission*. Since not all neutrons absorbed by fissionable nuclei cause fission—some are merely captured in the (n,γ) reaction—the number of fission neutrons *per* (*thermal*) *neutron absorbed* is less than quoted in the table.

† As the nuclear power industry develops, the additional plutonium-239 produced in fast reactors will be employed as fuel in thermal reactors. In these, there will be some regeneration of fissionable material, but the very best that can be anticipated, as in thermal reactors utilizing uranium-235, is a one-to-one conversion.

within the core or reflector, or a beam of neutrons, covering a range of energies, may be extracted through an opening (or beam hole) running into the reactor. Research reactors frequently have a layer of graphite, 4 or 5 feet thick, known as a *thermal column*, adjacent to the core, to provide a source of thermal neutrons. If a long column of graphite is employed, the emerging neutrons are exceptionally "cold" (§ 11.91).

15.51. The earliest (Chicago) reactors, using natural uranium as the fuel source and graphite as moderator, and ambient air as the coolant, were research reactors. A similar fuel-moderator system, but with forced air cooling so as to permit operation at higher power (and higher neutron flux), was subsequently employed in the Oak Ridge reactor and the one at the Brookhaven National Laboratory, Long Island, N. Y. The fuel elements in the latter, originally of the cylindrical slug type, have now been replaced by twisted, sandwich plates containing enriched uranium as an alloy with aluminum. The Oak Ridge and Brookhaven reactors are used both for direct research and for the production of isotopes for research purposes (see Chapter XVII). These reactors, and similar reactors in Great Britain and elsewhere, provide extensive research facilities, but they are very large, requiring a minimum of 30 tons of uranium metal and 300 to 400 tons of graphite, and so are not suitable for all locations.

15.52. Several other types of compact reactors for research purposes have been developed in recent years. One of these is based on the so-called *water boiler*, developed at the Los Alamos Scientific Laboratory during World War II "to provide," according to the Smyth *Report*, "verification of the effects predicted for reacting systems containing enriched U-235." The original water boiler, which went critical in May 1944, was the first (homogeneous) reactor to use an aqueous fuel solution as well as the first to employ an enriched fuel (14.6 per cent uranium-235). The water boiler reactor has the great merit of simplicity of design and construction.

15.53. The core consists of uranyl sulfate (20 to 90 per cent enrichment) dissolved in roughly 3¾ gallons (14 liters) of ordinary water; the total weight of uranium-235 is about 2 pounds. The solution is contained in a stainless steel sphere or cylinder, surrounded by a graphite reflector about 4½ feet thick. The heat generated by fission is removed by passing cold water through pipes in the containing vessel. In spite of its name, the fuel solution in the water boiler does not boil, although its temperature may be as high as 80°C (175°F). Recent forms of the water boiler operate at a heat power level of 50 kilowatts or more. Under these conditions there is appreciable decomposition of the water by the fission products, neutrons and gamma rays, and provision must be made for recombining the hydrogen and oxygen gases released.

15.54. Another type of research reactor is known colloquially as the *swimming pool*. The core consists of a number of flat fuel elements of the sandwich plate type, the center layer containing 20 to 90 per cent enriched uranium (or uranium dioxide) dispersed in aluminum (§ 15.16); the weight of uranium-235 required for satisfactory operation is 5 to 7 pounds. The fuel elements are suspended vertically near the bottom of a pool of water, about 20 feet deep; it is from this characteristic that the reactor has acquired its name (Fig. 15.2).

The water acts as moderator, reflector and shield, and by convection it provides adequate cooling at power levels up to 100 kilowatts. By circulating the water through an exterior heat exchanger, so as to increase the rate of heat removal, operation up to 1000 kilowatts (1 megawatt) or more is possible.

pool reactor went into operation in the early part of 1951. But the MTR itself, at the National Reactor Testing Station, Arco, Idaho, did not go critical until March 1952; the maximum power level is about 40 megawatts. It is more of an engineering test device than a pure research reactor, although it is used for a wide variety of pur-

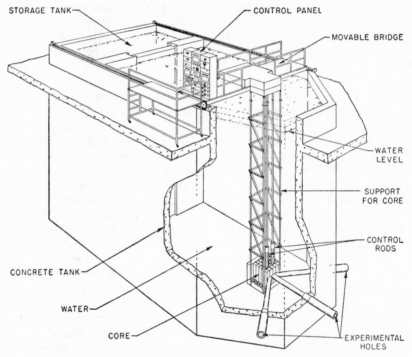

STORAGE TANK

CONTROL PANEL

MOVABLE BRIDGE

WATER LEVEL

SUPPORT FOR CORE

CONTROL RODS

CONCRETE TANK

WATER

CORE

EXPERIMENTAL HOLES

Fig. 15.2. Cutaway drawing of a reactor of the "Swimming Pool" type.

15.55. Historically, the swimming pool type of reactor originated from a mock-up of the Materials Testing Reactor (MTR). The latter was designed to provide a high neutron flux for experimental purposes, especially, as its name implies, for the study of the effects of radiation on various reactor materials. The mock-up was built at Oak Ridge National Laboratory in 1950, and the first swimming

poses (Fig. 15.3). Because of the great demand for the use of the MTR, another reactor of somewhat similar design, but with greatly improved facilities, called the Engineering Test Reactor (ETR), was completed at Arco in 1957. The maximum power level of the ETR is 175 megawatts, and the neutron flux is probably as high as can reasonably be attained in a thermal reactor.

15.56. The fuel elements of the MTR (and ETR) are of the aluminum sandwich-plate type, the fuel section containing uranium of about 90 per cent enrichment dispersed in aluminum. The core is surrounded by a tions (Chapter XIX). Cooling is achieved by forced convection with large volumes of water which enter the tank at some distance above the core, and flow downward through the fuel plates. The water leaves by an over-

FIG. 15.3. General view of the Materials Testing Reactor at Arco, Idaho, showing experiments in progress.

beryllium reflector and, in the case of the MTR, a second reflecting region of graphite. In the ETR, this outer reflector is made of aluminum. The whole is held near the center of a cylindrical tank containing water which acts as the moderator. The tank is enclosed in a thick concrete shield to minimize the escape of harmful radia- flow pipe fed from the bottom of the tank. A number of other research or test reactors similar to the design of the MTR (or ETR) have been constructed. They are generally referred to as being *tank-type reactors,* to distinguish them from the swimming pool (or pool-type) reactors which have a similar core but differ with respect to the method of heat removal, the reflector and the shielding.

15.57. A reactor of reasonable size, with natural uranium as fuel, can be designed by using heavy water as the moderator. Such reactors have a special appeal in countries which do not have means for the production of uranium-235. About 3 tons of uranium metal, in the form of vertical rods, in somewhat over 1000 gallons of heavy water, surrounded by a graphite reflector, will have an effective multiplication factor exceeding unity. Consequently, a reactor core with these components can be contained in a cylindrical tank roughly 8 feet high and 6 feet in diameter. An advantage of a heavy water-moderated research reactor with natural uranium as fuel source is that, since it contains less uranium-235, it follows from equation (14.4) that the neutron flux will be higher than for a graphite-moderated reactor operating at the same power level, i.e., for the same rate of heat removal.

15.58. The first reactor to use heavy water as moderator, with natural uranium metal as fuel, was completed at the Argonne National Laboratory in May 1944. Heat removal was achieved by circulating the heavy water through a cooler (heat exchanger) outside the reactor. The normal operating power was 300 kilowatts. The reactor was dismantled in January 1950, because of suspected corrosion of the aluminum cladding of some of the fuel rods. At that time the natural uranium was replaced by metal enriched to the extent of 2 per cent in uranium-235. This permitted a four-fold increase in neutron flux without any change in the rate of heat removal.

15.59. Outside the United States, the first reactor constructed was a natural uranium-heavy water system, which commenced operation in Canada in September 1945. Its power level was very low and reliance was placed on the ambient air to remove the small amount of heat generated. Some two years later, a Canadian reactor of the same basic type, but capable of operating at a power of 40 megawatts, was completed. Until the MTR started operation in 1952, the reactor provided the highest neutron fluxes available for experimental purposes. Another natural uranium-heavy water research reactor, of still higher power (200 megawatts) and neutron flux, has been built in Canada, and since 1951 others of moderate power have been constructed elsewhere.

15.60. With the greater availability of uranium-235, heavy water-moderated research reactors have been designed, using highly (90 per cent) enriched fuel. The advantage claimed for such reactors as compared with those of the MTR-type, which are moderated by ordinary water, is that, for a given amount of uranium-235, it is possible to have a larger core, thus providing somewhat more flexibility for experiments. The cost of the reactors using heavy water is, of course, greater. An enriched fuel reactor moderated by heavy water commenced operation at the Argonne National Laboratory in February 1954, and since then a few others of a similar type have been planned or completed.

15.61. A research reactor of an entirely different character to those described above was the Los Alamos Fast Reactor, nicknamed "Clementine." * Commencing operation in No-

---

* This name, derived from the well-known song, originated from a combination of circumstances: the location of the reactor in a canyon, and the fact that plutonium-239, for which the code number was "49," was the fuel.

vember 1946, it was the first fast reactor and also the first to have plutonium-239 as the fuel. The core, containing the vertical fuel rods clad with steel, was a cylindrical cage only 6 inches high and 6 inches in diameter; naturally, there was no moderator. The reflector consisted of ordinary uranium metal and steel, and the coolant was mercury. This liquid could not be used in a thermal reactor because it has a large cross section for the capture of slow neutrons, but the capture of fast neutrons is negligible. Neutron-absorbing rods, containing cadmium or boron, such as are used in thermal reactors, are of little value for the control of fast reactors. Consequently, control was achieved by rods which displaced some of the uranium from the reflector, thus permitting the fast neutrons to escape. The reactor was dismantled in 1953, when the corrosion of the steel cladding resulted in the mercury coolant becoming contaminated.

PRODUCTION REACTORS

15.62. The purpose of a production reactor is to convert fertile into fissionable material, the latter being employed as the source of energy in a nuclear fission bomb or as the fuel in other reactors, either for research or useful power. In the Hanford production reactors, the fuel is natural uranium, the moderator is graphite and water is the coolant. Because of the relatively large number of neutrons captured by hydrogen nuclei in the water, the number available for capture by uranium-238, with subsequent formation of plutonium-239, is considerably reduced. The efficiency of conversion, i.e., the ratio of plutonium-239 nuclei produced to the uranium-235 nuclei consumed in the reactor, may thus be appreciably less than

unity. It is conceivable that the British plutonium production reactors, at Windscale, which are cooled by air, have a higher conversion efficiency than do the Hanford reactors, but the power levels, and the production rate, may be lower.

15.63. The obvious method for increasing the efficiency of the conversion process is to design the reactor so as to have a relatively small resonance escape probability (§ 14.35). It is mainly by capture of neutrons in the resonance region that uranium-238 is eventually converted into plutonium-239. In natural uranium-graphite reactors, the maximum value of the infinite medium multiplication factor (about 1.07) is so close to unity that any appreciable decrease in the resonance escape probability would make it impossible to attain criticality. But, when heavy water is the moderator, with natural uranium fuel, the infinite medium multiplication factor can be as large as 1.25. Hence, a substantial decrease in the resonance escape probability is permissible without making operation of the reactor impractical. The conversion efficiency of a production reactor using heavy water as moderator can thus be greater than of one which is graphite moderated. It is of interest to record that heavy water is the moderator in the plutonium production reactors at Savannah River, South Carolina.

15.64. Most, if not all, of the fission energy released in the production reactors in the United States is wasted. Some consideration has been given to *dual-purpose reactors* which would produce both high-grade plutonium for weapons and useful power. But the general opinion is that, unless circumstances undergo a significant change in the United States, such reactors would not fulfill a useful function. In Great Britain, however, where conventional fuels, e.g., coal and oil, are relatively expensive, the first two Calder Hall reactors, intended for the large-scale production of electrical power from nuclear energy, were designed as dual-purpose reactors. They are natural uranium-graphite systems cooled by carbon dioxide gas under pressure. Similar reactors have been (or are being) constructed in France, where the situation with regard to power sources is somewhat the same.

15.65. In a broad sense, any reactor in which there is conversion of fertile to fissionable material is a production reactor. Whenever uranium-238 or thorium-232 is present, either within the core or in a blanket surrounding the core, as is the case in many power reactor designs, some production (or regeneration) of fissionable material is inevitable. But these are not called production reactors; the name is reserved for reactors in which production is the main objective.

15.66. Several reactors which are intended primarily for research, such as the graphite-moderated reactors at Oak Ridge and Brookhaven, are extensively used for the production of radioactive isotopes (§ 17.9, footnote). The method employed is to expose a suitable stable element to the neutrons in the reactor and, as a result of the radiative capture (n,γ) reaction, a radioisotope of the same element is obtained. A few additional radioactive species are produced as the result of other neutron reactions.

POWER REACTORS AND POWER REACTOR EXPERIMENTS

15.67. In a power reactor, the heat generated in the fission process is used, either directly or indirectly, to produce steam at high temperature and pressure or to heat a compressed gas. The steam or heated gas then passes on to a turbine, as in a conventional power plant; the turbine drives a generator, thereby producing electricity. In essence, therefore, the nuclear reactor is equivalent to a furnace of a boiler which "burns" a fuel of an entirely novel character. In some reactors steam or hot gas is produced within the reactor itself, but in most cases the steam is formed in an external heat exchanger which acts as the boiler.

15.68. Regarded purely as a generator of heat, there are some unusual aspects of a nuclear reactor that merit consideration. In the first place, there is no limit, in principle, to the rate (or power) at which a given reactor can generate heat. It will be evident from equation (14.4) that the heat power output depends on the weight of fissionable material, e.g., of uranium-235, and the neutron flux. The weight of the material does not vary greatly, but there is no theoretical reason why the flux should not be increased indefinitely. There is, however, a practical limitation to the power level. If the heat is not removed as fast as it is generated, the temperature of the reactor components will continue to rise and eventually they will get so hot that something will melt and the reactor will be destroyed. The operating power of a nuclear reactor is, therefore, determined by the maximum rate of heat removal. Nevertheless, it is because there is the possibility of a very rapid rate of heat generation, that increasing the power of a reactor to its operating level must be done with care (§ 14.61).

15.69. Even if heat can be removed very rapidly, there is another restriction to the power output, dependent upon the neutron flux. If the flux and, consequently, the fission rate are high, radiation damage to the fuel elements and other components of the reactor core may become too serious to permit operation for any length of time. Further, in a thermal reactor, certain fission products, notably xenon-135, have a peculiar effect. This particular nuclide has an extremely large cross section for the capture of thermal neutrons and is one of the worst known reactor poisons. It is formed mainly by the radioactive decay of a primary fission fragment (tellurium-135). As a result, its concentration in the fuel elements may increase considerably even after the reactor is shut down. Such is particularly the case when normal operation is at a high neutron flux, and the curious situation may then arise in which, due to the poisoning, the reactor cannot be re-started for some time after it is shut down. It may be necessary to wait many hours for the xenon-135, which is radioactive, to decay to a sufficient extent to permit start-up. Fast reactors do not suffer from xenon poison-ing, and this is often regarded as be-ing one of their advantages.

15.70. It is characteristic of nuclear reactors that they have a potential for high thermal efficiency, i.e., for the conversion of heat into electricity. A consequence of the laws of thermo-dynamics, with which engineers are familiar, is that heat can be more effi-ciently converted into useful energy if it is released at a high temperature. In a nuclear reactor, very high tem-peratures, and hence good thermal efficiency, would be possible were it not for the limitation imposed by the nature of the materials used. Such materials must not only be able to withstand high temperatures, but must also have small cross sections for neutron absorption. For one rea-son or another, thermal efficiencies hitherto attained in reactor systems have not exceeded those in conven-tional steam plants, but the situation may be changed in due course.

15.71. Another aspect of nuclear re-

POWER REACTOR COMPONENTS

Nuclear Fuel	Moderator	Coolant	Method of Heat Removal
Natural uranium	Heavy water, beryl-lium, beryllium oxide or graphite	Ordinary water, heavy water, organic liquid, helium, nitrogen, car-bon dioxide	Circulation of coolant through external heat exchanger (boiler)
Slightly enriched uranium	Same as above; also ordinary water or or-ganic liquid	Same as above or so-dium	Same as above or boil-ing water within reac-tor core
Highly enriched uranium	Same as above	Same as above or bis-muth	Same as above or cir-culation of homogene-ous solution through external heat ex-changer
Uranium-235 or plutonium-239 (plus uranium-238 for breeding)	None (fast reactor)	Sodium	Circulation of coolant through external heat exchanger

actors, to which attention should be called, is related to the fuel consumption. It is true that 1 pound of uranium-235 (or plutonium-239) can provide heat energy equivalent to that of 1500 tons of coal. But, whereas a fire can be started in a furnace with a small quantity of coal and then further amounts added gradually until all is consumed, fissionable material cannot be used in a similar manner. A power reactor capable of consuming 1 pound of uranium-235 without attention would have to contain a great deal in excess of this quantity. During the whole of its operation, the nuclear reactor must contain more than the critical amount of fuel material. This may range from a few pounds, in the case of a thermal reactor utilizing highly enriched uranium (or plutonium), to several tons, when natural uranium is the fuel source.

15.72. Within the limitations indicated above, there is still a large number of combinations, of fuel material, moderator (if any), reflector, coolant and method of heat removal, which appear to be practical for power reactor designs. Some idea of the reasonable possibilities are given in the appended table. To the fuel materials there will ultimately be added uranium-233, when this becomes avail-

able in quantity. Although some of the combinations of components are obviously better than others, there still remain about ten (or so) different reactor design concepts which appear to offer prospects for the economic production of power. In general, each system has both advantages and drawbacks, and without actual operating experience, it is not possible to state definitely that any one is to be preferred over the others. To build full-scale plants of each type would be too costly (and wasteful), and so a number of reactors have been (or are being) constructed that are in the nature of power reactor experiments. The reactors are generally prototypes of those which might be used for large-scale power production, but they may lack much of the subsidiary equipment. From the information gained in these experiments it will be possible to decide upon the best reactor types for the future development of nuclear power.*

15.73. Since the power reactor experiment of today may be the central station power reactor of tomorrow, the two categories will be considered together. In the ensuing section, some of the reactor types which seem to show the greatest promise will be reviewed.

TYPICAL POWER REACTORS

PRESSURIZED WATER REACTORS

15.74. A power reactor design which has received much attention in the United States is the *pressurized water system*, utilizing water under pressure, up to 2000 pounds per square inch, as the moderator-coolant. The

fuel elements are in the form of rods or plates of enriched uranium (or uranium dioxide) clad in a corrosion-resistant zirconium alloy or stainless steel. The temperature at the surface of the fuel elements may be as high as 315°C (600°F). The pressurized water

* In some countries, e.g., Great Britain, where conventional fuel sources are not as large as in the United States, it has been decided to build several full-scale power reactors of one or two types without waiting for the results of an extensive series of power reactor experiments.

is circulated through the reactor core, from which it removes heat, and then through an external heat exchanger where steam is produced. Fairly typical steam conditions would be a temperature of 255°C (490°F) and a pressure of 600 pounds per square inch.

15.75. A pressurized water system was used in the first nuclear reactor ever to produce substantial amounts of electrical power, starting on May 31, 1953.* This was the prototype (Mark I) of the reactor later installed in the submarine U.S.S. Nautilus, which commenced its sea trials in January 1955. The original fuel charge in the nuclear-powered submarine reactor was not replaced until more than two years later when the vessel had traveled some 60,000 nautical miles. It is estimated that in a Diesel-propelled submarine this would have required about 720,000 gallons of fuel oil. The nuclear fuel consumed has been described as being "about as large as a softball."

15.76. Because of the stringent space requirements, the fuel for the submarine reactor is highly enriched in uranium-235. With water as the moderator, it is then possible to construct a core of small size. Somewhat similar considerations apply to the very compact Army Package Power Reactor, which is also of the pressurized water type. This reactor is intended to act as a source of power in remote military bases, and it has been designed so that all its components can be transported by air.

15.77. Where space is not at a premium, e.g., in central-station electric power plants, a fuel of low enrichment can be used in a pressurized water reactor. The advantages over the highly enriched fuel system are the lower cost of the fuel material, the partial regeneration of fissionable material by conversion of the uranium-238 present into plutonium-239, and better conditions for heat removal due to the increased size of the core.

15.78. The first full-scale nuclear power plant in the United States, at Shippingport, Pennsylvania,† called the *Pressurized Water Reactor* (PWR), is based on a system of the type just described. Two kinds of fuel elements are employed: natural uranium (as the dioxide) in rods, and highly enriched uranium, alloyed with zirconium, in the form of plates, all clad with a corrosion-resistant zirconium alloy. The average uranium-235 content of the fuel is about 1.2 per cent. The steam temperatures and pressures are similar to those given in §15.74. The reactor is designed to produce 260,000 kilowatts of heat and the minimum electric power rating of the plant is 60,000 kilowatts. With an improved core design, this will probably be increased to 100,000 kilowatts.

15.79. An artist's sketch of the Shippingport nuclear power installation is shown in Fig. 15.4. As a safety precaution, in the event of an accident due to a series of unforeseen circumstances, the reactor and the four heat exchangers (or boilers) are completely enclosed in steel containers located under ground. These are seen at left-center of the sketch. The reactor itself is in the central container and two heat exchangers are in each of the others. A fourth container (not shown) holds the water pressurizing and other auxiliary systems.

15.80. Because operation of the pressurized water reactor in the U.S.S.

* The first nuclear reactor ever to produce electricity, although only in small amounts, was the experimental breeder reactor (§ 15.105) at Arco, Idaho.

† The reactor attained criticality on December 2, 1957, the fifteenth anniversary of the first nuclear chain reaction (§ 14.53).

Nautilus and its prototype (Mark I) has been so successful, others of this type, with fuels of various degrees of enrichment in uranium-235, are either under construction or being planned for central-station power plants and for the propulsion of surface ships and submarines. Since the temperature of the pressurized water is not very high, in terms of modern steam plants, some superheating is desirable. In certain nuclear power plant designs, therefore, the steam is superheated in an oil- (or coal-) fired furnace, so as to improve the operating efficiency of the turbine.

ployed as fuel. Power reactors based on these components are being favored in Canada and Norway, in particular, which have access to supplies of the necessary materials. A reactor design of the same type is also being studied in the United States. However, it has

Fig. 15.4. Artist's sketch of the Pressurized Water Reactor plant at Shippingport, Pa. The reactor is shown in the central cylindrical vessel of the three at the left; the vessels in front and back contain the heat exchangers or boilers. (Westinghouse Bettis Atomic Power Division.)

15.81. If pressurized heavy water is used as the moderator-coolant, instead of ordinary water, then natural uranium, either in the form of metal or as uranium dioxide, can be em-

been realized in this country, where the need for a new source of energy is not urgent, that reactors of the future must utilize plutonium-239, obtained from breeder reactors, as the main fissionable species. Thus, natural uranium as a fuel material can have only relatively short-range interest.

BOILING WATER REACTORS

15.82. It is well known that if boiling can be permitted, water is much more effective for heat removal than if there is no boiling. For several years it was felt that steam bubble formation in a reactor would lead to a dangerous instability, but since 1953 it has been shown, in a number of experiments carried out at Arco, Idaho, that water can be boiled quite safely in a properly designed reactor core by the fission-generated heat. Electric power was first generated from steam produced in such a *boiling water reactor* in June 1955. In order to determine the damage that might result from an accident, a reactor of this kind was deliberately allowed to go out of control, in July 1954, by increasing the power extremely rapidly. The reactor was destroyed as expected, but the consequences were not disastrous.

15.83. The boiling water reactor system, in which the water moderator-coolant is actually boiled directly within the reactor core, has many points in its favor. First, the elimination of the external heat exchanger results in a considerable decrease in capital expenditure. Further, the pressure in the reactor vessel does not have to be much greater than the required steam pressure. In a pressurized water reactor, the pressures used to prevent boiling are much larger, so that stronger and more expensive pressure vessels are required.

15.84. The Experimental Boiling Water Reactor (EBWR), at the Argonne National Laboratory, designed for 20,000 kilowatts of heat power, became critical on December 1, 1956, and first generated electricity on December 23, 1956. Electricity at the full rated power of 5000 kilowatts was produced six days later. The reactor employs plate-type fuel elements, partly of natural uranium and partly of highly enriched material; the average uranium-235 content is about 1.4 per cent. Steam is generated

at a pressure of 600 pounds per square inch. A modification of the boiling water reactor is being considered with natural uranium as the fuel and heavy water as the boiling coolant-moderator. If the loss of heavy water due to leakage, etc., can be kept small, a reactor of this design would have a strong appeal in countries which do not have facilities for the production of enriched uranium.

15.85. A number of boiling water reactors are being built for the production of electric power on a large scale. One of these is to have a heat capacity of over 600,000 kilowatts. Some doubt has been expressed concerning the stability of a boiling reactor operating at such a high power, but the problem can be resolved only by experience. Another question relating to a boiling water reactor is the possible contamination of the steam turbine system by radioactivity, thus adding to the difficulties of maintenance. The extent of this difficulty also remains to be seen.

HOMOGENEOUS (LIQUID FUEL) REACTORS

15.86. In the reactors described so far, solid fuel elements have been employed. When, for one reason or another (§ 15.18), the fuel is no longer effective, the elements are removed and put through the complex series of processes for the recovery of the residual fissionable and fertile materials (§ 15.109). These must subsequently be refabricated into new fuel elements. In order to avoid such costly procedures, *homogeneous reactor* systems have been proposed, using an aqueous solution of uranyl sulfate as fuel similar to that in the water boiler type of reactor (§ 15.52). Water acts as the moderator as well as the fuel-carrying coolant medium.

Heat is generated by fission in the fuel solution under pressure, and this is circulated through an external heat exchanger where steam is produced, just as in a pressurized water reactor. Apart from the savings due to the elimination of fuel fabrication, a significant advantage of a homogeneous reactor, indicated in § 15.21, is the possibility of continuous removal of fission products (and other impurities) during operation.

15.87. The major problem in connection with homogeneous reactors is the extremely corrosive nature of the fuel solution at the high operating temperatures, about 300°C (570°F). It is reported that, because of the corrosion problem, the British have abandoned their experiments with homogeneous aqueous systems. In the United States, however, experimental work on reactors of this type is proceeding actively. Corrosion is minimized by using a fairly dilute solution of highly (about 90 per cent) enriched uranium as the fuel material; the containing vessels, pipes, etc., are made of a corrosion-resistant alloy of zirconium.

15.88. The Homogeneous Reactor Experiment (HRE) at Oak Ridge National Laboratory was built to test the feasibility of maintaining a fission chain reaction in an aqueous circulating solution at high temperatures and pressures. The reactor attained criticality in April 1952 and was operated at heat power levels up to 1000 kilowatts. On February 24, 1953, about 150 kilowatts of electricity were generated, through its associated steam turbogenerator system. The HRE was dismantled in December 1954 to make room for a larger-scale homogeneous reactor experiment, known as the Homogeneous Reactor Test (HRT). In this form, the fuel carrier is heavy water, which permits the use of a low concentration (9.6 grams uranium-235 per 1000 grams of heavy water) of uranyl sulfate, because the neutron absorption cross section in heavy water is considerably less than in ordinary water. Heavy water is also the reflector (or blanket) medium.

15.89. Since the fuel material contains very little uranium-238 there is essentially no regeneration of fissionable material within the core. It is proposed, however, to add fertile material, probably in the form of a suspension of thorium dioxide, to the heavy water reflector so as to provide a blanket in which conversion can occur. It is hoped, in this manner, ultimately to achieve thermal breeding of uranium-233 (§ 15.46).

15.90. The evolution of the explosive hydrogen (or deuterium)-oxygen gas mixture, due to decomposition of the water (or heavy water) by fission products and nuclear radiations, represents a problem. The volume of gas evolved can be reduced by adding certain substances, e.g., copper salts, to the fuel solution, and by applying an excess pressure. In the HRT, the pressure on the core solution, for example, is 2000 pounds per square inch. The evolved gases, which carry with them fission product gases including the strong reactor poison xenon-135, are passed on to a vessel called a recombiner. This contains a catalyst which causes the hydrogen and oxygen to combine to re-form water (or heavy water). The radioactive fission product gases which remain are adsorbed on charcoal and allowed to decay.

15.91. A special feature of a homogeneous power reactor is that it can be controlled without the usual neutron-absorbing control rods. The operating temperature is increased by increasing the concentration of the fuel solution and the power level is adjusted by the rate of heat removal in the external heat exchanger. If heat is removed rapidly, the fuel solution returns to the reactor core at a relatively low temperature. This causes an increase in the multiplication factor and consequently the power level rises to balance the rate of heat removal. Similarly, a decrease in the heat demand causes the temperature of the core to increase and this is accompanied by a drop in the power level. To shut the reactor down, the fuel solution is diluted with water (or heavy water) until it is noncritical, the excess liquid being collected in storage tanks. In starting up again, the solution is concentrated to the required value by evaporating the added water (or heavy water). For emergency shutdown, the fuel solution is rapidly emptied into dump tanks.

15.92. A circulating fuel reactor of an entirely different type is the Liquid Metal Fuel Reactor Experiment (LMFR) designed by the Brookhaven National Laboratory. The fuel is a dilute solution of highly enriched uranium metal in molten bismuth. This permits operation, without pressurization, at high temperatures which are not practical with aqueous systems. The thermal neutron capture cross section of bismuth is quite small, but since its mass number is high, it does not slow down neutrons to any extent. Hence, a stationary graphite moderator is used in the reactor core. The fuel solution is circulated within the moderator and through an external heat exchanger for the production of steam of good quality, i.e., high temperature and pressure. Superheating of the steam can be achieved, if desired, without the conventional super-heater necessary in water-cooled reactors. The complete design of the LMFR calls for a regenerating (or breeding) blanket, surrounding the core, containing thorium as fertile material, in the form of the compound Th_3Bi_5, suspended in liquid bismuth.

GRAPHITE-MODERATED REACTORS

15.93. Although they differ somewhat in their individual characteristics, it will be convenient to consider next reactors with graphite as moderator and reflector and employing solid fuel elements. In the United States, attention is being given to a thermal reactor with liquid sodium as the coolant. The Sodium Reactor Experiment (SRE), with a heat power level of 20,000 kilowatts, is the first stage, and the Sodium Graphite Reactor (SGR) represents a full-scale development (250,000 kilowatts). The fuel rods of slightly enriched (about 1.7 per cent uranium-235) uranium metal, clad with stainless steel, are held vertically in channels through which the liquid sodium flows. The graphite moderator is contained in a number of zirconium cans, with a fuel and coolant channel at the center of each. The liquid sodium flows through the reactor core and then circulates through an external heat exchanger.

15.94. Since sodium acquires considerable radioactivity due to neutron capture (§ 15.31), it is desirable, from the safety standpoint, to incorporate two heat-exchanger circuits when this metal is used as reactor coolant. In the primary heat exchanger, which has a radiation shield, the heat is transferred from the radioactive reactor coolant to nonradioactive sodium (or sodium-potassium alloy). The latter is then circulated through an unshielded secondary heat-exchange system where steam is produced. By designing this heat exchanger in sections, saturated steam formed in one section can be superheated in another. The design temperature for the steam is about 440°C (825°F), the upper limit being determined by the possibility of corrosion of the cladding materials in the reactor core by the liquid sodium. The advantage of a sodium-cooled reactor is the high steam temperature attainable without pressurization, thus reducing the danger of the spread of radioactivity in the event of an accident. On the other hand, hot liquid sodium is by no means a simple material to handle.

15.95. As indicated earlier, natural uranium graphite reactors with gaseous coolants have received considerable attention in England. The interest in such reactors started with the air-cooled production reactors at Windscale which were considered to be less hazardous than the water-cooled Hanford reactors in the United States. In the Calder Hall reactors, as used in the world's first full-scale nuclear power plant, which commenced official operation on October 17, 1956, the carbon dioxide gas is at a pressure of 100 pounds per square inch. It is heated to 336°C (637°F) by passage around the magnesium (alloy)-clad fuel elements, arranged vertically in a matrix of graphite. In the heat exchangers, which consist of a boiler and superheater, steam is produced at 313°C (595°F) and 210 pounds per square inch pressure. Each reactor, containing 130 tons of uranium, has a heat power of about 180,000 kilowatts and an electrical output of some 39,000 kilowatts. Improvements in design, such as operation with carbon dioxide at higher pressures, and alternative cladding, to permit high reactor temperatures, may increase both heat and electrical power levels.

OTHER POWER REACTORS

15.96. The first nuclear power plant in the U.S.S.R. commenced operation on June 27, 1954; its electrical output is 5000 kilowatts, with a heat power of about 25,000 kilowatts, so that it is not really a full-scale industrial system. The reactor fuel is uranium metal of 5 per cent uranium-235 enrichment; the moderator is graphite and water under pressure is the coolant. The fuel elements are long tubes clad internally and externally with stainless steel, and effective heat removal is achieved by flowing pressurized water both along the inside and the outside of the tubes. The fabrication involves numerous welded joints and the cost would be prohibitive in the United States. The cooling water is circulated through an external heat exchanger where steam is generated at 260°C (500°F) and 185 pounds per square inch pressure.

15.97. The special advantages of an organic hydrocarbon, e.g., a polyphenyl, of high boiling point as moderator-coolant were mentioned in § 15.32. The purpose of the Organic Moderator Reactor Experiment (OMRE) in the United States is to test the effectiveness of such a moderator-coolant. By avoiding the use of pressurized water on the one hand, and liquid sodium, on the other hand, the possible hazards resulting from an accident are greatly minimized. Further, the problems of corrosion and of possible interaction of the coolant with the fuel material are insignificant. Organic hydrocarbons are, however, much less efficient in heat removal than are either water or liquid sodium; this may require an increase in the total area of the fuel elements. With an organic liquid of sufficiently high boiling point, it may be possible eventually to obtain super-heated steam of fair quality for operation of a turbogenerator. The OMRE is designed to produce steam at 288°C (550°F) and a pressure of 415 pounds per square inch.

15.98. Although gas cooling of the type used in British reactors has not been favored in the United States, partly because of the large amount of power required to pump the gas through the reactor and heat exchanger, and also because of the large fuel inventory, there is interest in some special applications of gas cooling. One of these arises from the fact that a gas-driven turbine of small size is less expensive than a steam turbine of the same power. Hence, a closed-cycle, gas-cooled reactor, with the hot compressed gas operating a turbine directly, would be of great interest, at military installations, for example, in remote areas. In order to attain good thermal efficiency, very high reactor temperatures are required, and for this purpose a refractory type of fuel element, e.g., of uranium dioxide, without cladding, is desirable. As moderator, either graphite or beryllium oxide could satisfy the requirement of being able to withstand high temperatures. Gas-cooled reactors for other purposes, e.g., merchant ship propulsion, are also being studied.

15.99. The foregoing descriptions have covered briefly essentially all of the most promising types of thermal power reactors. A number of others have been given more or less serious attention, including one moderated by heavy water and cooled by liquid sodium. This should be a very efficient system if the difficult engineering and constructional problems can be solved economically. Such a reactor would have an excellent coolant not requiring

pressurization combined with the best moderator. The latter would have to be kept cool enough to avoid the necessity for high pressures to prevent boiling. Special care must, of course, be taken to prevent access of the heavy water to the hot sodium; contact between these substances could be disastrous.

INTERMEDIATE REACTORS

15.100. As stated in § 15.10, only one intermediate reactor has been designed; two reactors have been constructed, one a prototype at the Knolls Atomic Power Laboratory and the other, the Submarine Intermediate Reactor, installed in the submarine U.S.S. Seawolf. These reactors have beryllium as (partial) moderator and are cooled with liquid sodium. They have operated successfully, although mechanical trouble was experienced in the steam superheater portion of the heat exchanger.

FAST REACTORS

15.101. The only type of power reactor remaining to be described is the so-called *fast breeder*, i.e., a reactor which produces power due to fissions by fast neutrons and at the same time regenerates more fissionable material than it consumes. Fortunately, the possible variations in the components of a fast reactor are limited and future developments will probably represent improvements in design based on operating experience with a number of reactor experiments. Strictly speaking, a breeder reactor should produce the same fissionable material as it consumes, e.g., plutonium-239 in a fast reactor using uranium-238 as the fertile material. Ultimately, such reactors must assume a prominent role in the nuclear power program. For the present, however, the fissionable species consumed in many fast reactors will be uranium-235, so that they are not strictly breeders. This name is, nevertheless, applied to such reactors, since they will, it is expected, have a conversion efficiency of over 100 per cent.

15.102. In reviewing the possible components of a fast reactor system, consider, first, the fuel material. This must contain a fairly large proportion of either uranium-235 or plutonium-239. Uranium-233 could be used if it were available, but there would be no point to utilizing this fissionable material in a fast reactor when almost as high a breeding gain can be achieved in a thermal reactor. Some dilution of the fuel with an element of high mass number is permissible, so as to increase the size of the core and facilitate heat removal. However, such dilution generally results in an increase in the quantity of fissionable material required to attain criticality, thereby increasing capital costs.

15.103. The coolant in a fast reactor must not contain elements of low mass number because they would slow down the neutrons. Further, solution of the problem of rapid heat removal from a relatively small reactor core demands operation at high temperatures and the use of a coolant with excellent heat-removal properties. There is only one substance, namely, liquid sodium, which can satisfy the requirements. An alloy of sodium and potassium was favored at one time, mainly because it remains liquid at ordinary temperatures, whereas sodium itself solidifies. But the alloy has inferior properties as a coolant and its use is no longer recommended.

15.104. There is, of course, no moderator in the core of a fast reactor, and the breeding blanket of uranium-238 serves effectively as a reflector. This may be surrounded by a moderating material and a neutron absorber to decrease the radiation hazard. Fast neutrons escaping from the exterior of the blanket would be difficult to absorb, but they can be captured much more readily after being slowed down in the moderator. In order to obtain as high a breeding efficiency as possible, a central "blanket" of fertile material may be located within the core, in addition to the one which surrounds it.

15.105. The first Experimental Breeder Reactor (EBR-I), designed by the Argonne National Laboratory, commenced operation at Arco, Idaho, toward the latter part of 1951 and produced over 100 kilowatts of electrical output on December 20 of that year. This date is of historical signficance, since it marked the first production of electricity using the energy of nuclear fission. The fuel elements consist of stainless steel tubes containing highly enriched uranium metal, the sodium-potassium alloy coolant flowing around these tubes. The core has been described as "about the size of a regulation football." The breeding blanket is in two parts: first a number of rods of natural uranium metal surrounding the core and next a number of keystone-shaped blocks of the same material. Control of the reactor is achieved by moving uranium metal rods in and out of the exterior blanket.

15.106. After operation for some time, analysis of the fuel and blanket materials of the EBR-I showed that the conversion efficiency achieved, i.e., the ratio of plutonium-239 produced to the total uranium-235 consumed, was just over 100 per cent. Since the conditions were not ideal, it may be assumed from this result that breeding of plutonium-239 should be practical. This has been confirmed by experiments in Great Britain on a fast reactor of very low power (2 watts) employing plutonium as the fuel. On the small scale used, it was found that at least two nuclei of plutonium were produced for each one consumed. The breeding gain was, therefore, very significant.

15.107. A second Experimental Breeder Reactor (EBR-II) in the United States is intended as a prototype for a fast-neutron reactor power plant. The fuel elements consist of a number of thin rods ("pins") of an alloy of uranium and plutonium enclosed in stainless steel tubes. The breeding blanket is in three parts: the central blanket in the middle of the core, an inner blanket around the core and, finally, an outer blanket. The reactor is controlled by movement of parts of the core section into and out of the reactor, thereby increasing or decreasing, respectively, the effective multiplication factor. The coolant is liquid sodium, producing steam through a system of two heat exchangers, as described in § 15.94. The temperature of the superheated steam is about 460°C (850°F) and the pressure is 1250 pounds per square inch. The heat power of the reactor is 60,000 kilowatts and the electrical capability is 20,000 kilowatts. Fast breeder re-

actors, of higher power, under construction in the United States and in Great Britain, are generally similar to EBR-II, although the composition of the fuel may differ.

15.108. A difficulty associated with the use of plutonium as a fuel is that the solid metal exists in six different modifications between normal temperatures and its melting point at 640°C (1185°F).* The change from one form to another, as the temperature is increased or decreased, is accompanied by a change in density. A fuel element made of plutonium metal would thus be dimensionally unstable and unsuitable for use in a reactor operating at a high power level. Possible solutions to the problem are to employ alloys of plutonium with other metals or to avoid the metallic state entirely by utilizing a compound, such as plutonium dioxide (PuO_2). Another promising possibility is to use the plutonium in a liquid alloy form; this is being studied at the Los Alamos Scientific Laboratory. Combination of a liquid-metal fueled reactor with a method for processing the spent fuel, without the necessity for fabricating solid fuel elements, would represent an important advance in power reactor technique.

SPENT FUEL PROCESSING

RECOVERY OF FERTILE AND FISSIONABLE MATERIALS

15.109. When the fuel elements are removed from a reactor, either due to the accumulation of fission product poisons, because of radiation damage or as a result of impoverishment in

fissionable nuclei, they will inevitably contain considerable amounts of fissionable, and often fertile, material which cannot be discarded. The effectiveness of the method of recovery to be employed depends on the nature of the fuel and the form in which it is

---

* Uranium metal exists in three modifications, but the first change does not occur until 662°C (1224°F), which is above the operating temperature of reactors using the metal as a fuel.

used in the reactor. In the case of a homogeneous reactor, for example, all that is required in processing is the removal of the worst of the fission product poisons. On the other hand, in a production-reactor or breeder with solid fuel elements, it may be necessary to extract the fissionable and fertile materials separately and to purify them to such an extent that the radiations emitted do not represent a hazard in refabrication of the fuel elements or breeding blanket. Efficient recovery of fissionable material is of special importance in the treatment of breeder blankets; a small loss in the recovery process, which might normally be regarded as quite tolerable, could completely nullify the breeding gain.

15.110. The first method devised for the recovery of plutonium from spent uranium fuel elements involved a complex precipitation procedure (§ 16.32), but this has now been superseded by a simpler treatment. The basic process is applicable to fuels of all types, with some modifications according to circumstances. After removal of the cladding, the spent fuel or breeder material is dissolved in nitric acid and an oxidizing agent added, if necessary, to insure that all of the uranium and plutonium is in the most highly oxidized (VI) state. The nitrates of these elements can then be extracted from the aqueous solution by means of certain organic solvents, which do not mix with water. The one commonly used in the United States is tributyl phosphate (TBP) diluted with a hydrocarbon, such as kerosene. The fission products remain in the aqueous solution and can be discarded. The fertile and fissionable materials can then be back-extracted from the organic liquid by means of water.

15.111. To separate plutonium from uranium, use is made of the fact that the former is fairly easily reduced to a lower oxidation (IV) state in which the nitrate is no longer soluble in the organic solvent. The uranium, on the other hand, is difficult to reduce and remains soluble. Thus, if the organic liquid containing uranium and plutonium is extracted with an aqueous solution of a reducing agent, the reduced plutonium passes into the aqueous medium but the uranium remains in the organic solvent.

15.112. The processing of spent fuel by the extraction method just described has proved quite successful. When solid fuel elements are involved, however, the fact that they have to be dissolved first, and subsequently have to be refabricated after recovery, adds considerably to the cost of nuclear power. Consequently, other methods of processing are being investigated which may have economic advantages. Two of these will be mentioned. One involves conversion of the spent fuel into a mixture of fluorides; upon distillation, the volatile uranium hexafluoride comes off as a vapor, leaving most of the fission products behind in the residual solid. Unfortunately, plutonium also remains, and so it must be extracted with an organic solvent. The fluoride method would appear to lend itself best to the separation of uranium-233 from thorium breeder blankets, since the thorium fluoride is not volatile. Another promising approach is to make use of high-temperature (pyrometallurgical) techniques such as are often employed in the extraction and purification of common metals. The spent fuel may perhaps be heated until it melts and impurities extracted with another liquid metal, by means of a suitable salt or as an oxide slag.

DISPOSAL OF FISSION PRODUCTS

15.113. No matter what method is used for treating spent reactor fuel, there always remains the problem of disposing of the highly radioactive fission product wastes. To some extent, it may be possible to find useful applications for certain of the fission products, as will be indicated in Chapter XVII, but it is reasonable to assume that much material will remain for disposal. In the United States considerable volumes of waste solutions are stored in underground tanks until the radioactivity decays sufficiently to permit their removal. The liquid wastes of low activity from the plutonium plants in Great Britain are pumped into the sea at a distance of about two miles from shore. These are probably temporary expedients and, as the nuclear power industry grows, other methods must be found for disposing of the radioactive wastes. One possibility, worked out at the Brookhaven National Laboratory, is to concentrate some of the main constituents in a special clay. Upon heating, the radioactive material becomes strongly attached to the clay and cannot be washed out; it can then be buried at sea or on land.

ECONOMICS OF NUCLEAR POWER

NUCLEAR FUEL RESOURCES

15.114. The future of fission as a source of useful energy depends, of course, on the availability of adequate supplies of uranium and thorium. According to estimates made by geologists, uranium is present to the extent of four parts per million (4 grams per ton) of the earth's crust, and the amount of thorium is nearly three times as great. This would make these fertile materials as plentiful as zinc, lead and tin, and more abundant than mercury, silver and gold. However, this information, although correct, is misleading. The reason is that, whereas most of the familiar metals occur in relatively concentrated forms in well segregated ores, much of the uranium and thorium is so widely dispersed that significant concentrations, in workable deposits, are the exception rather than the rule.

15.115. Only two sources of relatively high-grade uranium ores are known;* these are the deposits in the Belgian Congo and Canada, which contain 1 to 4 per cent of uranium oxide (U_3O_8). Ores of medium grade, with from 0.1 to 1 per cent of this oxide, are found in large quantities in Australia, Canada, Portugal, the United States and elsewhere. In the continental United States, the principal deposits are those of the Colorado Plateau, an area which includes parts of Arizona, Colorado, New Mexico and Utah. The average composition of the ores mined in this region is about 0.25 per cent of uranium oxide.†

15.116. Low-grade sources of uranium, containing less than 0.1 per cent of uranium oxide, are economic at the present time only if the uranium is a by-product of another process. Among the most important of these are the South African gold-ore residues, with about 0.02 per cent of

---

* The information given here applies only to countries outside the orbit of the U.S.S.R.
† The U. S. Atomic Energy Commission will purchase all domestic ores with a uranium content down to 0.1 per cent of U_3O_8 or its equivalent, i.e., 1.7 pounds of uranium element per ton of ore.

uranium. The mining costs in this case have already been assigned to the gold, so that economic recovery of the uranium is feasible. A similar, although less favorable, situation exists in connection with the extensive phosphate deposits in Florida and Idaho, which contain up to 0.01 per cent of uranium. The extraction of this element is then a by-product of the manufacture of phosphoric acid and of phosphate fertilizers. From the long-range viewpoint, recovery of uranium from the oil shales of Tennessee and the lignite beds in Wyoming is of some interest. Possible methods for extracting the nuclear fuel from these materials at a reasonable cost are being studied.

15.117. Although the total amount of thorium in the earth's crust exceeds that of uranium, the economically recoverable quantities of the former are probably much less. The only known commercially useful sources of thorium are the monazite-bearing sands of Travancore, India. Considerable quantities of these sands are also found in Brazil and smaller amounts occur in other parts of the world, including North and South Carolina, Florida and Idaho in the United States. The monazite sands almost invariably contain some uranium as well as thorium.

15.118. Because of the highly variable nature of uranium and thorium deposits, both as regards composition and extent, and the lack of reliable information, estimates of the total reserves of fissionable and fertile materials cannot be too accurate. A further complication is that the reserves depend upon the concentration of uranium in the mineral that can be extracted economically. In other words,

the quantity of uranium and thorium available is determined by the cost that can be paid for recovery of the metal from the ore. It has been estimated that, assuming a price of $100 per pound, and allowing for technological advance, the world's reserves are 25 million tons of uranium and 1 million tons of thorium.*

15.119. Since uranium-235, present to the extent of 0.7 per cent in natural uranium, is the only fissionable material in nature, the total reserves of this isotope would be roughly 175,000 tons. This is equivalent in heat energy to 1.25×10^{19} B.T.U. At the present rate of the world's power consumption (10^{17} B.T.U. per annum), this would represent a 125 year's supply. But, if power were used in all parts of the world at the same rate as in the United States at the present time, the directly fissionable material would supply the world's needs for not more than about 20 years.

15.120. With breeding as a practical possibility and, in fact, a necessity if nuclear fuel is to make a significant contribution to the world's energy resources, allowance must be made for the fertile materials. Assuming that one third of the latter can be converted into fissionable materials at a reasonable cost, the total heat energy available from fission would be 6.2×10^{20} B.T.U. This is about forty times as great as could be obtained from the uranium-235 alone. For purposes of comparison, it may be recorded that the heat content of the coal, oil, gas and oil shale, recoverable at not more than twice the present cost, is estimated to be about 4×10^{19} B.T.U. It is apparent, then, that nuclear fuels can make a substantial contribution to the world's energy resources.

* The price of uranium metal in the United States in 1957 is just over $18 per pound.

COST OF NUCLEAR POWER

15.121. Several attempts have been made to estimate the cost of electricity produced from nuclear fission. Until more data are available concerning the costs of constructing and operating large-scale nuclear power plants, the conclusions are largely in the nature of intelligent guesses. It seems certain that electricity from nuclear fuel will be initially more expensive than electricity produced in plants burning fossil fuels, i.e., coal or oil. But the order of the difference is such as to indicate that, in the course of time, the cost of nuclear power can be decreased so as to be competitive with power from more conventional sources.

15.122. In the meantime, there are circumstances where the use of nuclear energy can be justified, on economic or other grounds. In areas where neither fossil fuels nor water power is available and where the cost of transporting coal or oil is high, nuclear reactors might prove to be worth while even in their present early state of development. A transportable nuclear power system, for use in the event of a disaster or other emergency, represents a possible application where cost is a secondary consideration.

15.123. Another justifiable application of nuclear power arises from the fact that the space occupied by a reactor and its fuel is much less than for a conventional system of equivalent energy output. Thus, a nuclear power plant would be advantageous for the propulsion of ships, either warships or merchant vessels, which must at present give up valuable space to store large quantities of oil or coal. A somewhat similar situation arises in connection with the propulsion of an aircraft, and considerable work has been done on the development of a nuclear reactor for this purpose. During 1956, a turbojet engine, such as is used in aircraft, was driven (on the ground) for the first time, at least in the United States, by nuclear power. It appears, therefore, that a nuclear-powered airplane is a distinct possibility, although there are still problems to be solved before it is a practical proposition.

The New Elements

Chapter XVI

THE TRANSURANIUM ELEMENTS

DISCOVERY AND PROPERTIES OF NEPTUNIUM

16.1. The element plutonium, which was unknown and probably did not even exist to any appreciable extent in 1939, has become of great significance in the world's social and economic outlook. As seen in the preceding chapters, it can be employed as a source of energy of explosive violence, or it can be made to liberate energy more slowly in a manner that may make feasible the production of useful power. At the same time, it should be possible for the plutonium-239 to regenerate, by breeding, more than is consumed, thereby utilizing as a source of power material that might otherwise be of no value in this respect.

16.2. To the scientist, plutonium is also of special interest as a member of a group of elements, called the *transuranium elements*, that lie beyond uranium in the periodic system. These elements, with atomic numbers greater than 92, and of which several are known, are important not only because they have been obtained by artificial means; the arrangement of the orbital electrons (§ 4.63) in the atoms of these elements is an intriguing problem for both physicists and chemists. Further, the investigation and isolation of compounds of the transuranium elements in the pure state has led to the development of the remarkable new techniques of quantitative ultramicrochemistry; this makes possible experiments with fractions of a cubic centimeter of solutions containing a few millionths of a gram of dissolved substance.

16.3. As seen in Chapter XIII, the many radioactivities observed when uranium was irradiated with slow neutrons, which were at first attributed to transuranium elements, were later shown to be due to various fission products. Consequently, although elements of atomic number exceeding 92 were undoubtedly present, they were not definitely identified until later when the situation had been somewhat clarified by the discovery of fission. Among the several beta-particle decay periods which had been observed following the interaction of uranium with neutrons was one of 23 min. This could not be separated in any way from the uranium itself, and hence in 1936, O. Hahn, L. Meitner and F. Strassmann in Germany attributed it to the uranium-239 isotope formed by the radiative capture reaction,

$$_{92}U^{238} + _{0}n^1 \rightarrow _{92}U^{239} + \gamma.$$

Upon emitting a beta particle, the uranium-239 should form the transuranium element of atomic number 93, but this was not identified.

16.4. In the course of experiments designed to confirm the phenomenon of fission, made by E. M. McMillan in Berkeley early in 1939, in which a thin layer of uranium oxide was exposed to slow neutrons, a non-recoiling, beta-emitting product of 23 min. half life was observed. This was undoubtedly uranium-239; not being a fission fragment it would not be expected to recoil from the target. In addition, a non-recoiling beta activity of 2.3 days was detected, the chemistry of which followed that of the rare earths. In other words, when a rare-earth element, added as a carrier to the solution, was precipitated, the precipitate carried with it the 2.3-day activity. At first it was thought that the latter was due to a radioactive rare-earth isotope, but this interpretation was shown to be incorrect.

16.5. As a result of further investigation, E. M. McMillan and P. H. Abelson were able to show in 1940 that the 2.3-day product was generated from uranium-239 at a rate exactly that required by the 23-min. half life of the latter. Hence, the 2.3-day period is due to the element of atomic number 93, mass number 239, formed by beta decay of the uranium-239; thus,

$$_{92}U^{239} \rightarrow 93^{239} + _{-1}e^0.$$

The first true transuranium element, discovered in this manner, was later called *neptunium*, symbol Np, by McMillan, after the name of the planet Neptune, lying beyond Uranus in the solar system.

16.6. It was indicated in § 1.49 that there had been some uncertainty concerning the position in the periodic table of the elements following actinium. The most general view, which appeared to find support from the work done on the false, so-called transuranium elements from 1934 through 1938 (§ 13.2 *et seq.*), was that they were analogous to Period 5, rather than Period 6, containing the rare-earth (lanthanide) series (see Periodic Table in § 1.44). It is true that the elements actinium, thorium, protactinium and uranium resemble their Period 5 homologues yttrium, hafnium, tantalum and tungsten, respectively; consequently, it was to be expected, that the chemistry of neptunium should be similar to that of rhenium. But upon investigation, McMillan and Abelson proved that this was not the case.

16.7. Unlike rhenium, neptunium does not precipitate with hydrogen sulfide in acid solution; it is not reduced to the metallic state by zinc, neither does it have an oxide volatile at red heat. It was found, however, that in a reducing (sulfur dioxide) solution neptunium could be precipitated with cerium (III) as fluoride, CeF_3,* like a rare earth, or with thorium (IV) as iodate, $Th(IO_3)_4$. On the other hand, after oxidation with an acid bromate solution, the neptunium activity could be separated with sodium uranyl (VI) acetate. Subsequent work has shown that neptunium resembles uranium in the respect that both exist in (III), (IV), (V) and (VI) oxidation states. One of the main differences in the properties of the two elements lies in the fact that neptunium (VI) is more easily reduced to the (IV) and (III) states than is uranium (VI). The most stable compounds of the former element are those of the oxidation state (IV), such as

---

* The neptunium fluoride may have been $Np(III)F_3$ or $Np(IV)F_4$, both of which are insoluble, or a mixture of the two.

NpO_2 and NpF_4, but for the latter the uranyl (VI) compounds are the most stable.

16.8. Soon after the discovery of the 2.3-day Np^{239} isotope of neptunium, another isotope was identified by G. T. Seaborg, E. M. McMillan, J. W. Kennedy and A. C. Wahl of the Radiation Laboratory, Berkeley, at the end of 1940. By bombarding uranium oxide with fast deuterons from a cyclotron, the $(d,2n)$ reaction

$$_{92}U^{238} + _1H^2 \rightarrow _{93}Np^{238} + 2_0n^1$$

took place. The product Np^{238} is beta active, decaying with a half life of 2.0 days.

16.9. The two isotopes of neptunium mentioned so far are too unstable to make other than a tracer study of the chemistry of this element possible (§ 16.12). It is fortunate, therefore, that a third isotope, with a much longer half life, was discovered by A. C. Wahl and G. T. Seaborg early in 1942. In 1940, both G. Nishina and his associates in Japan, and E. M. McMillan in Berkeley had found that exposure of uranium to fast neutrons leads to the formation of the beta-active isotope U^{237}, having a half life of 6.8 days, as a result of the $(n,2n)$ reaction

$$_{92}U^{238} + _0n^1 \rightarrow _{92}U^{237} + 2\,_0n^1.$$

The beta-decay product of the uranium-237 should be neptunium-237, but because of the weak activity of the latter it was not detected for some time; however, it is now known to be an alpha emitter with a half life of 2.2×10^6 years. It is of interest to mention that traces of neptunium-237 found in uranium minerals probably originate in a similar manner from the $(n,2n)$ reaction of neutrons liberated in the spontaneous fission of uranium-238. Neptunium-237 is by far the longest-lived of the known isotopes of this element, and it is the nuclide after which the neptunium $(4n + 1)$ series of radioelements (§ 5.62) was named.

16.10. Because of its relatively long life, the rate of emission of alpha particles from neptunium-237 is low, and their penetrating power is small. By taking reasonable care, work with appreciable amounts of this isotope can be performed without the necessity for the special precautions required by more active elements (§ 19.69). In addition to this circumstance, it happens that neptunium-237 is formed to a small extent, due to the $U^{238}(n,2n)$ U^{237} reaction, followed by decay of the U^{237}, in nuclear chain reactors. Appreciable quantities of Np^{237} have thus been obtained by extraction from spent reactor fuel. With this material a very thorough study has been made of the chemistry of neptunium, and many of its compounds have been prepared in the pure state (§ 16.17).

16.11. Besides the three neptunium isotopes mentioned above, eight others, with mass numbers ranging from 231 through 241, have been identified. These are obtained mainly by bombarding either one or other of the isotopes of uranium by deuterons or alpha particles, or by the decay of other radioactive species. Some typical reactions are the following:

Np^{231}	$U^{233}(d,4n)$; $U^{235}(d,6n)$; $U^{238}(d,9n)$
Np^{234}	$Pa^{231}(\alpha,n)$; $U^{235}(d,3n)$; $U^{235}(\alpha,p4n)$
Np^{235}	$U^{235}(\alpha,p3n)$; $U^{235}(d,2n)$
Np^{236}	$U^{235}(d,n)$; $U^{235}(\alpha,p2n)$; $U^{238}(d,4n)$; $Np^{237}(d,t)$
Np^{239}	$U^{238}(d,n)$; $U^{235}(\alpha,p2n)$

Several of the neutron-deficient isotopes of low mass number decay by orbital-electron capture, whereas those of high mass number emit negative beta particles; neptunium-231 and -237 are alpha-particle emitters.

TRACER AND ULTRAMICROCHEMICAL METHODS

16.12. The earliest experiments on neptunium, and on the other transuranium elements, were made by what is called the *tracer technique,* in which an inactive carrier* is used to follow the behavior of a radioactive element present in unweighable and invisible, often referred to as tracer, amounts. Provided the material has a reasonably strong activity, it is possible to trace quantities as small as 10^{-10} gram or less (§ 17.35). At the extremely low concentrations of the radioactive compounds in the solutions, there is rarely precipitation of the substances themselves, although they may be carried down, either adsorbed or as a solid solution, by an insoluble compound of the carrier element. From the extent to which this occurs, it is possible to obtain a comparative indication of the insolubility of the corresponding compound of the radioelement.

16.13. For example, if an appreciable quantity of thorium is added as carrier to a solution containing a tracer amount of neptunium, in the reduced state, in aqueous hydrofluoric acid, it will be found that the thorium fluoride (ThF_4) precipitated contains essentially the whole of the neptunium activity. From this result it can be inferred that neptunium forms an insoluble fluoride, presumably NpF_4. According to G. T. Seaborg: "A great

deal can be learned by this [tracer] method of investigation, which is the only possible method when submicrogram† amounts are available. However," he points out, "care must be taken in interpreting the data, and in many cases completely positive deductions cannot be made." Where possible, therefore, it is desirable to confirm the conclusions reached with the tracer technique, which employs extremely dilute solutions, often less than 10^{-10} molar, by making observations with somewhat larger amounts at such concentrations that pure precipitates can be formed and carriers are not required.

16.14. Because the quantities of the transuranium elements usually available are very small, generally of the order of a few millionths of a gram, it is necessary to work on a scale very much below even that of microchemistry. The technique of qualitative chemical analysis on such a minute scale has been pioneered by A. A. Benedetti-Pichler, and also by P. L. Kirk, in the United States; the latter, who proposed the name *ultramicrochemistry* for this field of study, made important contributions to its adaptation to quantitative measurements. By using extremely small volumes, of the order of 10^{-5} to 0.1 cc., and weighing microgram amounts, it is possible to obtain solutions containing from 0.01 to 100 grams per liter. Such concentrations are those of ordinary chemistry, and are far greater than are involved in tracer work; consequently, the common chemical reactions can be performed without the use of carriers.

16.15. "The extremely small volumes [used in ultramicrochemical

---

* In general, a carrier may be an isotope of the element carried, or it may be an entirely different element, as in the present chapter, having a somewhat similar chemistry (§§ 5.29, 13.76).

† A microgram is one millionth part of a gram.

studies]," says Seaborg, "are handled with the help of specially constructed, small capillary containers, pipettes, burettes, micromanipulators, etc. Liquid volumes [from 10^{-5} to 10^{-1} cc.] ... are measured ... by means of finely calibrated tubing, the movement of liquid within the capillary being governed by air pressure under sensitive control. . . . The 'test tubes' and 'beakers' for this work are constructed from capillary tubing which has an inside diameter of 0.1–1 mm. The weights of solids which are handled in reagents and precipitates are usually in the range of 0.1–100 microgram. . . . This work is usually done upon a mechanical stage of a microscope, with the entire apparatus within the field of view [Fig. 16.1].

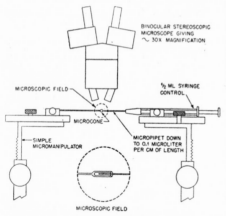

Fig. 16.1. Ultramicrochemical reaction performed under the microscope.

The test tubes, pipettes, etc., are handled by means of mechanical aids . . . [and] the separation of solids from liquids is usually done by means of centrifugation rather than by filtration."

16.16. The weighing of quantities of the order of millionths of a gram is often performed with some form of ultramicrobalance which makes use of the bending or torsion of a fine quartz fiber. These balances are calibrated by means of known small weights. In the quartz-fiber torsion balance used in much of the ultramicrochemical work, it is possible to weigh amounts as small as 1 microgram, or less, with an accuracy of 0.02 microgram. The beam and other parts of this balance are constructed of fibers of quartz "ranging in diameter from about four times that of a human hair down to fibers which are invisible to the unaided eye." The addition to a small platinum pan of the substance to be weighed causes a horizontal quartz fiber carrying the beam of the balance to be twisted; the weight is then estimated from the amount of torsion that must be applied to return the beam to its original position. In work of this kind the very greatest precautions must be taken to avoid sources of error which are quite negligible under normal conditions.

CHEMISTRY OF NEPTUNIUM

16.17. The first compound of neptunium free from carrier* was prepared by L. B. Magnusson and T. J. LaChapelle in the United States in 1944, working on the ultramicrochemical scale. The material secured by the bombardment of uranium by fast neutrons, and which contained the neptunium-237 in addition to unchanged uranium, some plutonium and fission products, was dissolved in nitric acid. Because of its low activity, neptunium-237 is difficult to trace; consequently, a small quantity of the 2.3-day Np^{239} isotope was added to the solution to permit the chemistry of the neptunium to be followed.

---

* The first transuranium compound to be prepared free from carrier was a compound of the element plutonium (§ 16.30), which was discovered after neptunium.

16.18. The nitric acid solution was then reduced, by sulfur dioxide, for example, and fluorides precipitated by hydrofluoric acid with a small amount of lanthanum as carrier. The precipitate included the neptunium and plutonium, together with rare-earth elements, but most of the uranium remained in solution as uranyl nitrate. The fluorides were then dissolved in sulfuric acid and oxidized by means of bromate at room temperature. The neptunium was thus converted to the (VI) state, and upon the addition of hydrofluoric acid, the lanthanum and plutonium were precipitated, leaving the neptunium in solution. The (VI) oxidation state of the latter was then reduced to the (IV) state by sulfur dioxide, and its hydroxide (or hydrous oxide) precipitated by ammonia. Upon removing the precipitate and heating it in air to red heat, 10 micrograms of product, which proved to be neptunium (IV) dioxide, NpO_2, were obtained.

16.19. The hydroxide can be dissolved in sulfuric acid and then oxidized to the neptunium (VI) state by means of bromate. Upon addition of concentrated sodium nitrate and acetate solutions, sodium neptunyl acetate, $NaNpO_2(C_2H_3O_2)_3$, isomorphous with the well-known sodium uranyl acetate, was precipitated. The nature of the compound was proved by means of its X-ray diffraction pattern (§ 2.93) obtained with only 15 micrograms of material.

16.20. Besides the substances mentioned above, other compounds of neptunium, notably the fluorides, have been prepared, mostly on the microgram scale. If the dioxide is heated in a mixture of hydrogen and hydrogen fluoride at 500°C, the trifluoride, NpF_3, is formed; thus,

$$NpO_2 + \tfrac{1}{2}H_2 + 3HF \rightarrow NpF_3 + 2H_2O.$$

Upon heating the trifluoride in a current of oxygen and hydrogen fluoride, also at 500°C, the product is the tetrafluoride, according to the equation

$$NpF_3 + \tfrac{1}{4}O_2 + HF \rightarrow NpF_4 + \tfrac{1}{2}H_2O.$$

The same compound also results from the reaction of mixed oxygen and hydrogen fluoride directly on heated neptunium dioxide. If the trifluoride is heated in fluorine, the hexafluoride, NpF_6, with properties similar to uranium hexafluoride, is formed. The three compounds NpF_3, NpF_4 and NpF_6 represent neptunium in the III, IV and VI oxidation states, respectively.

16.21. By heating the dioxide in carbon tetrachloride vapor, the reaction

$$NpO_2 + 2CCl_4 \rightarrow NpCl_4 + 2COCl_2$$

takes place, leading to the production of neptunium tetrachloride; this is exactly analogous to the method employed in the preparation of uranium tetrachloride. Further, as with uranium, neptunium tetrachloride is reduced to the trichloride by means of hydrogen at 450°C.

16.22. Two bromides and an iodide of neptunium have also been made by a method which is similar to one which has proved successful with uranium. A mixture of neptunium dioxide and excess aluminum was exposed to the action of bromine vapor, and the unreacted aluminum bromide was removed by sublimation at 250°C. Upon heating the residue to 800°C, neptunium tribromide volatilized and deposited on the cooler portions of the tube. If, in a similar experiment, excess of aluminum was avoided, the tetrabromide was obtained by sublimation at 500°C. Neptunium triiodide was prepared in an analogous manner from the dioxide, aluminum and iodine vapor; the iodide volatilized at 800°C.

The identity of all the halides was established by X-ray diffraction studies which showed them to have the same crystal structure as the corresponding uranium compounds.

16.23. Neptunium trifluoride was reduced to the elemental state by heating at 1200°C in the presence of barium vapor; the tetrafluoride could probably have been used but in the experiments being described the high temperatures caused this compound to soak into the beryllium oxide crucible. Neptunium is a silvery metal, not particularly affected by air. Its measured density is about 19.5 grams per cc. at normal temperatures, but changes occur on heating with the formation of two other modifications having lower densities. The melting point of metallic neptunium is 640°C. From studies of neptunium solutions, the existence of the (III), (IV) and (VI) oxidation states has been confirmed; the (IV) state is evidently the most stable, but it can be reduced to the (III) state by electrolytic reduction, and, as already seen, it is oxidized to the (VI) state by an acid solution of bromate in the cold. By the use of ferric ions or dilute nitric acid, neptunium (IV) solutions can be oxidized to the intermediate (V) state, which is more stable than the corresponding state of uranium.

Discovery and Separation of Plutonium

16.24. When the beta-active isotopes of neptunium decay, the daughter elements should have the atomic number 94. McMillan and Abelson, in their study of neptunium-239 (§ 16.5), were unable to detect any new activity when this nuclide decayed, and they concluded that the product, 94^{239}, was an alpha emitter of long life; this prediction was subsequently verified, as will be seen below. The first isotope of element-94 to be definitely identified, however, was the one of mass number 238, for this has a short half life, and has, consequently, a relatively higher activity. When Seaborg, McMillan, Kennedy and Wahl discovered the 2.0-day neptunium-238 in the winter of 1940-41, as mentioned above, they also noted that this substance developed an alpha activity which could be separated chemically from both uranium and neptunium. This was ascribed to the element of atomic number 94, which its discoverers subsequently named *plutonium*, symbol Pu, after Pluto, the planet beyond Neptune. Hence, plutonium-238, an alpha emitter of about 90-years half life, is formed in the beta decay of neptunium-238; thus,

$$_{93}Np^{238} \rightarrow {_{94}}Pu^{238} + _{-1}e^0.$$

16.25. Preliminary experiments using the tracer technique showed that plutonium, like neptunium, is precipitated as fluoride or iodate with a rare-earth element or thorium as carrier. Unlike neptunium however, it is not generally oxidized by an acid bromate solution, and this property can be utilized to separate plutonium and neptunium, as indicated in § 16.18. After bromate oxidation, the plutonium can still be precipitated as fluoride, with a rare-earth carrier, but the neptunium cannot, since it has been oxidized to the (VI) state. It was found, however, that by the use of a very strong oxidizing agent, such as persulfate with a silver ion catalyst, plutonium can be oxidized to a state, presumably (VI), which does not precipitate as fluoride or iodate.

16.26. The important fissionable Pu^{239} isotope of plutonium, which McMillan and Abelson had sought as the decay product of neptunium-239, was characterized in March 1941 by J. W. Kennedy, G. T. Seaborg, E. Segrè and A. C. Wahl, who worked with larger amounts of the latter species. The formation of plutonium-239 may be represented by

$$_{93}Np^{239} \rightarrow {}_{94}Pu^{239} + {}_{-1}e^0,$$

and in accordance with expectation, it turned out to be an alpha emitter with a half life of 24,400 years. Since the 239-isotope of element-94 was found to undergo fission by slow neutrons, the study of plutonium-239 assumed a special interest, as described in § 14.26. Incidentally, because of this interest, tests have been made for the presence of plutonium-239 in nature. It seemed possible that it might be found associated with uranium minerals, resulting from the interaction of uranium-238 with neutrons, produced in spontaneous fission or by the (α,n) reaction of alpha particles from uranium with various light elements. The results obtained indicate that the minerals pitchblende and carnotite do, in fact, contain minute traces of plutonium-239.

16.27. Brief mention may be made, in passing, of some fourteen other isotopes of plutonium which have been reported. Their mass numbers range from 232 through 246. The lower isotopes can be obtained by the interaction of alpha particles with uranium isotopes, accompanied by the emission of one or more neutrons. A few examples of such reactions are as follows:

Pu^{232}	$U^{235}(\alpha,7n)$
Pu^{234}	$U^{233}(\alpha,3n)$
Pu^{237}	$U^{235}(\alpha,2n)$; $U^{238}(\alpha,5n)$
Pu^{240}	$U^{238}(\alpha,2n)$
Pu^{241}	$U^{238}(\alpha,n)$

Several isotopes of plutonium are also formed by the beta decay of neptu-nium isotopes, with mass numbers 236, 238, 239, or 241. In addition, a useful method for the production of plutonium isotopes with mass numbers exceeding 239 is to expose plutonium-239 to neutrons in a nuclear reactor. As the result of a series of (n,γ) reactions, products up to (and including) plutonium-246 have been obtained. All the even-numbered isotopes, with the exception of mass number 246, as well as the familiar 239-isotope, are alpha emitters. As is the case with neptunium, the neutron-deficient plutonium isotopes of low mass number, some of which are also alpha emitters, exhibit orbital-electron capture. The beta-emitters are those of mass number 241, 243, 245 and 246.

16.28. When the decision was made to attempt the production of plutonium on a large scale by means of a nuclear reactor, it became necessary to work out a process which would permit the separation of plutonium from unchanged uranium and also from the numerous fission products. The first experiments on the chemistry of plutonium were made with the 238-isotope, obtained by the decay of neptunium-238 produced by bombarding uranium with deuterons from the Berkeley cyclotron. With this material, G. T. Seaborg, J. W. Kennedy and A. C. Wahl, using the tracer technique, were able during 1941 to determine many of the chemical properties of plutonium, and to evolve several possible processes for the separation of plutonium from the spent fuel material.

16.29. Four methods of separation, depending on volatility, adsorption, solvent extraction and precipitation, respectively, were considered, and a process making use of precipitation reactions was chosen as the basis of the large-scale separation. It was felt, for various reasons, that, although not necessarily the best procedure, it was the most likely to be successful when transferred from the laboratory to the production plant. The preliminary work on the separation process was performed with invisible tracer quantities of plutonium, but there was no certainty that the method would operate in practice with large amounts of material. As pointed out earlier, the concentrations in tracer work are so low that the results obtained might not apply to ordinary concentrations such as would be used on the production scale. Further, it was realized that the final isolation of the plutonium would require separation from carrier materials.

16.30. Hence it became necessary to obtain visible quantities of plutonium which could be used to study its chemistry by the ultramicrochemical technique described in § 16.14. A quantity of uranyl nitrate was consequently irradiated by neutrons, produced by bombardment of beryllium by means of cyclotron-accelerated deuterons, first at Berkeley and later at Washington University in St. Louis, and from it a few hundred micrograms of plutonium-239 were extracted by the end of 1942. With this material, information concerning the chemistry of the element, deduced from tracer-scale experiments, was confirmed. In addition, small quantities of pure plutonium compounds were prepared and analyzed.

16.31. In reporting on the work, G. T. Seaborg said: "The first pure chemical compound of plutonium, free from carrier material, and all other foreign matter, was prepared by B. B. Cunningham and L. B. Werner . . .

in Chicago on August 18, 1942, and the first weighing of such a compound occurred on September 10, 1942.* There was available . . . for the accomplishment of this feat only a couple of micrograms of plutonium produced by the bombardment of uranium by neutrons. . . . These memorable days will go down in scientific history to mark the first sight of a synthetic element, and the first isolation of a weighable amount [Fig. 16.2] of an artificially produced iso-

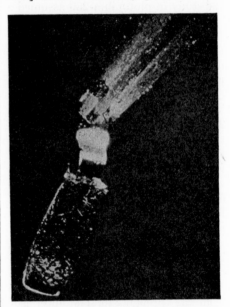

Fig. 16.2. Magnified picture of the first plutonium compound ever isolated, weighing 2.77 micrograms; it appeared as a golden incrustation on the small platinum shovel held by the forceps.

tope of any element." Subsequently, a number of pure plutonium compounds were prepared and their formulas determined by ultramicrochemical analysis.

16.32. With the microgram quantities of plutonium which were avail-

---

* The first solid compound obtained was a precipitate of the fluoride, probably PuF_4, and the first to be weighed was the oxide, PuO_2.

able, the methods of separating plutonium from uranium and its fission products, which had been developed from tracer experiments, were tested at the actual concentrations anticipated in large-scale operation. The process finally adopted was partly based on the stability of the (IV) oxidation state of plutonium, as compared with that of the (VI) state for uranium. With plutonium, a powerful oxidizing agent is required to convert the (IV) state into the (VI) state, while a relatively weak reducing agent will reverse the process. With uranium, on the other hand, the opposite is the case; the (IV) state is very easily oxidized, but the resulting (VI) state is reduced with difficulty. The method of separation "involves a precipitation of plutonium (IV) with a certain compound as a carrier, then dissolution of the precipitate, oxidation of the plutonium to the (VI) state, and reprecipitation of the carrier compound while the plutonium (VI) remains in solution. Fission products which are not carried by these compounds remain in solution when plutonium (IV) is precipitated. The fission products which carry are removed from the plutonium when it is in the (VI) state. Successive oxidation-reduction cycles are carried out until the desired decontamination [that is, elimination of the fission products] is achieved." *

16.33. The foregoing description of the separation procedure, as Seaborg has pointed out, "represents a gross oversimplification of the actual process [as performed on the large scale at Hanford (§ 14.75)]. There are carried out in all some thirty major chemical reactions involving hundreds of operations before the plutonium emerges from the process. The plants themselves defy description with their massive structures and their intricate maze of equipment, piping, and remotely operated controls. The preliminary design of these plants was under way at a time when the world supply of plutonium was invisible to the naked eye. This remarkable program of investigation [carried out in the United States in connection with the wartime atomic bomb project] with microscopic and submicroscopic quantities marks . . . one of the . . . amazing achievements of . . . chemistry." In spite of its complexity, the precipitation process, in which bismuth phosphate was the carrier for plutonium in the early purification stages and lanthanum fluoride in the later ones, was operated successfully for several years. It has now been replaced by the solvent extraction procedure described in § 15.110.

CHEMISTRY OF PLUTONIUM

16.34. Experimental investigations with plutonium are somewhat hazardous because of the relatively high alpha activity, which makes it preferable to work with very small amounts even though larger quantities may be available. In addition, great care must be taken to prevent entry of plutonium into the body; it tends to concentrate in the bones, where the continuous emission of alpha particles can have serious consequences (§ 19.19). Because of the importance of plutonium as a fissionable material, with great possibilities for use in peace or war, more is known of this

---

* Quoted from H. D. Smyth, *Atomic Energy for Military Purposes,* 1945. It is now known that the plutonium (IV) was first precipitated as the phosphate, with bismuth phosphate as the carrier. The uranium (VI) remained in solution. In the final cycle the plutonium was precipitated as the fluoride with lanthanum fluoride as the carrier.

artificially produced element and its compounds than of most other elements, in spite of the fact that the existence of four oxidation states, namely, (III), (IV), (V) and (VI), makes the situation very complicated. Like neptunium, plutonium resembles uranium in many of its chemical properties; the main difference, as mentioned above, lies in the stability of the (IV) state in plutonium, whereas with uranium it is the (VI) state which is the most stable.

16.35. The chemistry of plutonium is, in many respects, very similar to that of neptunium described above. The most stable oxide is PuO_2, but if it is heated to about 1500°C in a vacuum, it forms the lower oxide Pu_2O_3. By the oxidation of plutonium, a compound of approximate composition PuO may be formed. In addition, there is a mixed oxidation state, varying in composition from Pu_2O_3 to roughly Pu_4O_7. Uranium exhibits similar properties, the mixed oxides ranging from UO at one extreme to UO_3 at the other. The halides PuF_3, $PuBr_3$ and PuI_3 may be prepared by the methods described for the corresponding neptunium compounds. The tetrafluoride PuF_4 is stable, although it can be reduced to the trifluoride, but the tetrachloride and tetrabromide have not been obtained, at least not in the solid state. Plutonium hexafluoride is unstable, whereas that of uranium is quite stable. Reduction of the fluorides with barium vapor yields plutonium metal. The density at ordinary temperatures is 19.7 grams per cc., but upon heating this undergoes a number of changes corresponding to the formation of a total of six different solid modifications (§ 15.108). The melting point of the metal is 640°C.

16.36. Plutonium (III) can be precipitated from solution as the hydroxide, $Pu(OH)_3$, and the fluoride, PuF_3, thus behaving in a manner analogous to the rare-earth elements. Aqueous solutions of the positive plutonium (III) ion are oxidized in air to the plutonium (IV) state, although not as rapidly as are solutions of uranium (III). As already stated, the (IV) oxidation state of plutonium is the most stable, and many compounds in this category are known. The fluoride, PuF_4, the iodate, $Pu(IO_3)_4$, and the hydroxide, $Pu(OH)_4$ are insoluble, like those of thorium, and can be precipitated from aqueous solution; the chloride, nitrate, perchlorate and sulfate, however, are soluble in water. Numerous complexes, both inorganic and organic, of the plutonium (IV) state have been prepared; a soluble oxalate complex, for example, makes it possible to dissolve PuF_4 and other insoluble Pu(IV) compounds in water. On the other hand, several of the "chelate" complexes, formed with diketones and related compounds, are soluble in organic liquids. Plutonium (IV) solutions can be reduced to the plutonium (III) state by means of warm sulfur dioxide, by hydroxylamine, by iodide ion, or by zinc amalgam. The reactions can be reversed with relatively mild oxidizing agents.

16.37. The conversion of plutonium (IV) to the (VI) state requires the use of fairly strong oxidizing agents, such as acid solutions of permanganate or dichromate, ceric ions or persulfate in the presence of silver ions. This is in contrast with uranium, for which oxidation from (IV) to (VI) state in solution takes place in air. Solid plutonyl (VI) compounds, such as plutonyl nitrate, containing the ion PuO_2^{++} analogous to uranyl compounds, are known, and there is an insoluble sodium plutonyl acetate, $NaPuO_2(C_2H_3O_2)_3$, similar to the familiar compound of uranium. Some organic chelated complexes of the plutonyl ion have been prepared.

16.38. Evidence for the existence of plutonium in the (V) state has mainly been obtained from studies of solutions, for only one solid compound of this type has been reported. It appears, from measurements of the absorption spectrum, that a solution of Pu(VI) in dilute hydrochloric acid can be partially reduced electrolytically to the Pu(V) state. This is probably present as the $PuO_2{}^+$ ion, similar to the $UO_2{}^+$ ion of uranium. However, the (V) oxidation states of uranium and plutonium are relatively unstable, as compared with that of neptunium. Because of the different colors or, in general, of the absorption spectra, of the various oxidation states, it has been found possible to work out a method of analyzing plutonium solutions by studying the absorption of light of different wave lengths.

16.39. The first pure plutonium compound (PuF_4) free from carrier, referred to in the preceding section, was obtained by making use of the increasing difficulty of attaining the (VI) oxidation state in passing from uranium through neptunium to plutonium. Most of the unchanged uranyl nitrate, after the neutron bombardment, was extracted with ether, and the remainder was retained in solution while Pu(IV) and Np(IV), obtained upon reduction, were precipitated as fluorides with lanthanum and cerium as carriers. The fluorides were then converted into the soluble sulfates by evaporation with concentrated sulfuric acid. The addition of bromate to the solution resulted in oxidation of neptunium to the Np(VI) state, while the plutonium was unaffected; hence, the latter, free from neptunium, could again be precipi-

tated as fluoride with the rare-earth carrier. After redissolving the fluorides with sulfuric acid, precipitating the hydroxides with ammonia and dissolving them in nitric acid, persulfate and silver nitrate were added to oxidize the plutonium to the (VI) state. Upon addition of hydrofluoric acid, the rare-earth carrier was precipitated, but the plutonium remained in solution. This was evaporated with sulfuric acid, and diluted; when hydrofluoric acid was added a precipitate of plutonium fluoride, free from carrier, was obtained.

DISCOVERY AND PROPERTIES OF AMERICIUM

16.40. Although the element of atomic number 95, which its discoverers, G. T. Seaborg, R. A. James and L. O. Morgan, named *americium*, symbol Am, by analogy with its rare-earth homologue europium, is the third transuranic element, it was actually the fourth to be identified, late in 1944. When uranium-238 was bombarded with 40-Mev alpha particles from a cyclotron, the reaction

$$_{92}U^{238} + {}_2He^4 \rightarrow {}_{94}Pu^{241} + {}_0n^1$$

was expected to take place, and it was anticipated that the product, plutonium-241, would be a beta emitter, because of its high neutron-to-proton ratio. Upon separating the fraction which should have contained the plutonium, no activity was detected, apparently because of the very low energy of the beta particles emitted by the plutonium-241. But in due course an alpha activity developed, and this was presumably due to the new element americium, atomic number 95, formed by the decay of the Pu^{241}; thus,

$$_{94}Pu^{241} \xrightarrow{\sim 10 \text{ yr.}} {}_{95}Am^{241} + {}_{-1}e^0.$$

The same nuclide results from the $(\alpha,2n)$ reaction with plutonium-239. Its half life has been found to be about 500 years.

16.41. Carrier experiments with americium showed it to have a very stable (III) oxidation state in which it displays a striking resemblance to the rare-earth elements. Consequently, separation of americium from the rare-earth carriers at first proved difficult, although removal of uranium and any neptunium and plutonium that might be present can be readily achieved by oxidation of these elements. Two methods of purifying americium have been developed. Although americium fluoride, like the rare-earth fluorides, is sparingly soluble, the former is somewhat more soluble. It is possible, therefore, by fractional precipitation of the fluorides, with careful control of the fluoride ion concentration, to effect a separation. Preferably, americium may be separated from the rare earths by making use of the ion-exchange procedure described in § 13.81. The various ions, present in dilute acid solution in the (III) state, are absorbed by a suitable resin. This is then eluted, i.e., extracted, with concentrated hydrochloric acid, when the americium (and other transuranic elements) are removed well ahead of the rare earths. Separation from each other of the elements of high atomic number, e.g., neptunium, plutonium, americium, etc., in the (III) state, is best done by the ion-exchange method, using a slightly acid solution of ammonium citrate as the eluting agent. The procedure is similar to that employed for the separation of the rare earth elements. The elements absorbed on the resin are extracted in order of decreasing atomic number.

16.42. Some pure compounds of americium, such as AmF_3 and Am_2O_3, free from carrier, were prepared during the winter of 1945-46 by B. B. Cunningham, and studied on the ultramicrochemical scale. Since that time, a number of other solid compounds have been prepared, including $AmCl_3$, $AmBr_3$, AmI_3 and AmO_2. The latter shows that americium can exist in the (IV) state, at least in a solid compound. Because of the high alpha activity, due to the relatively short life of the Am^{241} isotope, special precautions must be taken when working with americium compounds, even though the amounts used are very small.

16.43. The (III) oxidation state of americium is undoubtedly the most stable, but there is evidence for the existence of both higher and lower states. When a solution of americium (III) hydroxide in concentrated potassium carbonate solution is oxidized by heating with sodium hypochlorite, a dark-colored precipitate is formed which is apparently an oxide of americium (V). By means of a very strong oxidizing agent, such as ammonium persulfate, americium (III) can be oxidized to the (VI) state. A compound, analogous to those formed by plutonium, etc., referred to in § 16.37, can then be precipitated by addition of sodium acetate. The (IV) state of americium is so unstable in solution that its presence has not been observed, although solid AmO_2 exists, as noted above. It may appear surprising that a state of lower oxidation number than the (III) state should be suspected, but it has long been known that europium, the rare-earth homologue of americium, exists in a (II) oxidation state. The reaction of americium (III) in aqueous solution with sodium amalgam indicates the possibility that an americium (II) state may be formed, and, in fact, the isolation of AmO has been reported.

16.44. The relative stability of the americium (III) state is shown by the fact that the methods used for the preparation of the tetrafluoride and tetrachloride of neptunium yield only the corresponding trihalides of americium. Thus, heating the hydroxide in a current of oxygen and hydrogen fluoride gives americium trifluoride, while the trichloride results from reaction of the dioxide with carbon tetrachloride. The tribromide and triiodide of americium are made, like those of neptunium and plutonium, by heating the oxide together with aluminum in the vapor of the appropriate halogen. The compounds have been identified by their being isomorphous with the corresponding halides of uranium. The preparation of americium tetrafluoride, but of no other tetrahalide, has been reported; it is definitely less stable than plutonium tetrafluoride. The action of barium vapor on americium trifluoride at temperatures over 1000°C gives elemental americium. It is a silvery metal with a density of 11.7 grams per cc. at ordinary temperatures. The melting point is somewhat above 840°C.

16.45. In addition to the Am^{241} isotope, with which most of the chemical work on americium has been carried out, nine other isotopes, with mass numbers from 237 to 246, have been discovered. As with plutonium, the higher isotopes are made by successive neutron captures in a nuclear reactor, starting with Am^{241}. Several of the isotopes of lower mass number have been obtained by bombardment of plutonium-239 with protons or deuterons, or of neptunium-237 by alpha particles.

DISCOVERY AND PROPERTIES OF CURIUM

16.46. The fourth transuranium element, atomic number 96, was identified by G. T. Seaborg, R. A. James and A. Ghiorso in 1944, before the discovery of its predecessor americium. The new element was called *curium*, symbol Cm, in honor of Marie and Pierre Curie who pioneered in the study of radioelements; this designation was proposed so as to correspond with that of its rare-earth homologue, gadolinium, named after J. Gadolin, the Finnish chemist who was one of the early workers in the rare-earth field. The first isotope of curium to be detected was obtained by bombarding plutonium-239 with alpha particles in the Berkeley cyclotron, the reaction being

$$_{94}Pu^{239} + {}_2He^4 \rightarrow {}_{96}Cm^{242} + {}_0n^1.$$

The same nuclide, an alpha emitter with a half life of 162.5 days, was later found to be formed in the beta decay of the 16-hr. isomeric state of americium-242; thus,

$$_{95}Am^{242} \rightarrow {}_{96}Cm^{242} + {}_{-1}e^0.$$

It was actually from this source that curium, in the form of the oxide Cm_2O_3, was first obtained as a pure compound, in September 1947, by L. B. Werner and I. Perlman in ultramicrochemical amounts free from carrier. Since that time Cm^{242} has become available in appreciable quantities from Am^{242} produced by exposure of Am^{241} to neutrons in a reactor.

16.47. As is to be expected, the (III) oxidation state of curium is extremely stable, and so far no evidence has been obtained that higher or lower states exist. Separation from the rare-earth elements of curium, together with any americium that may be present, is achieved by the methods described in § 16.41. Since the (III) states are stable for both americium and curium, the separation of these elements is not easy. The problem is, both in fact and in theory, analogous to that of separating neighboring rare-earth elements. A successful method has been devised, based on a partial precipitation of americium in its higher oxidation state by means of hypochlorite in potassium carbonate solution, as mentioned above, followed by absorption and elution with citrate from a column of ion-exchange resin.

16.48. One of the exceptionally interesting facts about curium, from the theoretical point of view (§ 16.69), is that its solutions are colorless, although it exhibits strong absorption of ultraviolet radiation. This behavior, which was expected from a consideration of the probable arrangement of the orbital electrons of curium, is exactly analogous to that of the homologous rare-earth element gadolinium, and calls attention to a striking similarity between these two elements.

16.49. The study of the absorption spectrum of curium, and, in fact, all experimental investigations with curium, are rendered difficult by the short life of the curium-242, and the consequent intense alpha activity which accompanies this radionuclide. The alpha particles are also the source of another difficulty; they cause decomposition, with the evolution of gas, and heating of the water in which the curium compound is dissolved. Because of the health hazard, work with curium-242 must be performed in closed systems. It may be noted that the product of alpha decay is plutonium-238, the properties of which are known well enough to provide a check

on the mass assignment of the curium-242.

16.50. Altogether, thirteen isotopes of curium, with mass numbers from 238 through 250, have been reported. The lower isotopes, such as Cm^{238} and Cm^{240}, result from the same bombardment process, i.e., plutonium-239 by alpha particles, as yields Cm^{242}. The higher isotopes are obtained either as the result of radioactive decay or by several stages of neutron capture. For the latter procedure, Cm^{244}, obtained as described below, may be a good starting point.

16.51. For future studies of the chemistry of curium, the isotope Cm^{244}, with a half life of about 18.4 years, may prove to be of interest. Although it is an alpha emitter, its relatively long life means that the effects of radiation indicated above are much less marked than with Cm^{242}. The curium-244 can be obtained in relatively pure form in the following manner, based on a series of neutron captures and radioactive decay stages. First, americium-241 is exposed to neutrons in a reactor to produce Am^{242}; in addition to undergoing beta decay, this nuclide also exhibits orbital-electron capture, leading to the formation of Pu^{242}. The latter is separated, e.g., by ion exchange, and exposed to neutrons to yield the beta emitted Pu^{243}, of which the decay product is Am^{243}. This can also be separated by ion exchange and transformed into Am^{244} by neutron capture; beta decay of the latter gives the required Cm^{244}, which can be purified by the ion-exchange procedure.

THE DISCOVERY OF BERKELIUM
AND CALIFORNIUM

16.52. At the end of 1949, S. G. Thompson, A. Ghiorso and G. T. Seaborg, of the University of California, announced that they had produced the element of atomic number **97**, which they called *berkelium*, symbol Bk. The name was given in honor of the city of Berkeley, where the discovery of this and of other related elements was made, by analogy with its rare-earth homologue, terbium, which was named for the small town of Ytterby, Sweden, where several rare-earth minerals have been found. The new element was obtained by bombarding americium-241 with alpha particles accelerated to about 35 Mev energy by means of a cyclotron. The process occurring was found to be

$$_{95}Am^{241} + _{2}He^{4} \rightarrow _{97}Bk^{243} + 2_{0}n^{1},$$

so that the mass number of the product was 243. The berkelium was separated from the target americium, and also from curium formed at the same time, by the ion-exchange method. The indications are that, although berkelium exists predominantly in the (III) state, there is evidence for a (IV) oxidation state. In this respect, the element resembles its rare-earth homologue terbium.

16.53. A total of eight isotopes of berkelium, with mass numbers from 243 through 250, have been described. Several of these have considerably longer half lives than that of berkelium-243, which is only 4.5 hours, so that they are useful for further studies with the element. Notable among these is Bk^{247}, an alpha emitter with a half life reported to be about 7000 years. Most of the heavier isotopes are obtained by a series of neutron captures, and occasional beta decays, re-

sulting from the prolonged exposure of plutonium, americium and curium in a nuclear reactor.

16.54. In March 1950, the discoverers of berkelium, in conjunction with K. Street, Jr., reported that element number **98**, which they named *californium*, symbol Cf, for the state and University of California,* had been made by the action of 35-Mev alpha particles on curium-242. The reaction occurring is of the (α,n) type and the product is californium-245, i.e., $_{98}Cf^{245}$, half life 44 min. The new element was separated by the ion-exchange procedure and identified, although the amount obtained in the initial work was extremely small, estimated to be about five thousand atoms, i.e., 2×10^{-18} gram, since only a few millionths of a gram of curium-242 was used as target material. As far as is known at present, californium exists only in the typical (III) oxidation state.

16.55. A total of eleven isotopes of californium, in the mass number range from **244** through **254**, have been identified. In addition to the use of alpha-particle reactions and successive neutron capture processes, some of the isotopes of californium have been obtained by bombardment of uranium-238 with so-called heavy ions, e.g., carbon and nitrogen (§ 9.113). Examples of such reactions are $U^{238}(C^{12},6n)Cf^{244}$, $U^{238}(C^{12},4n)Cf^{246}$ and $U^{238}(N^{14},p3n)$ Cf^{248}. Special interest attaches to californium-254, half life 55 days, since it decays almost entirely by spontaneous fission, rather than by alpha (or other particle) emission. It has been sug-

---

* In this case, there is no direct analogy with the name of its rare-earth homologue dysprosium, although it is pointed out "that dysprosium is named on the basis of a Greek word meaning 'difficult to get at' [and] that the searchers for another element [gold] a century ago found it difficult to get to California."

gested that the fission of this isotope is responsible for the tremendous output of energy in certain extra large new stars, called type I supernovae. These are seen to flare up to high brilliance (or explode) and then fade, the rate of fading corresponding to a half life of 55 days. It is believed that the californium-254 in these stars is formed by a series of neutron captures and beta decays, just as can occur in a nuclear reactor.

THE DISCOVERY OF EINSTEINIUM AND FERMIUM

16.56. An examination of the residues collected after the thermonuclear test explosion of November 1952 at Eniwetok Atoll, by scientists at the Los Alamos Scientific Laboratory and the Argonne National Laboratory, revealed the presence of new heavy isotopes of plutonium and americium, namely Pu^{246} and Am^{246}. It seemed that nuclides with such a high neutron content could arise only from successive neutron captures, such as occur much more slowly in a reactor.* This suggested the possibility that isotopes of elements beyond americium, and even beyond californium, might be present in the explosion residues. Preliminary ion-exchange experiments at the Radiation Laboratory, Berkeley, indicated that this was indeed the case, and in order to facilitate the isolation of the new elements several hundred pounds of coral were collected from the vicinity of the explosion. In this material, the new element of atomic number 100 was identified at Berkeley, by the ion-exchange separation technique, although in the first experiments only about 200 atoms were obtained. Later, element number 99 was observed both at Berkeley and at the Argonne National Laboratory. By agreement among the many workers in the three Laboratories involved in the project, element 99 was called *einsteinium* (symbol Es) and number 100 was given the name *fermium* (symbol Fm), in honor of A. Einstein and E. Fermi, respectively. These elements are precipitated as fluorides with lanthanum fluoride as carrier, and appear in the proper order in the ion-exchange elution procedure; these facts suggest that they normally occur in the (III) state.

16.57. The foregoing work was carried out during 1953, but before it was announced in June 1955, several isotopes of the two new elements had been obtained by other methods. Chief among these was the neutron capture (and beta decay) procedure in a nuclear reactor, which is similar to that in the thermonuclear explosion. Starting with plutonium-239, long exposure in the Materials Testing Reactor at Arco, Idaho, led to the production of Es^{253}, which was separated and identified, by a group at Berkeley, using the ion-exchange method. An isotope of lower mass number was reported in November 1953 as resulting from the bombardment of uranium with nitrogen ions, i.e., $U^{238}(N^{14},5n)Es^{247}$. Altogether, eleven isotopes, with mass numbers from 246 to 256 are known. Of these, Es^{254}, with a half life of 270 days, may be obtainable in weighable amount which can be used for further investigations and production of elements of even higher atomic number.

16.58. Seven isotopes of fermium, in the mass number range of 250 through 256, have been made, mainly by neutron capture and beta decay

---

* Nuclear reactions among the hydrogen isotopes, as given in § 14.102, can produce neutrons in large numbers.

processes. In addition, H. Atterling and his collaborators, in Sweden, reported in February 1954 the production of the element of atomic number 100, probably the isotope of mass number 250, by bombardment of uranium with oxygen ions; the reaction was apparently U^{238} (O^{16}, $4n$) Fm^{250}.

DISCOVERY OF MENDELEVIUM

16.59. The discovery in April 1955 of element number 101, named *mendelevium* (symbol Md), in honor of D. I. Mendelyeev, by A. Ghiorso, B. G. Harvey, G. R. Choppin, S. G. Thompson and G. T. Seaborg, at the Radiation Laboratory, Berkeley, was a remarkable achievement since it was based on observation of a single atom. An invisible amount of einsteinium-253, consisting of a billion atoms, deposited on a gold foil, was bombarded with 48-Mev alpha particles. The product nuclei were collected, by recoil, on an adjacent gold foil, so that they were relatively free from einsteinium. The foil was dissolved and the new element isolated by the ion-exchange method.

16.60. It was at first thought that this element, with atomic number 101, would be an alpha emitter, but owing to interference by other nuclides, especially radon, it proved impossible to identify the single atoms in this way. The procedure which proved satisfactory was based on the fact that the new species exhibited orbital-electron capture, as a result of which the element of atomic number 100, i.e., ferminum, was produced. The particular isotope formed undergoes spontaneous fission and this could readily be detected. Because of the small amount of einsteinium-253 used in the bombardment with alpha par-

ticles, only one, and sometimes two, atoms of the new element, at best, were separated (by ion exchange) in each experiment. Nevertheless, this was sufficient to identify it as having an atomic number of 101, and a half life of about 30 minutes. Later, larger quantities were obtained, and the decay to the spontaneously fissionable isotope of fermium (half life 3 hours) was confirmed by chemical separation. The mass number assigned to the isotope of mendelevium, as well as to that of fermium formed by orbital-electron capture, is 256.

DISCOVERY OF NOBELIUM

16.61. The preparation of element 102, announced in July 1957, was the result of a joint effort of scientists from the United States, Great Britain and Sweden. The basic idea, which apparently originated with P. R. Fields and A. M. Friedman of the Argonne National Laboratory, was to bombard curium-244 with high-energy (accelerated) carbon-13 ions in the hopes of bringing about one (or both) of the reactions

$$Cm^{244}(C^{13},4n)102^{253}$$

or

$$Cm^{244}(C^{13},6n)102^{251},$$

leading to the formation of element number 102. The reason why the relatively rare carbon-13 was chosen, rather than the much more common carbon-12, was that the product in the former case was expected to have an odd mass number, as indicated above. It is known from the general behavior of the heavy nuclides that those with even atomic number are more stable against spontaneous fission if they have an odd mass number.* Isotopes with odd mass numbers

---

* It should be noted, however, that these nuclides undergo fission *due to neutron capture* more readily than do those with even mass numbers (cf. § 13.63, *et seq.*).

also generally have longer half lives for alpha decay than do those with even mass numbers. In view of the expected instability of the isotopes of element 102 against both spontaneous fission and alpha decay, the chances of detection would be enhanced if the nuclide produced had an odd mass number.

16.62. Since the necessary facilities for performing the bombardment experiments were not available, Fields and Friedman interested J. Milstead of the British Atomic Energy Research Establishment, Harwell, in the project. The latter then arranged with H. Atterling and his colleagues (see § 16.58) to make use of the cyclotron at the Nobel Institute of Physics in Sweden, since this was the only instrument in operation at the time capable of producing a sufficiently strong beam of accelerated carbon-13 ions. The sample of curium-244 (as the nitrate) was coated as a film on aluminum and then bombarded with $C^{13(4+)}$ ions, at energies of 65 to 100 Mev, for periods up to about half an hour. The recoiling reaction products were collected on a thin film of plastic, which was then placed on a platinum plate and burnt off. The residue was found to emit alpha particles of 8.5-Mev energy at a rate corresponding to a half life of approximately 10 minutes; there was no significant spontaneous fission activity. By dissolving the residue in acid and performing the familiar ion-exchange separation, the 8.5-Mev alpha activity was found in the position expected for element number 102. The discoverers of this new element have proposed the name nobelium, symbol No, in honor of Alfred Nobel and of the Institute where the experimental work was done. It should be mentioned that the observed alpha activity may not arise

directly from nobelium-251 (or -253), half life 10 minutes. It may possibly be emitted by a shorter-lived isotope of mendelevium, with the same mass number, formed by electron-capture decay of the nobelium isotope. With the techniques available, these two alternatives could not be distinguished.[*]

ELEMENTS OF ATOMIC NUMBER 103 AND BEYOND

16.63. For the production of elements having atomic numbers of 103 or more, two methods may be considered: one is that of successive neutron captures and beta decays, by which einsteinium and fermium were obtained, and the other is to make use of bombardment by positive ions. The method of neutron captures does not appear to be very promising, because the half lives of some of the intermediate stages will be so short that they cannot accumulate to a sufficient extent to permit further build-up by neutron capture. The situation with regard to alpha-particle bombardment, used in the discovery of mendelevium, is somewhat the same. The quantities of target materials available become increasingly smaller, and they decay more rapidly, as the atomic number increases. The most promising approach to the synthesis of new elements of high atomic number is by bombardment with ions heavier than alpha particles. As seen above, by using carbon, nitrogen and oxygen ions as projectiles, the elements 99 and 100 were prepared and 102 was discovered. With the new linear accelerators (§ 9.116), capable of providing fairly strong beams of ions as heavy as argon, it should be possible to obtain elements of high atomic number, even starting with uranium.

16.64. After the new elements are

---

[*] Workers at the University of California have been unable to confirm the results described in § 16.62. However, the nuclide 102^{254} was identified among the products of bombardment of Cm^{246} by C^{12} ions.

prepared, there will be the problem of identifying them. With increasing atomic number, the half lives for radioactive decay or spontaneous fission will become shorter and shorter; this difficulty can be alleviated, to some extent, by attempting to prepare nuclides with odd mass numbers. It will be seen below that element 103 will probably complete the series capable of existing in the (III) oxidation state which can be readily separated by ion exchange. For the higher elements, new chemical methods of separation would have to be used, but it is believed that even the more stable isotopes will exist barely long enough to permit such separations to be carried out. For these elements, therefore, reliance will probably have to be placed in other methods of identification. A study of the numerous artificially prepared isotopes of the elements of high atomic number has revealed certain regularities in connection with the half lives (and energies) for alpha particle emission and for spontaneous fission (§ 16.102). Consequently, from observations of the method of production and the decay properties of the new short-lived isotopes, it should be possible to assign to them correct atomic and mass numbers.

THE ACTINIDE SERIES

16.65. In reviewing the properties of uranium and the new elements described above, the striking nature of their similarity is at once evident. All the elements exist in the (III) oxidation state, although its relative stability, with reference to the other states, increases with increasing atomic number. Thus, the uranium (III) ion in solution is oxidized by air, but the (III) state is the most stable for americium and the elements be-

yond it. In fact, for curium and, probably, californium and beyond, it is the only state that has been detected. The trihalides, of the general formula MX_3, where M is the metal and X a halogen, are all isomorphous with one another, and also with the corresponding halides of actinium. It is of interest to note, too, that they have the same crystal structure as the trihalides of the rare-earth series.

16.66. The elements uranium, neptunium, plutonium, americium and berkelium form compounds of the (IV) state, and for neptunium and plutonium these are the most stable. The known tetrahalides, of the MX_4 type, are isomorphous with each other and with thorium tetrachloride. The (V) oxidation state has been observed in solutions of the three elements uranium, neptunium and plutonium; although in no case is this state particularly stable, neptunium (V) is relatively more stable than the (V) states of the other two elements. The same three elements and americium also exist in (VI) states, that of uranium being the most stable for this element; compounds analogous to the uranyl compounds, containing the MO_2^{++} ion, have the same crystal structures.

16.67. An approximate attempt to indicate the relative stabilities of the various oxidation states of the elements from actinium onward is made in the table on page 502; four stars represent a very stable, and one star a relatively unstable state of each element. Although the complete gradation of properties cannot be shown, the general trend is evident.

16.68. It is not possible here to consider the significance of the foregoing facts in connection with the problem of the arrangement of the orbital electrons in the atoms of high atomic number. It can be seen in general, however, that the existence of (III) oxidation states which are related to that of actinium, and (IV) states similar to that of thorium, would appear to justify the grouping of actinium

RELATIVE STABILITIES OF
OXIDATION STATES

Element	Atomic Number	Oxidation State			
		III	*IV*	*V*	*VI*
Actinium	89	****			
Thorium	90	*	****		
Protactinium	91	*	*	****	
Uranium	92	**	***	*	****
Neptunium	93	**	****	***	***
Plutonium	94	***	****	**	***
Americium	95	****	*	*	*
Curium	96	****			
Berkelium	97	****	**		
Californium	98	****			
Einsteinium	99	****			
Fermium	100	****			
Mendelevium	101	****			
Nobelium	102	****			

and the elements which follow it into a series analogous to the rare-earth elements. The suggestion that there might be such a group of elements, for which G. T. Seaborg revived the name *actinide series,*[*] was made by N. Bohr in 1923. But there was no real evidence for its existence until 1940, when E. M. McMillan and P. H. Abelson discovered neptunium and pointed out the similarity of its properties to those of uranium. The facts brought to light since that time have shown that the resemblances, accompanied by expected gradations, continue through the elements of still higher atomic number.

16.69. The parallelism between the rare-earth (lanthanide) and the actinide elements is also quite marked, especially as regards the (III) oxidation states. Certain similarities exist among the atomic spectra and the magnetic properties in the two series. Perhaps the most striking resemblance is the absence of any absorption of light in the visible region of the spectrum by curium in the actinide series and by gadolinium, its lanthanide homologue (§ 16.48). This fact argues very strongly for the analogous arrangement of the electrons in the two elements. The critical test of the similarity between the actinide and lanthanide series will come with the identification of element number 104. It will be seen from the periodic table in Chapter I that, if the number of elements in the two series is the same, element 103 should be the last member of the actinide series. Thus, with element 104 there should be a change in chemical properties; this element should be definitely tetravalent, like zirconium and hafnium.

16.70. Further, it has long been known that the trivalent (III) ions of the rare-earth series show a decrease in size with increasing atomic number; this has been referred to as the *lanthanide contraction*, and has been the subject of theoretical speculation. A similar contraction has been observed among the ions of the actinide series; the radii of the ions of the (III) and (IV) oxidation states, as determined by X-ray diffraction of the appropriate crystalline compounds, are given in the table. The results are expressed in Angstrom units, that is, in units of 10^{-8} cm. (§ 1.68).

---

[*] The term "actinide," among others, was first used in 1937 by the Swiss-born geochemist V. M. Goldschmidt, who also invented the name "lanthanides" for the rare-earth elements (§ 1.48).

The "actinide series" of elements following actinium in the periodic system should not be confused with "actinium series," the radioactive disintegration ($4n + 3$) series of which actinium-227 is a member (§ 5.56).

IONIC RADII IN THE ACTINIDE SERIES IN
ANGSTROM UNITS

Element	III State	IV State
Actinium...........	1.11 A	— A
Thorium............	—	0.95
Protactinium........	—	—
Uranium............	1.04	0.89
Neptunium.........	1.02	0.88
Plutonium..........	1.01	0.86
Americium.........	1.00	0.85

16.71. Incidentally, this table points up one of the complexities, already indicated above, concerning the actinide series. Although the (III) state is evidently the most characteristic oxidation state, there is only slight evidence for the existence of thorium (III) and of protactinium (III) states. In fact, in some respects, the four elements actinium, thorium, protactinium and uranium resemble lanthanum, hafnium, tantalum and tungsten, which would be their respective homologues in Groups IIIA, IVA, VA and VIA of the periodic system, if they were not included in the actinide group. However, there is not the slightest doubt that the transuranium elements do not in any way resemble the elements which follow tungsten. Attempts have been made to explain the situation in terms of the arrangements of the orbital electrons among the various possible energy levels. But many problems, which lie outside the scope of this book, still remain to be solved.

THE MISSING ELEMENTS

ELEMENT-87: FRANCIUM

16.72. In the middle thirties of the present century, four elements lying below uranium in the periodic system were still unknown; these were the elements of atomic numbers 43, 61, 85 and 87. It is true that various claims had been made to the discovery of all these elements, and names had even been assigned to them. The general opinion among scientists was, however, that the claims had not been fully substantiated, and that the occurrence of the elements 43, 61, 85 and 87 in nature was still in doubt. In 1939, Mlle. M. Perey in France showed that actinium-227, the isotope for which the actinium $(4n + 3)$ series of radioelements is named (§ 5.56), exhibits a branched disintegration. Besides undergoing beta decay, as has long been known, it also simultaneously emits an alpha particle, with the resultant formation of a nuclide of mass number 223 and atomic number 87. The previously unknown element formed in this manner was first designated actinium K, but later its discoverer proposed the name *francium*, symbol Fr, after her native country.

16.73. In addition to the Fr^{223} isotope, which thus occurs in nature, at least six other isotopes have been obtained artificially. One, Fr^{221}, is a member of the neptunium $(4n + 1)$ series and there are four, with mass numbers 217, 218, 219 and 220, which are members of other disintegration series (§ 16.92 *et seq.*). Finally, francium-222 has been detected as a product of the spallation of thorium by high-energy protons. From the observations made so far, the properties of francium appear to be, as they should, those of a typical alkali-metal element.

16.74. The claim was made in 1943 by B. Karlik and T. Bernert of Austria to have detected isotopes of the element 85 as a result of certain branched beta-particle decays in the natural radioactive series. Previous to this date, however, the element had been obtained artificially and its interesting chemical properties had been elucidated, as will be seen shortly (§ 16.88).

ELEMENT-43: TECHNETIUM

16.75. In 1937, C. Perrier and E. Segrè, in Italy, secured from the United States a specimen of molybdenum which had been bombarded with deuterons, together with neutrons produced incidentally, from the Berkeley cyclotron. The atomic number of molybdenum is 42, and Perrier and Segrè considered that the following reactions might have occurred: $42(n,\alpha)40$, $42(d,\alpha)41$, $42(n,\gamma)42$, $42(d,n)43$, the various elements being indicated by their atomic numbers. The products could thus be isotopes of zirconium (40), niobium (41), molybdenum (42) or the element-43. The irradiated molybdenum was dissolved in aqua regia, and by making use of the carrier technique, it was found that its radioactivity was not carried down with either zirconium, niobium or molybdenum; hence, it appeared probable that it was due to the presence of element-43. This element should lie in Group VIIA of the periodic system, with manganese and rhenium as its homologues, the former above and the latter below it in the vertical group; it is to be expected, therefore, that element-43 would be carried by either or both of its homologues.

16.76. A small quantity of rhenium was added to the solution of the irradiated molybdenum in aqua regia, and the mixture was evaporated to dryness. The residue was dissolved in aqueous ammonia and saturated with hydrogen sulfide; a manganous salt was then added and the whole allowed to stand for twelve hours. The precipitate of manganous sulfide formed carried some of the rhenium and nearly the whole of the radioactivity. By treating with hydrochloric acid, the manganous sulfide was dissolved out, leaving black rhenium sulfide together with the activity; it was thus evident that the active product closely resembles rhenium. Further, both the active sulfide and the rhenium sulfide are soluble in hydrogen peroxide. A partial separation of the sulfides can be achieved by means of concentrated hydrochloric acid; rhenium sulfide separates slowly, but the activity, presumably due to element-43, remains in solution.

16.77. Subsequent work has confirmed the production of element-43 in the manner described above, and its discoverers have called it *technetium*, symbol Tc; this name, derived from the Greek word *technetos*, meaning artificial, was suggested because it was the first element, previously unknown on earth, which had been made artificially.* Altogether, fourteen radioisotopes of technetium, in the mass number range from 92 to 105, have been reported. Some are fission products, and others have been obtained by bombardment of molybdenum with protons, deuterons or alpha particles and of niobium by alpha particles. Negative beta-active molybdenum isotopes of mass number 99, 101, 102 and 105 are transformed into technetium when they decay, as also is ruthenium-97, which exhibits K-capture.

---

* Traces of technetium undoubtedly exist in nature, formed by fission of uranium-235 and uranium-238 and by the capture of cosmic-ray neutrons by molybdenum. Spectroscopic evidence indicates, however, that certain stars, e.g., R. Andromedae, contain larger amounts of technetium than would be expected from these sources. Since there is no isotope of this element with a half life exceeding 2×10^5 years, it appears possible that the synthesis (or building up) of elements is still proceeding in some stellar bodies.

16.78. A considerable clarification of the problem of assigning masses to the various isotopes of technetium has resulted from the availability of the separated stable isotopes of molybdenum with mass numbers 92, 94, 95, 96, 97, 98 and 100; these have been subjected to the action of deuterons, and the products studied. It has been found that technetium can be removed from its neighboring elements by distillation from concentrated sulfuric acid. This avoids the use of rhenium as carrier, from which it is difficult to separate. Where a carrier is necessary, platinum has been found useful, for the sulfide carries down the technetium with it.

16.79. One of the most interesting of the isotopes of technetium is the long lived Tc^{99} discovered by G. T. Seaborg and E. Segrè in the United States in 1939. The interaction of molybdenum-98 with slow neutrons yields molybdenum-99, by the (n,γ) process, and this decays, with a half life of 67 hours, to form technetium-99. The latter undergoes an isomeric transition, and the product is Tc^{99} with a half life of 2.1×10^5 years. Microgram amounts of Tc^{99} were at first obtained by neutron bombardment of molybdenum, but considerably larger quantities have since been separated from the products of uranium fission. As seen in § 13.93, the 67-hour Mo^{99} mentioned above is a fission fragment, and hence its decay product, the long-lived isomer of Tc^{99}, accumulates in the course of time.

16.80. A study of the chemistry of technetium shows it to have, as expected, properties intermediate between those of its homologues manganese and rhenium, the resemblance to the latter being perhaps greater than to the former. Like rhenium, technetium apparently exists in (IV),

(VI) and (VII) oxidation states. Pure technetium metal has been prepared by passing hydrogen gas at 1000°C over the sulfide obtained by precipitation with hydrogen sulfide from hydrochloric acid solution. The metal has been shown to have the same crystal structure as rhenium and the adjacent elements osmium and ruthenium.

ELEMENT-61: PROMETHIUM

16.81. The work of Moseley (§ 4.24) on the characteristic X-rays of the elements and their relationship to the atomic numbers showed that there should be a rare-earth element of atomic number 61 lying between neodymium and samarium. For the past quarter of a century, numerous claims have been made by scientists both in America and in Europe to have discovered this missing element; these were usually based on either the ordinary optical spectrum or the X-ray spectrum of the product supposed to contain the missing element. None of the claims seemed to inspire any real confidence, and there was a feeling of doubt concerning their validity. In view of the arguments presented in § 12.104, it would appear that the existence of a stable isotope of element-61 is unlikely, and if this element does occur in nature it would probably be a long-lived radioactive species of mass number 145. There is no evidence, however, that any of the substances claimed to be compounds of element-61 were radioactive.

16.82. In the course of a series of studies made in the United States by M. L. Pool, J. D. Kurbatov, L. L. Quill and their associates, between 1938 and 1942, on the interaction of neutrons, protons, deuterons and alpha particles with neodymium and praseodymium, there were obtained a number of activities, some of which were ascribed to element-61. Isotopes of this element were undoubtedly formed, but the assignments of the various activities were made without adequate chemical separation. Consequently, not all of the conclusions drawn proved to be correct.

16.83. A definite separation and identification of element-61 was achieved by J. A. Marinsky and L. E. Glendenin, working in C. D. Coryell's group in connection with the fission product identification program of the wartime atomic energy project (§ 13.76 *et seq.*). From the fraction of the fission products containing the rare-earth elements and yttrium, which is invariably associated with the rare-earths, the cerium was precipitated as iodate, and the yttrium, samarium and europium were largely removed by repeated digestion with a carbonate solution. The residue, consisting mainly of praseodymium, neodymium, element-61 and a small amount of yttrium, was absorbed on an Amberlite resin in an ion-exchange column, and then eluted with a slightly acid solution of ammonium citrate. Fractions of the eluate were collected and their radioactivity determined; from a plot of the activity against the volume of liquid passing through the column, as described in § 13.83, the element-61 was found to be associated with a 2.5-year beta activity.*

16.84. The same half life was observed to be formed as the product of negative beta-decay of 11-day $_{60}Nd^{147}$, so that it is presumably due to 61^{147}; this mass assignment has been verified by direct measurement in the mass spectrograph. Appreciable quantities of this nuclide in a pure state have been separated, by means of the ion-exchange technique, from the products of uranium fission. In

accordance with anticipation, the element-61 is a typical member of the rare-earth series, bridging the gap between neodymium and samarium. The wave lengths of the K-lines of the characteristic X-rays of the supposed element-61 have been measured, and the values were found to be exactly as expected.

16.85. Several other isotopes of element-61 have been definitely identified, while others are still uncertain. The 52-hour 61^{149} isotope has been found among the fission products, where it probably results from the negative beta-decay of the 2-hour Nd^{149}. The latter nuclide is also formed when slow neutrons interact with neodymium-148 and the 52-hour isotope of element-61 has been confirmed as the decay product. A 5.3-day isotope of this element, an isomeric state of mass number 148, has not been detected as a fission product, but it is produced in the (p,n) reaction with neodymium, presumably $Nd^{148}(p,n)61^{148}$.

16.86. As stated in § 12.104, the isotope of element-61 with mass number 145 would be of particular interest, since it might be expected to be of a relatively long life. This nuclide has been found to have a half life of about 30 years. Although it has a longer life than any other isotope of element-61, it is much too short to expect that it can be detected on earth.

16.87. The naming of element-61 has been the subject of a controversy, which has now been resolved. The appellation "illinium" was widely used at one time, especially in the United States, but it was based on a claim to the discovery of the element that is still open to confirmation. Because they considered element-61 to have been produced in their bombard-

* The half life was originally given as 3.7 years, but this is now known to be incorrect.

ment of neodymium with particles accelerated in the cyclotron, Pool and Quill suggested it be called "cyclonium." Finally, the name "promethium" was proposed by Marinsky and Glendenin, who separated element-61 from uranium fission products; Prometheus, according to mythology, brought fire from heaven for the use of man, just as fission has made available the energy of the nucleus.* At its meeting in 1949, the International Union of Chemistry recommended the adoption of the name *promethium*, symbol Pm, thereby acknowledging the claim of Marinsky and Glendenin to the first isolation of element-61.

ELEMENT-85: ASTATINE

16.88. It was mentioned in § 16.74 that isotopes of element 85 have been reported as products of natural radioactivity, but this element was first obtained by D. R. Corson, K. R. Mackenzie and E. Segrè in the United States in 1940. They found that when bismuth is irradiated with 32-Mev alpha particles from a cyclotron, a 7.2-hour activity develops which can be separated from all the adjacent elements, and which is presumably due to element-85 formed by the reaction

$$_{83}Bi^{209} + _2He^4 \rightarrow 85^{211} + 2_0n^1.$$

The decay of the 85^{211} nuclide by orbital-electron capture results in the formation of Po^{211}; thus

$$85^{211} + _{-1}e^0 \rightarrow _{84}Po^{211}.$$

This is the substance commonly known as actinium C′, which has a very short half life, estimated to be 5×10^{-3} sec., and expels a long-range alpha particle. The fact that these energetic particles always accompany

the 85^{211} supports the assignment of the mass number. There are, in addition, alpha particles of shorter range, and these are attributed to a branched disintegration. The production of element 85 in the manner described has been confirmed, and its discoverers have proposed the name *astatine*, symbol At, from the Greek *astatos*, meaning unstable, since it is the only member of the halogen group having no stable isotope.

16.89. The chemistry of astatine, which was worked out by means of the tracer technique, is exceptionally interesting because it shows marked differences from that of the halogens, yet is in keeping with the regular transition of properties with increasing atomic number in Group VIIB of the periodic table. It is well known that the electronegative, that is, the acidic or non-metallic, properties of the halogens diminish steadily in passing from fluorine to iodine; in the latter, some electropositive, or metallic, character is already apparent, although the properties are essentially those of an electronegative element. With astatine, however, the electropositive character appears to be more marked.

16.90. After reduction by sulfur dioxide or by zinc, the astatine activity is carried either by silver or thallium iodide, so that it evidently forms insoluble silver and thallium salts. This represents astatine in the univalent negative state which is characteristic of the halogens. However, astatine is very readily oxidized by bromine and by ferric ions, there being indications of at least two oxidation states. Although there is no evidence from migration experiments of the presence of positive ions in the solution, astatine deposits on the cathode, as well as

* The analogy was suggested by Mrs. C. D. Coryell.

on the anode, in the electrolysis of oxidized solutions. Elemental astatine can be volatilized, although not so readily as iodine, and it has a specific affinity for metallic silver. The similarity to iodine is also shown by the observation that astatine concentrates in the thyroid glands of animals.

16.91. According to Karlik and Bernert (§ 16.74), isotopes of astatine result from branched disintegrations of radium A (Po^{218}), thorium A (Po^{216}) and actinium A (Po^{215}), accompanied by the emission of beta particles; the mass numbers would thus be 218, 216 and 215, respectively. Subsequent investigations, however, suggest that the production of the 216-isotope in this manner is doubtful, although the other modes of decay have been confirmed.

Both At^{215} and At^{218}, which thus occur in nature, are alpha-particle emitters of very short half life. Their decay products, radium C and thorium C, respectively, are normal members of the uranium and actinium series, respectively. In addition to the two naturally occurring isotopes, sixteen others, with mass numbers in the range from 202 to 219, have been reported. Some have been obtained by bombardment of bismuth with alpha particles or by the spallation of uranium-238, whereas most of the remainder are members of one of the several known artificial radioactive series, described in the next section. Astatine-205 has resulted from the action of accelerated carbon nuclei on gold, i.e., $Au^{197}(C^{12},4n)At^{205}$.

NEW RADIOACTIVE SERIES

THE NEPTUNIUM SERIES

16.92. The first three known members of the neptunium ($4n + 1$) series of radioactive elements, mentioned in § 5.62, are plutonium-241, americium-241 and neptunium-237; these have been described in the present chapter. The next element is protactinium-233, which was, incidentally, the first member of the series to be discovered. When E. Fermi and his collaborators in Italy bombarded thorium with slow neutrons in 1935 (§ 11.46) the product* was identified as thorium-233 produced by the (n,γ) reaction

$$_{90}Th^{232} + _{0}n^{1} \rightarrow _{90}Th^{233} + \gamma.$$

This is known to have a half life of 23.5 min., and the product should be protactinium-233, formed by the negative beta-decay process

$$_{90}Th^{233} \rightarrow _{91}Pa^{233} + _{-1}e^{0}.$$

The Pa^{233} was found, by L. Meitner, F. Strassmann and O. Hahn in Germany in 1938, to be a negative beta-emitter, with a half life of 27.4 days. The decay of the protactinium-233, represented by

$$_{91}Pa^{233} \rightarrow _{92}U^{233} + _{-1}e^{0},$$

leads to the formation of uranium-233, another member of the neptunium series. This important nuclear fuel material (§ 15.12) was discovered and first isolated in 1942 by G. T. Seaborg, J. W. Gofman, and R. W. Stoughton in the United States; they showed that it is an alpha emitter, with a half life now taken to be 1.62 $\times 10^5$ years, and that it is fissionable by slow neutrons.

16.93. By bombarding thorium with a high density of neutrons from a nuclear-chain reactor, and allowing the intermediate products to decay,

---

* The situation, in this case, was not complicated, as it was with uranium, by fission products, since thorium-232 does not suffer fission with slow neutrons.

several milligrams of uranium-233 were obtained. Its immediate daughter, thorium-229, has a relatively long life, but because adequate amounts of uranium-233 were available, it was possible to accumulate sufficient of this isotope of thorium to permit a complete study of its disintegration products, all of which have relatively short lives. One of these is seen to be francium-221, the daughter of which is astatine-217.

Collateral Radioactive Series

16.94. In addition to the three main natural and the one artificial disintegration series of radioelements (Chapter V), each has been found to have at least one parallel or *collateral series*. The main series and the collateral series have different parents, but they become identical when, in the course of disintegration, they have a

uranium-238. Similarly, mendelevium-256 appears to be a direct progenitor of thorium-232. Many others, however, fall on collateral series which join with the main series at a later stage.

16.95. Because of the large number of isotopes of the elements of high atomic number, several collateral series have been identified. A few of the shorter ones, representing mostly those first discovered, will be described here. Collateral with the natural uranium series is an artificial $4n + 2$ series discovered in the United States by M. H. Studier and E. K. Hyde.* Its parent is protactinium-230 formed by the bombardment of thorium with alpha particles or deuterons of high energy, according to the reactions $Th^{232}(\alpha,p5n)Pa^{230}$ and $Th^{232}(d,4n)Pa^{230}$. The decay scheme of the series has been found to be as follows:

$$_{91}Pa^{230} \xrightarrow[17.7\ d.]{\beta^-} {}_{92}U^{230} \xrightarrow[20.8\ d.]{\alpha} {}_{90}Th^{226} \xrightarrow[30.9\ m.]{\alpha} {}_{88}Ra^{222} \xrightarrow[38\ s.]{\alpha} {}_{86}Rn^{218} \xrightarrow[0.02\ s.]{\alpha} {}_{84}Po^{214}\ (RaC') \rightarrow U\ series.$$

member in common. Actually, the nuclides of all the actinide elements must be members of one or other of the four so-called main series or of their collateral series, since there are only four possible end-products of the radioactive decay chains, namely, $Pb^{208}(4n)$, $Bi^{209}(4n + 1)$, $Pb^{206}(4n + 2)$ and $Pb^{207}(4n + 3)$. Thus, some of the artificial species are progenitors of the existing parents of the naturally occurring (or main) radioactive series. For example, einsteinium-254 undergoes beta decay

The loss of an alpha particle by the emanation, radon-218, leads to the formation of polonium-214, which is identical with radium C' of the uranium series; the subsequent decay of the collateral series thus coincides with that of the main uranium series at this point.

16.96. Another collateral $4n + 2$ series has for its progenitor protactinium-226 which is found among the products of bombardment of thorium with 150-Mev deuterons. The decay scheme is represented by

$$_{91}Pa^{226} \xrightarrow[1.8\ m.]{\alpha} {}_{89}Ac^{222} \xrightarrow[5.5\ s.]{\alpha} {}_{87}Fr^{218} \xrightarrow[5\times10^{-3}\ s.]{\alpha} {}_{85}At^{214} \xrightarrow[2\times10^{-6}\ s.]{\alpha} {}_{83}Bi^{210}\ (RaE) \longrightarrow U\ series.$$

and this would be followed by four stages of alpha decay to produce

16.97. Two collateral $4n$ (thorium) and one $4n + 3$ (actinium) series were

---

* The name *protactinium series* has been suggested for this artificial $4n + 2$ series, because protactinium-230 is the first known member. However, as will be seen below, other protactinium isotopes are also the progenitors of the $4n$ and $4n + 3$ collateral series.

identified by G. T. Seaborg and his associates in the United States. The first member of one of the $4n$ series is protactinium-228 resulting from the irradiation of thorium with 80-Mev deuterons, by the reaction $\text{Th}^{232}(d,6n)\text{Pa}^{228}$. The decay scheme is

$$_{91}\text{Pa}^{228} \xrightarrow[22\ \text{h.}]{\alpha} {}_{89}\text{Ac}^{224} \xrightarrow[2.9\ \text{h.}]{\alpha} {}_{87}\text{Fr}^{220} \xrightarrow[27.5\ \text{s.}]{\alpha} {}_{85}\text{At}^{216} \xrightarrow[3\times10^{-4}\ \text{s.}]{\alpha} {}_{83}\text{Bi}^{212}\ (\text{ThC}) \to \text{Th series,}$$

the Bi^{212} being identical with thorium C of the natural thorium series. The second collateral $4n$ series starts with plutonium-232 produced when uranium-235 is bombarded with alpha particles; thus $\text{U}^{235}(\alpha,7n)\text{Pu}^{232}$. The decay stages are

$$_{94}\text{Pu}^{232} \xrightarrow[36\ \text{m.}]{\alpha} {}_{92}\text{U}^{228} \xrightarrow[9.3\ \text{m.}]{\alpha} {}_{90}\text{Th}^{224} \xrightarrow[1\ \text{s.}]{\alpha} {}_{88}\text{Ra}^{220} \xrightarrow[3\times10^{-2}\ \text{s.}]{\alpha} {}_{86}\text{Rn}^{216} \xrightarrow[10^{-4}\ \text{s.}]{\alpha} {}_{84}\text{Po}^{212}\ (\text{ThC}') \to \text{Th series.}$$

16.98. The progenitor of the collateral $4n + 3$ series is protactinium-227 obtained by the reaction $\text{Th}^{232}(d,7n)\text{Pa}^{227}$; its decay scheme is as follows:

$$_{91}\text{Pa}^{227} \xrightarrow[38\ \text{m.}]{\alpha} {}_{89}\text{Ac}^{223} \xrightarrow[2.2\ \text{m.}]{\alpha} {}_{87}\text{Fr}^{219} \xrightarrow[0.02\ \text{s.}]{\alpha} {}_{85}\text{At}^{215} \xrightarrow[\sim10^{-4}\ \text{s.}]{\alpha} {}_{83}\text{Bi}^{211}\ (\text{AcC}) \to \text{Ac series.}$$

16.99. It can be seen from the tabulation in § 5.58, that uranium-235 (actinouranium) is the first naturally occurring member of the actinium $(4n + 3)$ series, but the three nuclides U^{239}, Np^{239} and Pu^{239} may be regarded as artificial precursors. The rapid decay of the first two leads, of course, to the formation of plutonium-239 (§ 16.26), and as the latter is an alpha emitter, its daughter will be uranium-235;* thus,

16.100. A collateral $4n + 1$ series that, it is of interest to note, includes an emanation (Rn^{217}), which the main neptunium series† does not (§ 5.64), has for its progenitor uranium-229, formed by the $(\alpha,7n)$ reaction on thorium-232 with 100-Mev alpha particles. The decay scheme is

$$_{92}\text{U}^{229} \xrightarrow[58\ \text{m.}]{\alpha} {}_{90}\text{Th}^{225} \xrightarrow[8.0\ \text{m.}]{\alpha} {}_{88}\text{Ra}^{221} \xrightarrow[30\ \text{s.}]{\alpha} {}_{86}\text{Rn}^{217} \xrightarrow[\sim10^{-3}\ \text{s.}]{\alpha} {}_{84}\text{Po}^{213} \to \text{Np series.}$$

16.101. In addition, a few other collateral members of the neptunium series are known. One example is protactinium-229, formed by the bombardment of the natural radioactive element ionium (Th^{230}) by means of deuterons, according to the process $\text{Th}^{230}(d,3n)\text{Pa}^{229}$. This nuclide has a half life of 1.5 days, decaying by orbital-electron capture and also by the emission of an alpha particle; the products are thorium-229 and actinium-225, which, as seen in § 5.63, are both members of the neptunium series. The plutonium mentioned in § 16.27 as resulting from the $\text{U}^{238}(\alpha,5n)\text{Pu}^{237}$ reaction, decays by orbital-electron capture with a half life of 40 days; the product is neptunium-237, for which the artificial $4n + 1$ series is named.

$$_{92}\text{U}^{239} \xrightarrow{\beta} {}_{93}\text{Np}^{239} \xrightarrow{\beta} {}_{94}\text{Pu}^{239} \xrightarrow{\alpha} {}_{92}\text{U}^{235}\ (\text{AcU}) \to \text{Ac series.}$$

* It is of special interest to note in this connection that the decay of plutonium-239 leads to the formation of uranium-235; since both parent and daughter are fissionable, and the half life of the latter is nearly 10^9 years, it is evident that plutonium-239 could be stored for thousands of years without appreciable loss of fissionable properties.

† Since the neptunium series does not occur in nature, the assignment of the "main series" is actually quite arbitrary. The name is given here to the first $4n + 1$ series to be discovered.

ALPHA-PARTICLE ENERGIES

16.102. One of the consequences of the study of the various collateral series is the availability of a total of over one hundred alpha emitters, compared to the less than thirty occurring in nature. A comparison of the masses, half lives and alpha-particle energies of these nuclides has revealed some interesting facts. Considering the alpha-emitting isotopes of any given element, from bismuth onward, it has been noted that the energies of the alpha particles increase, in general, with decreasing mass of the isotope. In other words, the nuclides with the lowest mass numbers, and which are consequently the most neutron deficient, emit alpha particles with the highest energies. This is to be expected, since the larger ratio of protons to neutrons should favor alpha activity. For the elements of lower atomic number, namely, bismuth, polonium and astatine, the heaviest isotopes show the trend mentioned above, but with decreasing mass number a point is reached where the alpha energy decreases, passes through a minimum and then increases again. These minima must represent nuclides of relatively greater stability, and it is significant that Bi^{209}, Po^{210} and At^{211}, all of which have the stable number 126 of neutrons, occur at or near the minima for the respective elements (§ 12.105). There is evidence of similar minima for those isotopes of the elements beyond curium containing 152 neutrons in their nuclei.

16.103. If the energies of the alpha particles expelled from the nuclides of the even-even type, that is, with even numbers of protons and neutrons, are plotted against the logarithms of the corresponding half lives, the values for the various elements of even atomic number, from polonium to curium, fall on a series of approximately parallel lines. The results are in general agreement with the wave-mechanical theory of alpha decay (§ 7.30), the half life, for a given energy value, increasing with the atomic number, i.e., with the nuclear charge of the radioactive species. However, alpha emitters with an odd number of neutrons or protons, or both, have half lives considerably longer than expected. Incidentally, all these nuclides emit alpha particles of relatively high energy, namely, 5 Mev or more. It is possible that the comparatively long half lives and high energies of the isotopes containing odd numbers of protons or neutrons, or both, in which one or more of the nucleons must have unpaired spins, is due partly to the "forbidden" character of the decay.

16.104. In view of the relationships between mass number and alpha-particle energy on the one hand, and half life and alpha-particle energy on the other hand, it is to be expected that certain regularities will exist between half lives and mass numbers. This is indeed the case, especially for even-even nuclides. Similarly, relationships have been obtained between mass number and the half lives for spontaneous fission. The accumulation of systematic data of this kind has helped in predicting the decay properties of hitherto undiscovered species, and should be useful, as mentioned above, for the identification of nuclides of such short life that other methods will not be applicable.

The Uses of Isotopes and Radiations

Chapter XVII

ISOTOPES AS TRACERS

LABELING WITH ISOTOPES

17.1. It has been predicted that when the achievements of the present-day atomic energy program are reviewed in the light of history it will be found that the greatest contribution to humanity will have resulted from the variety of isotopes, both radioactive and inactive, that have been made available for experimental purposes. The isotopic method represents, as will be seen below, a powerful tool for the solution of numerous problems in biology, physiology, chemistry, physics and other sciences. Some of these problems, particularly those having an important bearing on life processes, could not have been solved without the use of isotopes. In others, possible solutions, which have been arrived at by laborious procedures, have been confirmed or disproved by utilizing the information that can quickly be supplied by the proper application of the isotopic method. It is true that the use of isotopes as a scientific tool is not new; but it is only in recent years that isotopes have become available in such variety and in such quantity as to make their use as widespread as it is at the present time. Results of considerable interest and practical value have already been reported, and further discoveries of great significance may be confidently expected.*

17.2. The more important applications of isotopes depend on the fact that the chemical properties of the isotopes of a given element are essentially identical. Some variations, as mentioned in § 8.74, which are due to differences in reaction rates, occur with the lightest elements, but these are usually unimportant. A radioisotope can be detected by its radioactivity, and an inactive isotope of particular mass can be identified by means of the mass spectrometer. Consequently, the characteristic property of the isotope, namely, its radioactivity or its mass, can act as a "tag" or "label" which permits the fate of the element, or of a compound con-

* From August 2, 1946 through July 31, 1957, the Oak Ridge National Laboratory, in its capacity as primary distributor for the U. S. Atomic Energy Commission, made 98,807 shipments of radioisotopes to groups in the United States and 6,464 shipments to foreign countries. As of June 30, 1957, there have also been made 3,798 shipments of stable isotopes.

taining this element, to be traced through a series of chemical and physical changes. The element which has been labeled or tagged is consequently called a *tracer element*.

17.3. In general, an element can be labeled by changing its natural isotopic composition; for example, ordinary carbon contains 1.1 per cent of the heavier isotope C^{13}, but if the proportion of this isotope in a particular compound is increased, the carbon has become labeled. Similarly, the radioactive isotopes C^{11} and C^{14} may be used to label carbon, since the natural element contains neither of these nuclides. If a carbon compound contains two or more carbon atoms, it is often feasible to label a particular one or more. Thus acetic acid, CH_3COOH, has a methyl carbon atom, in the $—CH_3$ group, and a carboxyl carbon atom, in the $—COOH$ group. It is possible to prepare acetic acid in which the isotopic composition of either or both of the carbon atoms differs from the normal value for the element carbon as found in nature. This change has a negligible effect on the chemical and physiological properties of the substance, and so the behavior of each particular portion of the molecule can be traced.

17.4. Suppose that acetic acid, in which only the methyl carbon atom is labeled, is supplied to an organism; then, among the metabolic products appears carbon dioxide gas. Upon testing the latter by a particle counter for radioactivity or by a mass spectrometer for mass, the carbon is found to be inactive or to have the normal isotopic composition. The obvious conclusion to be drawn is that the carbon in the carbon dioxide originated from the carboxyl group and not from the methyl group of the acetic acid. The carbon in the methyl group is evi-

dently utilized for some other process, the nature of which might be discovered by further investigation.

17.5. The foregoing example is an illustration of the type of problem for which an unequivocal solution could not possibly be obtained without the use of an isotopic tracer, for the chemist has otherwise no way of distinguishing between the two carbon atoms. There are many other instances of a similar character. Plants and other living organisms produce carbon dioxide in respiration, but it was not possible to state whether the gas was being assimilated at the same time. By means of carbon dioxide tagged with a radioactive carbon isotope, it has been found that absorption occurs simultaneously with respiration. When a plant grows it takes up phosphorus both from the soil and from added fertilizer; it is important to know what proportion comes from each source. Ordinary analytical methods cannot answer this question, but the use of radioactive phosphorus can supply the information. In blood transfusion, what happens to the red corpuscles in the body of the patient? Once the transfusion has taken place, it is normally impossible to distinguish between the corpuscles previously present and those which have been added. But by labeling the iron in the hemoglobin, the red coloring matter of the transfused blood, its behavior can be determined in the body of the recipient.

17.6. One further example may be given in concluding this general outline of the unique properties of the isotopic tool. In sunlight, green plants can take up carbon dioxide and water, which are converted into sugars and starches, and at the same time they give up oxygen. Carbon dioxide and water each contain oxygen, and the question is: Does this oxygen originate from the carbon dioxide or from the water molecule, or from both? It had long been suspected that it came from the water molecule, but definite proof required the use of water and of carbon dioxide, in one or other of which the oxygen atoms were labeled by increasing the proportion of the O^{18} isotope.

RADIOACTIVE AND STABLE ISOTOPES

17.7. In 1913, soon after the discovery of isotopes (Chapter VIII), G. Hevesy and F. A. Paneth, in Germany, showed that minute amounts of radium $D(Pb^{210})$ could be used as a *radioactive tracer*, or *indicator*, as they called it, for lead in the determination of the solubilities of sparingly soluble lead salts. Five years later, in 1918, Paneth employed naturally occurring radioisotopes of lead and bismuth to study the behavior of the unstable hydrides of these metals. The hydrides were detected by the radioactivity associated with them, since the respective isotopes had the same chemical properties as the inactive forms of the elements. The first application of radioactive tracers to a biological problem was made by Hevesy in 1923; he investigated the uptake by plants of lead from solution, using thorium $B(Pb^{212})$ to label a lead salt. After various time intervals, the plants were burned and the amounts of lead taken up were calculated from the thorium B present. It was Hevesy, too, who in 1935, in conjunction with O. Chiewitz, initiated the use of artificial radioisotopes as tracers, by

studying the absorption by plants of phosphorus from a nutrient solution.

17.8. The first nonradioactive isotope to become available in an enriched form was heavy hydrogen or deuterium (§ 8.66); this immediately found numerous applications as a tool for the study of a variety of chemical problems. Subsequently, the heavier stable isotopes of carbon and nitrogen, namely C^{13} and N^{15}, were concentrated by the chemical exchange method, and in 1937, R. Schoenheimer and his associates in the United States, started a highly significant series of physiological investigations making use of deuterium and of N^{15} as tracers. Later, enriched isotopic forms of carbon, nitrogen and sulfur were employed in connection with a number of biochemical studies.

17.9. Until recently, the application of isotopic tracers was restricted, for two main reasons: first, the number of stable isotopes that had been concentrated was very small; and second, although many radioactive isotopes were known, only very limited amounts were obtainable, and then only by those who had access to a cyclotron, or other particle accelerator, or to a strong source of neutrons. Since 1946, the situation has changed completely; stable isotopes of over fifty elements, including deuterium, carbon-13, nitrogen-15 and oxygen-18, are now readily available. Many radioisotopes which had previously been obtained in the merest traces are now being made in appreciable quantities by various neutron reactions, using the intense neutron flux of nuclear reactors.* In addition, other radioiso-

---

* "Materials to be activated are placed in small aluminum containers. The containers are then inserted into holes in a graphite block or 'stringer' which composes part of the graphite and uranium structure of the pile [see Fig. 14.4]. The block, loaded with containers, is pushed into the interior of the pile through an opening in the surrounding thick concrete shield and is irradiated for a period varying from a few days to several months." (Quoted from *Radioisotopes Catalog and Price List,* issued by the Isotopes Division, U. S. Atomic Energy Commission.)

topes are being extracted from the fission products. Some useful radioactive nuclides cannot be conveniently derived from neutron reactions, and they are usually made by irradiation of a suitable element with accelerated deuterons from a cyclotron, or similar device.

17.10. When the decision is made to undertake an experimental investigation requiring the use of an isotope of a particular element, there is frequently, although not always, a choice possible between a stable and a radioactive isotope. This is the case, for example, with carbon for which the stable C^{13} as well as the radioactive C^{11} and C^{14} are available. The final selection will be determined by a number of considerations, which can be indicated by reviewing the advantages and disadvantages of stable and unstable nuclides as tracers.

17.11. The main point in favor of the employment of radioisotopes is their ease of detection, and even of quantitative determination, in extremely small amounts by utilizing the ionizing or photographic effects of the emitted radiations (Chapter VI). It may be mentioned, incidentally, that virtually all the artificial radioisotopes used in tracer work are beta emitters, positive or negative; some evolve gamma radiations in addition. On the other hand, the spontaneous decay of the radioactive nuclei means that the amount of the tracer is steadily decreasing, so that observations of long duration may not be possible. As a very rough generalization, a radioisotope is effectively useful in a given experiment lasting about ten times the half life. Before the discovery of C^{14}, the only known radioactive isotope of carbon was C^{11}, with a half life of 20.4 min., and it is a tribute to the skill of the scientists that they were able to prepare suitable compounds and study their behavior in living organisms before the material had become undetectable.

17.12. Where there is a choice between a short-lived and a long-lived isotope, the latter would appear, at first sight, to be preferable. But it must be remembered (§ 7.78) that there is an approximate inverse relationship between the life of a radionuclide and the energy of the emitted beta particle. A long-lived isotope, such as C^{14}, with a half life of 5600 years, expels a feeble beta particle of short range which is not easy to detect. This difficulty is, fortunately, not insuperable, and a number of different methods have been proposed for adapting Geiger-Müller tubes and other devices for the counting of the so-called "soft" beta particles of feeble energy and low penetrating power.

17.13. Another aspect of the use of radioisotopes as tracers is the possible harmful effects of the radiations, both on the operating personnel and on living organisms that may form the subjects for biological studies. Methods of protecting the workers have been devised, and provided the recognized precautions are taken, as described in Chapter XIX, all danger can be avoided. In this respect isotopes, such as carbon-14, which emit beta particles of low energy and no gamma rays, present an advantage, since protection from the external effects of the radiation is relatively simple. Care must, of course, be exercised in the introduction of radioisotopes into the body; some, radiocarbon, for example, are distributed throughout the tissues, while others, notably iodine and calcium, tend to be fixed in particular parts of the organism (§ 19.16). However, by keeping the quantity of radioactive material below certain specified limits, depending on the half life of the isotope and the ease with which it is eliminated from the body, the possibility of deleterious effects due to radiation can be obviated.

17.14. The great advantages of stable isotopes is their permanency, so that they are invaluable for experiments which require considerable time for completion. Further, provided only small amounts of the tracer isotope are introduced, as will undoubtedly be the case because of its scarcity, the physiological effects on a living organism will be negligible. The use of stable isotopes is restricted to a great extent by the necessity of employing a mass spectrometer for their detection. It is true that this instrument has been greatly improved and its operation simplified, but it is still more expensive and complicated than the common detectors of beta and gamma radiations. In general, therefore, it may be stated that, because of its ease of detection in extremely small amounts, and the consequent possibility of using high dilutions, preference would be given to a radioisotope, if one suitable for the required purpose could be obtained.

17.15. In certain instances, the nature of the experiment is such that it cannot be completed in a short time. Occasionally, too, complicated molecules are needed, and the process of synthesis may take several weeks or months. By the time the compound has been prepared, the activity of the material may have decayed to a negligible amount and it will be contaminated, in any event, by what may be an undesirable daughter element. The discovery of the long-lived carbon-14 has been a great boon, the benefits of which are becoming increasingly apparent, but unfortunately the situation is not so satisfactory with regard to the biologically important elements nitrogen and oxygen, and also, but to a lesser extent, with phosphorus and sulfur. The longest-lived radioisotopes of nitrogen and oxygen, N^{13} and O^{15}, have half lives of 10.1 min. and 2.1 min., respectively, which are too short for the great majority of investigations. Consequently, the stable isotopes N^{15} and O^{18}, which are available in fair quantities, must usually be employed.

Isotopes for Biological Studies

17.16. It will be of interest to review, at this point, the elements of most importance in the study of biological problems, and to consider what isotopes are available and how they can be obtained. Actually something like thirty different elements are known to play a part in the life processes of various organisms, but the discussion here will be restricted to the following, given in order of increasing atomic number: hydrogen, carbon, nitrogen, oxygen, sodium, phosphorus, sulfur, chlorine, potassium, calcium, manganese, iron, cobalt, copper, zinc and iodine.

17.17. For hydrogen, two isotopes are possible for tracer work: these are the stable isotope deuterium, mass number 2, and the radioactive tritium, mass number 3. The latter has a half life of 12.26 years, but it emits a beta particle of extremely low energy, so that special techniques of measurement must be employed unless large quantities of the tracer are used. The chief difficulty in experimental work with the isotopes of hydrogen, and especially with tritium, is that the masses are so different from that of ordinary hydrogen that differences in reaction rates have a noticeable effect. It has long been known, for example, that appreciable proportions of heavy water are harmful to certain living organisms, presumably because the processes necessary for the maintenance of life occur at abnormal rates. This effect would be even more marked with tritium. Care must therefore be exercised in the use of hydrogen isotopes and in the interpretation of the results.

17.18. As already indicated, three isotopes of carbon, namely C^{11}, C^{13} and C^{14} are obtainable for experimental purposes. Of these C^{13} is stable, and is enriched by the chemical exchange method described in § 8.115. The long-lived C^{14}, with a half life of 5600 years, is obtained by irradiation of nitrogen with neutrons in a nuclear reactor, according to the process $N^{14}(n,p)C^{14}$ mentioned in § 11.51. This is one of the few cases where slow neutrons have a large cross section for an (n,p) process. If the short-lived C^{11}, half life 20.4 min., is required it is best made by the bombardment of boron with fast deuterons from a cyclotron, according to the reaction $B^{10}(d,n)C^{11}$.

17.19. No radioisotopes of nitrogen or oxygen having a reasonably long life have yet been discovered, as stated above, and so tracer work with these elements is restricted to the stable nuclides N^{15} and O^{18}, respectively. Fortunately, both of these isotopes are now readily available. The nitrogen-15 is concentrated by the chemical exchange procedure, and oxygen-18 is a by-product of the manufacture of heavy water, but this isotope could undoubtedly also be enriched by chemical exchange methods. Because of their gaseous nature and the consequent difficulty of retaining the deposits, it is unlikely that the isotopes of nitrogen and oxygen will be separated electromagnetically (§ 8.90).

17.20. Sodium exists in nature as a single nuclide (Na^{23}) and so there is no possibility of using a stable tracer, but two radioisotopes, namely Na^{22}, half life 2.6 years, and Na^{24}, half life 15 hours, are known. The former is made by the bombardment of magnesium by deuterons in the reaction $Mg^{24}(d,\alpha)Na^{22}$ and requires the use of a cyclotron or similar instrument. The Na^{24} isotope, prepared by the action of reactor neutrons on sodium, thus, $Na^{23}(n,\gamma)Na^{24}$, is available and can be used for short-term investigations.

17.21. Phosphorus is another element occurring naturally as a single nuclide, so that a radioisotope must be employed in tracer work. Only one of these, P^{32}, has a sufficiently long half life, viz., 14.3 days, to permit its use as a tracer; this isotope can be readily made in a nuclear reactor either by the (n,γ) reaction $P^{31}(n,\gamma)P^{32}$, or by the (n,p) process $S^{32}(n,p)P^{32}$. The latter method is preferred because the phosphorus can be chemically separated from the sulfur target material, thus yielding a product of high specific activity (§ 17.36).

17.22. The element sulfur offers three possibilities for isotopic tracing. The stable isotopes S^{34} and S^{36} can be separated by the electromagnetic method, and the former has also been enriched by chemical exchange. In addition, the 87.1-day radioactive S^{35} is available from the interaction of reactor neutrons with chlorine, according to the process $Cl^{35}(n,p)S^{35}$. The energy of the beta particle from S^{35} is similar to that emitted by C^{14}, and so analogous detection procedures are employed for these two nuclides.

17.23. The situation with regard to the isotopes of chlorine is not too good. The long-lived radioisotope Cl^{36}, with a half life of 3.2×10^5 years, is obtainable from the irradiation of Cl^{35}, the most-abundant stable isotope, with reactor neutrons, by the $Cl^{35}(n,\gamma)Cl^{36}$ process. Because of the very long half life, however, the activity is low, and relatively large quantities of material are required for experimental work. A second, shorter-lived isotope, Cl^{38}, half life 37.5 min., can be obtained by the analogous $Cl^{37}(n,\gamma)Cl^{38}$ process with the less abundant natural isotope, or by the $Cl^{37}(d,p)Cl^{38}$ reaction in the cyclotron, but it is probably too evanescent to find much application. The possibility of concentrating one of the stable isotopes has been considered, but since chlorine normally contains about 25 per cent of Cl^{37}, an appreciable change in the natural isotopic abundance ratio, which is essential for tracer work, would require the addition of relatively large quantities of enriched material.

17.24. Potassium-42, with a half life of 12.5 hours, is made by the reaction $K^{41}(n,\gamma)K^{42}$ in a nuclear reactor, but its short life limits its usefulness. The other known radioisotopes of potassium have even shorter lives, and so the enrichment of the naturally occurring nuclides offers better prospects for tracer work. Both K^{40} and K^{41} have been concentrated electromagnetically; the former isotope is feebly radioactive, being one of the few naturally occurring radionuclides of low mass number, but its activity is so weak that Geiger-Müller counters and similar devices can hardly be used for its detection in small amounts. The employment of a mass spectrometer would thus be necessary for K^{40} as well as for K^{41}.

17.25. Several isotopes of calcium have been separated by the electromagnetic procedure and are available for tracer work. In addition, limited quantities of the 164-day Ca^{45} can be obtained as a result of the reaction $Ca^{44}(n,\gamma)Ca^{45}$ taking place with slow neutrons in a reactor. An alternative possibility is to utilize the $Sc^{45}(n,p)Ca^{45}$ process, although the cross section for slow neutrons is small; the advantage of this method of making Ca^{45} is that the latter can be extracted from the scandium target by ordinary chemical procedures, and thus obtained with high specific activity.

17.26. Since manganese occurs naturally as a single nuclide, radioactive isotopes are mandatory for tracer work. Neither the 5.6-day Mn^{52} nor the more useful 300-day Mn^{54} can be conveniently made by neutron bombardment, because the stable nuclide of manganese has a mass number of 55. Manganese-56, which could be obtained in a reactor by the process $Mn^{55}(n,\gamma)Mn^{56}$, has a half life of only 2.6 hours, and is of little value for investigations involving the tracing of manganese. The two former isotopes are made by fast deuteron bombardment in the cyclotron according to the processes $Cr^{52}(d,2n)Mn^{52}$ and $Fe^{56}(d,\alpha)Mn^{54}$, respectively.

17.27. In view of the importance of iron as a tracer element, it is fortunate that several isotopes, both stable and radioactive, are available. It has consequently been possible to obtain interesting results by labeling with two isotopes, as will be seen in § 17.82. The stable isotopes Fe^{57} and Fe^{58} have been concentrated electromagnetically and, in addition, the radionuclides Fe^{55}, half life 2.94 years, and Fe^{59}, half life 45.1 days, have been made. As obtained by neutron bombardment in a reactor, the product is a mixture of these two species, due to the reactions $Fe^{54}(n,\gamma)Fe^{55}$ and $Fe^{58}(n,\gamma)Fe^{59}$. The Fe^{59} isotope could be obtained more or less exclusively if enriched Fe^{58} were used as target material. Another possibility is to allow the mixture containing Fe^{55} and Fe^{59} to stand for a year or so, in which time the Fe^{59} will have largely decayed, but the amount of Fe^{55} will be reduced only slightly. Where a cyclotron is available the individual radioisotopes of iron can be made by $Mn^{55}(d,2n)$ Fe^{55} and $Co^{59}(n,p)Fe^{59}$, respectively, fast neutrons being required for the latter process.

17.28. Cobalt has two radioactive isotopes of value in tracer work, to compensate for the fact that it has but a single stable nuclide. The longer-lived, 5.3-year Co^{60} is readily obtained by means of slow neutrons, according to the reaction $Co^{59}(n,\gamma)Co^{60}$, but the 72-day Co^{58} requires deuterons from a cyclotron to make the Fe^{57} $(d,n)Co^{58}$ process possible.

17.29. The situation with regard to copper is not too promising. The longest-lived known radioisotope is Cu^{64}, but its half life is only 12.8 hours, so that its use as a tracer is restricted to short range investigations. It is true that the stable isotope Cu^{65} can be enriched, but since the natural material already contains nearly 30 per cent of this nuclide, large quantities would be needed to make an appreciable change in the isotopic composition. Without such a change, tracer work is, of course, impossible.

17.30. Stable Zn^{70} has been concentrated by the electromagnetic method and is available for use as a tracer element. In addition, the 245-day Zn^{65} is made by the irradiation of zinc with reactor neutrons, thus, $Zn^{64}(n,\gamma)Zn^{65}$. Because the radioisotope cannot be separated from the stable target material, the specific activity of the Zn^{65} as obtained in this way is low. If a product of higher specific activity is required, the reaction $Cu^{65}(d,2n)Zn^{65}$ is used, the deuterons being supplied by a cyclotron.

17.31. Iodine exists in nature as a single species and consequently there is no possibility of using stable iodine in tracer studies. Of the many radioisotopes of this element, only two, namely, 8.05-day I^{131} and 60-day I^{125}, offer any practical prospects in this connection. The former is obtained from the products of the fission of uranium, where it results from the beta decay of 24.8-min. Te^{131}. The iodine is readily extracted from the mixture on account of its volatility. The longer-lived isotope I^{125}, which is less readily available, is made by the $Te^{124}(d,n)I^{125}$ reaction in a cyclotron.

SPECIFIC ACTIVITY: THE CURIE

17.32. The extreme sensitivity of the radioactive tracing procedure can be readily understood by considering some simple calculations. According to equation (5.1), the rate of disintegration of a radioelement is equal to λN, where λ is the decay constant and N is the number of atoms of the element present. If each disintegration may be supposed to be accompanied by the expulsion of a single particle, for example, a beta particle, then λN is also the rate at which such particles are expelled from the N atoms of radioactive material. By equation (5.9), the decay constant λ may be replaced by $0.693/T$, where T is the half life of the radionuclide; hence,

$$\frac{\text{Rate of emission}}{\text{of particles}} = \frac{0.693N}{T}. \quad (17.1)$$

If T is expressed in seconds, then this equation gives the emission rate in terms of the number of particles expelled per second from N atoms of the given nuclide.

17.33. A particle counter, such as an ionization device or a scintillation counter, can, in principle, detect a single particle, but if reasonably accurate measurements are to be made, the counting rate must appreciably exceed that due to extraneous causes, such as cosmic rays and atmospheric radioactivity. A minimum practical value for the rate of counting may be taken to be about 20 counts per minute. In general, unless special precautions are taken, something like 10 per cent of the particles from a given source will actually enter the counter; and hence it may be supposed that a quantity of radioactive material emitting particles at the rate of approximately 200 per minute, or about 4 per second, is the smallest amount that can be measured satisfactorily.

17.34. Consequently, the expression in equation (17.1) may be set equal to 4 per second, and the resulting value of N, that is,

$$N = \frac{4T}{0.693} = 6T \text{ atoms}, \qquad (17.2)$$

then gives, roughly, the minimum number of radioactive atoms, having a half life of T seconds, which can be conveniently detected. In order to see what this quantity implies in grams of the isotope, the result given by equation (17.2) should be multiplied by the mass number A, and divided by the Avogadro number, 6×10^{23} (§ 1.56). In this manner it is found that the minimum weight of a radioactive species capable of detection can be expressed in the following approximate form:

Minimum detectable weight
$$= 10^{-23}TA \text{ gram}. \qquad (17.3)$$

The smallest mass of a particular

radionuclide which can be used in a tracer experiment is thus proportional to its half life and to its mass number. The shorter the half life and the lower the mass number the smaller will be the minimum weight suitable for convenient detection.

17.35. The general order of magnitude of these minimum weights may be seen by considering two species which have been widely used as tracers, namely, carbon-14, which has a long life, and phosphorus-32, with a relatively short life. The half life T of radiocarbon C^{14} is about 5600 years, i.e., 1.8×10^{11} seconds, the mass number A is 14, and so the minimum detectable weight of this isotope is found from equation (17.3) to be close to 2×10^{-11} gram. For 14.3-day P^{32}, on the other hand, the half life T is roughly 1.3×10^6 seconds and the mass number A is 32, so that the smallest weight which could be conveniently measured in an ionization counter is about 4×10^{-16} gram. It is evident, therefore, that extremely small amounts of a radioactive tracer, which are much too small for observation in any other way, can be detected by means of a suitable particle counter.

17.36. The material used for tracer work rarely, if ever, consists of the pure radioisotope. The required nuclide can usually be freed from other elements, but separation from stable isotopes of the same element is in most cases a matter of great difficulty. The proportion of the active species is frequently expressed in terms of the *specific activity* of the material, defined as the ratio of the number of atoms of the given radioactive isotope to the total number of atoms of the same element. The specific activity, as defined in this manner, is thus the fraction of the given element that is present in the form of the particular radioisotope. In order to avoid undesirable addition of large amounts of stable nuclides to a system under investigation, attempts are made to have the specific activity as high as convenient, especially in metabolic studies with small animals.

17.37. For practical purposes, another quantity, also called the specific activity,* is used to express the rate at which unit weight of radioactive material decays or, in other words, to indicate the rate at which it emits charged particles. Since the detection of the radionuclide depends on these particles, this form of the specific activity gives a more useful practical indication of the amount of the tracer element present in a particular specimen. In order to understand the alternative definition it is necessary to consider the unit called the *curie,* which is frequently encountered in radioactive studies. At the present time the curie is defined as the quantity of any radioactive material giving 3.70×10^{10} disintegrations per second.† Two subsidiary units, representing smaller amounts of active material are the *millicurie,* which is a one-thousandth part of a curie and a *microcurie,* representing a one-millionth of a curie; these would correspond to amounts of active material producing 3.7×10^7 and 3.7×10^4 dis-

integrations per second, respectively. The specific activity of a given substance is then expressed as the number of curies (or millicuries) per gram (or per milligram) of the element present, the weight to include both active and stable isotopes. On this basis, the specific activity of pure elemental radium is 1 curie per gram.

17.38. The use of the specific activity may be illustrated by reference to an example. In the Radioisotope Catalog issued by the Isotopes Division of the U. S. Atomic Energy Commission, it will be seen that P^{32} is available as a product having a specific activity of 50 millicuries per gram. This means that for every gram of total phosphorus in the material there are $50 \times 3.7 \times 10^7 = 1.85 \times 10^9$ disintegrations taking place per second, so that 1.85×10^9 beta particles are expelled per second. Since an emission of 4 particles per second can be detected conveniently, a quantity of this material containing 1 gram of total phosphorus would go a long way in performing tracer experiments.

17.39. In order to determine the specific activity of a particular product according to the definition just given, use may be made of equation (17.1). If N is taken as the number of atoms in 1 gram of a radionuclide, i.e., the Avogadro number, 6.02×10^{23}, divided by the mass number A, then

* It is unfortunate that the same term is used for the two quantities, which are quite different, although they are related to one another. Some writers use the two indiscriminately, relying upon the units to distinguish them.

† At the Radiology Congress held in Brussels in 1910, it was decided to give the name "curie" to the quantity of radium emanation (radon) in equilibrium with 1 gram of radium. In 1930, however, the International Radium Standard Commission extended the definition, so that the curie became the equilibrium quantity of any decay product of radium. Since 1 gram of radium undergoes about 3.7×10^{10} disintegrations per second, the definition of the curie in the text came into general, but unofficial, use. In 1948, the Committee on Standards and Units of Radioactivity of the National Research Council (United States) recommended that this definition of the curie be made official. At the same time, the Committee favored the adoption of the proposal made by E. U. Condon and L. F. Curtiss of the U. S. National Bureau of Standards in 1946, that the term "rutherford" be used to designate a quantity of radioactive material giving 10^6 disintegrations per second. In spite of the convenience of this latter unit, there seems to be little inclination for its adoption as an alternative to the curie.

this equation gives the rate of disintegration of 1 gram of the pure isotope; thus, replacing N by $6.02 \times 10^{23}/A$, it follows that

Rate of disintegration per gram of nuclide $= \dfrac{0.693 \times 6.02 \times 10^{23}}{TA}$. (17.4)

Upon dividing this by 3.7×10^{10}, and expressing the half life T in seconds, the result is the specific activity in curies per gram of the pure isotope; thus, making the appropriate calculation, it is found that

Specific activity of pure nuclide $= \dfrac{1.13 \times 10^{13}}{TA}$ curies per gram. (17.5)

The specific activity in curies per gram of the pure nuclide is seen to be inversely proportional to both the half life and the mass number.

17.40. To return to the particular case of phosphorus-32, for which the mass number A is 32 and the half life T is 1.3×10^6 seconds, it is found from equation (17.5) that the specific activity of pure P^{32} is 2.7×10^5 curies per gram.* The specimen referred to above has an activity of 50 millicuries, that is 0.05 curie, per gram of phosphorus so that the actual weight of P^{32} is $0.05/2.7 \times 10^5 = 1.8 \times 10^{-7}$ gram. Consequently, for each gram of total phosphorus, including both active and stable isotopes, there is present only 1.8×10^{-7} gram of P^{32}. This extremely small quantity is nevertheless adequate for a considerable amount of tracer work, since, as seen above, 4×10^{-16} gram is sufficient for a single determination. The foregoing calculation has been pre-sented in some detail, not only because it is the type of information often used in tracer work, but also because it indicates the minuteness of the amounts which can be employed.

17.41. Although the weights of radioactive tracer elements are quite small, it must be remembered that the number of atoms is nevertheless large; 10^{-7} gram of phosphorus-32, for example, contains about 10^{15} atoms. Since the radionuclide is made, as a general rule, by bombardment of the target nuclei with individual neutrons or deuterons, according to circumstances, a considerable exposure to these particles is necessary to produce even a small amount, in weight, of a radioactive isotope.† For this reason, it is frequently desirable to concentrate the latter in order to increase the specific activity of the final material. If the product resulting from irradiation is a different element, that is, it has a different atomic number, from that of the target material, the problem of separation is not too difficult. This will be the case for the few (n,p) reactions, such as $N^{14}(n,p)C^{14}$, $S^{32}(n,p)P^{32}$ and $Cl^{35}(n,p)S^{35}$, using slow neutrons, and for all reactions, except those of the (d,p) or (d,t) type, involving deuterons. The concentration can then be achieved by the methods of radiochemistry described earlier (§§ 5.29, 13.76); for example, precipitation with a small amount of a carrier, which might be a stable isotope if no suitable nonisotopic carrier could be found, extraction by means of a solvent, volatilization, electrodeposition or displacement of one metal by another, and, finally, ion exchange.

---

* It should be noted that the specific activity of pure phosphorus-32, expressed in curies per gram, is considerably greater than that of radium itself; because of its considerably longer half life, the specific activity of pure carbon-14 is only 5 curies per gram.

† The relationship between the number of nuclei produced and the flux of the incident particles and the cross section is given by equation (11.7).

17.42. As the majority of slow-neutron reactions are of the (n,γ) type, the product is isotopic with the target material, and none of these separation methods can be employed. There is, however, one interesting phenomenon, discovered in England by L. Szilard and T. A. Chalmers in 1934, which has been utilized to some extent to separate the radioactive product of an (n,γ) reaction from the target material. The emission of the gamma-ray photon following the absorption of a neutron causes the residual nucleus to recoil, and the recoil energy is often sufficient to break the chemical bond attaching this particular atom to the remainder of the molecule. The product atom, although isotopic with the target atom, will thus be in a different chemical form, and a separation from the original material becomes possible. For example, if an aqueous solution of sodium chlorate $(NaClO_3)$ is subjected to the action of slow neutrons, the reaction $Cl^{37}(n,\gamma)Cl^{38}$ takes place, but many of the Cl^{38} atoms formed are detached from the chlorate and pass into solution as chloride ions.* By adding a small amount of inactive chloride to the solution and precipitating with silver nitrate, the resulting silver chloride is found to carry nearly the whole of the Cl^{38} activity. Additional cases of similar behavior have been observed with other halogen derivatives, such as ethyl iodide, in which the effect was first observed by Szilard and Chalmers, and also with manganese and arsenic compounds.

17.43. It is not certain that the separation by recoil, accompanying the (n,γ) process as described above, is effective under the conditions existing in the fission-chain reactor. Fortunately, the neutron flux in the nuclear reactor is so high that reasonably high activities can be obtained by direct irradiation with neutrons. In some cases, however, the exposure to neutrons must be continued for a considerable time in order to obtain the desired specific activity.

SYNTHESIS OF LABELED COMPOUNDS

17.44. In much of the work in which an isotope is used as a tracer it is necessary to introduce the tracer element into a certain compound to be studied. Sometimes all that is being determined is either the path or the distribution of a particular element or compound in an organism. For example, it may be required to ascertain the manner in which a particular element, such as phosphorus, is taken up by a plant. In cases of this kind, it is a relatively simple matter to prepare the desired compound containing a suitable proportion of the tracer isotope. However, in many biochemical investigations the object of the study is to determine the fate of different portions of a given compound; it is then essential that the tracer atom be inserted in a definite position, thus labeling that part of the molecule. The preparation of labeled compounds has become an important aspect of tracer studies, and the methods used to introduce an isotopic atom at a particular point have required considerable ingenuity.

17.45. Because of the possible radiation hazard, it is usual to work with quite small quantities in a closed, gastight system. If the nuclide being employed as the tracer has a short half life, the difficulties are increased. In some instances, months have been spent working with inactive material, developing a suitable technique which will permit a desired product contain-

* This is an example of a "hot atom" reaction (§ 10.122 footnote).

ing an active isotope to be prepared in a few minutes. Where rapid synthetic procedures have not proved feasible, and a long-lived radioisotope is not available, the only alternative is to make use of a stable isotope as the tracer.

17.46. Before the discovery of the long-lived C^{14}, the only radioactive isotope of carbon suitable for tracer studies was the 20.4-min. C^{11}, yet organic chemists were able to prepare a number of compounds, with the active carbon atoms in precisely defined positions. The availability of carbon-14 has changed the situation, and although it is still necessary to work with very small quantities, the time factor is no longer a limitation. At present, many labeled organic compounds can be purchased commercially by properly authorized laboratories. A few simple examples of synthesis will be outlined here to indicate the type of procedure adopted in the preparation of such compounds. Because of the necessity for preventing loss of the active material, the various stages are chosen so as to give the highest possible yields of the prospective products containing the radioactive carbon.

17.47. Consider, for simplicity, the familiar compound acetic acid, CH_3COOH; it has been prepared in three isotopic forms, one with C^{14} labeling the methyl carbon atom, another with the carboxyl carbon labeled, and a third with molecules in which both carbon atoms were tagged with the radioisotope. The action of acid on barium carbonate containing C^{14} yields carbon dioxide; this can be reduced catalytically to methanol, by means of hydrogen under pressure at a high temperature. Upon treating with phosphorus and iodine, methyl iodide is formed, which can be con-

verted into methyl cyanide (acetonitrile) by ordinary sodium cyanide containing no radiocarbon; hydrolysis of the acetonitrile then produces acetic acid in which the methyl carbon is labeled. The series of reactions can be represented in the following manner, an asterisk being used to mark the position of the C^{14} carbon atom:

$$Ba\overset{*}{C}O_3 \rightarrow \overset{*}{C}O_2 \rightarrow \overset{*}{C}H_3OH \rightarrow \overset{*}{C}H_3I \rightarrow$$
$$\overset{*}{C}H_3CN \rightarrow \overset{*}{C}H_3COOH.$$

17.48. The action of potassium on a mixture of carbon dioxide and ammonia at 500°C yields potassium cyanide; reaction with methyl iodide then gives acetonitrile, which can be converted into acetic acid as shown above. This series of processes may be used to prepare acetic acid with the C^{14} in the carboxyl group; thus,

$$\overset{*}{C}O_2 \rightarrow K\overset{*}{C}N \rightarrow CH_3\overset{*}{C}N \rightarrow CH_3\overset{*}{C}OOH.$$

If the labeled potassium cyanide is made to interact with labeled methyl iodide, the resulting acetonitrile has C^{14} in both carbon positions. Upon hydrolysis, acetic acid is obtained in which both carbon atoms are labeled.

17.49. Considerable use has been made of syntheses with the Grignard reagent, that is, alkyl (or aryl) magnesium halide, RMgX, where R is an alkyl or aryl group and X is a halogen. Reaction with isotopic carbon dioxide, followed by hydrolysis, yields a carboxylic acid containing labeled carbon in the carboxyl group; thus, where R is the methyl group, the result is acetic acid obtained as follows:

$$CH_3MgBr + \overset{*}{C}O_2 \rightarrow CH_3\overset{*}{C}OOH.$$

Other acids have been made in this manner and have been used to synthesize a variety of compounds.

17.50. One further reaction is worthy of mention. By heating barium carbonate with magnesium, barium carbide is formed, and this with water produces acetylene. If the original carbonate contained C^{14}, then both carbon atoms in the acetylene will be labeled. The isotopic acetylene is a very useful starting material for a number of syntheses. With water, in the presence of a catalyst, it gives acetaldehyde which can be reduced to ethanol or oxidized to acetic acid, and so on. Acetaldehyde is also a convenient intermediate for the preparation of the biologically important lactic and pyruvic acids. The action of ordinary potassium cyanide on labeled acetaldehyde, to form the cyanhydrin, followed by hydrolysis, gives lactic acid, in the following manner:

which either cannot be synthesized at all, or can be synthesized only with difficulty, by chemical methods. If a green plant is grown in the presence of carbon dioxide containing C^{14}, the starch deposited is labeled with the isotope; acid hydrolysis then yields labeled glucose. This may be combined with unlabeled fructose, in the presence of a suitable enzyme, to yield sucrose in which only the glucose portion contains the C^{14} isotope. Sucrose, in which both portions contain labeled carbon, can be extracted from sugar beets grown in the presence of radioactive carbon dioxide.

17.53. Starting with carbon dioxide or glucose a large number of acids can be prepared by biosynthesis using various bacteria. Among the compounds obtained are formic, acetic,

$$\overset{*}{\text{BaCO}_3} \rightarrow \overset{*}{\text{BaC}_2} \rightarrow \overset{*}{\text{CH}}\equiv\overset{*}{\text{CH}} \rightarrow \overset{*}{\text{CH}_3}\overset{*}{\text{CHO}} \rightarrow$$

$$\overset{*}{\text{CH}_3}\overset{*}{\text{CH}}(\text{OH})\text{CN} \rightarrow \overset{*}{\text{CH}_3}\overset{*}{\text{CH}}(\text{OH})\text{COOH}.$$

17.51. If it is desired to label the carboxyl carbon, then the same general reaction may be used except that the C^{14} is in the potassium cyanide; the latter is prepared from labeled carbon dioxide in the manner indicated above. The reaction stages are then

$$\text{CH}_3\text{CHO} \rightarrow \text{CH}_3\text{CH}(\text{OH})\overset{*}{\text{CN}} \rightarrow$$

$$\text{CH}_3\text{CH}(\text{OH})\overset{*}{\text{COOH}}.$$

17.52. The method of *biosynthesis*, in which the synthesis of a desired organic compound is performed by a living organism, has been used for the preparation of various labeled molecules. This procedure is likely to be developed considerably in the future for the production of biologically significant substances, such as hormones, vitamins, alkaloids and antibiotics,

propionic, butyric, valeric, and higher fatty acids, lactic and citric acids, and several ketoacids. In addition to substances with labeled carbon several amino acids, in which the nitrogen has a higher proportion of the stable N^{15} than normal, have been isolated from microorganisms grown in media containing excess of this isotope.

17.54. Deuterium, the stable isotope of hydrogen, has been used in tracer work, quite frequently, as a means of labeling a carbon atom to which it is attached. In many instances synthesis of a molecule containing a particular marked carbon atom is difficult, but it may be possible to label the atom by replacing one or more of its associated hydrogen atoms by deuterium. Further, since deuterium is relatively cheap, in comparison with the chemically enriched, stable C^{13}, it may be used as a tracer for carbon where, for one reason or another, the employment of radioactive C^{14} is not feasible. Many deutero-compounds have been prepared since 1932, when deuterium was first available in an enriched form. By acting on calcium carbide with heavy water, dideuteroacetylene, C_2D_2, can be obtained, and this can be the starting point for numerous syntheses. In addition, the catalytic reduction of carbon monoxide or dioxide with deuterium gas yields tetradeuteromethanol, CD_3OD, which can be converted into CD_3I by means of phosphorus and iodine, thus providing a useful method for labeling a methyl group.

17.55. The addition of deuterium itself or of a deuterium derivative to a double bond of an unsaturated molecule is an obvious method for preparing deutero-compounds. This procedure has been used to label fatty acids for the study of fat metabolism (§ 17.69). Another possibility, which is sometimes practicable, is to make a direct exchange of a hydrogen atom for a deuterium atom in the presence of a suitable catalyst. A simple example is the partial conversion of ethylene (C_2H_4) into monodeuteroethylene (C_2H_3D) by passing a mixture of ethylene and deuterium over a nickel catalyst at 120°C. The hydrogen atoms in benzene or in a fatty acid may be replaced by deuterium in a similar manner.

17.56. As an alternative to deuterium, use can also be made of the radioactive isotope tritium. Although its beta radiation is very weak it can, nevertheless, be detected in smaller amounts than deuterium. Compounds labeled with tritium can be prepared by direct laboratory methods or they may be produced by biosynthesis, the organisms being supplied with water containing an appreciable proportion of tritium. Provided deuterium or tritium is used merely to label a carbon atom, the difference in reactivity from that of ordinary hydrogen, to which reference was made in § 17.17, is probably of little significance.

17.57. The fact that the exchange of one isotopic atom for another is sometimes possible, points up the necessity for the exercise of caution in the performance of tracer experiments. The effect of isotopic exchange is most likely to be troublesome with deuterium, especially if it is present in an —OD, —COOD, or —ND$_2$ group, but it may take place with other elements. If isotopic exchange does occur at an appreciable rate the results obtained may be completely misleading. Suppose, for example, the hydrogen atoms in the amino (—NH$_2$) group of an amino acid were replaced by deuterium in the hopes of tracing their chemical path (or that of the nitrogen atom) in a living organism. As soon as the acid labeled in this manner passed into aqueous solution, there would be an exchange between the deuterium in the amino group and the hydrogen in the water. Consequently, the latter would automatically be found to contain deuterium, irrespective of any role that might be played by the organism. If the possibility of exchange were not realized, the almost immediate appearance of deuterium in the water would lead to the erroneous conclusion that the organism rapidly oxidizes the hydrogen of the amino-group to form water.

ISOTOPIC TRACER METHODS

17.58. As already implied, several different types of tracer studies have been made with biological systems. A particular labeled compound may be supplied to an organism, and then the distribution of the isotopic element may be investigated by studying the various portions of the body. For example, an animal may be fed an amino acid with nitrogen enriched in N^{15}, and then the amounts present in several organs, such as the kidneys, liver, heart and lungs and in the blood, may be determined after the lapse of a certain time. This work can be carried a stage further, by a more detailed analysis which will reveal how much of the N^{15} is present in the form of a particular amino acid in various parts of the organism. A search for intermediate compounds containing the isotopic tracer may throw light on the mechanism of the processes taking place. Similar observations can, of course, be made with green plants and with bacteria.

17.59. When a stable isotope is used as the tracer, analysis is usually carried out by means of the mass spectrometer, as stated in § 17.14, but with deuterium density measurements may be employed, thus simplifying the experimental technique. The material containing the deuterium is burned in a current of oxygen and the resulting water is collected and its density determined. Since the density of heavy water is about 10 per cent greater than that of ordinary water, the presence of a very small excess of deuterium can be detected. Satisfactory measurements can be made with less than 0.1 gram, but this quantity, although not large, is much more than is necessary for the detection of a radioisotope.

17.60. The use of a radioactive tracer in biological investigations offers certain advantages with regard to the localization of the active material. For example, a small quantity of radiosodium, as the chloride, may be injected at one point of the body and the time taken to reach another point can be determined by placing a Geiger counter in the latter position. In this way, it was found that sodium injected intravenously in one arm appeared in the sweat of the other arm within 75 seconds.* Another illustration of a similar type is associated with the use of radioiodine for the treatment of hyperthyroidism, to which reference will be made in § 17.87. The amount of radioactive material accumulated in the thyroid gland can be estimated by means of an external counter placed in the close vicinity of the gland.

17.61. Greater precision in the localization of radioactive material, although on a much smaller scale, has been achieved by means of what has been called *radioautography*.† This technique makes use of the influence on a photographic emulsion of the radiations from radioactive bodies discovered by Becquerel (§ 2.98). The effects observed by the latter were the first crude examples of radioautographs, in which a radioactive substance is made, in a sense, to record its own photograph. Some early observations on the distribution of radioactive elements in biological material by utilizing the photographic activity, were made in France in 1904, by E. S. London, and later, in 1922, by A. Kotzareff. But the modern developments stem essentially from the experiments of the French biologists A. Lacassagne and J. Lattés, reported in 1924, on the distribution of the radioelement polonium injected into various organs.

---

* Calculations based on experiments of the movement of radiosodium in the body indicate that in an average adult there is a diffusion of sodium ions equivalent to about 50 lbs. of sodium chloride (salt) per day, back and forth, through the walls of the blood vessels.

† The name *autoradiography* has also been used by some writers.

Thin sections of the organ, such as are used for histological study under the microscope, were placed in contact with a photographic plate which was later developed. The regions in which the plate was blackened represented the areas where the polonium had been concentrated.

required, thicker material may be used; thus, Fig. 17.1 is a reversed radioautograph of a group of tomato leaves taken from a plant which had been placed in a solution containing a small amount of radiophosphorus. The lighter parts here represent higher concentrations of the radioactive iso-

Fig. 17.1. Reversed radioautograph due to radioactive phosphorus taken up by tomato plant (P. R. Stout and D. R. Hoagland).

17.62. In recent years the radioautographic technique has been greatly improved so that it is now a highly valuable tool in biological research. Good definition is obtained by the use of thin sections of the material being examined, in conjunction with a fast, fine-grained photographic emulsion. Where such high resolution is not

tope, and since the distribution is probably the same for the stable isotope, it is seen that phosphorus tends to concentrate in the stem and in the conducting system of the leaves. Among the many applications of the radioautographic method, mention may be made of the study of the distribution of natural radioelements and of phosphorus in body tissues, of carbon, phosphorus, yttrium, cerium, strontium and plutonium in bone, of iodine in the thyroid gland, and of carbon and phosphorus in plants.

APPLICATIONS OF ISOTOPIC TRACERS

DYNAMIC STATE OF BODY CONSTITUENTS

17.63. During recent years, particularly since 1945, several thousand reports have been published on the use of isotopes for the study of problems in various areas of science and industry. Much of the work, especially that in biology and chemistry, is highly technical in nature, and a detailed knowledge of these subjects is necessary for an adequate comprehension of the significance of the results obtained. In brief, it may be stated that one of the main purposes of the use of isotopic tracers in biological studies is to secure information that will make possible a better understanding of the many complex processes which take place in living organisms. In chemistry, isotopes are being used to throw light on the problems of reaction mechanism, and in industry radioactive tracers are playing a part in a variety of processes. Although isotopic tracing is essentially a new tool, which may be expected to prove extremely useful in the future, many important results have already been obtained by its use; some of the more interesting and more significant, which do not require detailed technical explanation, will be described below.

17.64. In the opinion of many biologists, probably the most outstanding contribution to the understanding of life processes to come from the use of isotopes is that made in the United States since 1938, by R. Schoenheimer and D. Rittenberg and their associates. Prior to this time, it had been universally believed that degradative changes in the living animal took place slowly, the purpose of food being largely to supply the currently required energy, while a small proportion went to replace worn out tissue. As a result of experiments carried out with the aid of deuterium and stable nitrogen-15 as tracers, this long-established concept of an essentially static or dormant state of the organism has been shown to be entirely wrong. The present view is that there exists, as Schoenheimer has called it, "a dynamic state of the body constituents," in which there is a continual interchange between the fats, proteins and carbohydrates already present in the animal body and those ingested in the form of food.

17.65. Linseed oil, which contains fats derived from doubly and triply unsaturated acids,* was partially "hydrogenated" by means of deuterium, so as to yield a mixture of both saturated and slightly unsaturated fats, in which two or four of the hydrogen atoms attached to carbon were replaced by deuterium. The resulting deutero-fats, labeled in this manner, were fed to animals, and the surprising fact was observed that only a small proportion of the deuterium was excreted for several days. The major part of the deuterium was found to have been deposited in the fatty portions of the body. Even when the diet was very deficient in fat, and the total

---

* These are acids with two and three double bonds, respectively.

calorie supply was inadequate, so that the animal was drawing upon its reserves, the deutero-fat was mainly stored and not put to immediate use, as might have been expected. Obviously the view that the organism was in a more or less static state, using such food as was needed and storing the remainder, if any, was unsound.

17.66. After the natural diet of the animals had been resumed, the labeled fats were found to disappear gradually, the deuterium leaving the body in the form of water. However, if the water included in the normal diet of other animals was enriched in heavy water, so as to maintain a constant level of deuterium in the body fluids, the stored fat was found to gain deuterium at the same rate as it was lost by the animals which had previously been fed the deutero-fats. These results indicated that reversible (dynamic) equilibria, involving fats and water, occur in the living organism. The saturated fats are "desaturated" by the removal of hydrogen (or deuterium) and at the same time the unsaturated fats are "saturated" by the addition of hydrogen (or deuterium) from water.

17.67. Further investigations showed that it was only the singly unsaturated fats which could take part in this equilibrium. The more highly unsaturated fats, such as those derived from linoleic and linolenic acids, could not be saturated, neither could they be formed by removal of hydrogen from saturated fats in the body. This conclusion, reached unequivocally by labeling the various fats with deuterium and tracing their behavior in the animal, confirmed the opinion held by nutritionists that the highly unsaturated fats are "indispensable," in the sense that they must be supplied in the diet, the body being unable to synthesize them.

17.68. In the continuation of their studies on animal metabolism, Schoenheimer and Rittenberg prepared a number of amino acids in which the nitrogen atom of the amino ($-NH_2$) group was labeled with the N^{15} isotope. Among the many interesting observations which were made after adding a labeled acid to the diet of an animal was the following: nearly all the amino acids isolated from the tissue protein contained N^{15}, but the concentration was greatest in the acid corresponding to the one which had been included in the diet. It would thus appear, first, that the dietary amino acid is taken up directly and rapidly into the body protein and, second, that there is a biological transfer of nitrogen from one protein amino acid to another during metabolism.

17.69. The latter conclusion implies a remarkable and unexpected state of affairs. The fact that the isotopic nitrogen appears in the "indispensable" amino acids, such as leucine and histidine, which the animal body is unable to synthesize, shows that the presence of N^{15} is not due to a complete breakdown of the labeled amino acid, followed by synthesis of another. This was confirmed by labeling the carbon chain of dietary leucine by means of deuterium, in addition to marking the nitrogen by means of N^{15}. The leucine extracted from the resulting tissue protein was found to have lost some of its isotopic nitrogen, as a result of exchange with other amino acids, but the proportion of deuterium remained unchanged, showing that the carbon chain remained unbroken. The exact mechanism of the nitrogen exchange between the amino acids is not clearly understood, but several different processes are possible.

17.70. As a consequence of the nitrogen-transfer reactions, the nitrogen fed to an animal in the form of one amino acid should eventually be distributed among all those present in the body protein. There is, however, one exception to the rule: the indispensable amino acid lysine does not seem to be able to take part in this exchange of the amino groups. Incidentally, lysine is also known to be unique in another respect: unlike the other indispensable acids, it cannot be replaced in the diet by the corresponding alpha-hydroxy acid. These two properties of lysine are undoubtedly related.

17.71. For many years, since 1905 in fact, it had been widely agreed among physiologists that a distinction could be made between "endogenous" and "exogenous" nitrogen of the diet; the former was supposed to represent the amount of protein required to replace worn out tissue protein, and the latter that utilized to supply energy. The proof that body proteins are in a dynamic state, undergoing continual exchange with amino acids of the diet and also among themselves, renders untenable the concept of endogenous and exogenous nitrogen.

17.72. It is of interest, in this connection, to refer to the nitrogenous compound creatinine, an approximately constant amount of which is excreted daily in the urine. This was regarded as a measure of the endogenous nitrogen metabolism, because the quantity liberated by the body does not vary greatly with the protein consumption. Creatinine is the anhydride of the amino acid creatine, an important constituent of animal tissue, and from experiments made *in vitro*, that

is, outside the animal body, it appeared that creatinine and creatine could be reversibly converted into one another. But work with isotopic nitrogen as tracer has shown that in the living organism, that is, *in vivo*, creatine is converted into creatinine, but the reverse is not possible. If labeled creatine is supplied to the animal, the creatinine in the urine is found to contain excess of N^{15}, but if labeled creatinine is assimilated no isotopic nitrogen appears in the creatine. Without the use of an isotopic tracer, there seems no way in which this fact could have been established.

17.73. By labeling various dietary amino acids with both isotopic nitrogen and deuterium it has been shown, further, that the formation of creatine in the body requires contributions from three amino acids, namely, glycine, arginine and methionine. The creatine is produced in this manner, and is converted into creatinine, at a fairly steady rate. This accounts for the observation, which was misinterpreted, as indicated above, that there is an approximately constant excretion of creatinine independent of the amount of the dietary protein.

17.74. The problems associated with the metabolism of the three energy-providing constituents of the diet, namely, carbohydrates, fats and proteins, are extremely complicated. Phosphorus is known to have a role in the utilization of both carbohydrates and fats, and much work has already been done with radioactive P^{32} for the purpose of elucidating the mechanism of metabolic processes taking place in the animal organism. Both stable and radioactive carbon isotopes have been used as tracers in the investigation of the manner in which the energy of carbohydrates becomes available. As seen above, stable N^{15}, in the absence of a suitable radioisotope of nitrogen, is being applied to the study of proteins, and deuterium is proving a valuable tool in the investigation of fat metabolism.

17.75. Because of the complex nature of the subject it is difficult to provide a general summary of the conclusions reached so far, but attention may be called to the significance of the dynamic state of the body constituents as established by isotopic tracer experiments. The fact that there is a continual exchange between the elements supplied in the diet and those already present in the animal, means that the atoms of the body are undergoing continual replacement. This exchange extends even to the phosphorus, and probably also to the calcium, in the accessible portions of the bones, so that the body undergoes virtually complete renewal in the course of time. The element iron seems to be an exception to the general behavior, as will be seen in the next section.

Tracer Studies of Blood

17.76. Some of the most valuable information in the biological field has come from investigations made in the United States with the isotopes of iron. As just indicated, this element differs from other elements in the respect that iron supplied in the food, or injected into the animal, does not exchange to any appreciable extent with iron already present in the body. From observations on the feeding of iron labeled with radioactive Fe^{59} to normal animals it appeared that very little of the iron found its way into the blood, where most of the iron in the body occurs as hemoglobin, the coloring matter of the red corpuscles (erythrocytes). In animals depleted of iron, however, a larger proportion of this element is absorbed. Shortly after the loss of blood, iron is not absorbed even though there is a deficiency of hemoglobin; but, in due course, as the hemoglobin is replaced by drawing upon the animal's store of iron, there is considerable absorption of iron from the food. Similarly, it has been shown that in cases of pernicious anemia iron is absorbed only after the reserves have been depleted by the administration of liver extract.

17.77. The extent to which iron is taken up evidently depends on the state of the reserves of the element in the body. The view generally held at the present time, based largely on studies with radioactive iron as a tracer, is that iron is stored in the body in the form of an iron-protein combination known as ferritin. When the store of ferritin has attained its normal value, it does not increase further, no matter how much iron may be supplied orally. However, if for some reason the iron reserves are drawn upon, so that the amount of ferritin is decreased, the body is able once more to absorb iron.

17.78. The remarkable fact about iron, which makes its behavior so different from that of the other body elements, is that it is utilized over and over again. By employing radioiron as tracer, it has been found that iron remains in the hemoglobin as long as the red blood-corpuscles are intact. But when the corpuscles are destroyed the iron is not lost; it is almost wholly retained in the body, and is rapidly incorporated into the hemoglobin of new red corpuscles. It is this phenomenon which accounts for the small absorption of iron from the food under normal conditions,* and the absence of exchange between administered and stored forms of the element.

17.79. The stability of the iron in the red corpuscles has led to the development of a method for determining the total amount of red cells in the blood. A small quantity of iron, containing some Fe^{59}, is supplied to an animal under such conditions that the element is absorbed and forms hemoglobin. Some of the red corpuscles, labeled in the hemoglobin, are withdrawn and injected into the subject. As there is no appreciable exchange of iron, all the Fe^{59} in the injected blood remains in the system. By comparing the radioactivity of the red cells in the subject's blood, after time has been allowed for thorough circulation, with that of the injected cells the extent of dilution can be calculated. If the quantity of red cells injected is known, the total amount in the subject can be determined by proportion. A simpler procedure than that just described is to take a sample of the patient's blood and label the red cells with chromium-51 (half life 27.8 days) by adding sodium chromate outside the body. The labeled red cells are then separated and a known amount injected into the patient for the dilution study. The same general (dilution) principles can be used to determine the total blood volume of the patient, by injecting a known volume of labeled blood.

17.80. One way of determining the average life of the red corpuscles of the blood is to make use of the stable N^{15} isotope of nitrogen. Hemoglobin, which plays a vital part in the transport of oxygen in the body, is itself a combination of two units: one is the red pigment called hemin, and the other is a protein, known as globin. In hemin the element iron is present in association with a nitrogen-containing molecule, belonging to the group of complex compounds referred to as porphyrins. From experiments made with animals which had been fed the simple amino acid glycine labeled with N^{15}, it was known that this substance is an important source of the nitrogen in the porphyrin, and hence in the hemin of the red corpuscles. In a continuation of this study, labeled glycine was fed to a human adult for three days; samples of blood were withdrawn, from time to time, during the ensuing months. The crystalline hemin was extracted from the blood, and its N^{15} content determined by means of a mass spectrometer.

17.81. It was observed that the amount of N^{15} in the hemin increased steadily for about 25 days after feeding of the labeled glycine had ceased; it then remained fairly constant for the succeeding 80 days or so, after which it declined steadily. The interpretation of these results is as follows. The glycine, after ingestion, is rapidly stored in the body, as is known to be the case from other experiments. During the course of some 25 days it is gradually released to form hemin, which in combination with globin, produces the hemoglobin of the red blood-corpuscles. Since the N^{15} content then remains the same for some time, it is evident that the hemin contained in these corpuscles is not continuously broken down and rebuilt. Once it has formed it has a fairly definite life span, estimated, from the

---

* In pregnancy or during the period of rapid growth, when the total amount of hemoglobin in the body is increasing, the ferritin reserve is being drawn upon continuously and it must, of course, be replaced by absorption of iron from the food.

change in the amount of isotopic nitrogen, to be about 127 days. At this age, a red corpuscle apparently disintegrates, releasing the hemin, which then breaks up into iron and the nitrogen-containing porphyrin. As seen above, the iron is reutilized, combining to form more hemin, but the porphyrin part passes out of the body, as is shown by the steady decline in the proportion of N^{15} in the blood.

17.82. A notable practical application of isotopes in connection with the study of the characteristics of blood for transfusions makes use of both Fe^{55} and Fe^{59} isotopes. The blood volume of the recipient, before transfusion, is first determined by introducing a small quantity of red cells labeled with Fe^{59}, as explained above. Transfusions of whole blood including red cells labeled with Fe^{55} are then given. Since the two radioactive isotopes have different half lives, they can be determined separately in the blood of the recipient. In this way, the fate of the transferred blood can be followed through the behavior of the Fe^{55}, while the concentration of Fe^{59} gives the effective blood volume. As a result of the knowledge obtained in this manner, valuable advances have been made in the storage of blood.

17.83. The foregoing discussion has referred particularly to the red corpuscles of the blood. But the study of other constituents of the blood by means of radioisotopes has not been neglected. Radiophosphorus has been employed in experiments on the complex substances known as phospholipids and nucleic acids which are present in both the plasma and the red cells, and also to study the behavior of the white cells in blood transfusion. In addition, this radioactive isotope has been used for therapeutic purposes

in the treatment of blood diseases, as will be seen in § 17.89. Thus, at least three radioisotopes and one stable isotope have contributed to an understanding of the behavior of the blood in the animal body; most of the results could not have been obtained without the use of these isotopic tracers.

APPLICATIONS OF RADIOISOTOPES IN MEDICINE

17.84. Several instances have been reported of the use of radioisotopes both as diagnostic tools and for therapeutic purposes. The former are more common, in medicine, for only very small amounts of the active material are needed. One example of this type of application is provided by the employment of radiosodium to diagnose cases of restricted circulation of the blood. A small quantity of sodium chloride solution, in which the sodium has been labeled with Na^{24}, is injected into a vein of the patient's forearm; a G-M counter is then placed in contact with one of the feet. If the blood circulation is normal, the presence of radioactivity is very soon detected in the foot; it increases rapidly and reaches a maximum value within less than an hour. If there is a circulatory impairment of some kind, however, the radioactivity will increase slowly, showing that the blood has difficulty in reaching the foot. By moving the counter to different parts of the body the position of the restriction can be located and the necessary treatment can be applied.

17.85. A modification of this scheme has been proposed for studying the pumping action of the heart. Labeled sodium chloride is injected into the blood stream, as before, and a counter, attached to an automatic pen-recorder, is placed over the heart. As the radiosodium enters the right side of the heart the pen of the recorder rises and then drops as the venous blood enters the lungs. A few seconds later, the radiosodium appears with the arterial blood on the left side of the heart and there is another rise and fall of the recording pen. By studying the nature of the resulting curves the pumping action of the two sides of the heart can be compared and abnormalities can be discovered.

17.86. Most medical applications of radioisotopes, both diagnostic and therapeutic, depend on the property exhibited by certain elements of being preferentially absorbed at certain locations. A relatively small preferential uptake is generally adequate for diagnosis, but satisfactory therapy requires considerable activity to be concentrated in the tissues or organ to be treated. It is necessary, therefore, that the latter should exhibit marked preferential absorption of the radioelement, in order that administration of dangerous quantities of radioactive material to the body as a whole may be avoided.

17.87. Iodine, which is rapidly taken up by the thyroid gland, provides an instance of the use of a radioisotope for both diagnosis and therapy. A great deal of useful information concerning the functioning of the thyroid gland, and the storage in it of iodine as thyroxine, has resulted from experiments with radioiodine as tracer. But this aspect of the subject will not be considered here; the discussion will be limited to the application of the results. In cases of hyperthyroidism the thyroid gland is overactive, and the condition can be readily demonstrated and diagnosed following the oral administration of small quantities of sodium iodide containing some radioiodine. The iodine, including the radioisotope, concentrates in the gland, as stated above, and this fact has been utilized in the treatment of hyperthyroidism. The gamma radiations emitted by the radioiodine act like X-rays in causing a partial destruction, and hence a decrease in the physiological activity, of the thyroid gland. Radioiodine therapy has consequently become recognized for the alleviation of certain cases of overactive thyroid, and successful results have been reported in a number of instances. The same treatment has proved beneficial in some, but not all, types of cancer of the thyroid gland. In the use of radioiodine and of similar isotopes for therapeutic purposes, based on the ability of the radiations to destroy abnormal growths, very great precautions must, of course, be taken to avoid the possible serious consequences of overdosage.

17.88. An exceptionally interesting diagnostic application of radioisotopes has been made in the study of brain tumors. The position of such tumors is not only difficult to determine from outside, but once located, the tumorous mass is not readily distinguishable from the normal tissue. In this connection use is made of the fact that the albumin from human blood can be labeled with iodine-131 and upon injection into the patient, the iodinated albumin is taken up preferentially by the undesired growth in the brain. Since the radioiodine emits gamma rays, the position of the tumor can be found by mapping the exterior of the skull with a scintillation counter having highly directional properties.

17.89. Radiophosphorus has found some application in the treatment of two diseases of the blood, both of which are fatal; these are leukemia, which is an overproduction of the white corpuscles (leukocytes) of the blood, and polycythemia vera, characterized by an excess of red cells. Very frequently, sufferers from the latter disease develop the former, to which they succumb in a short time. Both types of blood corpuscles are formed in the bone marrow, which, incidentally, exhibits preferential absorption of phosphorus to a small extent. The oral ingestion of radioactive phosphorus has, therefore, been used with some success, particularly in the treatment of polycythemia vera. The beta radiations emitted by the P^{32} isotope, which has concentrated in the bone marrow, inhibit the excessive formation of the red blood-cells. By the administration of small doses of radiophosphorus at intervals, polycythemia can often be arrested, although not cured; however, this is regarded as the treatment of choice of many physicians for the disease. The radiophosphorus therapy has not been successful with acute leukemia, although some improvement has been claimed in certain instances of chronic leukemia.

17.90. For many years, both gamma rays from radium and X-rays have been used externally to inhibit the growth of malignant tissue in the treatment of cancer. Radium is very expensive because of its rarity, and it is not too satisfactory, because its decay products have undesirable radiation characteristics. Further, X-ray equipment capable of producing radiation of sufficient penetrating power, e.g., 1 Mev energy, is large and expensive. Consequently, the radioactive isotope cobalt-60 with a half life, in its ground state, of 5.3 years, has been widely used in different ways as a substitute for radium and for X-rays. The active material is prepared by exposing either pure cobalt (Co^{59}) or

an alloy of cobalt and nickel to the neutrons in a reactor, so as to form Co^{60} by the (n,γ) reaction. The 5.3-year cobalt-60 emits gamma rays with energies of 1.17 and 1.32 Mev. Because it can be made relatively cheaply with a high specific activity, it has many advantages as a source of radiation for therapeutic purposes. The chief drawback to radiocobalt is its short life, although it can be reactivated by exposure in a reactor. As an alternative to cobalt, interest is growing in the fission product cesium-137 (half life 30 years), the decay of which is accompanied by 0.66-Mev gamma radiation. Incidentally, the removal of this isotope from reactor fuel residues will go a long way toward solving the problem of waste disposal (§ 15.113).

17.91. Apart from diagnostic and therapeutic uses of isotopes and radiations in the field of medicine, there have been many applications in medical and biological research. Among these, mention may be made of the employment of tritium and carbon-14 to study the suspected relationship between cholesterol, found associated with fats in the diet, and the disease called arteriosclerosis (hardening of the arteries). The experiments have led to indications of a possible method for early diagnosis of the disease and are throwing light on the metabolism of cholesterol in the body.

PHOTOSYNTHESIS

17.92. In the study of plants, the most significant, fundamental problem which is being attacked with the aid of isotopic tracers is photosynthesis, that is, the ability to convert simple combinations of carbon, hydrogen and oxygen into complex, energy-containing materials in the presence of sunlight. It is well known that, in sunlight, green plants are able to take in carbon dioxide and water and build them up into sugar, starch and cellulose, which fall into the general category of carbohydrates. At the same time oxygen gas is liberated by the plant. There is no doubt that the processes leading to the formation of carbohydrate and oxygen are very complicated, involving several intermediate stages, but the over-all action may be represented approximately by the equation

$$xCO_2 + yH_2O + energy \xrightarrow{\text{chlorophyll}} C_xH_{2y}O_y + xO_2,$$

where $C_xH_{2y}O_y$ is the general formula for a carbohydrate, and the energy is that of sunlight. It will be noted that chlorophyll, the green coloring matter of plants, is indicated as playing a part in the reaction. In the absence of chlorophyll, or possibly some equivalent substance, photosynthesis cannot occur.

17.93. Carbohydrates are important because, as sugar, potato and grains of various kinds, they supply either directly or indirectly much of the food energy of human beings. In addition, in the form of wood, or in the fossilized state as coal and oil, the carbohydrates are, at the present time, the main source of energy for heating and lighting, and for industrial use. It has been estimated that about 150 billion tons per annum of the element carbon are fixed in photosynthesis by plants on land and in the sea. This is equivalent to power production at an average rate of 1.6×10^{11} kilowatts. In spite of its already enormous value, the energy stored as a result of photosynthesis is actually a small proportion of the sun's energy falling on the earth. Quite apart, therefore, from its own great intrinsic interest, an

understanding of the mechanism of photosynthesis could lead to the possibility of utilizing a larger fraction of the sun's almost limitless energy. This might be achieved either by finding the conditions under which green plants could store energy more efficiently or, ultimately, by devising means for performing photosynthesis without the aid of plants.

17.94. Since 1771, when the famous English chemist Joseph Priestley found that air that had been vitiated by burning a candle could be restored, or, in modern scientific terms, carbon dioxide could be replaced by oxygen, by means of a green plant, the subject of photosynthesis has attracted the interest of investigators. Although numerous important facts had been discovered before 1940, these were limited to the study of the reacting species, namely, carbon dioxide, water, light and chlorophyll, on the one hand, and the products of photosynthesis, on the other hand. The study of the intermediate stages presented a virtually insuperable problem, until the advent of isotopes as a tool opened up new possibilities. Some preliminary observations were made in 1940, with the short-lived C^{11} radioisotope of carbon, but the quantity obtainable by cyclotron bombardment was very small, and its rapid decay made experimentation difficult. The availability of relatively large amounts of the radioactive 5600-year C^{14} at a reasonable price has encouraged further studies, whose purpose is the interpretation of the mechanism of photosynthesis.

17.95. One method of investigation is to permit simple plants, such as certain algae, to carry out photosynthesis, in the presence of light, with carbon dioxide containing a small proportion of radioactive carbon-14. The product formed after a period of time is then extracted and analyzed. By following the radioactivity, some indication may be obtained of the path taken by the carbon in the complex photosynthetic process. Another approach is based on the view, which has long been held by some biologists, that upon exposure to light the green plant interacts with water to liberate oxygen, and the chlorophyll forms an unstable intermediate compound containing active hydrogen. The subsequent reaction of this intermediate with carbon dioxide, leading ultimately to the formation of carbohydrates, presumably does not require the presence of light and can take place equally well in the dark. Consequently, algae suspended in water are first exposed to light for some time; they are then allowed to react in the dark with carbon dioxide containing radiocarbon. By making the period of this reaction very short, e.g., a few seconds, only a small number of compounds, presumed to be those formed in the earliest stages of photosynthesis, are obtained. Identification of the extremely minute quantities of these substances is facilitated by taking advantage of their radioactivity.

17.96. It may be mentioned that some studies of the mechanism of photosynthesis have also been made by means of deuterium and tritium. As indicated in § 17.6, water and carbon dioxide in which the oxygen was labeled with O^{18} have been used to prove that the oxygen gas formed in photosynthesis originates almost entirely in the water, and not in the carbon dioxide. In view of the possibility that phosphorus compounds are involved as intermediates in photosynthesis, radiophosphorus is also finding application in this important field of investigation.

ISOTOPIC TRACERS IN AGRICULTURE

17.97. In the realm of agriculture, radioactive isotopes are being used to provide information which could not be secured in any other way. It is recognized as good farming practice to apply phosphorus to the soil, but there are several types of phosphate fertilizers which can be used for this purpose, and it is not always obvious which is most effectively utilized by any given type of soil. Although it is possible to determine by ordinary chemical analysis the total amount of phosphorus taken up by a plant, there has, until recently, been no way of distinguishing between the phosphorus derived from the soil and that taken up from the added fertilizer. The use of radiophosphorus as a tracer permits the distinction to be made, and provides a means of ascertaining the kind of phosphate which is best for a given soil and crop.

17.98. The procedure adopted is to start with phosphoric acid containing a known proportion of the radioactive P^{32}, and to convert this into a phosphate, such as calcium superphosphate, tricalcium phosphate or hydroxyapatite, suitable for use as a fertilizer. A definite quantity of the labeled phophorus is then applied to the soil in which plants are grown. At certain intervals a number of these plants are harvested, and the total phosphorus, derived from both soil and fertilizer, is determined by chemical analysis of their ash. Assuming, as is very probable, that the plant does not distinguish between ordinary and radioactive phosphorus atoms in the fertilizer, the radioactivity of the plant ash, combined with the measured specific activity of the fertilizer, immediately gives the amount of phosphorus which the plant takes up from the latter. In this way the individual quantities derived from the soil and from the fertilizer can be estimated.

17.99. Because experiments of this type, which depend on the growth of plants, require a considerable time, the data are being accumulated relatively slowly. Nevertheless, a number of interesting points have become apparent, and a few of them will be mentioned here. The proportion of phosphorus absorbed from a given soil and fertilizer depends on the nature of the plant and on the period of growth. Tobacco and corn, for example, both derive about 65 per cent of their phosphorus from the fertilizer in the early stages of growth, but near maturity the proportion has dropped to 45 per cent for the former, and to only 15 per cent for the latter. Evidently, in this particular, rather poor, soil, corn requires most of its phosphorus fertilizer at the beginning, and less toward the end of its growth. With potatoes on a similar soil, from 50 to 60 per cent of the phosphorus uptake came from the fertilizer during the whole period of growth.

17.100. The ratio of phosphorus derived from the soil to that obtained from the fertilizer varies with the type of soil, its phosphorus content, the amount of fertilizer added, and the nature of the crop being grown. In general, the higher the amount of phosphorus in the soil, the larger is the proportion which the plant obtains from this source. In greenhouse experiments made in Canada, in which wheat plants were grown in soil, to some of which ammonium phosphate was added as fertilizer, it was found that the plants actually took up more phosphorus from the soil in the presence of the fertilizer than they did in its absence.

17.101. A study of great interest was made of the availability of phosphorus in green manure. Wheat fertilized with labeled phosphate was grown as a green manure crop; it was then analyzed for its total phosphorus content and mixed with soil so as to give the equivalent of 65 pounds of phosphoric acid per acre. To another quantity of the soil was added an equal amount of phosphoric acid in the form of superphosphate, also labeled with the P^{32} isotope. Rye grass was planted in both cases, and from the radioactivity of the crops it appeared that the green manure phosphate is nearly as effective in supplying phosphorus to the plant as is superphosphate.

17.102. The relationship between root growth and the uptake of phosphorus from the soil has been investigated by placing fertilizer labeled with radiophosphorus at several depths and distances from growing plants. After various time intervals, the plants were harvested and analyzed for radiophosphorus. The results provided information on the manner in which the phosphorus is taken up by the roots. With corn and certain other plants, for example, it was found that, as the plant develops, the root feeding system is below the usual depth at which phosphate fertilizer is placed in the soil. Hence, when the plant was beginning to mature it was getting no advantage from the added phosphorus. Deeper location of the phosphate should give better yields of these plants.

17.103. Radioisotopes have provided a unique method for studying the feeding of plants through their leaves. It has been found, with radiophosphorus as the tracer, that nutrients are frequently absorbed much more readily from the leaves than through the root system. Absorption can also take place through the fruit, twigs and even the flowers.

17.104. Most of the tracer investigations relating to soil and plant growth have been performed hitherto with radiophosphorus. Some work has also been done with radioactive calcium as tracer in connection with the efficiency of the "liming" of soils. The difficulty here is that the only radiocalcium that can be employed is Ca^{45}, with a half life of 180 days. Appreciable radioactivity will thus persist in the soil for two or three years, or more. However, experiments in greenhouses, with restricted amounts of soil, may be possible.

17.105. Reference may also be made to the application of radioiron, in conjunction with radiophosphorus, for the purpose of determining the cause of chlorosis, that is, the inability of plants to form sufficient chlorophyll to maintain growth. It appears that, under certain conditions, phosphorus is able to block the entry of iron into the plant, this element being required for the proper formation of chlorophyll. The discovery of a method for combating chlorosis would be of considerable economic significance.

17.106. It has been known for many years that both animal and vegetable life are dependent on very minute quantities of certain elements, such as boron, cobalt, copper, manganese, molybdenum and zinc, called *micronutrients*.[*] For example, cattle fed on forage containing less than four parts of cobalt in one hundred million of their diet will lose their appetite and actually starve to death although adequate pasture is accessible. Cobalt is also essential for other ruminants, such as sheep, but horses apparently do not require this element in their diet. The difficulty associated with the study of micronutrients has been the problem of detecting the extremely small quantities of the different elements, both in the diet and in the living animal. The advent of radioactive tracers has provided a means for overcoming this obstacle. The minute amount of a micronutrient element can be readily detected by incorporating a radioactive isotope into the food. One of the facts ascertained, by means of cobalt-60, is that the traces of this element are required for the synthesis of vitamin B_{12}.

INDUSTRIAL APPLICATIONS OF ISOTOPES

17.107. Radioactive isotopes are finding applications in industry, both in research and in process control. Many of these applications, as will be seen below, are based on the use of the radiations emitted rather than on the atomic tracer characteristics of the isotopes. Because of the great variety of the ways in which radioisotopes have been employed in industry, it will not be possible here to do more than present some typical examples. Several of the applications, it will be noted, deal with surfaces and thin films, where the quantities of material involved are extremely small and where, consequently, radioactive tracers offer a distinct advantage. The subject of catalysis is of great importance to the oil industry, and radiocarbon-14 is being used to label hydrocarbons undergoing catalytic reactions. A related process, also being investigated with the aid of the same isotope, is the Fischer-Tropsch

---

[*] These are sometimes referred to as "trace elements," because minute traces only, generally much less than 1 part per million, are necessary. In order to avoid confusion between "trace" and "tracer" elements, the term "micronutrients," favored by biologists, is used.

synthesis, which involves the passage of a mixture of carbon monoxide and hydrogen over an iron catalyst. The products include various hydrocarbons as well as a number of valuable oxygenated compounds. The process has great possibilities, and a better understanding of the reactions taking place may have important industrial consequences. Wetting, detergency, the flotation of minerals, adsorption and metallic corrosion are all examples of surface phenomena upon which researches are being performed with the aid of radioactive tracers.

ferred from the piston can be detected by its radioautograph (§ 17.61); in this way the areas of greatest wear are easily located. Improvements in lubricating oils and in the composition of sliding surfaces so as to reduce friction may be expected from experiments of this kind.

17.109. In the metallurgical industry, radioactive isotopes are finding some interesting uses, in addition to the study of friction just mentioned. Metals, and particularly alloys of several elements, are frequently subjected to different treatments, such as age-

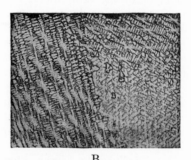

A   B

FIG. 17.2.   Radioautograph (A) and ordinary photomicrograph (B) of nickel-chromium-tungsten alloy containing radioactive tungsten.

17.108. Efforts are being made to understand the mechanism of friction, another surface property of considerable significance. One method being used is to expose a steel piston ring to the action of neutrons in a nuclear reactor, so that it becomes radioactive. This piston ring is fitted into the cylinder of an internal combustion engine which can then be operated, with suitable lubrication, in the ordinary way. By determining the radioactivity removed by the lubricating oil, the extent of wear of the piston ring can be studied. In addition, if a photographic film is placed against the walls of the cylinder, after running the engine, the radioactive material trans-

hardening, annealing, quenching and cold rolling, and it is important to know what is happening to the various constituents in the course of the treatment. Radioactive isotopes of the metals provide a simple and effective tool for following the movements of the different species, for the radioactive atoms will behave in exactly the same way as the stable atoms of a given element. In Fig. 17.2 is shown a radioautograph (A) and an ordinary photomicrograph taken by reflected light (B) of an alloy of nickel, chromium and tungsten to which a small amount of a radioactive tungsten isotope was added. The dark portions in the radioautograph clearly indicate the distribution of the tungsten.

17.110. The phenomenon of self-diffusion in a metal, that is, the movement of the atoms of a metal within the crystal lattice, is of interest in connection with the properties of metals under stress at high temperatures. Since it is not normally possible to follow the diffusion among identical atoms, there is no way, without the use of a radioactive tracer, to obtain experimental data on this subject. Now, a block of metal, such as copper, consisting of the stable isotopes, can have a layer of the same metal containing a radioisotope deposited on it, e.g., by electroplating. After subjecting the block to heat treatment, stress, etc., successive thin layers are shaved off the surface and their activity measured. In this way, the penetration or diffusion of the radioactive into the stable metal, which is the same as ordinary self diffusion, can be determined.

17.111. Metallurgists have long been interested in the sulfur present in coal; some of this remains in the coke made from the coal, and a part ultimately finds its way into steel, where it is not desired. In one particular instance it was required to know whether it was organic sulfur in the coal or inorganic sulfur, usually present as the mineral pyrite, which remained in the coke. The problem was readily solved by adding to the coal a small quantity of pyrite containing some radioactive sulfur, which could be traced into the coke. Since the stable and radioisotopes of sulfur in the pyrite behave alike chemically, the results provided the desired information. It was found that the proportion of organic to inorganic sulfur in the coke was the same as that in the coal from which it was made.

17.112. Another practical example of the use of radioisotopes in process metallurgy originated in the attempt to determine whether a fine powder of iron ore, obtained by concentration from a low-grade source, could be charged into a blast furnace or whether it would be blown out by the air blast. A quantity of the fine ore was exposed to neutrons in a reactor, so that it became radioactive. This was mixed with a large amount of the original fine ore and then with a different ore of a coarser type. After treatment in the blast furnace, the pig iron, slag and dust were examined for radioactivity. The results showed that 60 per cent of the fine ore remained in the furnace as pig iron. Although this proportion was higher than expected, the loss was too large to be tolerated. The results showed that further studies are needed to determine how to increase the retention of the fine material.

17.113. It is well known that X-rays are used to investigate the interior of metallic castings without the necessity of destroying them. The source of the rays is placed on one side of the casting and a photographic plate on the other side. The X-rays penetrate the metal, and affect the photographic emulsion; from the nature of the image obtained the presence of flaws or defects can be detected. The apparatus required for the production of X-rays powerful enough to pass through a considerable thickness of metal is cumbersome and inconvenient to manipulate. In some instances, therefore, radioactive materials, e.g., radium, which emit highly penetrating gamma rays, have been used instead of X-rays. As seen in preceding chapters, the two types of radiation are essentially identical, the only possible difference being in the wave length or energy.

17.114. Instead of using radium, the process of *radiography*, as it is called, may be conveniently performed with a compact source of gamma rays, such as a specimen of Co⁶⁰, described above. The advantage of Co⁶⁰ is that a form of any desired shape may be made of ordinary cobalt, or a cobalt-nickel alloy, and then irradiated with neutrons in a nuclear reactor. Further, it can be moved to locations not accessible to X-ray equipment.

17.115. A number of such radiation sources with cobalt-60 have been used for industrial radiography, but there is increasing interest in the longer lived cesium-137, mentioned in § 17.90. As a small and convenient portable source of radiation of moderate energy, suitable for relatively thin layers of metal or for medical radiography, thulium-170 has been recommended. It is made by exposing the rare-earth element thulium-169 to neutrons in a reactor. It does not emit gamma radiation, but the bremsstrahlung from the beta radiation serve the same purpose. The disadvantage of thulium-170 as a radiographic source is its short half life of 127 days.

17.116. Various applications have been made of radioisotopes in process control where, as in the case of radiography, the radiative, rather than the chemical, properties of the material are used. One example is a gauge which can be used in checking the thickness of paper, cellophane, plastic, or other sheet material without actual contact. A source of beta rays is placed below the sheet and an ionization chamber or a Geiger-Müller counter above it. The proportion of the radiation absorbed and, hence, the number of particles reaching the counter depend on the thickness of the material through which the rays pass. A device of this kind can be used to give a continuous record, and can even be adapted to automatic control. When material of one kind is coated on another, the thickness of the coating can be determined by making use of what is known as the "backscattering" of beta particles. The extent to which these particles are reflected or scattered back by the coating is a measure of its thickness.

17.117. The absorption of radiation is also employed in a means for indicating the level of a liquid in a closed vessel. If a gamma-ray source is placed at the side of the vessel, the radiation proceeding in a horizontal direction will traverse the liquid if its level is above the position of the source; on the other hand, the rays will pass through air (or vapor) if the liquid level is below the source of radiation. Consequently, if the latter is moved vertically, the proportion of the gamma rays transmitted, as indicated by a G-M counter at the same height on the opposite side of the vessel, will change abruptly at the level of the liquid surface.

17.118. Liquid level gauges, such as those described above, are extensively used in oil refineries and there are, in addition many other applications of radioisotopes in the control of the operations. Some examples are the following: tracing the flow of fluidized (solid) catalyst in the catalytic cracking of hydrocarbons; measuring flow rates of liquids; determining the extent of mixing in surge tanks and stills; and detection of leaks in enclosed pipes, e.g., in heat exchangers. Uniformity of mixing during the blending of gasolines, lubricating oils, greases and waxes can be followed by means of isotopic tracers.

17.119. Information concerning the

location of the surface of separation, its velocity of flow, and the degree of intermixing of different oil stocks flowing in a pipe-line can be obtained by the use of a radioactive indicator injected between two different oil stocks. The 12.8-day barium-140 was originally employed for this purpose, but on account of its short life it lost a large proportion of its activity during the preparation and transportation of the material. Consequently, antimony-124, with a half life of 60 days, is now used; this nuclide emits, in addition to beta particles, gamma rays of long range which can be detected by means of a Geiger-Müller counter placed outside the pipe-line. In this manner the position and sharpness of the interface between the oil stocks can be determined. The decay product of antimony-124 is a stable isotope of tellurium, and hence the radioactivity disappears in a short time, so that it does not constitute a hazard.

Analytical Applications

17.120. Several of the illustrations given above of the use of isotopic tracers are, of course, analytical procedures for determining the quantity of a particular element present in a system. It is of interest, however, to consider the analytical applications in a more systematic manner. These applications may be divided into three categories: the first, called *tracer analysis*, involves the addition of a known amount of isotopic material* to the system, in which the total quantity of the element has been determined by chemical analysis. In view of the essential identity in properties of the isotopes, the proportion of radioactive to stable isotopes, i.e., the specific activity, will always re-

main the same after allowing for natural decay. A determination of the radioisotope at any time by means of a particle counter will then immediately indicate the total amount of the element present in the system.

17.121. An example of tracer analysis is the tracing of pyrite sulfur from coal to coke, as described above. Other uses are for the measurement of low vapor pressures and small solubilities, where ordinary analytical methods are usually inaccurate. The principle has also been used to test the effectiveness of precipitation processes, which is, in a sense, equivalent to the determination of low solubilities.

17.122. In *isotopic dilution analysis* a compound of a particular element, for which the analysis is to be performed, is prepared containing a known fraction of the tracer isotope. A definite amount of this mixture is then added to the system under study, and the quantity of the element present in the system can then be evaluated from the decrease in concentration e.g., in the specific activity, of the tracer isotope. The procedure differs from tracer analysis in not necessitating an initial chemical (or other) analysis for the element under consideration. The methods described in § 17.79 for estimating the quantity of red cells in the blood and in § 17.98 for studying the uptake of phosphorus from fertilizers are instances of isotopic dilution analysis with radioisotopes.

17.123. The dilution principle has also been applied to determine the volume of water in the body. For this purpose, either the stable isotope deuterium or the radioactive tritium can be used as a tracer. A definite volume

---

* It should be understood that for a radioactive isotope a "known amount" refers to a known rate of particle emission as determined by a G-M or other counter.

of water, containing a known amount of one of these isotopes, is injected into the body, and after allowing about an hour for uniform mixing to take place, a sample of serum is withdrawn and its isotope content is measured. From the change in concentration, the volume of water in the body can be calculated. If the isotope concentration is found to be decreased by a factor of 1000, for example, then the volume of water in the body is 1000 times that originally injected. The sodium space of the body, ascribed to its extracellular volume, has been estimated in a somewhat similar manner by injecting a solution containing a known concentration of radioactive sodium as sodium chloride.

17.124. A highly useful adaptation of the isotopic dilution method has been made in connection with the extremely difficult and tedious process of analyzing the mixture of amino acids resulting from the chemical hydrolysis of protein outside the body. In order to determine the amount of glycine, for example, this amino acid is synthesized with the inclusion of a known concentration of glycine labeled with the N^{15} isotope. A definite weight of this mixture is added to the system to be analyzed, and from it is extracted a specimen of glycine, which may be a small proportion of the total present. The concentration of N^{15} in this sample is determined by a mass spectrometer, and from the extent of dilution undergone, the total amount of glycine in the system under investigation can be readily calculated.*

17.125. The third method of analysis by means of isotopes is called *activation analysis;* it offers attractive possibilities for determining minute traces of elements, even beyond the limits of detection by spectroscopic methods. A specimen, containing a very small quantity of an element which it is required to determine, is exposed to deuterons in a cyclotron or, better, to neutrons in a nuclear reactor. One or more of the stable isotopes of the element are thus "activated," that is, they are converted into radioisotopes which can then be detected by their characteristic radiations and half lives. By the use of a comparison sample containing a known proportion of the given element, and treating it in the same way, it is even possible to make the analysis quantitative. If the activation is carried out in a nuclear reactor, the sensitivity of the method depends on the cross section of the isotopes of the element being studied for the radioactive capture of slow neutrons. For the activation analysis to be satisfactory, the radioisotopes formed by irradiation must have a half life which is neither too long nor too short, so that convenient measurement is possible. Further, other elements present, which may also become activated, must not yield products with similar half lives or radiation characteristics, for otherwise they will interfere with the determinations.

17.126. The activation method has been employed for the analysis of mixtures of rare-earth elements, which is usually a difficult matter, and also for estimating traces of gallium and palladium in iron meteorites. Minute quantities of molybdenum, copper, iron and gallium have been detected in aluminum. In the biological field it has been used to investigate the distribution of gold in the tissues of an

---

* Isotopic exchange of nitrogen between the various amino acids, referred to in § 17.69, does not arise here, since the enzymes responsible for the exchange reactions have been destroyed.

animal to which this element has been supplied in connection with the study of rheumatoid arthritis.

ISOTOPES AND THE STANDARD OF LENGTH

17.127. Since 1889, the metric standard of length has been a bar of platinum-iridium alloy at Sèvres, near Paris, France. But it has long been realized that this is unsatisfactory because it is liable to undergo change or be destroyed, and the suggestion was made that the wave length of a particular line in the spectrum would be more reliable as an absolute standard. After considering various possibilities, the red line in the spectrum of cadmium was chosen; however, this line is not as sharp as would be desirable, and measurements with it are tedious. The green line of mercury seemed to be better in some respects; it is sharper and easier to measure than the cadmium line, it can be produced at ordinary temperatures, whereas cadmium must be heated to form the vapor, and finally the line is in the region of maximum sensitivity of the human eye. On the other hand, since mercury has six stable isotopes present in relatively large amounts, besides small quantities of others, the "line" has a complicated structure in which a particular component is not easy to identify.

17.128. If a single isotope of mercury could be observed in a pure form, the wave length of its green spectral line would evidently constitute an ideal standard of length. The problem was solved in an elegant manner by irradiating pure gold, which consists of a single nuclide Au^{197}, with neutrons from a nuclear reactor; the product of the (n,γ) reaction is the 2.70-day

Au^{198}, which decays rapidly, by the emission of a negative beta-particle, to yield the stable Hg^{198} isotope of mercury. This product can then be evaporated off and condensed in a form completely free from other isotopes.[*] Mercury-vapor lamps, containing Hg^{198} as the sole isotope, have been made at the U. S. National Bureau of Standards. The green line, as expected, is sharp and eminently suited to accurate measurement; its wave length is **5460.752 A.**

DATING WITH ISOTOPES

17.129. In 1907, the American physicist, B. B. Boltwood (§ 5.44), then working in E. Rutherford's Laboratory in Manchester, England, suggested that the age of a radioactive mineral could be determined from the known half life of the parent, e.g., uranium-238, and the quantity of helium that had accumulated from the emitted alpha particles. Although quite sound in principle, this method is not too accurate in practice because some of the helium gas escapes from the mineral in the course of the many millions of years since it was first formed. With the proof, after 1913 or so, that different isotopes of lead were the end products of the natural radioactive series, an improvement in the technique of dating uranium minerals was possible.

17.130. Consider the radioactive decay equation (5.3), i.e., $N_t = N_0 e^{-\lambda t}$; N_0 may be taken as the amount of uranium-238 originally present in a mineral at the time it was formed, N_t is the amount still left after the lapse of the time t, which represents the age of the mineral. Since essentially all the uranium-238 which has decayed has been converted into lead-

---

[*] As the Au^{198} accumulates in the nuclear reactor, some 3.15-day Au^{199} is formed by the (n,γ) process; it decays to stable Hg^{199} which causes some difficulty.

206, it follows that $N_0 - N_t$ is equal to the quantity of the latter present. It follows, therefore, that

$$U^{238} = (U^{238} + Pb^{206})e^{-\lambda t},$$

where the symbols U^{238} and Pb^{206} refer to the amounts of the respective nuclides existing at the present time in a given piece of mineral. These quantities can be determined by experiment, and λ, the decay constant (equal to $0.693/T$, where T is the half life) of uranium-238, is known; hence the age t of the mineral can be calculated. A similar expression will hold for the relationship between uranium-235, the parent of the actinium series, and its end product lead-207, i.e.,

$$U^{235} = (U^{235} + Pb^{207})e^{-\lambda' t},$$

where λ' is the decay constant of uranium-235. Thus, two sets of measurements on a uranium mineral, containing both isotopes, will serve as a check on one another.

17.131. A simpler procedure is to divide one of these equations by the other, and upon rearrangement it is found that

$$\frac{Pb^{206}}{Pb^{207}} = \frac{U^{238}(e^{\lambda t} - 1)}{U^{235}(e^{\lambda' t} - 1)},$$

since U^{238}/U^{235} is equal to λ'/λ, as may be seen from equation (5.6). Since λ and λ' for the two isotopes of uranium are known, from the half lives, age of the mineral can be calculated if the ratios of Pb^{206} to Pb^{207} and of U^{238} to U^{235} are determined by means of a mass spectrometer.

17.132. A difficulty in applying these methods arises from the possibility that the lead may not all be of radioactive origin. If this is the case, then the mineral will contain some lead-204, since this is not an end product of any radioactive series. The

problem may be overcome in two ways. The most reliable is to make use only of materials which do not contain lead-204; this restricts the applicability of the method. The alternative procedure is to determine the amount of Pb^{204} by means of a mass spectrometer and from this to estimate (and allow for) the Pb^{206} and Pb^{207} that is not of radioactive origin. This can be done if the proportions of these three lead isotopes in a completely nonradiogenic mineral are measured. The oldest known uranium minerals have an age of 4.5×10^9 years.

17.133. Minerals containing rubidium may be dated by making use of the fact that Rb^{87} present in nature undergoes beta decay and forms Sr^{87}. It follows, therefore, that

$$Rb^{87} = (Rb^{87} + Sr^{87})e^{-\lambda t},$$

where λ is now the decay constant of rubidium-87. Hence, if the ratio of Rb^{87} to Sr^{87} can be determined, the age t of the mineral can be calculated. It is by no means easy to measure this ratio, and the method commonly employed is to determine spectroscopically the ratio of total rubidium to total strontium, and then to use isotopic analysis by the mass spectrometer to allow for nonradioactive and nonradiogenic isotopes. A similar method has been proposed for determining the ages of minerals containing potassium based on the decay of the K^{40} isotope. This has two products, namely gaseous argon-40 (by beta decay) and calcium-40 (by orbital-electron capture); the decay scheme is somewhat uncertain, so that the results are not yet too reliable. The age of the oldest known rubidium mineral has been reported to be about 3.4×10^9 years; from the argon-40 in the atmosphere, its age has been estimated to be about 4×10^9 years. The age of the earth is believed to be 4.5 × 10⁹ years.

RADIOCARBON DATING

17.134. The methods described above are useful for dating minerals of considerable age. For more recent objects, especially those of animal or vegetable origin, the radiocarbon method is proving to be of great value. In 1934, A. V. Grosse in the United States indicated the possibility that radioactive isotopes could be formed in nature by the action of cosmic rays (Chapter XVIII). Twelve years later, W. F. Libby, also in the United States, made the specific suggestion that carbon in living matter might be expected to contain a definite, if small, proportion of the long-lived C^{14} radioisotope, formed by the $N^{14}(n,p)C^{14}$ reaction between atmospheric nitrogen, which is 99.6 per cent N^{14}, and neutrons from cosmic rays. Any radiocarbon formed in this way will soon be converted into carbon dioxide; it will thus be taken up by plants in photosynthesis, built up into carbohydrates to be consumed by animals, who will then return part to the atmosphere in respiration. As a result of the operation of the familiar plant-animal carbon cycle, an equilibrium will be established in the course of time, and all carbon present in living matter will contain a constant equilibrium concentration of the C^{14} isotope. This amount will be determined by the rate of formation from the cosmic-ray neutrons, and the natural decay of C^{14} back to nitrogen (N^{14}). An examination of specimens of new wood obtained from sources in various distant parts of the world has indicated that, in every case, there is a constant radioactivity, equivalent to 15.3 counts per minute per gram of carbon, within the limits of experimental error.

17.135. Once a carbonaceous material has been separated from equilibrium with the plant-animal cycle, it is expected that the C^{14} will decay, with its normal half life of about 5600 years. In this event, the activity of "old" carbon, such as that present in petroleum, which has been removed from the life cycle for hundreds of millions of years, should be extremely small. This expectation has been confirmed by the failure to detect any appreciable particle count in excess of the normal background value.

17.136. The interesting prospect opened up by the theory outlined above is the possibility of being able to determine the age of various carbon products in the range of about 1000 to 50,000 and possibly up to 100,000 years. The assumption made is that when formed these substances had the same activity as "new" carbon compounds do at the present time, and that since removal from the life cycle the C^{14} has decayed with a half life of 5600 years. Thus, in the decay equation $N_t = N_0 e^{-\lambda t}$, the value of N_0 is taken as 15.3 counts per minute per gram of carbon, N_t is the corresponding number of counts as determined at present, that is, at the age of t, and λ is the decay constant for carbon-14. Since the half life of the latter is 5600 years, λ is 0.693/5600 in reciprocal years. Hence, if the number of counts per minute per gram of old carbon is determined, its age can be readily calculated.

17.137. The method of radiocarbon dating has been extensively used in recent years for a great variety of age measurements, especially of specimens of archeological and geological interest. These include textiles, wood and charcoal from Egyptian tombs, American cave dwellings and many other sources, and wood, peat and mud from the latest glacial age. The older the material, the more difficult it is to date it exactly, because the count rate becomes smaller and smaller in comparison with that of the normal background. By improving the counting techniques, the limit of radiocarbon dating has been increased from 10,000 to 50,000 years, and it has been claimed that this may be increased to 100,000 years in due course.

17.138. The validity of the radiocarbon method depends on the postulate that, when originally formed, the dated materials had the same content of carbon-14 as new material has at the present day. Since this isotope results from the capture of neutrons from cosmic rays, a basic assumption is that the intensity of cosmic rays has not changed appreciably during the course of the past 50,000 years or more. In order to test this point, J. L. Kulp, of the Columbia University Geological Observatory, determined the ages of certain ocean-bottom sediments by the radiocarbon method and also by measurements based on the content of ionium (Th^{230}). Good agreement was obtained for deposits dating back to 25,000 years. Since the ionium method is independent of cosmic-ray intensities, it is concluded that the latter has not changed by more than 10 to 20 per cent for any sustained period for the past 30,000 years.

17.139. On the other hand, from measurements of the magnetism of ancient bricks, going back over 1700 years, the French geophysicists E. Thellier and O. Thellier concluded, in 1956, that the earth's magnetic field has been decreasing steadily during that period. In this event, as W. Elsasser, E. P. Ney and J. R. Winckler, in the United States, have pointed out, there would have been a corresponding increase in the flux of cosmic rays reaching the atmosphere. As a result, ages determined by the radiocarbon method would be about 240 years too small in specimens 1700 years old, and, if the same rate of decrease in the earth's magnetic field were extended back 4000 years, the error would be as much as 1000 years in specimens of that age. It should be pointed out, in this connection, that in dating materials from Egyptian tombs up to 5000 years old, the carbon-14 method has given results in excellent agreement with the most reliable archeological data. It is highly improbable that the latter are in error by more than about 100 years, and so it must be concluded that, if there has been a change in cosmic-ray intensity, it has not been continuous.

DATING WITH TRITIUM

17.140. Another radioisotope formed in nature by the action of cosmic rays is tritium; like carbon-14, it can be used, although to a more limited extent, for determination of age. Because of its short half life of 12.26 years, the tritium method cannot be applied to specimens that are more than about 30 years old. Tritium is produced in the atmosphere mainly in two ways: by the interaction of fast neutrons with nitrogen, i.e., $N^{14}(n,t)C^{12}$, and as a product of the disintegration of nuclei which have captured protons or mesons of very high energy. Dating with tritium is much more involved than with radiocarbon, because of the variations in the amounts present in water at different latitudes and under different rainfall conditions. The proportion of tritium in ordinary water is so small, a few parts per billion billion (10^{18}), that special methods of analysis, including concentration, by evaporation of the water, by a factor of at least 10,000, have had to be developed.

17.141. In spite of the difficulties in dating with tritium, some interesting results have been obtained by W. F. Libby and his collaborators, since 1953. For example, from the tritium content of rain, it has been possible to calculate how long moisture has remained in the air between evaporation from the sea and its ultimate precipitation. A rough estimate indicates that water remains in the air over the ocean for about nine days, on the average. Agricultural products less than 30 years old have been dated by determining the tritium content and comparing it with the estimated original value, in a manner similar to that described for radiocarbon. Another application is to determine how long water has been stored in underground reservoirs. In general, it appears that analysis for natural tritium may prove a useful tool in meteorology and in the solution of water supply problems.

Isotopes and Geological Temperatures

17.142. An entirely different application of isotopes, having some geological interest, deals with a method originated by H. C. Urey in 1947 for the determination of the temperature of the sea in prehistoric times. Reference has been made earlier to the fact that isotopes of a given element can exchange in certain chemical compounds until a state of equilibrium is attained. The position of the equilibrium, as with chemical equilibria in general, depends on the temperature. A case in point is the isotopic exchange equilibrium between the oxygen in water and that in calcium carbonate deposited from it. Calculations show that if the carbonate sepa-

rates at $0°C$, it will be enriched in the O^{18} isotope of oxygen by a factor of 1.026 over that in the water; at $25°C$, the corresponding factor will be 1.022. This difference for a change of $25°C$ is quite small, but it should be detectable by means of a mass spectrometer. Hence, accurate determination of the isotopic abundance of O^{18} in calcium carbonate which has separated from water should make it possible to estimate the temperature of the water.

17.143. "It is evident," says Urey, "that if a [marine] animal deposits calcium carbonate in equilibrium with water in which it lives, the shell * sinks to the bottom of the sea and is buried securely in the earth and remains unchanged . . . it is only necessary to determine the ratio of the isotopes of oxygen in the shell today, in order to know the temperature at which the animal lived." The theory connecting the isotopic composition of the calcium carbonate with the temperature of the water is not exact, and is, in any event, applicable to pure water; consequently an empirical relationship was established by examining a number of shells of marine animals existing at the present time in seas ranging in temperature from $0°$ to $28°C$. From the proportion of O^{18} present in fossil belemnites, the temperatures of the Upper Chalk layers of the Upper Cretaceous system of the county of Hampshire, England, were estimated to have changed steadily from $26.5°$ to $18.8°C$ over a period of about 10 million years.

Applications of Radiations

17.144. Some uses of radiation for control and testing in industry have been given earlier. In this section, a few possible industrial applications of an entirely different character will be

* The shells and sometimes the skeletons of marine animals consist of calcium carbonate.

described. Several of these are of interest because they do not require radiations of any specific energy; hence, they may provide a practical use for the fission products that will be a by-product of the nuclear (fission) power industry.

17.145. It has long been known that mixtures of small amounts of a radioactive substance with certain phosphors, such as zinc sulfide, produce a luminescence visible in the dark. This basic phenomenon led to the discovery of X-rays and radioactivity, and is also the origin of the present-day scintillation counters (Chapter VI). A number of beta emitters, such as carbon-14, strontium-90, promethium-147 and thallium-204 have been suggested for the production of luminescent materials. These are easier to handle than natural (alpha-emitting) radioactive substances and the beta particles cause less deterioration of the phosphor than do alpha particles.

17.146. The ionization produced by beta particles is being used for the elimination of static electricity, which is a serious fire and explosion hazard in the paper, textile, rubber and plastic industries. Another use of the ionization from radioactive sources is to control the firing voltage in certain types of voltage-regulator tubes and in the spark gaps of ignition systems. Similar ionization sources have been included in a variety of instruments where operation depends on the passage of an electrical discharge. By keeping the residual gas in a vacuum tube in a state of partial ionization, more dependable operation is possible.

17.147. An important application of nuclear radiation is in bringing about certain chemical changes, particularly in plastics. Many of these products consist of more or less parallel long chains of atoms. By suitable controlled exposure to radiation, the chains can be connected together, by what are called cross linkages, thereby improving the properties of the plastic. Polyethylene, for example, is a product which has benefited from treatment by radiation. It should be remembered that excessive exposure to radiation can lead to serious disruption of the atomic bonds, so that the material may be rendered useless (§ 15.27).

17.148. Since gamma radiation can destroy bacteria and enzymes which cause deterioration and spoilage of food, considerable interest has developed in the possibility of cold sterilization of meats, vegetables and even antibiotics. The nutritional value of the irradiated food appears to be unimpaired, but there are sometimes undesirable changes in taste and appearance. If these difficulties can be overcome, sterilization by gamma radiation may result in a considerable change in methods of food packaging. Striking improvements in the storage quality of potatoes has been achieved by exposure to radiation. It should be mentioned here that, provided gamma rays of moderate energy are used, the chances of the food having radioactivity induced into it are negligible.

17.149. An attractive possibility is the direct conversion of radioactive energy into electrical energy. Several ways of doing this have been proposed and a number of *nuclear batteries*, as they are called, have reached a practical stage of development. A few of the ideas proposed will be outlined below. The radioactive materials used are generally substances emitting only beta particles, because the relatively heavy shields required to decrease the gamma-ray intensity are undesirable. In one case, however, an alpha-particle emitter is preferred.

17.150. The simplest type of nuclear

battery, called the *beta-current cell*, was first demonstrated by H. G.-J. Moseley (§ 4.24) in 1913. It consists of two conducting electrodes, an emitter, coated with a beta-active material, and a collector; the electrons (beta particles) emitted from one electrode are collected on the other and flow through an external circuit to produce an electrical current in the usual manner. By filling the space between the electrodes with a plastic material, such as polyethylene or polystyrene, the electrons of high energy from the emitter can penetrate to the collector, but the flow of low-energy electrons in the reverse direction is prevented, thereby giving an increase in efficiency. Using the fission product strontium-90, half life 28 years, a cell having a high voltage but extremely small current output has been constructed.

17.151. In the *contact potential difference* type of cell, first demonstrated by J. V. Kramer in 1924, the electrodes consist of two conductors, e.g., zinc and carbon, which differ markedly in the respective amounts of energy required for the release of orbital electrons. The gas between the electrodes is ionized by the radioactive material, and the resulting charged particles, consisting mainly of positive ions and electrons (§ 4.31), serve to carry current from one electrode to the other. The gas commonly used between the electrodes is tritium. Since each beta particle can produce as many as 200 ion-pairs, by avalanche ionization (§ 6.22), there is some internal amplification of current in batteries of the contact potential difference type which does not occur in the beta-current cells. The potential differences in the battery are of the order of 1 volt and the currents are very small.

17.152. A third type of nuclear cell, which has much to recommend it, makes use if a *positive-negative* (or *p-n*) *junction*, similar to that employed in the familiar transistors used for current amplification. The junction is made of silicon, to one (positive) side being added a trace of boron and to the other (negative) side a trace of antimony. The presence of a source of beta particles causes a flow of electrons, and hence a flow of electric current, across the junction. There may be as many as 200,000 electrons flowing for every initiating beta particle and so the current amplification is considerable. The cell voltage is quite small, e.g., about 0.2 volt, but the currents, although not large, are much greater than those from nuclear cells of most other types. Because of the radiation damage caused by the beta particles, it is necessary that the energy of the latter should be less than 0.2 Mev, otherwise the voltage of the cell fails in a short time. For this reason, strontium-90, which was the material used in the first designs, has proved to be unsatisfactory. Better results may be obtained with the fission product promethium-147 (half life 2.5 years); the maximum beta-particle energy from this source is 0.22 Mev and the average energy about 0.08 Mev.

17.153. A proposed modification is to combine the p-n junction with a scintillator and a photoelectric surface (§ 2.48). The radioactive particles falling on the scintillator produce light flashes which serve to eject electrons from the photosensitive p-n junction. The principle is exactly the same as that now being used in devices for conversion of sunlight into electrical energy, in what are called solar batteries.

17.154. Although several others

have been proposed, one final type of nuclear cell will be mentioned. This requires the use, preferably, of an alpha emitter, so that the particles are completely absorbed in a small thickness of material. The heat liberated as a result of this absorption raises the temperature of a thermal junction and an electric current is produced. Using polonium-210, which emits no gamma radiation, as the source of alpha particles, a 0.75-volt cell, producing a current of 0.025 ampere, has been constructed. However, the high cost of the polonium makes this a laboratory curiosity rather than a practical reality.

17.155. None of the cells described above appears to offer any immediate prospects for conventional battery uses, e.g., domestic or industrial power or for automobile starting. There are special purposes, however, where the possible long life and reliability of a nuclear battery, as compared with the familiar chemical dry cell or storage battery, may be advantageous. The very small size possible with a p-n junction type of nuclear cell has led to its adoption as a source of power in an electric watch.

CONCLUSION

17.156. It should be understood that the uses of isotopes and radiations described in the present chapter represent a selection, chosen either because of the relative completeness of the conclusions, or because of their general interest. A great deal of other work has been done, which for one reason or another, could not be included here. The range of applications given, from photosynthesis to the treatment of polycythemia vera, and from the determination of the uptake of phosphorus by plants to the temperature of the sea in geological times, should be sufficient, however, to indicate the tremendous power and versatility of the isotopic tool. In view of the progress already made, there is no doubt, as stated earlier, that the future holds great promise for discoveries that will be of benefit to mankind.

Cosmic Rays and Strange Particles

Chapter XVIII

THE PROPERTIES OF COSMIC RAYS

THE DISCOVERY OF COSMIC RAYS

18.1. The study of cosmic rays, which has revealed some of the most striking and complex phenomena of nuclear science, owes its origin to the attempts by physicists, at the beginning of the present century, to account for the continuous leakage of current from charged electroscopes. For example, around 1900, C. T. R. Wilson (see § 6.64) in England, and J. Elster and H. Geitel in Germany reported a loss of charge, presumably due to ionization of the air in the electroscope, even when precautions were taken to prevent access of known ionizing radiations. Wilson suggested the possibility that the ionization might be caused by unknown rays coming from outside the earth, and this view appeared to find support in the observations made in Canada, two or three years later, by J. C. McLennan and E. F. Burton, and by E. Rutherford and H. L. Cooke. The former workers studied the rate of discharge of an electroscope on the surface of frozen Lake Ontario, at some distance from land, and the latter noted the effect of thick layers of iron and lead. In both cases, the loss of charge was diminished, but there was always a residual ionization which could not be eliminated.

18.2. The effects observed were undoubtedly small, and they could be decreased by the use of sufficient shielding; hence there was some feeling of doubt concerning their significance. In a review of the subject written in 1909, the conclusion was drawn that the ionizing radiations were entirely of terrestrial origin. It was thought that they were due either to radioactive minerals in the earth, or to traces of the gaseous emanations (§ 5.18) arising from such minerals, or to both. There is no doubt that ionizing rays of radioactive origin are present in the atmosphere, and it seemed reasonable to attribute to them the observed ionization. However, since such radiations are completely absorbed by a few inches of lead, there was a sufficient element of doubt to make the matter worthy of further investigation.

18.3. In the years 1909 and 1910, T. Wulf made observations on the discharge of electroscopes at the top of the Eifel Tower in Paris, France, and the Swiss scientist A. Gockel studied the same phenomenon at high altitudes in the course of balloon ascents. If the ionizing radiations come from the earth, their intensity should diminish at great heights, because passage through a considerable layer of air would be accompanied by absorption and consequent attenuation. The data obtained indicated that a small decrease in intensity actually occurred, at first, but at higher altitudes the ionization commenced to increase. At an elevation of 4500 meters (14,800 ft.) Gockel found that an electroscope was discharged even more rapidly than at the earth's surface.

18.4. On the basis of the foregoing results it would appear that the ionizing radiations could not be exclusively of terrestrial origin, but the experimental techniques were not too reliable, and the obvious conclusion was not widely accepted. In the succeeding years, more careful quantitative measurements were reported by V. F. Hess in Austria, in 1911 to 1913, and by W. Kolhörster in Germany, in 1913 and 1914; both these investigators made balloon ascents, to heights of about 5000 and 9000 meters, i.e., about 16,500 and 30,000 feet, respectively, and found a marked increase in the ionizing radiations at high elevations. Consequently, Hess suggested that the rays were "of cosmic origin," and referred to them as "Höhenstrahlung," which might be translated as "high-altitude rays." If these radiations originated from outside the earth, yet reach the surface after passing through the atmosphere, it is evident that they must have great penetrating power. It is thus possible to understand how the rays can traverse the thick layers of metal which were used to shield charged electro-

scopes in some of the early experiments, mentioned above.

18.5. The war in Europe interrupted the study of these highly penetrating radiations, but in 1922 investigation of the subject was resumed, particularly by the noted American physicist, R. A. Millikan (see § 2.33) and his collaborators. Millikan used so-called "free" balloons, that is, unmanned balloons, containing recording instruments, and was thus able to obtain measurements at altitudes of 15,500 meters (51,000 ft.). In addition, observations were made in airplane flights and on mountain tops, as well as at considerable depths in the water of mountain lakes. The existence of the penetrating radiations under all these conditions was confirmed, and since they appeared to come from an extraterrestrial source, Millikan in 1925 called them *cosmic rays*, a name now universally adopted. Although it is the practice to speak of cosmic rays as if they were a single type of radiation, they are actually very complex, as will shortly appear. The primary rays in outer space are believed to be fairly simple, but, because of their interaction with matter, their nature changes as they pass through the atmosphere.

METHODS AND OBJECTIVES
OF COSMIC-RAY STUDIES

18.6. During recent years the phenomena associated with cosmic rays have formed the subjects of numerous investigations. Their remarkable penetrating power has been proved by their detection at considerable depths in water, and under the surface of the earth in mines. By the use of free balloons observations have been made at altitudes up to 100,000 feet, and by introducing the instruments into the heads of rockets, data have been obtained for short time intervals at very much greater heights.

18.7. All the early work on cosmic rays was done with some form of ionization chamber (§ 6.10) in conjunction with a suitable electrometer. Instead of counting individual particles, the instrument was used as an integrating device to measure the total amount of ionization produced by the cosmic rays entering the chamber. By grounding the central electrode at definite intervals, the ionization charge collected in a given period of time could be determined. With the vacuum-tube amplifiers at present available, the ionization chamber can be adapted to indicate individual events or groups of events accompanying the passage of cosmic rays.

18.8. In 1927, the Russian physicist, D. Skobelzyn, adapted the Wilson cloud chamber (§ 6.68), with an associated magnetic field, to the study of cosmic rays. With certain modifications, to be described below, this instrument has proved of great value; its use has led to the discovery of new fundamental particles and of new phenomena of considerable interest. In order to slow down the rapidly moving particles, thus increasing the specific ionization in their paths, and also to observe, if possible, the end of their tracks, cloud chambers for cosmic-ray work are filled with gas at high pressure.

18.9. The development of the Geiger-Müller tube in 1928 (§ 6.26) led to its almost immediate use for cosmic-ray work in 1929, by W. Bothe and W. Kolhörster in Germany. By making use of two or more of these counters, either alone or in conjunction with a cloud chamber, a number of highly ingenious devices have been constructed for investigating a variety of effects associated with cosmic rays. An illustration is provided by what is sometimes known as a *cosmic-ray telescope;* in its simplest form this consists of two or more G-M tubes oriented horizontally, with one placed vertically above the other, and connected by a coincidence circuit. A system of this kind will respond only to ionizing particles (or radiations) passing through all the counters, which means it will only count penetrating particles traveling in a vertical direction. If the relative positions of the tubes are changed, the number coming from other directions can be recorded.

18.10. By placing a Wilson cloud chamber between two G-M counters, as did Blackett and Occhialini in the work described in § 2.72, it is possible to make the cosmic-ray particle record its own cloud track. The coincidence circuit is connected to a relay which causes the expansion of the cloud chamber to take place when an ionizing particle has passed through the two G-M tubes and the chamber. Since the ions formed persist for an appreciable time, it is possible to record the cloud track during a short interval after the actual passage of the particle. This delay is often an advantage because the track is somewhat diffused, and so the number of droplets present and hence of ions formed can be counted. Previous to the use of G-M tubes to cause cosmic-ray particles to trigger the cloud chamber, it was the practice to make many random expansions in the hope of hitting upon an interesting event. This wasteful procedure has now been obviated.

18.11. As seen in § 6.87, a photographic emulsion behaves somewhat like a cloud chamber in recording the paths of ionizing particles. The simplicity and lightness of the photographic plate are a great asset in connection with observations made in free balloons and on mountain peaks. Further, the continuous sensitivity of the emulsion is an advantage for there is no way of knowing in advance when an interesting nuclear event is about to occur. Photographic plates were first employed for the studies of cosmic rays by (Frl.) M. Blau in Austria in 1936, and their use has led to many important discoveries in the realm of cosmic rays. A number of nuclear track plates or pellicles, in the form of a pack, are placed in a light-tight box, which the cosmic rays can easily penetrate, and exposed at high altitudes for some time. Since the stopping power of the emulsion is considerably greater than that of air, tracks frequently terminate in the emulsion producing events of particular interest. Measurements made on the tracks, which are observed under the microscope, provide information on the properties of the particles causing them.

18.12. In the subsequent sections of this chapter an outline will be given of the more significant phenomena, many of which are highly complicated, associated with cosmic radiations. An attempt will also be made to interpret the results as far as possible, within the limitations of present day knowledge. It should be understood, however, that in this rapidly developing field new facts are being discovered almost daily, and many of these new facts require the erection of new theories.

18.13. Before going into details, however, it may be asked: What is the purpose of studying these rays which appear to have their origin in distant space? The answer is two-fold. In the first place, the investigation of cosmic rays is an area of research having an intrinsic interest to the physicist, partly because of the variety and complexity of the related phenomena, and partly because of the intriguing problem of the origin of these rays. In the second place, the presence of radiations of tremendously high energies makes the cosmic rays a weapon for attacking the atomic nucleus, more powerful than any of the laboratory particle-accelerators that are at present in existence.

18.14. Already the study of cosmic rays has resulted in the identification of the positron (§ 2.67) as well as several types of mesons (§ 2.124 *et seq.*) which will be described more fully below. Nuclear disintegrations ("stars") and other striking effects have also been brought to light in the course of work with cosmic rays. It is thus not difficult to understand why the subject has attracted so much attention in recent years.

THE LATITUDE EFFECT

18.15. If cosmic rays consist of electrically charged particles coming from outside the earth, as seems possible from their ionizing and penetrating properties, then it is to be expected that they should be affected by the earth's magnetic field, just as are the electrons responsible for the aurora borealis. The rule relating to the deflection of electrically charged particles in the field of a magnet is well known to physicists; from this rule it can be readily shown that charged particles coming from an extraterrestrial source will suffer maximum deflection if they approach in the direction of the earth's geomagnetic equator.* The extent of the deflection

---

* The geomagnetic equator is the imaginary great circle on the earth's surface, everywhere equidistant from the earth's *magnetic* poles. Degrees of latitude with respect to the geomagnetic equator and the magnetic poles are referred to as *geomagnetic latitudes.*

should decrease, however, as the direction of approach is changed toward the polar regions, and will be essentially zero in the direction of the earth's magnetic poles. It can be seen, therefore, that if cosmic rays do indeed consist of charged particles, a variation of intensity with the geomagnetic latitude should be observed. The intensity should be greatest near the poles, where the approaching particles are not appreciably deflected, and least in the region of the geomagnetic equator, where the deflection is a maximum.

18.16. Early attempts to observe what is now called the *latitude effect* were unsuccessful, but in 1927, the Dutch physicist, J. Clay, first reported a noticeable decrease in intensity of cosmic rays, observed on shipboard, in the region of the geomagnetic equator. The variation of intensity with geomagnetic latitude depends to some extent on the longitude,* and this fact led to a certain amount of confusion. However, as a result of the comprehensive investigations made by A. H. Compton (see § 3.36) and his coworkers the existence of the latitude effect was definitely established. Lines drawn on a map, passing through points of equal cosmic-ray intensity, are found, as expected, to be parallel to the lines of geomagnetic latitude. These results provide strong evidence for the view that cosmic rays consist, at least partly, of electrically charged particles originating outside the earth.

18.17. If the cosmic-ray intensities at various geomagnetic latitudes, for a given longitude, are plotted, the result is a curve like that in Fig. 18.1. It is seen that between the magnetic poles and latitudes of about 50°, the

intensity remains almost constant, the observed decrease taking place only between 50° latitude and the geomagnetic equator.

18.18. It should be noted that the form of the curve in Fig. 18.1 is in-

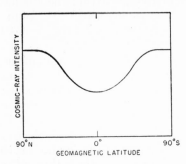

Fig. 18.1. Approximate variation of cosmic-ray intensity with geomagnetic latitude.

tended to be qualitative only, since it varies with the conditions of measurement of the cosmic-ray intensity. At the top of the atmosphere, for example, the relative difference between the ionization intensities at geomagnetic latitudes of 0° and 90° are considerably greater than at sea level. This is due to the many changes occurring in the cosmic rays in their passage through the atmosphere, as will be seen later. The shape of the curve also appears to be related to sun spot activity, although this may well be a secondary effect.

18.19. There is some uncertainty as to whether the curve in Fig. 18.1 is actually flat between geomagnetic latitudes of about 50° and 90°, implying a constancy of the cosmic-ray intensity in these regions. If the intensity is indeed constant, the implication would be that no primary cosmic-ray particles with energy less than

---

* This arises because a line joining the magnetic poles does not pass through the center of the earth. In other words, the magnetic field of the earth is not symmetrical with respect to the earth itself.

about 1500 Mev (or 1.5 Bev)* can reach the earth's atmosphere. Thus, by geomagnetic latitude 50°, all particles with energies of 1.5 Bev or more will have arrived, and a further increase in the number would not be possible. If this is the case, what then happens to particles with energies less than 1.5 Bev? It has been suggested that such particles are deflected by the magnetic field of the sun. However, this explanation is of doubtful validity, since calculations based upon it do not agree with the experimental facts.

18.20. More recent investigations of cosmic-ray intensities have indicated that the values may not be constant at latitudes greater than 50°; they probably increase to some extent, although less markedly than from the geomagnetic equator to latitude 50°. In this event, there is no sharp cutoff of the energy of the primary particles reaching the earth's atmosphere. There is evidently some relationship between the sun and cosmic rays, but the exact nature of the connection has not been established. For example, it has been claimed that the cosmic-ray intensities are highest in years when sun-spot activity is least, and vice versa. Further, the appearance of "flares" on the sun's surface are associated with a definite increase in cosmic-ray intensities.

East-West Asymmetry Effect

18.21. It was pointed out by B. Rossi in Italy in 1930 that, if cosmic rays contain a large proportion of electrically charged particles, there should be a difference in the intensity of the rays coming from easterly and westerly directions. A moving stream of charged particles is deflected by a magnetic field in a direction perpendicular both to the field and to that of their motion. If the particles are positively charged, then the earth's magnetic field will deflect them toward the east; on the other hand, they will be deflected toward the west if the particles are negatively charged. It follows, therefore, that if most of the cosmic-ray particles are positively charged, an observer on the earth will find a greater intensity apparently approaching from a westerly than from an easterly direction. There should thus be what has been called an east-west asymmetry effect. This effect is expected to be most marked near the geomagnetic equator and should fall off to zero as the poles are approached.

18.22. By making use of the ability of a system of two or more G-M tubes, arranged in coincidence, to act as a cosmic-ray telescope, it is possible to count particles coming from a specific direction. In this way the existence of the east-west asymmetry in cosmic rays has been proved. From measurements reported in 1935 near the magnetic equator in Peru, and elsewhere, the American physicist T. H. Johnson established definitely that more particles approach the earth from the west than from an easterly direction. This result not only confirmed the view that cosmic-ray particles are electrically charged, but it also showed that the majority are positively charged.[†] These and other considerations led Johnson to suggest that the primary particles, that is, the particles present in cosmic rays before interacting with nuclei present in the atmosphere, are mainly protons. This view is now

---

* The abbreviation Bev is used, as in § 9.96, for a billion electron volts, i.e., 10^9 ev.

† The ionization measured at or near the earth's surface is mainly due to secondary particles, as will be explained later; hence, it is strictly to these that the observed east-west effect applies. It seems reasonable to suppose, however, that the charge which is predominant in the primary particles will also be that of the secondaries.

widely adopted as providing the most satisfactory interpretation of numerous cosmic-ray phenomena.

THE ALTITUDE EFFECT

18.23. It will be recalled that one of the essential arguments in favor of the extraterrestrial origin of cosmic rays was the marked increase of intensity observed with increasing altitude (§ 18.3). With the improved apparatus that later became available a more careful and detailed examination of the effect of altitude has been made at several different geomagnetic latitudes. The intensities obtained for cosmic-ray particles reaching the instrument from all angles, at the given observation point, are depicted in Fig. 18.2. In accordance with a common practice in cosmic-ray studies, the intensities are plotted against the corresponding values of the atmospheric pressure expressed in terms of meters of water, a pressure of 1 atm., or 76 cm. of mercury, being equivalent to 10.33 meters of water.*

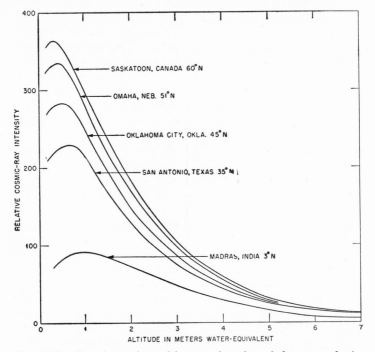

FIG. 18.2.   Cosmic-ray intensities as a function of the atmospheric pressure, at latitudes from 3° to 60°N.

tensity observed with increasing altitude (§ 18.3). With the improved apparatus that later became available a more careful and detailed examination of the effect of altitude has been made at several different geomagnetic latitudes. The intensities obtained for cosmic-ray particles reaching the instrument from all angles, at the given **18.24.** The curves reveal a number of interesting points. As already noted, the total cosmic-ray intensity increases with increasing altitude or decreasing pressure, i.e., in passing from right to left of the figure. But at high altitudes, usually in excess of 50,000 feet, the intensity starts to fall off with increasing height. The intensity at

* A pressure of 1 meter water-equivalent corresponds to an altitude of 53,600 feet. One reason why the water equivalent of altitude is used is that cosmic-ray intensities determined under water, above or below sea level, can be included in the same figure.

any pressure or, in other words, at a given altitude, is seen to increase with geomagnetic latitude, as recorded in a preceding section.

18.25. Very briefly, the general shape of the intensity-altitude curve may be explained in the following manner. Near the top of the atmosphere, the primary cosmic-ray particles, believed to be protons, interact with matter, for example, the molecules of oxygen and nitrogen, producing considerable numbers of secondary particles, mostly electrons, both positive and negative, and photons, as will be explained in § 18.37. The instrument which measures the total number of charged particles, or total ionization, thus registers an increase of intensity with decreasing altitude. This accounts for the small, rising portions of the curves at the left of Fig. 18.2. As the secondary particles pass down through the atmosphere, they are absorbed, that is to say, they are slowed down until they no longer produce ionization. Hence, as the instrument descends, the ionization intensity recorded decreases at first rapidly, and then more slowly as sea level is attained at the extreme right of the figure.

18.26. As already seen, the difference in the intensities at different latitudes, as shown by the several curves in Fig. 18.2, is due to the fact that a proportion of the cosmic-ray particles which can overcome the earth's magnetic field at San Antonio, Texas (geomagnetic latitude 38°), for example, do not have sufficient energy to do so at Madras, India (geomagnetic latitude 3°). For each geomagnetic latitude, between 0° and 50°, at least, there is a certain minimum energy necessary for the primary cosmic-ray particles to reach the earth.

18.27. The area under each curve represents the total (integrated) ionization, and thus is a measure of the total energy,* of the cosmic rays reaching the earth's surface at that latitude. Hence, it is proportional to the total energy of the rays in excess of the calculated minimum energy for the given latitude. The difference in the areas under any two curves in Fig. 18.2 is thus related to the total energy carried by the cosmic-ray particles whose individual energies lie between the two minimum values for the latitudes corresponding to the chosen curves. Consequently, if the average energy of the individual particles were known, it would be possible to determine the actual number of particles with energies lying between these minimum energies. Estimates of the average energies have been made, and with their aid an indication has been obtained of the distribution of energies among the primary cosmic-ray particles.

18.28. From the results, it appears that primary particles with energies in the vicinity of 6 Bev are more frequent than those with other energies. This does not mean that the majority of all the particles in cosmic rays have 6 Bev energy, but that more particles have this energy than any other individual value. The calculations, based on the data in Fig. 18.2 show that the mean energy of all primary cosmic-ray particles is approximately 10 Bev. However, cosmic rays contain a fair proportion of particles with energies of 30 to 40 Bev, and more. It will be seen later that there is evidence, in fact, for the occasional occurrence in cosmic rays of particles with energies up to the fantastic figure of 10^8 Bev, that is, 10^{17} ev.

---

* The formation of one ion-pair in air requires about 33.5 ev of energy (§ 6.4).

THE SOFT AND HARD COMPONENTS

18.29. The extraordinary penetrating power of cosmic rays is shown, in the first place, by their ability to pass through the earth's atmosphere, the absorptive power of which for ionizing radiations is approximately equivalent to 1 meter thickness of lead. But that is not all. The rays have been detected underground and under water at distances equivalent to 1400 meters of water below the earth's surface. Only particles with many billions of electron volts of energy could have penetrated to such depths.

18.30. A study of the absorption of cosmic rays in matter has revealed the fact that the intensity does not decrease regularly with the thickness of the absorbing material. With lead as absorber, for example, the intensity of the cosmic rays diminishes rapidly for the first 10 cm. thickness, and then falls off much more slowly. This indicates that the cosmic rays consist of at least two different types of radiation. That part which is absorbed by 10 cm. of lead is called the *soft component* of the cosmic rays. The portion of the cosmic radiation which is able to pass through 10 cm. of lead, and which is absorbed only with difficulty, is called the *hard component*. Actually, the distinction between hard and soft components, based on the penetration of 10 cm. of lead, is somewhat arbitrary, but it has proved very convenient. The properties of the two types of cosmic rays, defined in this manner, are quite characteristic, as will be evident in due course.

18.31. The soft component constitutes about 20 per cent of the total cosmic radiation at sea level at 50° geomagnetic latitude, but the proportion increases, at first, with increasing altitude. This is to be expected since the soft component is more easily absorbed than the hard component in passing through the atmosphere. At very great heights, where the total cosmic radiation commences to decrease, as indicated by the turning downward of the curves at the left-hand side of Fig. 18.2, the amount of the soft component also decreases. Actually, the decrease in the total intensity is due to the decrease in the soft component at high altitudes, for the intensity of the hard component has been observed to increase steadily up to the greatest heights attained.

18.32. Taken in conjunction with the interpretation of the shape of the curves in Fig. 18.2, given above, it may be concluded from these data that the hard component is more closely related to the primary cosmic radiation, whereas the soft component is equivalent to the secondary radiation resulting from the interaction of the primary rays with matter, or from spontaneous changes undergone by the hard component. This view, which will be elaborated more fully at a later stage (§ 18.36 *et seq.*), is supported by the observation that the soft component can still be detected at great depths below sea level. Because of its relatively easy absorbability, it is inconceivable that the soft component will have penetrated to such distances from the earth's surface. It would appear, therefore, that the soft component is produced by, and is consequently secondary to, the extremely penetrating, hard component.

18.33. On the basis of numerous detailed studies of the ionizing and penetrating powers of the hard and soft components of cosmic rays, at various altitudes and latitudes, it is generally accepted that the hard component consists mainly of highly energetic mesons, the charged and neutral particles of intermediate mass and short life to which reference was made in Chapter II, and which will be considered more fully below. A small number of fast protons, and a still smaller number of nuclei of heavier atoms, all of which are believed to be primary cosmic-ray particles, are also present in the hard component. In addition, there are a few neutrons, electrons and photons (§ 3.34) of extremely high energy. The great penetrating power of the mesons largely accounts for the ease with which the hard component of cosmic rays passes through considerable thicknesses of matter.

18.34. The soft component, on the other hand, is made up essentially of positive (positrons) and negative electrons, and about an equal number of photons; there are, in addition, possibly a small number of slow mesons, neutrons, protons and heavier particles. For practical purposes, the soft component may be thought of as approximately equal proportions of positrons, electrons and photons with energies less than about 200 Mev. Since it is doubtful if electrons are present to any great extent in the primary cosmic radiation, the soft component must, presumably, be secondary in nature, as indicated above. The electrons of the soft component of cosmic rays are believed to originate chiefly in three ways. First, charged pi-mesons decay into mu-mesons and the latter then emit electrons, either positive or negative according to the sign of the meson. Second, the decay of neutral mesons is accompanied by the liberation of gamma-ray photons of high energy which can produce positron-

electron pairs when they encounter atomic nuclei (§ 7.88). And, finally, many of the electrons in the soft component of cosmic rays, referred to as *knock-on electrons,* result from direct impact of the fast mesons with the orbital electrons of the oxygen and nitrogen atoms in the atmosphere. The foregoing mechanisms account for the occurrence of the soft component of cosmic rays at considerable depths underground where the mesons can penetrate, but electrons cannot.

18.35. In their passage through the air (or other matter), the electrical interaction of the electrons with atomic nuclei results in the formation of X-rays of the continuous type, i.e., bremsstrahlung (or braking radiation), as explained in § 4.75.* This accounts for the presence of photons in the soft component. If these photons have energy in excess of 1 Mev, as many do, initially at least, they can produce positron-electron pairs. Thus, one electron may cause the liberation of one photon, which is then converted into two electrons, one positive and one negative; this multiplication undoubtedly plays some part in maintaining the electron concentration of the soft component of cosmic rays. By using a special device, this multiplication can be greatly amplified to produce some interesting phenomena, as will be seen below. It is worth noting that the positron was first discovered, and evidence for positron-electron pairs was first obtained, from cloud tracks resulting from the passage of cosmic rays through a Wilson chamber (§ 2.67 *et seq.*).

---

* Radiations of the bremsstrahlung type are also produced by charged mesons, but since the probability (or cross section) for this process is inversely proportional to the square of the mass of the moving particle, it is very small for mesons, as compared with electrons.

COSMIC-RAY PHENOMENA

CASCADE SHOWERS

18.36. In 1929, shortly after he had adapted the cloud chamber to the study of cosmic rays (§ 18.8), D. Skobelzyn noted that sets of associated tracks were often obtained indicating the passage of particles in groups. Subsequently a variety of similar effects were observed with both cloud chambers and G-M counters. Any grouping of cosmic-ray particles is referred to as a *shower,* following the suggestion made by P. M. S. Blackett and G. P. S. Occhialini in 1933. Actually, numerous types of showers, many of them of great complexity, have been studied, but only those which appear to be moderately well understood will be described here.

18.37. Showers are readily observed in a cloud chamber by placing one or more lead plates across it; a cosmic-ray particle entering the chamber may then initiate a shower which is seen to originate in the lead. An illustration of a simple type of shower is to be found in Fig. 2.6 which was used in §2.70 to depict the formation of electron-positron pairs. The initiating particle may be extremely penetrating, so that it is seen to continue its motion without deflection. On the other hand, there is often no observable track of an initiating particle, so that the latter is believed to be a photon of high energy arising from the decay of a neutral pi-meson. By placing several lead plates across the cloud chamber the striking phenomenon of a *cascade shower* is observed, as shown in Fig. 18.3. A cascade can be initiated by a single particle; the number of resulting particles increases in the first few plates and then decreases until it is terminated. If penetrating particles are present, they may pass right through the chamber virtually unaffected.

18.38. The fact that cascade showers are almost invariably stopped before

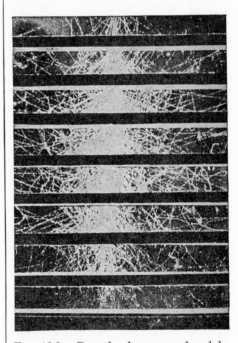

FIG. 18.3. Cascade shower produced by cosmic rays in a cloud chamber containing lead plates.

passing through lead plates with a total thickness of about 10 cm. indicates that they are related to the soft component of cosmic rays. The particles producing the tracks are thus essentially positive and negative electrons and photons. This is in harmony with the interpretation of cascade showers first suggested by the French physicist P. Auger in 1935, and developed quantitatively in 1937 by J. F. Carlson and J. R. Oppenheimer in the United States, and by H. J. Bhabha and W. Heitler in Eire. According to the theory, a shower of the type under consideration is usually initiated by a high-energy electron. This may be a knock-on electron, liberated by the impact of an energetic mu-meson with an extranuclear electron of an atom or, more probably, a member of a positron-electron pair liberated by gamma-ray photons from neutral pi-meson decay.

18.39. The initiating electron, whose energy may be many billions of electron volts, will emit bremsstrahlung photons of high energy in its passage through matter, a lead plate for example. Each of the highly energetic photons formed in this manner will produce a positron-electron pair, with each particle carrying off half of the excess energy. Thus, in the first generation, within the lead plate, one primary electron will produce two secondary electrons, as outlined in § 18.35. Each of these secondaries can then behave in a similar manner, so that there is a very rapid multiplication of the number of particles; by the time these emerge from the first plate, there may be many hundreds or even thousands of electrons, positrons and photons which form the shower. In the next plate, the less energetic particles are absorbed, but there may be sufficient of high energy to cause further multiplication in the manner described above. A succession of events of this type will produce a cascade shower (Fig. 18.3). Since photons act as intermediates in the propagation of cascade showers, it is evident that photons of high energy, produced in other ways, can themselves initiate showers, as they undoubtedly do.

18.40. It should be clearly understood that, in the cascade process, although the number of particles increases, at least in the early stages, the total energy cannot increase. In fact, the energy of the initiating particle is gradually distributed among those formed in successive stages of the cascade. In addition some energy is transferred, by the Compton effect (§ 3.36), to orbital electrons of the lead absorber, and these make only a minor contribution to the shower. Hence, after passing through several plates, the number depending on the original energy, the energy of the individual positive and negative electrons and photons has fallen to such an extent that they are completely absorbed by the lead. From the total number of tracks produced in a cascade shower the energy of the initial particle can be estimated; for a large shower this may be as high as a thousand billion electron volts, i.e., 10^3 Bev or 10^{12} ev, or more.

18.41. Important results have accrued from the investigation of cosmic rays by means of Geiger-Müller tubes arranged in a coincidence circuit. Sup-

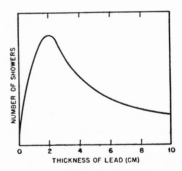

Fig. 18.4. Number of cosmic-ray showers observed under lead plates of various thicknesses (Rossi curve).

pose three such tubes, for example, are placed in one plane below a lead plate; a count will be recorded only if particles pass simultaneously through the three tubes. This is likely to occur only if a shower has been initiated in the plate. If the thickness of the lead plate is increased and the number of coincidences, representing the number of showers, in a given time is recorded for each thickness, there is obtained a characteristic curve known as *Rossi curve,* named for B. Rossi who first plotted such a curve in 1932. The number of showers always increases at first with increasing thickness of the lead, until a maximum is reached at a thickness of about 2 cm.; the shower frequency then commences to diminish until a thickness of 10 cm. of lead is attained, after which the decrease is extremely gradual (Fig. 18.4).

18.42. The characteristic shape of the Rossi curve has been interpreted as follows. The initial increase in shower formation with the thickness of the lead plate is due to the multiplication process, analogous to that for the first two or three plates in a cascade shower observed in a cloud chamber. When the thickness of the lead exceeds about 2 cm., the loss of energy, accompanied by absorption of the secondary particles, tends to reduce the number of particles which can pass through the plate and excite the coincidence circuit. Thus the number of counts decreases until a thickness of 10 cm. of lead is attained. As seen above, this amount of lead will remove the soft component of the cosmic radiation, and hence the showers observed for greater thicknesses must be caused by highly penetrating particles. The view generally accepted is that mesons, which can penetrate considerable thicknesses of absorber, give rise to energetic electrons in one way or another (§ 18.34). Any of these electrons, with sufficient energy, formed in the lower portion of the lead, can produce showers which will be detected by the G-M coincidence counter. Since the mesons are only slightly absorbed in the lead, the number of showers decreases slowly, as seen in Fig. 18.4.

AIR SHOWERS

18.43. In the work described above, cosmic-ray showers were produced deliberately, and in a limited space, by the use of plates of a heavy element which provided the required conditions for slowing down electrons, followed by the formation of electron-positron pairs from the resulting photons. The same processes undoubtedly occur in the atmosphere in nature, except that the smaller density of the medium, through which the cosmic-ray particles pass, results in a considerable spread of the distance in which a cascade shower occurs.

18.44. In studying these atmospheric showers, P. Auger arranged a number of G-M counters for the detection of coincidences; with the counters a few centimeters or decimeters apart, about one shower per minute could be detected, on the average, near sea level. As the distance between the counters was increased, Auger and his associates found in 1938 that the number of coincidences decreased sharply, but did not drop to zero. Even for large distances, an approximately constant rate of five or six coincidences per hour was observed. This result suggested that, in addition to the small or local showers, occurring about once each minute, there were other showers covering a much larger area. The latter are known as *extensive air-showers,* or as *Auger showers.*

18.45. Encouraged by the discovery of these extensive atmospheric cosmic-ray showers, Auger carried out further experiments at high altitudes and was able to record coincidences at the rate of one per hour even when the counters were about 1000 feet apart. Still more extensive showers have been reported as the result of experiments made by American scientists at an altitude of about two miles above sea level, at Echo Lake, Colorado. By using 200 G-M tubes in a coincidence circuit, gigantic showers, approximately a mile across, were found to occur about once a week. The tremendous spread of these extensive air-showers, which are presumably formed in a manner similar to the cascade showers described above, suggests that they traverse the entire atmosphere.

18.46. It has been estimated that the initiation of an extensive air shower requires a primary particle with an energy of about 10^{16} to 10^{17} ev, i.e., 10^7 to 10^8 Bev, and hence, as stated earlier, particles with such enormous energies must be present in the primary cosmic radiation reaching the atmosphere. It was thought at one time that these particles were electrons, but it is now known that there are very few, if any, electrons in the primary radiation. Neutral pi-mesons of high energy appear to be a more probable source of extensive air showers, the actual showers being initiated by the photons resulting from their decay.

18.47. The more common local cosmic-ray showers, observed at sea level and even below, obviously require much less energy than do the extensive showers. Energies of the order of 10^8 or 10^9 ev are probably sufficient for the purpose. The local showers are originated at lower levels in the atmosphere from secondary electrons produced either by meson decay, or by the knock-on of orbital electrons of atmospheric oxygen or nitrogen. The great majority of electrons and pho-

tons constituting the soft component of cosmic rays near sea level are due to local showers produced in this manner at moderate altitudes.

18.48. Attention may be called here to the similarity between the variation of atmospheric cosmic-ray intensity, mainly that of the soft component, with decreasing altitude, as shown in Fig. 18.2, and the change in intensity of a cascade shower in a cloud chamber (Fig. 18.3). In each case the ionization increases toward a maximum, due to the multiplication effect, and then decreases, as a result of absorption. The parallelism between the two cases is not exact, as many showers are initiated at different levels in the atmosphere, but it is nevertheless significant.

18.49. There is one other type of cosmic-ray shower to which brief reference may be made. In 1937, L. Fussell of the United States obtained a cloud-chamber photograph showing tracks of a group of particles penetrating several lead plates without deviation or multiplication. Since that time, much evidence has accumulated for the occurrence in the atmosphere of groups of two or more highly penetrating particles; these groups are referred to as *penetrating showers.* Two kinds of penetrating showers, namely, local and extensive, are distinguished, according to the area they cover. The local penetrating showers are believed to consist mainly of mesons produced in the vicinity of the detecting apparatus by collision of an energetic nucleon, either a neutron or a proton, with an atomic nucleus (§ 18.52). The phenomena associated with the extensive penetrating showers are complex and it appears that these showers may originate in two or more different ways. The main components are mesons and nucleons (neutrons or protons), probably produced in a nuclear reaction involving a particle of very high energy.

OTHER COSMIC-RAY PHENOMENA

18.50. Associated with atmospheric showers is the phenomenon of cosmic-ray *bursts*, first observed by G. Hoffmann in Germany in 1927. A burst is a large instantaneous increase of the electrometer current in an ionization chamber accompanying the passage of cosmic rays. The total energy released when a large burst is recorded is of the order of 10^2 to 10^3 Bev, i.e., 10^{11} to 10^{12} ev. Several different effects may be responsible for bursts. The formation of a large shower either in the atmosphere above the chamber, or within its walls or shielding, for example, will result in a sudden ionization current which would be recorded as a burst. There appears to be some evidence that ionization bursts are frequently found to be associated with penetrating showers.

18.51. During 1936, and even before, several investigators of cosmic rays reported cloud-chamber photographs showing several tracks meeting at a point, somewhat like a star in shape. In the following year similar *cosmic-ray stars* were detected in photographic emulsions, by (Frl.) M. Blau and H. Wambacher in Austria, and this technique has proved very convenient for the study of the phenomenon. There is no doubt that stars are due to nuclear disintegrations or explosions in which several strongly ionizing particles are emitted. The nuclei which produce stars in an emulsion are probably those of silver or of bromine, since a large amount of silver

bromide is present. However, the fact that stars have also been observed in cloud chambers shows that they also occur in the air, the disintegrating nuclei being those of atmospheric oxygen or nitrogen.

18.52. There is evidence that the particles ejected in the star-forming process may be mesons, protons, alpha particles and even heavier nuclei. In addition, it is probable that nonionizing neutrons are produced in these nuclear disintegrations; in fact, this appears to be an important source of the neutrons present in cosmic rays. The number of prongs to a star, indicating the number of ionizing particles produced in disintegrations, presumably due to the capture of negative pi-mesons, generally varies from 2 to 10.* The average number is 3 to 4, there being some increase with altitude, presumably because of the higher energy of the particle causing the disintegration. The frequency of the occurrence of stars increases markedly with the altitude; a fifty-fold increase has been reported in going from sea level to an elevation of 15,000 feet.

18.53. Although many stars are produced by the nuclear capture of negative pi-mesons, they can also result from other nuclear interactions. In support of this view is the fact that the frequency of star formation increases with altitude more rapidly than does the pi-meson density. Some stars are initiated by protons, but many are evidently caused by neutral particles, which may be either neutrons or photons of high energy. The general consensus at the present time is that fast neutrons are responsible for a good portion of cosmic-ray stars.

18.54. One of the interesting effects

* As many as 50 prongs have been observed in stars resulting from the interaction of a relatively heavy cosmic-ray nucleus with either silver or bromine present in a photographic emulsion.

associated with stars is the formation of what are called *hammer tracks*, in which a prong, representing an ejected particle has a "head," resembling that of a hammer. These were described by C. Franzinetti and R. M. Payne in England in 1948. These hammer tracks are attributed to the expulsion of a Li^8 nucleus, which is radioactive, undergoing beta decay, with a half life of less than one second, to form Be^8; this nucleus is extremely unstable and so it splits instantaneously into two alpha particles. The latter are expelled in opposite directions, at right angles to the track of the Li^8 particle, thus producing a hammerlike track.

18.55. In concluding this discussion of cosmic-ray phenomena, mention may be made of the important discovery during 1948, by P. Freier, E. J. Lofgren, E. P. Ney, F. F. Oppenheimer, H. L. Bradt and B. Peters, in the United States, of very heavy tracks in cloud chambers and in photographic emulsions. These tracks were produced in free balloon flights at altitudes up to 94,000 feet and were undoubtedly due to relatively heavy particles with atomic numbers (nuclear charges) ranging from 11 to 41. Tracks due to helium, lithium, carbon, nitrogen and oxygen nuclei, as well as to other elements with atomic numbers up to 49, have been detected subsequently. It is improbable that such nuclei are due to secondary causes, and so they must be primary cosmic-ray particles.

The Nature of Cosmic Rays

18.56. Because of the great complexity of the effects associated with cosmic rays, a satisfactory interpretation of their behavior is a matter of some difficulty. The views which will be expressed here must be regarded only as an outline, providing a working hypothesis that seems to account for the more obvious facts.

18.57. At one time it was thought that cosmic rays consisted of photons of high-energy radiation, of shorter wave length, and hence carrying more energy, than gamma rays. This theory accounted for the remarkable penetrating power of cosmic rays, but the discovery of the latitude and east-west effects indicated that the primary particles were electrically charged. The possibility was considered that they might be positrons but, as stated earlier, it is now generally accepted that they are very largely protons of high energy. It appears from observations, such as those described in § 18.55, that about 78 per cent of the primary particles in cosmic rays are protons (hydrogen nuclei), almost 20 per cent are helium nuclei (alpha particles), and the remainder, some 2.5 per cent, are nuclei of heavier elements. These proportions are quite similar to those in which the elements occur in the various parts of the universe, e.g., in the sun, in the outer portions of many stars, and in interstellar gas and dust clouds. If there are any electrons in the primary cosmic radiation, they constitute probably less than 0.2 per cent of the total number of particles reaching the top of the atmosphere.

18.58. Turning now to the major component of cosmic rays, the protons, it appears that many of them interact with oxygen and nitrogen nuclei at the top of the atmosphere producing nuclear disintegrations of various kinds. It is probable that in most of these processes several pi-mesons, positive, negative and neutral, are produced. If heavier (K) mesons are liberated in the interaction of protons with other nuclei, they will break up in a very short time to produce pi-mesons in most instances (§ 18.90). The experimental evidence indicates that the majority of mesons are created at altitudes above 16,000 meters or 53,000 feet. Some are undoubtedly also formed at lower levels, down to 5,000 meters or 16,500 feet above sea level, in nuclear reactions induced mainly by nonionizing particles, either neutrons or photons of high energy, and to a lesser extent by protons and mesons. These nuclear disintegrations, in many of which pi-mesons are evidently expelled, are manifested as stars in a cloud chamber. Neutrons are themselves probably emitted in such star-forming disintegrations, although others may result from (p,n) processes between the primary protons and nitrogen and oxygen nuclei.

18.59. At this point it may be considered if mesons could not be the primary cosmic-ray particles, since they satisfy the conditions of being electrically charged and highly penetrating. There is no doubt, however, that this could not be the case. The average life of a pi-meson is about 10^{-8} sec., and that of a mu-meson about 10^{-6} sec., near sea level. At higher altitudes, when traveling more rapidly, the effect of relativity would be to extend somewhat the mean life, but in any event, it is doubtful if a meson can traverse a distance greater than about 30,000 meters or 100,000 feet before decaying completely. It is inconceivable, therefore, that mesons formed in outer space, where the cosmic radiation originates, would ever reach the earth's atmosphere. Hence, it must be concluded that mesons in cosmic rays are secondary in nature. Incidentally, a similar argument applies to neutrons. The fact that in the free state these particles undergo

spontaneous decay (§ 11.8) means that neutrons present in cosmic rays are also secondary products.

18.60. In their descent through the atmosphere, nearly all the positive pi-mesons undergo pi-mu decay, thus producing the positive mu-mesons found at lower altitudes. Of the negative pi-mesons, however, some decay into mu-mesons, but the majority are captured by atomic nuclei resulting in star-producing disintegrations of the latter. These disintegrations, like those initiated by protons, neutrons or photons, are accompanied by the expulsion of pi-mesons, protons and neutrons, and possibly also by heavier particles, such as the Li^8 believed to be responsible for the so-called hammer tracks (§ 18.54).

18.61. In the course of their downward flight, the mu-mesons, both positive and negative, collide with orbital electrons and accelerate them by the knock-on process. In addition, at the end of an average period of about 2×10^{-6} sec. following their formation, the mu-mesons decay and liberate energetic electrons and positrons. Electron-positron pairs of very high energy are also produced by the photons resulting from the decay of neutral pi-mesons. These electrons, especially the latter, initiate air-showers, and the electrons and photons of these showers constitute the major part of the soft component of cosmic rays. Very few mesons are found in the lower regions of the atmosphere because they disappear by decay, but are not replaced by nuclear disintegrations, as at very high altitudes, since particles of sufficient energy are not available. However, a small number of highly energetic mesons do reach sea level, and even penetrate to considerable depths under the

earth's surface. These are essentially the hard component of cosmic rays.

18.62. In view of the fact that hydrogen is by far the most common element in the universe, it is not difficult to believe that protons are the chief primary particles of cosmic radiation, even though their origin is somewhat of a mystery. In any event, it is still necessary to explain how they acquire such high energies, sometimes up to 10^{17} ev, before they reach the earth's atmosphere. The sun undoubtedly plays some part in connection with cosmic-ray phenomena, but it is generally accepted that its role is of a secondary nature. It has been suggested that the energy is derived from the fusion of protons to form heavier elements or, alternatively, from the annihilation of matter, but neither of these hypotheses is satisfactory. Several other proposals, which seem to be more adequate, have been made in which it is postulated that the cosmic-ray particles are accelerated by magnetic or electric fields in space.

18.63. One of these theories, developed in the United States by E. Fermi in 1949, appears to have some merit, although its author realized that it is incomplete. In 1943, the Swedish scientist H. Alfvén put forward the idea that magnetic fields of enormous size wander about between the stars in the galaxy, known as the Milky Way, of which the earth is a part. Fermi has suggested that the cosmic-ray protons obtain their energy by repeated interactions with these magnetic fields; in other words, the energy is not acquired in one step, but in a large number of stages. In this way considerable energies could be built up, although not all the particles would necessarily have the same energy, since some would escape sooner than others from the containing magnetic fields.

18.64. In order that particles may acquire energy from the galactic magnetic fields, they must be injected, as nuclei, with a certain minimum energy. For nuclei of low atomic number, such as hydrogen and helium, these minimum energies are not unreasonable in magnitude, e.g., 0.2 to 1 Bev, but for heavier nuclei, which are undoubtedly present as primary particles in cosmic rays, the required injection energy would be several hundred billion electron volts. It has been suggested that the initial particles are produced by certain stars which are known to have strong magnetic fields, and (alternatively) from the exploding stars known as supernovae. Nevertheless, the high energies required for injection of the heavier nuclei, so that they may be further accelerated in the wandering galactic magnetic fields, represent a basic difficulty.

18.65. It may be wondered what happens to the energy of the cosmic-ray particles falling upon the earth: all of this energy is ultimately degraded to heat. As seen above, the large amounts of energy carried by the primary particles are subdivided among the secondary particles; these are eventually absorbed by matter, so that the energy is transferred mainly to the molecules of oxygen and nitrogen in the atmosphere. In these it appears as kinetic energy of motion or, in other words, as heat. The total amount of heat produced in this manner can be calculated by utilizing the fact that, at geomagnetic latitudes greater than 50°, about twenty cosmic-ray particles, on the average, fall on each square centimeter at the top

of the earth's atmosphere per minute.* At this rate, making allowance for the decrease of intensity toward the equator, it is estimated that a total of about 10^{20} particles fall on the whole of the earth per minute.† If the average energy per particle is 10^{10} ev, the total energy is approximately 10^{30} ev per minute, which corresponds to power production at the rate of less than 10^6 kilowatts. This is a very minute fraction of the energy derived from the sun, and is, in fact, about the same as reaches the earth from starlight! Hence, in spite of the enormous energies carried by individual cosmic-ray particles, the total energy is of little significance.

STRANGE PARTICLES

HISTORICAL INTRODUCTION: LIGHT MESONS

18.66. A brief review of the subject of mesons was given in Chapter II. It would seem appropriate, however, to present a more detailed discussion here, since many of the original discoveries in this remarkable area of nuclear physics were made in connection with cosmic-ray studies. With the development of machines for the acceleration of particles to high energies, approaching those in cosmic rays, it has been possible to duplicate many of the phenomena in the laboratory. As a result, some light has been thrown on the manner in which mesons and other particles arise in nature. After a historical introduction, showing how these new and strange particles were discovered, their fundamental physical properties, which are independent of the mode of origin of the particles, will be described.

18.67. Before the existence of the meson was established in 1937, scientists experienced difficulty in accounting for the nature of the hard component of cosmic rays. The possibilities that the particles might be protons, photons or electrons were considered, but these views were found to meet with many difficulties and had to be abandoned. The discovery of the meson provided the solution to the problem, for it had the properties necessary to account for the observed facts.

18.68. In the summer of 1935, C. D. Anderson and S. H. Neddermeyer made some cloud-chamber exposures on Pike's Peak in Colorado, and upon examining the photographs, during the following year, they observed a few tracks which could not be attributed to either protons or electrons. An example of such a track is shown in Fig. 18.5; it is the short, heavy track

FIG. 18.5. Cosmic-ray tracks in cloud chamber which led to discovery of the meson by Anderson and Neddermeyer. (From *Phys. Rev.*, **50**, 270 (1936))

---

* At the earth's surface (sea level) the average number of cosmic-ray particles of all kinds is about one per sq. cm. per min. at latitudes greater than 50°.
† Since 1 gram of hydrogen contains 6.0×10^{23} individual atoms, the total rest mass of the primary cosmic-ray particles falling on the earth per minute, assuming them to be protons, is less than a one-thousandth part of a gram!

with a slight curvature, pointing upward, originating in the lead plate across the cloud chamber.* The curvature of this track indicated that the particle had a positive charge; but Anderson and Neddermeyer concluded that it must be lighter than a proton, although considerably heavier than an electron. Almost simultaneously, and independently, J. C. Street and E. C. Stevenson obtained a cloud-chamber photograph of a cosmic-ray particle which had passed through an 11 cm. block of lead, and which was near the end of its path. From the specific ionization, and the length and curvature of the path, the track was found to be that of a negative particle, with a mass estimated to be about 130 m_e, where m_e represents the mass of an electron.

18.69. During 1937 and 1938, confirmation was obtained from various sources of the existence in cosmic rays of particles lighter than a proton but about 200 times as heavy as an electron; such particles were found to carry either a positive or a negative charge. Anderson and Neddermeyer proposed to call them *mesotrons*, from the Greek *meso*, meaning intermediate, since their mass lies between that of a proton and that of an electron. However, the abbreviated form *meson*, suggested by the Indian physicist, H. J. Bhabha, has now been universally adopted.†

18.70. As stated in § 2.125, there appeared to be good reasons for believing that the meson described above did not have the properties of the particle postulated by H. Yukawa (§ 12.22) to account for nuclear forces. It was calculated that the mass of the latter should be greater than 200 m_e, but before 1947 there was no evidence of the existence of more than one type of intermediate particle. In that year, however, C. F. Powell and G. P. S. Occhialini, and their collaborators in England, showed that the two kinds of mesons, with different masses, exist. Upon developing photographic plates with emulsions of a special type suitable for recording cosmic-ray and nuclear phenomena, after exposure for some time at high altitudes in the Bolivian Andes, tracks were obtained which indicated the presence of a meson, with a mass approximately 300 m_e and consequently heavier than the previously known meson. Further, the interesting point was noted that toward the end of its path in the emulsion, when the heavier meson had slowed down, it changed spontaneously into the lighter meson, with a mass about 200 m_e. In order to distinguish the two mesons, the heavier one is called the *pi* (π) *meson*,‡ and the lighter is known as the *mu* (μ) *meson*, and the change from pi-meson to mu-meson is referred to as pi-mu decay. Mesons of each type were found to exist with either a positive or a negative charge.

18.71. Speculations concerning the origin of the mesons in cosmic rays suggested that they were formed by a primary proton of high energy in-

* A cloud-track photograph, produced by cosmic rays, published by P. Kunze in Germany in 1933, is reported to contain a track due to a meson, but its significance was not realized at the time.

† The Cosmic Ray Commission of the International Union of Physics approved the term "meson," at its meeting in October, 1947. Other names which had been proposed earlier for the particle are "heavy electron," "barytron" (from the Greek *barys*, heavy), and "yukon," after Yukawa, who had predicted the existence of such a particle (§ 12.22).

‡ The symbol π was used by C. M. G. Lattes, G. P. S. Occhialini and C. F. Powell because it is the Greek equivalent of p, for primary, since the pi-mesons are evidently primary mesons.

teracting with another proton, either in the free state or, more probably, one bound in an atomic nucleus. If this were the case, then it should perhaps be possible to produce mesons artificially in the laboratory by the use of particles accelerated by means of a cyclotron, or in a similar manner (Chapter IX). According to equation (3.16), the energy, in Mev, equivalent to a mass in grams, is obtained upon multiplying the latter by the factor

in 1948 by E. Gardner and the Brazilian physicist C. M. G. Lattes. They allowed a beam of 380-Mev alpha particles from the Berkeley synchro-cyclotron (§ 9.66) to impinge on the edge of a target, the nature of which was not critical; actually, carbon was used for most of the studies, but similar results were obtained with targets of beryllium, copper and uranium. A stack of photographic plates, suitably protected from extraneous radiations,

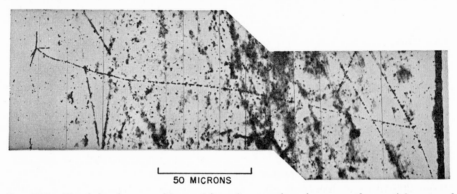

50 MICRONS

Fig. 18.6.   Track in photographic emulsion of a negative pi-meson; the particle entered at the right and was captured by a nucleus, forming a star, at the left. This is the first instance of the artificial production of mesons. (University of California Radiation Laboratory.)

5.6×10^{26}. The mass of an electron is 9.1×10^{-28} gram (§ 2.56), and the mass of the pi-meson is approximately 300 times this amount. Consequently, the energy which must be available for the creation of a pi-meson is $300 \times 9.1 \times 10^{-28} \times 5.6 \times 10^{26} = 150$ Mev. This energy is a minimum and does not allow for the fact that some energy (or momentum) is carried off by various nucleons which may be present (§ 9.105). It seemed, therefore, that if particles of about 300-Mev energy were allowed to interact with atomic nuclei, mesons should be produced.

18.72. The first report of the identification of artificially produced mesons was made in the United States early

was placed in the region where the mesons were expected to arrive, and upon development a number of tracks, definitely due to pi-mesons, were observed. The first mesons to be detected in this manner were negatively charged, because of the particular experimental arrangement used (Fig. 18.6). Later, the position of the target was changed so as to permit the detection of positive mesons which were deflected by the magnetic field in a direction opposite to that of the negative mesons mentioned above. In addition to pi-mesons, positive mu-mesons were observed, and also a few negative mu-mesons. Perhaps because of the short distances involved, no pi-mu decay was noted in flight. It appears that the mu-mesons detected resulted from the decay of pi-mesons which remained in the target.

18.73. The mesons in cosmic rays do not, of course, originate from alpha particles, and these are not essential to the artificial production of pi-mesons. During 1949 such mesons were detected, using either protons or deuterons accelerated by the synchrocyclotron, or recoil neutrons produced by 345-Mev protons. These pi-mesons presumably resulted from nucleon-nucleon interactions. In addition, it was reported by E. M. Mc-Millan and J. M. Peterson that pi-mesons can be produced by the action of energetic photons, i.e., radiation of high energy, with atomic nuclei. It is of interest to record that this was the first discovery to be made with the aid of the Berkeley Radiation Laboratory electron synchrotron, described in § 9.88. The accelerated (335-Mev) electrons were allowed to fall on an anticathode, thus yielding the high-energy X-rays which produced the mesons in their passage through a stack of photographic plates or through a slab of matter in the vicinity of these plates. The great majority of the mesons formed were negative pi-mesons and a few cases of pi-mu decay were observed.

18.74. Although the existence of a neutral meson had been postulated by Yukawa in 1935 and its properties had been predicted by others, on theoretical grounds, the first definite evidence for the existence of such a particle was obtained in 1950 by R. Bjorklund, W. E. Crandall, B. J. Moyer and H. F. York at the University of California Radiation Laboratory. When targets of carbon, beryllium and other elements were struck by protons with energy exceeding 175 Mev, gamma-ray photons were produced with characteristics best explained by assuming that they were formed by the spontaneous decay of a neutral pi-meson into two photons. Shortly thereafter, J. Steinberger, W. K. H. Panofsky and J. S. Steller obtained conclusive evidence for the existence of neutral pi-mesons, in the bombardment of a beryllium (or other) target by high-energy protons. These scientists used scintillation counters, appropriately located with respect to the target, to detect coincidences between pairs of gamma-ray photons produced simultaneously by the decay of neutral pi-mesons. The observed minimum energy per photon (about 70 Mev) was in agreement with that expected from the disappearance of a particle with a mass of roughly 280 m_e, that is, a pi-meson. These experiments proved that positive, negative and neutral pi-mesons are produced simultaneously in high-energy nucleon interactions.

HISTORICAL INTRODUCTION: HEAVY MESONS AND HYPERONS

18.75. In 1944, L. Leprince-Ringuet and M. L' heretier in France obtained a single cloud-chamber photograph suggesting the existence, in cosmic rays, of a particle of mass about 1000 m_e. Some three years later, G. D. Rochester and C. C. Butler, of the University of Manchester (England) cosmic-ray group, observed a branched (or V-shaped) track in a Wilson cloud chamber. One branch was shown to be consistent with a charged particle of roughly 1000 m_e, whereas the other was probably due to a pi-meson which was one of the decay products of the heavier particle. What was being observed was the decay in flight of the 1000 m_e particle into a pi-meson and at least one other (neutral) particle, probably also a pi-meson, which left no track in the cloud chamber. Because of the shape of the visible tracks, the heavy particle was originally called a charged V-particle, but this name is no longer used, since V-shaped tracks are produced by particles of different types, as will shortly be apparent. At the present time, the practice is to speak of these phenomena as V-events, rather than V-particles.

18.76. In addition to the charged V-event described above, Rochester and Butler also noted a V-shaped track representing the decay in flight of a neutral particle, with a mass estimated to lie between 700 and 1200 m_e, into two oppositely charged mesons. The original particle, being neutral, produced no visible track and the two branches of the V-shaped track were due to the mesons formed by its decay. There was thus evidence for the existence of both neutral and charged particles; the former was represented by the symbol V_2^0 (to distinguish it from another neutral V-particle called V_1^0) and the latter by $V^\pm$, but these representations are no longer used.

18.77. Since 1949, evidence has been obtained from tracks in cloud chambers and photographic emulsions of the existence of several different types of mesons, all of which have a mass of about 1000 m_e but which decay in different ways. These are now called K-particles (or K-mesons), although some have specific symbols, as will be indicated below. Prior to 1953, all the information concerning K-mesons was obtained from cosmic-ray studies, but in that year the Brookhaven Cosmotron (and later the Berkeley Bevatron) commenced production of these mesons in quantity. One method used

is to bombard copper (or other heavy element) with protons of 2-Bev (or more) energy; alternatively, a beam of 1.5-Bev (at least) negative pi-mesons, produced by the interaction of high-energy protons with matter (§ 18.73), is allowed to impinge on a stack of photographic emulsions, just as if the latter were exposed to cosmic rays. Although K-mesons are less abundant than pi- or mu-mesons, all the types observed in nature, i.e., in cosmic rays, can now be readily obtained artificially and studied in the laboratory.

18.78. When Rochester and Butler reported the two V-events referred to above, they also described a third such cloud-chamber event: a neutral particle, called V_1^0, with a mass of approximately 2000 m_e, decayed into two charged particles, one of which was apparently a proton and the other a negative pi-meson. This was the first evidence for the existence of a new kind of particle, now referred to as a *hyperon*,[*] with a mass greater than that of a neutron (or proton). In addition to the neutral hyperon, charged hyperons of somewhat higher mass have been detected. One of these is called a *cascade particle;* it is a negatively charged hyperon which decays into a lighter neutral hyperon and a negative pi-meson. Within a very short time, the neutral hyperon decays, mainly into a proton and another pi-meson. Subsequently, the pi-mesons, if not captured, decay into mu-mesons, which finally yield electrons (and neutrinos), as explained below. It was on account of this succession of decay stages that the term cascade was used to describe the particle.

18.79. The latest type of strange particles to be discovered are called *hyperfragments*, the existence of which was inferred by the Polish scientists

* From the Greek prefix *hyper-*, meaning over or above.

M. Danysz and J. Pniewski in 1953 from the tracks in photographic emulsions exposed to cosmic rays at an altitude of 85,000 feet. Similar tracks have since been produced in the laboratory, by bombardment with negative pi-mesons of high energy. They are due to nuclei, most commonly of light elements, such as hydrogen, helium, lithium, beryllium, carbon, etc., in which a neutron has been replaced by a neutral hyperon.

18.80. Because of the somewhat haphazard manner in which the various mesons and hyperons were originally named, the International Congress on Cosmic Radiation, at its meeting in France in 1953, suggested a system of nomenclature which will be adopted here.* Excluding hyperfragments, which are really nuclei of a special kind, three mass categories are recognized, indicated by the letters *L, K* and *Y* respectively; thus,

L (light mesons): mass between electron and pi-meson (1 to 283 m_e)

K (heavy mesons): mass between pi-meson and proton (283 to 1836 m_e)

Y (hyperons): mass between proton and deuteron (1836 to 3670 m_e).

A specific particle, falling within one or other of these groups, may be represented by a Greek letter—a lower case letter for *L*-mesons, e.g., π and μ, and *K*-mesons, e.g., τ, θ, κ, and a capital for hyperons, e.g., Λ, Σ and Ξ. Ordinary capital letters, such as V (indi-cating a V-shaped track) and S (for a particle stopped in a plate across a cloud chamber), are used to describe events, e.g., V-event and S-event, respectively. Some of the particles which have been formerly described as V-particles and S-particles are actually *K*-mesons.

EXPERIMENTAL METHODS

18.81. Three general techniques are used for determining the masses and observing the general behavior of particles either present in cosmic rays or produced in the laboratory; these involve (1) the Wilson cloud chamber in a magnetic field; (2) the cloud chamber with several parallel metal plates across it; and (3) stacks of photographic emulsion, preferably in the form of pellicles (§ 6.88). For laboratory work, the bubble chamber, with liquid hydrogen or pentane (§ 6.81), has been much used in recent years, since it combines the attributes of the cloud chamber with some of the photographic emulsion. Cloud and bubble chambers are best adapted to the study of decay of a particle in flight, whereas the multiplate cloud chamber and photographic emulsions provide information on the behavior of the particle when brought virtually to rest.

18.82. A cloud (or bubble) chamber in a magnetic field can be used to determine the mass of the particle, provided its velocity is less than about 80 per cent of the velocity of light. From the number of droplets (or bub-

---

* Another system of nomenclature, which has a more theoretical basis, classes electrons, mu-particles and neutrinos together as *leptons*, from the Greek prefix *lept-*, meaning small or weak; pi- and *K*-particles are called *mesons;* and neutrons, protons and hyperons are referred to as *baryons*, from the Greek *barys*, meaning heavy. The leptons and baryons all have a spin of ½ and are, consequently, in the category of *fermions*, obeying Fermi-Dirac statistics. Mesons, on the other hand, have spins of 0 or 1, and so are *bosons*, which follow the Bose-Einstein statistics. Leptons are formed in what are called "weak interactions," occurring relatively slowly and involving moderate energies (§18.98). Mesons are produced only in "strong interactions" which involve large amounts of energy and take place very rapidly.

bles) per unit track length the velocity of the ionizing particle can be estimated. By combining this result with the momentum derived from the curvature of the track in a magnetic field, the mass of the particle can be calculated. From the tracks in photographic emulsions, the particle mass is most conveniently estimated from such information as the number of visible grains per unit track length, the range of the particle and the deviation in the trajectory due to small-angle Coulomb scattering (§ 6.90).

18.83. An important and characteristic property of the unstable particles under consideration is their *average life*, often referred to as the *lifetime*. This is defined in very much the same way as the average life of a radioactive nuclide (§ 5.39); thus, if N_0 is the number of mesons or other particles present at a certain time, arbitrarily taken as the zero time, and N_t is the number at a time t later, then, as in equation (5.3),

$$N_t = N_0 e^{-\lambda t},$$

where λ is the meson decay constant. The lifetime τ is the reciprocal of the decay constant and so $N_t = N_0 e^{-t/\tau}$, or

$$N_t/N_0 = e^{-t/\tau}. \qquad (18.1)$$

Consequently, if the ratio of the numbers of mesons present at two different times can be measured, the lifetime τ can be readily calculated. Because meson speeds, especially in cosmic rays, are sometimes very high, the effect of relativity in expanding the time dimension, by the factor $\sqrt{1 - v^2/c^2}$, as given in § 3.69, will be significant. The lifetimes (and masses) of mesons and hyperons are usually recorded for low velocities, generally referred to as the "rest" values. When

the velocity approaches that of light, however, both the lifetime and the mass are larger than the respective rest values.

18.84. Although the determination of the lifetime of an unstable particle, based on equation (18.1), is simple in principle, the experimental technique is very complicated for several reasons. In the first place, the longest observed lifetimes are about a millionth (10^{-6}) of a second and may be as small as 10^{-14} sec. Further, the "beams" occurring in nature or obtained in the laboratory invariably contain many different particles, and it is necessary to make sure that only one kind is being counted. In any case, the number of mesons is usually small, so that statistical errors in counting are relatively large. Finally, measurements must be made on particles of low velocity, i.e., "stopped" particles, in order to avoid the relativity effect. A correction for the latter could be made if the particle velocity were known, but this is an added complication. These difficulties have been largely overcome, so that the longer lifetimes, at least, can be measured with reasonable accuracy. The particles are slowed down by passage through so-called "absorbers," and accurate timing of short intervals is achieved by means of special electronic circuits. For counting the particles after different intervals, various coincidence and anticoincidence circuits are employed to make sure, as far as possible, that unwanted particles are eliminated.

Properties of *L*-Mesons

18.85. The main characteristics of the five known *L*-mesons, namely, positive, negative and neutral pi-mesons (pions) and positive and negative mu-mesons (muons), are given in the accompanying table. In the decay schemes, the symbol ν refers to a neutrino (or antineutrino) and e^+ and e^- represent positive and negative electrons, respectively. Since the neutrinos and electrons have spins of

that interaction occurs with a nuclear proton (p^+), i.e.,

$$\pi^- + p^+ \text{ (in nucleus)} \to n + \text{energy.}$$

As a result of the energy available to the nucleus, one or more neutrons are

CHARACTERISTICS OF *L*-MESONS

Particle Name	Symbol	Mass (m_e)	Lifetime (sec.)	Spin	Decay Scheme
Positive pi-meson	π^+	273.3	2.5×10^{-8}	0	$\mu^+ + \nu$
Negative pi-meson	π^-	272.8	2.5×10^{-8}	0	$\mu^- + \nu$
Neutral pi-meson	π^0	264.3	$\sim 5 \times 10^{-15}$	0	2γ (or $e^+ + e^- + \gamma$)
Positive mu-meson	μ^+	206.7	2.15×10^{-6}	$\frac{1}{2}$	$e^+ + 2\nu$
Negative mu-meson	μ^-	206.7	2.15×10^{-6}	$\frac{1}{2}$	$e^- + 2\nu$

$\frac{1}{2}$, there is conservation of spin in all the indicated decay schemes. Positive pions do not interact with nuclei to any appreciable extent and so they almost invariably decay into a positive muon and a neutrino, with a mean lifetime of 2.5×10^{-8} sec. Slowed-down negative pions, on the other hand, are often trapped in the mesonic orbits of atoms, as explained in § 4.77, *et seq.* Most of the trapped negative pions are captured by the nucleus, in a very short time, and as a result the nucleus is disintegrated, as is evident from star formation, either in a cloud (or bubble) chamber or in a photographic emulsion (Fig. 18.6). These stars usually have one, two or three prongs; occasionally, the number is larger, but stars with six (or more) prongs are relatively rare. The products are mainly alpha particles, protons and neutrons, the latter leaving no tracks. In some (about 25 per cent) instances, capture of the negative pion produces no visible effect, and it is believed

emitted. Since neutrons produce no ionization in the photographic emulsion, they leave no tracks.* Negative pions which survive capture by nuclei, decay in the same way as do positive pions, and with approximately the same lifetime.

18.86. When a negative pion is captured by a free proton, i.e., one not part of a more complex nucleus, two particles must be formed, in order that momentum may be conserved. Two reactions have been identified, namely,

$$\pi^- + p^+ \to n + \gamma$$

and

$$\pi^- + p^+ \to n + \pi^0 \to n + 2\gamma.$$

In the first, the products are a neutron and a gamma-ray photon; in the second, a neutron and a neutral pion are initially formed, but the latter very rapidly decays into two photons. Recalling that the photon has a spin of unity, it will be seen that spin is conserved in each case. It is of interest to note that a deuteron behaves in a

---

* Before the phenomena were well understood, negative pions, forming stars upon capture, were called sigma-mesons, the Greek letter *sigma* being the equivalent of *s*, the initial letter of star. The term rho-mesons (Greek *rho*, equivalent to *r* for rest) was applied to those mesons which came to rest in emulsions without producing any observable event; most negative muons, as well as some negative pions, behave in this manner.

manner intermediate between a free proton, on the one hand, and more complex nuclei, on the other hand. The main reaction with negative pions is

$$\pi^- + d^+ \rightarrow n + n + \text{energy},$$

as with heavier nuclei, but the formation of gamma radiation, i.e.,

$$\pi^- + d^+ \rightarrow n + n + \gamma,$$

also occurs to some extent. There is, however, no evidence that a neutral pi-meson is produced.

18.87. Positive mu-mesons, like positive pions, generally decay without interaction with nuclei; the products are a positron and two neutrinos, and the mean life is 2.15×10^{-6} sec. Although slow negative muons are frequently trapped in appropriate orbits to form mu-mesonic atoms, the probability of nuclear capture is much less than with the corresponding pi-mesonic atoms. As seen earlier, the interaction between muons and atomic nuclei is relatively weak. For nuclei with atomic number less than 12 or so, negative muons generally survive capture; they then decay, like the positive muons, into a negative electron and two neutrinos with a lifetime of 2.15×10^{-6} sec. With nuclei of increasing atomic number, the probability of capturing the negative muon increases, and for atomic numbers of 12 or more, most of the muons are absorbed in the nuclei by which they have become trapped. The final result of the absorption is the conversion of a neutron into a proton, plus a neutrino; thus,

$$\mu^- + p^+ \text{ (in nucleus)} \rightarrow n + \nu.$$

The neutron may be ejected, but the event is not visible in a cloud (or bubble) chamber or in a photographic emulsion. Thus, muons do not produce stars.

18.88. Neutral pions have an extremely short life of not more than 5×10^{-15} sec. The chief mode of decay results in the formation of two gamma-ray photons, but some neutral pions yield a positron-electron pair and one photon. There is no evidence that a neutral muon is an intermediate stage in either case. In fact, theoretical considerations make it seem probable that a neutral muon does not exist.

18.89. Provided sufficient energy is available, it appears that almost any interaction with a nucleon can result in the production of pi-mesons. This is in agreement with the view (§ 12.36, footnote) that the virtual pi-mesons, which are believed to be associated with all nucleons, can be converted into free pi-mesons by means of a projectile having the required amount of energy. In the laboratory, pi-mesons—positive, negative and neutral—have been produced by bombarding various materials with high-energy protons, alpha particles, neutrons or photons. Similarly, the pi-mesons in cosmic rays undoubtedly result from the interaction of the primary protons with protons and neutrons in various nuclei. Pi-mesons are often emitted in nuclear disintegrations, apparent as stars, brought about by particles of high energy. Mu-mesons, on the other hand, are never observed in nucleon reactions, but only as the decay products of other (pi- or K-) mesons.

PROPERTIES OF K-MESONS

18.90. Because of the complex character of the experimental observations made in connection with K-particles, the situation regarding the nature and identity of these particles was at first somewhat confused. However, by bringing newly developed theoretical concepts to bear on the problems, considerable clarification has resulted. It now appears that there are four mesons: one positive (K^+), one negative (K^-) and two neutral (K_1^0 and K_2^0) particles. The charged K-mesons have essentially equal masses (966.5 m_e), but the neutral particles may be somewhat lighter (965 m_e). Each of the charged K-mesons decays in six different ways, the mean lifetime being the same in each case, namely, about 1.2×10^{-8} sec. The neutral K_1^0-meson has a much shorter life, close to 10^{-10} sec., and has apparently only two modes of decay, in each of which only two particles are formed. On the other hand, the K_2^0-meson decays in six ways, producing three lighter particles in each case; its lifetime, which is close to that of the charged mesons, is greater than 10^{-8} sec.

18.91. The characteristics of the K-mesons are summarized in the accompanying table. The decay symbol represents a method sometimes used to specify the decay mode. The Greek or Roman letter in the subscript, i.e., π, μ or e, indicates the charged particle formed and the numeral gives the total number of particles produced in the decay process. The Greek letters in the last column, which also describe particular modes of decay, are a relic of the historical development of the subject of K-mesons. When the discoveries of the new particles were first made and their nature was not apparent, they were identified by the letters τ, κ, θ, etc. It will be noted that all the modes of decay are consistent with the view that K-mesons have zero spin.

18.92. It is probable that, after slowing down, K^--mesons are trapped in orbital levels surrounding atomic nuclei, so that K-mesonic atoms may

Characteristics of K-Mesons

Particle Name	Mass (m_e)	Lifetime (sec.)	Decay Scheme	Decay Symbol	Type
K^+-meson	966.5	1.2×10^{-8}	$\mu^+ + \nu$	$K_{\mu2}^+$	—
			$\pi^+ + \pi^0$	$K_{\pi2}^+$	θ^+ (or χ^+)
			$\pi^+ + \pi^+ + \pi^-$	$K_{\pi3}^+$	τ^+
			$\mu^+ + \pi^0 + \nu$	$K_{\mu3}^+$	κ^+
			$e^+ + \pi^0 + \nu$	K_{e3}^+	—
			$\pi^+ + \pi^0 + \pi^0$	$K'^+_{\pi3}$	$\tau^{+\prime}$
K^--meson	966.5	1.2×10^{-8}	$\mu^- + \nu$	$K_{\mu2}^-$	—
			$\pi^- + \pi^0$	$K_{\pi2}^-$	θ^- (or χ^-)
			$\pi^- + \pi^- + \pi^+$	$K_{\pi3}^-$	τ^-
			$\mu^- + \pi^0 + \nu$	$K_{\mu3}^-$	κ^-
			$e^- + \pi^0 + \nu$	K_{e3}^-	—
			$\pi^- + \pi^0 + \pi^0$	$K'^-_{\pi3}$	$\tau^{-\prime}$
K_1^0-meson	965	$\sim 10^{-10}$	$\pi^+ + \pi^-$		θ^0
			$\pi^0 + \pi^0$		
K_2^0-meson	965	$> 10^{-8}$	$\pi^+ + e^- + \nu$		
			$\pi^- + e^+ + \nu$		
			$\pi^+ + \mu^- + \nu$		
			$\pi^- + \mu^+ + \nu$		
			$\pi^+ + \pi^- + \pi^0$		
			$\pi^0 + \pi^0 + \pi^0$		

CHARACTERISTICS OF HYPERONS

Particle Name	Symbol	Mass (m_e)	Lifetime (sec.)	Decay Scheme
Lambda	Λ^0	2182	3×10^{-10}	$p^+ + \pi^-$ and $n + \pi^0$
Sigma	Σ^+	2327	0.7×10^{-10}	$p^+ + \pi^0$ and $n + \pi^+$
Sigma	Σ^-	2343	1.5×10^{-10}	$n + \pi^-$
Sigma	Σ^0	~ 2325	?	$\Lambda^0 + \gamma$
Xi (Cascade)	Ξ^-	2585	$\sim 2 \times 10^{-10}$	$\pi^- + \Lambda^0\ (\rightarrow p^+ + \pi^-)$

well exist. If this is the case, these mesons will be even closer to the nucleus than are pi-mesons. Capture of K^--mesons apparently results in nuclear disintegrations in which hyperons and hyperfragments are often produced. If captured by a proton, a positive hyperon (Σ^+) is formed together with a negative pi-meson; thus,

$$K^- + p^+ \rightarrow \pi^- + \Sigma^+.$$

Subsequently, both the hyperon and pion undergo further reactions.*

18.93. Since K-mesons are formed by bombardment of nuclei with high-energy protons or negative pions, and are also known to be frequently emitted in nuclear disintegrations (stars), it may be assumed that, like pi-mesons, they are direct products of nucleon-nucleon interactions. It is possible, therefore, that K-mesons may be involved in some way in internuclear forces. From their mass, it can be inferred that the effective range of such forces must be even less than those due to pions (§ 12.29).

PROPERTIES OF HYPERONS

18.94. Five hyperons appear to be definitely established, although more may be discovered as research in the field continues; one of these was the original V_1^0 particle (§ 18.78), now called Λ^0 (Greek, *Lambda*) because this Greek letter looks like an inverted V. Another hyperon is the cascade particle, represented by Ξ (Greek, *Xi*); the three others are Σ^+, Σ^- and Σ^0 (Greek, *Sigma*). The essential characteristics are presented in the table given above. Like the neutron and proton, the hyperons have a spin of ½ unit. According to a theory which has proved highly successful in correlating the known mesons and hyperons and in predicting others, three other Σ particles, representing the anti-particles (§ 2.80) of those given in the table, should exist. In addition, there should be a neutral Ξ particle, as well as two anti-particles, one positive and one neutral.

18.95. Hyperons appear to be formed by the interaction of K^-- or L^--mesons with nucleons. They have been observed in cosmic-ray events and also in the laboratory by exposing a bubble chamber, containing liquid hydrogen (or a compound of hydrogen), to high-energy negative pi-mesons. They are also emitted from

* The hydrogen bubble chamber tracks in Fig. 6.11 show these processes. A K^--meson enters at the top somewhat right of center; it moves downward, slightly to the right, and collides with a proton but does not interact. The proton is scattered to the right and the K^--meson to the left. After traveling a short distance, the scattered K^--meson comes to rest and is captured by a proton forming Σ^+ and π^-. The π^- moves diagonally downward to the left, while the Σ^+ goes a short distance diagonally upward to the right. The latter particle then decays into a neutron, which produces no track, and a π^+ which travels upward to the left, thus giving a V-like event.

stars accompanying the capture of K-mesons. The formation of hyperons differs in one important respect from the production of K- or L-mesons. In the latter instances, sufficient energy must be available to "create" or "materialize" the particle. But such is not the case for hyperon formation; in other words, they are produced from pre-existing nucleons and are not materialized out of energy. This suggests that a hyperon may be regarded as a kind of excited nucleon which subsequently emits a pion (or two pions), just as a conventional excited nucleon emits a photon.

THE "STRANGENESS" NUMBER

18.96. There is strong evidence that

in Japan, there has been developed a new kind of quantum number, called the "strangeness" number, for nucleons, mesons and hyperons.

18.97. The strangeness number is related to a quantity called, somewhat misleadingly, isotopic spin. If I is the isotopic spin of a particle, then $2I + 1$ particles of similar mass, but with different electrical charges, should exist. For example, nucleons have $I = \frac{1}{2}$, so that there are two such particles, namely, protons and neutrons. The isotopic spin components are $+\frac{1}{2}$ (for protons) and $-\frac{1}{2}$ (for neutrons). In the table on page 584 are given examples of common isotopic spins.* The strangeness number is then defined by

Strangeness number
$$= 2 \text{ (Charge } - \text{ Isotopic spin component)} - \text{ Number of nucleons.}$$

the formation of a hyperon is generally, if not always, accompanied by the production of another particle, usually a K-meson, and vice versa; this is referred to as *associated production*. For example, a negative pimeson and a proton give rise to at least two pairs of products; thus,

$$\pi^- + p^+ - \begin{cases} \rightarrow \Sigma^- + K^+ \\ \rightarrow \Lambda^0 + K^0 \end{cases}$$

and possibly also $\Sigma^- + K^0$. The phenomenon of associated production, the realization of which is largely due to A. Pais (1952) in the United States, is believed to imply the operation of some kind of conservation principle, although exactly what is conserved is not altogether clear. As a result of the theoretical studies, made independently in 1953 by M. Gell-Mann in the United States and K. Nishijima

Consider, for example, the Σ^+-particle; the charge is $+1$, the isotopic spin component is $+1$, and its mass ($2327\ m_e$) shows that it contains one nucleon; hence,

Strangeness number of Σ^+
$$= 2\ (1 - 1) - 1 = -1.$$

18.98. Based on the information given above, the strangeness numbers for various particles have been determined and are quoted in the following table. It will be observed that pimesons, like protons and neutrons, have zero strangeness and so are not really "strange" particles. In what are called "strong" interactions, re-

STRANGENESS NUMBERS

Strangeness number	Particle
$+1$	$K^+,\ K^0$
0	$p,\ n,\ \pi^+,\ \pi^-,\ \pi^0$
-1	$\Lambda^0,\ \Sigma^0,\ \Sigma^+,\ \Sigma^-,\ K^-$
-2	$\Xi^-,\ \Xi^0$

* In some cases—viz., Λ^0; p^+, n; K^+, K^0; Ξ^-, Ξ^0; and Σ^+, Σ^0, Σ^-—anti-particles are expected to exist. Some of these are known, while others remain to be discovered.

ISOTOPIC SPIN CHARACTERISTICS

Isotopic Spin (I)	Number of Particles (2I + 1)	Spin Components	Examples
0	1	0	Λ^0
½	2	$+½, -½$	p^+, n K^+, K^0 Ξ^0, Ξ^-
1	3	$+1, 0, -1$	π^+, π^0, π^- $\Sigma^+, \Sigma^0, \Sigma^-$

quiring large amounts of energy and taking place very rapidly, e.g., within 10^{-22} sec. or so, the strangeness number is conserved. This is, for example, the case for the two $\pi^- + p^+$ reactions given above; the net value of the strangeness number is zero for the reacting species and also for the products. Unless there were associated production, it would not have been possible for the strangeness number to be conserved. For "weak" interactions, with lifetimes of the order of 10^{-10} sec. or more, such as K-meson and hyperon decays, the strangeness number is not conserved; the change, in all known cases, is $+1$ or -1.

18.99. The scheme based on the strangeness number has been found to be consistent with experimental observations. It has also proved useful in interpreting cloud (and bubble) chamber and photographic emulsion phenomena due to cosmic rays and to mesons produced in the laboratory. However, it has not yet been possible to assign any obvious physical significance to the strangeness number. It may, in fact, prove to be a manifestation of a fundamental, but yet unknown, property of material particles, including nucleons.

HYPERFRAGMENTS

18.100. Evidence for the existence of hyperfragments has been obtained mainly from a study of stars produced by the interaction of negative mesons or hyperons in photographic emulsions. Among those which have been detected, mention may be made of the following: H^{2*}, H^{3*}, H^{4*}, He^{4*}, He^{5*}, Li^{6*}, Li^{8*}, Be^{7*}, Be^{8*}, Be^{9*} and C^{11*}. The superscript gives the integer nearest to the actual mass, and the asterisk is used, by convention, to represent a hyperfragment. In each case, a hyperon, usually a Λ^0 particle, is bound in (or to) an atomic nucleus. The binding energy is in the million electron volt range, but is less than for a neutron or a proton, so that the hyperfragments are unstable. Their average life is about 10^{-11} or 10^{-12} sec.

18.101. Hyperfragments can decay in two different ways. The first, called *mesonic decay*, involves the emission of a negative pi-meson and sometimes a nucleon in addition; thus, one mode of decay of He^{5*}, among others, is

$$He^{5*} \rightarrow He^4 + p^+ + \pi^-,$$

where p^+ and π^- are equivalent to the loosely bound Λ^0 particle. When the nuclear charge (or atomic number) of the hyperfragment is greater than 2, *nonmesonic decay* occurs preferentially. In this case, the Λ^0 hyperon may be emitted as such together with a nucleon, or a neutron and smaller nuclei may result from a star-like disintegration.

MESONS AND THE PARITY CONCEPT

18.102. One of the most intriguing problems in nuclear theory has arisen in connection with the decay of K-mesons. The fact that each of these particles decays in several (up to six) different ways is interesting, but perhaps not altogether remarkable. The situation may be regarded as being different only in degree from the behavior of certain radioactive nuclei which are known to decay with the same half life in two different ways, e.g., simultaneous emission of alpha and beta particles (§ 5.60) or of positive and negative beta-particles (§ 10.100). However, another factor entered in connection with the decay of K-mesons that appeared to be contrary to certain basic ideas in nuclear physics.

18.103. In order to understand the problem, it is necessary to refer to the wave-mechanical (mathematical) concept called *parity*. Although parity is a fundamental attribute of a particle in wave mechanics, it has no analogy in ordinary mechanics and so it is impossible to express its significance in ordinary physical terms. In wave mechanics, every particle has a characteristic property, known as its *wave function,* which is determined by the position (or coordinates) of the particle in space. The square of the wave function then represents the probability of finding the particle at a specified point.*

18.104. The next step in the development of the parity principle is to make what appears to be a reasonable assumption: namely, that the physical description of the state of a particle (or combination of particles), which depends on the square of the wave function, is independent of whether a right-handed or left-handed set of coordinates (or frame of reference) is used in expressing the wave function. This means that if the coordinates are, in fact, changed from x, y, z to $-x$, $-y$, $-z$, by going from what might be described as right-handed to left-handed coordinates, by a series of reflections, the wave function will either remain the same or it will merely change its sign. In each case, the square of the wave function will be unaffected, as postulated above, since x^2 is the same as $(-x)^2$, and so on.

18.105. In the event that the wave function remains unchanged as a result of the reflection of the coordinates, the particle (or system of particles) is said to have *even* parity, but if it changes sign, the parity is *odd.* It is then a requirement of wave mechanics that in any isolated (or closed) system, i.e., one which no particles enter or leave, parity must be conserved. That is to say, there must be no change in parity when there is a rearrangement (or reaction) among the particles in such a system. If the initial state has even parity, then so also must the final state; alternatively, if the parity of the initial state is odd, the final state must also have odd parity.

18.106. Until the discovery of the K-mesons, in the early 1950s, all the evidence available from nuclear reactions indicated that parity was indeed conserved. The law of conservation of parity was consequently accepted as a basic and inviolable principle. However, a comparison of the decay of tau (τ)-mesons, which break up into three pions, and of

---

* This is strictly true only if the wave function does not contain any imaginary terms; however, the general arguments are unaffected even if it does.

theta (θ)-mesons, which form two pions, as may be seen from the table in § 18.91, showed that parity could not be conserved in both cases. The parity of the pi-meson is odd, and so the over-all parity of three mesons, which may be regarded as the product of the individual parities, is also odd. This means that the tau-meson should have odd parity. On the other hand, the theta-meson should have even parity, since its decay results in the formation of two pions, each having odd parity. From their masses and lifetimes, the tau and theta-mesons are identical, and so it would appear impossible that one should have odd parity and the other even parity.

18.107. A way out of this dilemma was proposed toward the end of 1956 by T. D. Lee and C. N. Yang in the United States. It was suggested that the conservation of parity applied only to strong (extremely rapid) interactions, but not necessarily to weak (relatively slow) interactions. Failure of the parity principle would mean the basic postulate, that the description of a particle is the same irrespective of whether a right- or left-handed frame of reference is used, is not always valid. In order to test this possibility, Lee and Yang proposed, among others, the experiment on cobalt-60, with the nuclear spin axes aligned in a magnetic field, described in §7.70. The result, namely, that the beta particles were emitted mainly in one particular direction, supported the view that there was indeed a distinction between left- and right-handedness in the decay process. If the parity principle had applied, beta particles would have been expelled almost equally in each direc-tion along the common spin axis of the aligned cobalt-60 nuclei.

18.108. Back in 1929, H. Weyl had shown that, for an uncharged particle of zero mass, the quantum electrodynamics equations of P. A. M. Dirac (§ 12.25) had two possible solutions, corresponding to opposite spins for a given direction of motion. Some two or three years later, however, these were rejected by W. Pauli (§ 4.64, 7.50) as being physically inadmissible because they would violate the parity principle. Early in 1957, soon after the announcement of the remarkable results obtained in the beta-decay of cobalt-60, Lee and Yang in the United States, L. Landau in Russia and A. Salam in England independently revived the work of Weyl. It was seen that if the mass of the neutrino (or antineutrino), which is, of course, uncharged, were taken as zero, the particle would inevitably fail to satisfy the basic postulate of the parity concept.*

18.109. The situation may be viewed in the following simplified manner. Consider a particle moving forward and at the same time spinning in a clockwise direction, somewhat similar to the motion of a right-handed screw. Imagine this particle to be reflected in a mirror. Although mov-

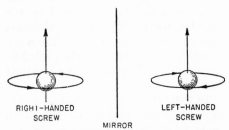

RIGHT-HANDED SCREW   LEFT-HANDED SCREW

MIRROR

Fig. 18.7. Motion and spin of a particle and the reflection in a mirror.

* The more widely accepted theoretical treatment requires the mass of the neutrino to be actually zero, but there is an alternative theory according to which the mass need only be very small and not necessarily zero.

ing in the same direction, the particle in the reflection will be spinning in an anticlockwise direction, like a left-handed screw, as may be seen in Fig. 18.7. If the parity principle is to be obeyed, then the postulate of § 18.104 requires the particle and its mirror image to be physically identical. (In the case shown, the parity would be negative since the spin coordinates change sign upon reflection.) However, according to the theory of the neutrino outlined in § 18.108, which is apparently supported by the experimental results described in § 7.70, *et seq.*, one of the particles (right-handed screw) corresponds to a neutrino and the other (left-handed screw) to an antineutrino. If these two particles are different, as appears to be the case (§ 7.68), then the fundamental assumption of the parity concept must be invalid. Consequently, in processes involving a neutrino (or antineutrino), such as beta-decay and the decay of charged pi- and mu-mesons, all of which are weak interactions, parity cannot be conserved.

18.110. During 1957 experimental evidence was obtained of the breakdown of the parity concept in mu-meson decay by L. M. Lederman, R. L. Garwin and M. Weinrich of Columbia University and in both mu- and pi-meson decay by V. L. Telegdi and J. I. Friedman of the University of Chicago. In the work of the former group, a pulse of pi-mesons was produced by bombarding a target with high-energy protons from a cyclotron. In flight, the pions decayed to form muons and antineutrinos. Since the pi-meson has zero spin and each of the product particles has ½ unit of spin, it seemed probable that the re-

sulting mu-mesons would all have their spin axes aligned in the same direction. The muons were stopped in a carbon block, where decay into an electron, together with a neutrino-antineutrino pair, occurred. If the parity principle were obeyed, there should be no preferred direction for the emission of the electrons. By applying a variable magnetic field to the carbon block, for a period roughly equal to the lifetime of the muons, the direction in space of their common spin axis could be varied. It was found that there was always a preferred direction in which the electrons were emitted, so that the parity principle failed.

CONCLUSION

18.111. It will be apparent from the foregoing discussion of the "strange" particles and their behavior that their discovery has presented nuclear science with a number of bewildering problems. Are the pi-mesons really the field particles, as postulated in Chapter XII, which account for nuclear forces? If so, why do mu-mesons exist and what part, if any, do they play in the structure of matter? What is the role of the K-mesons and why do they decay in so many different ways? Does the strangeness number have any obvious physical significance? Why is parity conserved in strong interactions and not in some (but not all) weak interactions? What is the significance of right- and left-handedness in matter? Many theories will, no doubt, be developed, and experiments will be devised to test them; the ultimate result will be a much more incisive understanding of the nature of matter than is possible at present.

Radiation Protection and Health Physics

Chapter XIX

RADIATION HAZARDS

HEALTH PHYSICS

19.1. Within about six months of the discovery of X-rays, that is, toward the middle of 1896, experimenters already began to notice the harmful effects of these rays on the skin. In the years that followed, and before the dangers were fully realized, cases of X-ray "burn" and X-ray dermatitis were all too common among physicists and radiologists. Similarly, it was not long after the isolation of radium, that it was realized that exposure of the skin to the radiations from this element could lead to painful results. Although Pierre Curie was not the first to experience the unpleasant consequences, Madame Curie in her biography of her husband describes how he "voluntarily exposed his arm to the action of radium during several hours. This resulted in a lesion resembling a burn that developed progressively and required several months to heal."

19.2. The danger of overexposure to X-rays or to the radiations from ra-

dioactive bodies was consequently well known during the first two decades of the present century. But there was little or no organized effort to establish suitable procedures to insure adequate protection until the early 1920s, when radiologists in the United States and in Great Britain gave some consideration to the matter, and recommended measures for use in the manipulation of X-rays and radium. Later, various national and international committees were set up to study the control of radiation hazards. Among these was the United States Advisory Committee on X-Rays and Radium Protection, whose suggestions relating to permissible levels of exposure to radiation are the basis of those now accepted.*

19.3. Prior to 1942, the use of X-rays or the handling of radioactive material was restricted to trained scientists, apart from the relatively few workers employed in the extraction of such material and in industries using them. With the development of

---

* At the present time the National Committee on Radiation Protection, established under the auspices of the U. S. National Bureau of Standards, is responsible for setting up radiation standards in the United States and for recommending permissible limits and tolerances.

the atomic energy project, not only has there been a large increase in the number of personnel engaged in work involving radiation hazards, but the intensity of the radiation is far greater than anything that had previously been experienced. The radioactivity due to the fission products in the "spent" uranium slugs from a nuclear reactor, for example, is many thousand times greater than that due to all the radium—about two and one-half pounds—extracted in nearly sixty years. The problem of radiation protection has thus become one of considerable importance.

19.4. Actually, all work with radioactive substances, from the use of isotopes as tracers to the large-scale processing of spent reactor fuel, involves some danger and requires that safety precautions be taken. As a result there has been developed the new field of *health physics*, the purpose of which is to insure the protection of personnel who are either ignorant of the hazards of radiation or are too preoccupied with other duties to pay adequate attention to them. The responsibilities of the health physicist include, among other things, the setting of standards for safe levels of exposure to radiations of different types, the detection of these radiations under a wide variety of conditions so as to give warning of the possibility of excessive exposure, and, finally, the development of suitable methods for protection against radiation. The great success of the efforts of the health physics group has been proved by the virtually complete absence of radiation accidents. By taking suitable precautions, almost any intensity of radiation can now be handled with safety, so that, as K. Z. Morgan, of the Health Physics Division, Oak Ridge National Laboratory, has said: "Radiation

need not be feared, but it must be respected." In the present chapter it is proposed to deal with the main aspects of the work of the health physicist.

BIOLOGICAL EFFECTS OF RADIATION

19.5. In the atomic energy field, the chief sources of harmful radiation are the cyclotron and other particle accelerators, nuclear chain reactors, including handling of spent fuel elements and fission products, and the production of radioisotopes for tracer work. In addition, the radioactive materials obtained by means of a cyclotron or a nuclear reactor always represent a possible radiation hazard. The alpha, beta, gamma and X-rays emitted by various radionuclides, and neutrons from reactors or other devices, are all known to have deleterious biological effects. Because of their relatively small penetrating power, of only a few centimeters of air, the dangers associated with external alpha particle sources are not serious. Unfortunately, if accidentally ingested or inhaled, some alpha particle emitters, such as plutonium, tend to accumulate in certain portions of the body where their continued action can be harmful. Gamma and X-rays and neutrons can penetrate quite deeply into the body, and it is with these radiations that precautions must be taken against external exposure. Beta particles occupy an intermediate position, for although they can travel some distance through air, they are able to penetrate only a few millimeters of tissue. However, in contact with the skin, beta-particle emitters can produce serious burns. The entry of any source of radiation into the body should, of course, be avoided.

19.6. It is generally believed that the harmful consequences of various radiations* are due to their ionizing effect; that is to say, to their ability to eject orbital electrons from atoms present in various compounds of which the body is constituted. Alpha, beta and gamma rays produce ionization more or less directly, as seen in Chapter VI, but with neutrons it is the indirect result of various possible interactions. Thermal (slow) neutrons undergo (n,γ) reactions with several body elements, particularly hydrogen which constitutes such a large proportion of the living organism. The highly energetic gamma radiations then cause ionization. Another process involving slow neutrons is $N^{14}(n,p)$ C^{14}; the protons emitted have a considerable ionizing effect. It will be noted that the product of this reaction, carbon-14, is itself radioactive, emitting beta particles. Other radionuclides can be formed within the body by the interaction of slow neutrons with stable isotopes. The effect of fast neutrons is essentially due to the production of recoil protons (§ 11.30) by the impact of the neutrons on hydrogen in the body. The fast protons formed in this manner produce ionization in their paths.

19.7. It is known that the radiations affect the individual cells of which the body is composed, possibly by destroying the enzymes that determine their particular functions. In brief, all cells contain protoplasm, consisting of a central body, or nucleus, suspended in a viscous liquid medium, called the cytoplasm. The cell as a whole is surrounded by a membrane through which pass the salts, sugars and so on, required for its maintenance. Within the nucleus is the substance chromatin which, at the times of cell division, forms the thread-like chromosomes; the latter, whose number and shape are characteristic of each species, carry the hereditary factors.

19.8. The exact mechanism whereby ionizing radiations produce their effects on the body is uncertain. One view is that the unstable molecular (or atomic) particles, called free radicals, known to be produced by the action of the radiations in water, react with and render inactive some important cell constituents, especially the enzymes. There is also a possibility that these substances may be directly decomposed by the ionizing radiation. However, even if the details are not understood, the over-all effects on the cell are well known. Among the results observed have been the breaking of the chromosomes, swelling of the nucleus and of the entire cell, destruction of the cell, increase in viscosity of the protoplasm, and greater permeability of the cell membrane. The broken cells and other biological debris tend to clog the capillaries and so interfere with the circulation of the blood.

19.9. In connection with the behavior of individual cells it has been noted that the process of cell division, known to biologists as mitosis, is delayed by exposure to radiation. Frequently the new cells that are formed are unable to undergo mitosis, so that their number does not increase. It is possible that this effect, together with cell destruction referred to above, underlies the use of gamma radiation for inhibiting the proliferation of the cancerous cells in malignant tumors (§ 17.90). There is, however, a curious paradox in this connection, which

* As used in this chapter, the word "radiation" is intended to refer to alpha and beta particles, electrons, protons, neutrons, gamma and X-rays, and, presumably, mesons, but not to visible, infrared and ultraviolet light and radiowaves, which are all forms of electromagnetic radiation having wave lengths longer than X-rays (§ 3.25).

emphasizes the difficulty in understanding the biological effects of radiation. While controlled treatment with gamma rays can stop cancerous growth, continued exposure to radiation in excess of certain limits may cause a cancer to be formed.

19.10. Unfortunately, the animal body has not developed an instinctive defense against radiation as it has against heat and, to some extent, against ultraviolet light. Consequently, there can be severe radiation damage without any realization at the time on the part of the subject. The nature and extent of the symptoms which develop later may vary with the individual. They depend on the type of radiation, on the depth to which the radiation has penetrated, on the extent of the body exposed, on the amount of radiation absorbed, and also upon whether the exposure was chronic, that is, repeated or prolonged so as to lead to a cumulative effect, or acute, that is, received in one large dose. All types of excessive exposure to radiation appear to have one factor in common:* there is invariably a delay, which may be weeks, months or years, before the final, and worst, effects become apparent.

19.11. Chronic local exposure leads first to a reddening of the skin (erythema); this is followed by blistering and formation of lesions which are very slow in healing. Loss of hair also results from the action of radiations. Because of this effect, X-rays were used at one time for the removal of superfluous hair, but in several reported instances the consequences were disastrous. Cancerous growths are likely to develop, sometimes years after there has been chronic overex-

posure of part of the body to pen ing ionizing radiations. The foregoing effects may be regarded as external or visible symptoms. Of those of an invisible character, the most important are genetic effects, which become apparent only in succeeding generations (§ 19.82), and changes in the constituents of the blood. The latter are many and varied, but a decrease in the number of white cells (leukocytes) seems to be one of the most characteristic. As in the case of cell development, mentioned earlier, considerable overexposure may lead to a reversal of behavior. Thus, one of the ultimate consequences may be leukemia, in which there is an overproduction of white corpuscles (§ 17.89).

19.12. A great deal of information on the consequences of acute overexposure to radiation has been accumulated from a study of Japanese victims of the atomic bomb, as well as from observations made on more than 250 persons in the Marshall Islands, who were inadvertently exposed to the radiations from the fission product debris (fallout) following the test explosion of March 1, 1954.† There have also been a few cases of laboratory accidents, where workers received known amounts of radiation, the results of which have been recorded. As stated above, the effects vary with the individual patient and the nature of the exposure, but certain broad conclusions have been reached. There are, as a rule, four phases in the response of the body to overexposure to radiation. In the first phase, the early symptoms are nausea and vomiting, accompanied by general lassitude; they are similar to those long known as being associated with "radiation sickness" suf-

---

* Very large doses are not included, since they lead to death in a short time, sometimes within two weeks or less.

† See *The Effects of Nuclear Weapons*, U. S. Government Printing Office, 1957, Chapter XI.

fered by patients undergoing intensive treatment with radium or X-rays. If the exposure has not been excessive, this is usually followed by a second phase of relative well-being which may last for a few days or for several weeks. The more severe the radiation dose, the shorter is this apparent latent period.

19.13. In the third phase the reaction of the body reaches its height, and the survival of the patient depends on the ability of his system to withstand the effects. Some of the symptoms are prostration, loss of appetite, loss of weight, fever, rapid heart action, severe diarrhea, bleeding of the gums and loss of hair. This phase may last days or weeks, depending on the extent of the radiation exposure. In severe cases, the patient becomes progressively worse and succumbs, but where the dose has not been so great, a period of prolonged convalescence is the fourth phase. During this time, which may last up to six months, there is a gradual recovery. The patient then appears to be quite normal, although changes in the blood constituents may persist for a long time. There is also a possibility of certain consequences which will not become apparent for some years after exposure. Among them, apart from the genetic effects, are leukemia and the formation of cataracts.

19.14. As in the case of chronic exposure, the acute radiation sickness is accompanied by significant changes in the blood, the most obvious of which is a marked decrease, with some fluctuations, in the number of white blood cells, following upon an initial temporary increase. Since the function of the white cells is to defend the body against infection and to remove toxic products, the decrease in their number

accounts, in part at least, for the increased susceptibility to infection that is characteristic of radiation sickness. Another change observed in the blood is in the platelets, a constituent which plays an important role in connection with blood clotting. The number of platelets falls steadily from the time of exposure to radiation and reaches a minimum, at the end of a few weeks, and then it increases slowly over a period of months or even years.

19.15. The influence of radiation on the blood is, to a large extent, a manifestation of the fact that the lymphoid tissue and the bone marrow, where various constituents of the blood are formed, are regions of the body which react most quickly as a result of exposure. For this reason, these, together with the reproductive organs and the gastro-intestinal tract, are said to be *radiosensitive* tissues. The muscles, nerve cells and fully-grown bone, on the other hand, are *radioresistant* for they show little evidence of change as a result of radiation exposure. Intermediate in their sensitivity are the skin, kidney, liver and lungs.

INTERNAL RADIATION HAZARDS

19.16. The foregoing descriptions of the effects of radiation have referred, in particular, to exposure from an external source. The general biological effects of nuclear radiations from ingested radioactive materials are essentially the same, but there are certain circumstances in which even a very small quantity of such sources within the body can produce considerable injury. Any radioactive nuclide entering the body is a potential hazard, but the situation can become very serious if the element is one which tends to concentrate in specific cells or tissues that are highly radiosensitive. For example, calcium and the chemically similar strontium, barium and radium are called *bone seekers,* since these elements are largely deposited in the skeleton. Plutonium and cerium are also bone seekers, although they are found in other parts of the bone. Radioisotopes of these elements can thus be very hazardous since, if they enter the body, they will collect, to a considerable extent, in the bone, where the radiations, even if of short range, can injure the sensitive bone marrow, where many blood cells are produced. Further, the continuous bombardment of bone tissue by radiations may eventually lead to necrosis and tumor formation.

19.17. In addition to the tendency for a particular element to be taken up by a radiosensitive organ or tissue, the main consideration in determining the hazard of a given radioisotope inside the body is the total radiation dose delivered while it is in the body or in a critical region. The most important factors in determining this dose are the mass of radioactive material deposited, its half life, the nature and energy of the radiations emitted, and the length of time it is effective in the body. This time is dependent upon two factors: one is the ordinary radioactive half life, and the other is the *biological half life.* The latter is defined as the time taken for the amount of a particular element in the body to decrease to half its initial value due to elimination by natural (biological) processes. Combination of the radioactive and biological half lives gives rise to the *effective half life,* which is the time required for the amount of a specified radioisotope in the body to fall to half of its original

value as a result of both radioactive decay and natural elimination.

19.18. The nuclides representing the greatest potential internal hazard are those with a relatively short radioactive half life and a comparatively long biological half life. A certain mass of a radioisotope of short radioactive half life will emit particles at a greater rate than the same mass of another isotope, possibly of the same element, having a longer half life. Further, the long biological half life means that the active material will not be readily eliminated from the body by natural processes. As an illustration, the case of iodine-131 may be quoted; this has a radioactive half life of only 8 days, but the biological half life of the element iodine is about 6 months, because it is rapidly taken up by the thyroid gland from which it is eliminated slowly (§ 17.87). Consequently, if sufficient iodine-131 should enter the body, it is capable of causing serious damage to the healthy thyroid gland.

19.19. Both radium-226, the common form of this element, and plutonium-239 are serious internal hazards; since they have long radioactive and biological half lives, once these nuclides are deposited in the skeleton, they remain there, essentially unchanged in amount, during the lifetime of the victim. The continued action of the emitted alpha particles, which deposit their energy in a limited region, over a period of years can cause significant injury. A somewhat similar situation arises in connection with the beta-emitting bone-seeker, strontium-90, which is one of the most abundant products of the fission of uranium-235 and plutonium-239. It has a radioactive half life of 28 years and a biological half life estimated to be about 10 years.

RADIATION UNITS AND DOSAGES

RADIATION UNITS

19.20. In order to express radiation exposure in quantitative terms, it is necessary to describe certain appropriate units. The first of these is the *roentgen*, named for the discoverer of X-rays (§ 2.86) ; it may be defined, on the basis of the recommendation of the Radiological Congress held in Chicago in 1937, as the quantity of X-rays or gamma rays which will produce, as a consequence of ionization, one electrostatic unit of electricity (§ 2.24 footnote), of either sign, in 1 cc. of dry air, as measured at 0°C and standard atmospheric pressure. Since a singly charged ion carries 4.80×10^{-10} electrostatic units (§ 2.41), 1 roentgen, abbreviated to 1 r, forms in 1 cc. of dry air the reciprocal of this number, i.e., 2.08×10^9, of ions of either sign, which is the same as the number of ion-pairs. The mass of 1 cc. of dry air under the standard conditions specified is 0.00129 gram, and consequently in 1 gram of air the absorption of 1 r would result in the formation of $2.08 \times 10^9 / 0.00129 = 1.61 \times 10^{12}$ ion-pairs. The average amount of energy expended in the production of one ion-pair in air is known to be about 33.5 ev (§ 6.4) ; hence, the energy for 1.61×10^{12} ion-pairs is 5.40×10^{13} ev or nearly 86 ergs, since 1 ev is equivalent to 1.60×10^{-12} erg (§ 3.81). The energy gained by the absorption of 1 r of X-rays in 1 gram of air is thus 86 ergs.

19.21. As stated above, the roentgen unit was intended to refer to photons of electromagnetic radiation, namely, X-rays and gamma rays, but in view of the similar biological effects due to ionization caused by particle radiations, such as alpha and beta particles, protons and neutrons, its use has been extended to cover such radiations. In order to make this extension possible, H. M. Parker, of the Hanford project (§ 14.74), suggested the adoption of a new unit, called the *roentgen equivalent physical*, abbreviated to *rep*. This was originally defined as the quantity of radiation which upon absorption in the body liberated the same amount of energy as 1 r of X-rays or gamma rays, i.e., 86 ergs per gram of tissue. However, it was found that exposure to a dose of 1 r of X-rays was accompanied by the absorption of something more like 97 ergs in a gram of soft tissue. The rep has, therefore, been used to denote a dose of 97 ergs of any nuclear radiation absorbed (or liberated) per gram of body tissue.

19.22. The foregoing definition of the rep, based on the energy (or physical) equivalent of the roentgen, is unsatisfactory, for several reasons. Perhaps the most important is the fact that the figure for the number of ergs absorbed is based on a calculation involving the value of the energy required to produce an ion-pair in air. This quantity is not known with certainty and, as new experimental data have become available, the number of ergs in the definition of the rep has been changed. For several years, for example, it was accepted that 32.5 ev were required to produce one ion-pair in air, and this led to 83 ergs per gram of air as the energy absorbed for 1 r and 93 ergs per gram of tissue for 1 rep. The newer value of 33.5 ev per ion-pair has required these numbers to be changed to 86 and 97 ergs, respectively.

19.23. In order to avoid this difficulty, the International Commission on Radiological Units adopted a new unit of absorbed radiation dose, called the *rad*, which does not suffer from the drawback of the rep. The rad is defined as the absorbed dose of any ionizing radiation which is accompanied by the liberation of 100 ergs of energy per gram of absorbing material. For soft tissue, the difference between the rad and the rep is very small, and numerical values of absorbed dose formerly expressed in reps are essentially unchanged when converted to rads. This is not true, however, for bone where the difference is quite considerable.

19.24. Because the absorption of quantities of different ionizing radiations which provide the same amount of energy may not have the same biological effect in the human (or animal) body, H. M. Parker introduced another unit, the *roentgen equivalent man*, abbreviated to *rem*. The rad is useful as a physical quantity which can be measured, but, ultimately, it is the biological changes produced by the absorbed radiation which are important. Consequently, 1 rem was defined as the quantity of radiation which produces the same biological damage in man as that resulting from the absorption of 1 rep of X-rays or gamma rays.

19.25. At the present time, the rem is defined in a somewhat different manner based on the *relative biological effectiveness* (or RBE) of a particular radiation. This is the ratio of the absorbed dose in rads of X-rays or gamma rays (of a specified energy) to that of the rads of the given radiation having the same biological effect. The value of the RBE for a particular type of nuclear radiation, e.g., alpha or beta particles or neutrons, depends upon a number of factors, such as the energy of the radiation, the kind and degree of biological damage, and the nature of the organ or tissue under consideration. The rem is then defined by the relationship

$$\text{Dose in rems} = \text{Dose in rads} \times \text{RBE},$$

so that the dose in rems provides a measure of the extent of biological injury, of a given type, that would result from the absorption of nuclear radiation. Thus, the rem may be regarded as a unit of biological dose, whereas the rad is one of absorbed radiation dose; in this scheme, the roentgen is considered to be a unit of exposure dose.

19.26. According to the definition given above, the RBE for X-rays and gamma rays may be taken as unity, although it varies to some extent with the energy of the radiation. Hence, for gamma rays, the biological dose in rems is equal to the absorbed dose in rads. Further, in view of the similarity between the rad and the rep in soft tissue, it is also roughly equal to the exposure in roentgens. This equality does not necessarily apply to other radiations, as is shown by the values in the accompanying table, the

RELATIONSHIPS AMONG RADIATION UNITS

Type of Radiation	r	rads	rems (or RBE)
X-rays and Gamma rays.	1	1	1
Beta particles	—	1	1
Fast neutrons	—	1	10
Thermal neutrons	—	1	4–5
Alpha particles	—	1	10–20

rads referring, for simplicity, to absorption in soft tissue. The number of rems is equal to the RBE in each case. As stated earlier, the RBE depends on the type of effect considered; it also depends on the location of the radiation source, especially for alpha-particle emitters. The values in the table apply, in particular, to cataract formation by neutrons and the production of tumors by alpha-particle sources within the body. For general radiation injury, such as that described above, the RBE for neutrons is probably not more than 2, and may well be less. With the results given, it is possible to make a rough assessment of the biological effect resulting from simultaneous or consecutive absorption of different kinds of radiation.

19.27. Attempts have been made to correlate the RBE with some physical property of the radiation. If a particular physiological effect is considered in a given organism, there appears to be a general relationship between the RBE of the radiation and its specific ionization (§ 6.3). In this connection, however, it has been found preferable to use a related quantity called the *linear energy transfer* (or LET), defined as the energy released by the radiation per unit length of the absorbing tissue. In general, when comparing different ionizing radiations, it is found that the RBE increases with the LET, although for very high values of the latter the RBE may decrease somewhat.

MAXIMUM PERMISSIBLE RADIATION EXPOSURE

19.28. In view of the harmful nature of the radiations from radioactive substances, and from particle accelerators and nuclear reactors, and the lack of any established method of treating the resulting injuries, the obvious procedure is to take all precautions necessary to avoid overexposure. The term "overexposure," rather than "exposure," is used here deliberately. There are reasons for believing that, provided the radiation dosage is small, the body is able to recover from the effects. An exception to this arises in connection with the action of radiation on the reproductive organs, where the injury to the germ cells is permanent and cumulative, as will be seen later. The reason for the recovery from small doses, in many cases, is that the majority of the cells damaged or killed by radiation are replaced by new cells. The rate of cell replacement varies from one part of the body to another, but it is a property possessed by many living tissues.

19.29. All human beings are subjected to the continuous action of cosmic rays (Chapter XVIII), the extent increasing with the geomagnetic latitude, up to a point, and, especially, with the altitude. In addition, there are sufficient radium and other radionuclides in the earth, and radium and thorium emanations in the atmosphere to produce an appreciable amount of ionizing radiation. Further, the amount of radioactive material, radium or mesothorium, in a luminous watch-dial is by no means negligible. It is seen, therefore, that human beings are continuously exposed to radiation at low intensity without any apparent harmful effects. Two other surprising sources of radiation are the C^{14} and the K^{40} in the body itself; the disintegration of the former causes the liberation of about 190,000, while the latter expels over a million, beta particles per minute in the average adult. It is true that the maximum energy of the particles from C^{14} is small (0.156 Mev), but K^{40} emits beta particles with a maximum energy of 1.35 Mev as well as 1.46-Mev gamma rays. It has been estimated that, in most parts of the United States, every individual receives about 0.14 to 0.16 roentgen per year due to natural radiation, from body constituents and the surroundings.

19.30. It is evident that a restricted exposure to radiation is not serious. But what needs to be known is the limit below which there will be no harmful consequences. Unfortunately, it is a matter of great difficulty to obtain reliable information on this vital matter. Long-range experiments with a large number of human beings subjected to various radiation dosages might supply the necessary data, but this is hardly a practical approach to the problem. Observations on animals would appear to provide a partial solution, but the differences between animals of different species, and even among those of the same species, are quite considerable. In any event, the extrapolation from a small animal to man is fraught with uncertainty.

19.31. In spite of these difficulties, there is a general agreement among radiologists and health physicists upon the limit of safe exposure. From the extensive experience of radiologists, in connection with X-rays, and in the use of radium in cancer therapy, and from the more limited information gathered by health physicists associated with the atomic energy program, there seems every reason to believe that the accepted tolerance limit is indeed a safe limit (see, however, § 19.82).

19.32. After considering all the available information, the U. S. Advisory Committee on X-Rays and Radium Protection concluded in 1936 that the maximum human tolerance dose of X-rays or gamma rays, which could be taken upon successive working days, was 0.1 r per day over the whole body, for individuals whose occupation may lead to radiation exposure. Thus, it was generally agreed, at that time, that the whole body can receive up to about 0.1 r of radiation per working day for long periods with-out experiencing any permanent harm. This was accepted as the *maximum permissible exposure dose* of X-rays and gamma rays until the latter part of 1949 when the U. S. National Committee on Radiation Protection recommended that the limit be reduced to 0.3 r per week. It should be understood that this dose applies to absorption over the whole body. Small areas can be exposed to very much larger quantities of radiation without serious injury. Thus, a dose of 5000 r can be used to treat a small skin cancer; this will leave a scar, but there will be no other permanent effect. On the other hand, exposure of the whole body to 600 r would be fatal to nearly all humans. Since different parts of the body may not all receive the same dose of radiation, the total permissible dose of 0.3 r per week for the whole body is to be regarded as a weighted mean value.

19.33. There is a further difficulty in assessing the body dosage. A quantity of 0.1 r of radiation spread over an 8-hour day, for example, is equivalent physically to 48 r for 1 minute, but is it the same biologically? The answer is undoubtedly in the negative. The same amount of radiation would cause more injury in the latter case than in the former. Similarly, a permissible dose of 0.3 r per week, spread over five working days, would be less harmful than a single dose of 0.3 r in one day and none on the other days. Consequently, care must be taken that the whole body is never exposed to a high radiation intensity, even for a short period of time.

19.34. In extending the maximum permissible dose to other radiations, use is made of the biological equivalence of 1 r and 1 rem. The permissible dose for any kind of ionizing radiation is therefore taken as 0.3 rem per week over the whole body, with the understanding that there is no exposure to excessive intensities even for short periods of time. Although limited parts of the body may receive fairly large doses without permanent harm, it is advisable to keep such doses as small as possible, not more than 0.3 rem per week. Taking into account the relationships between the rem and rad units for different types of radiation, as recorded in the table given above, it is seen that, while the maximum permissible absorption of X-rays and beta and gamma rays is 0.3 rad per week, it would be only 0.03 rad for fast neutrons, 0.06 rad for slow neutrons and 0.015 to 0.03 rad for internal alpha particles. In the event of exposure to two or more kinds of radiation, the equivalent of the total absorption must not exceed 0.3 rem per week.

19.35. The maximum permissible radiation dose of 0.3 rem per week would amount to 15 rem per year. Because the genetic effects of radiation are cumulative, the National Committee on Radiation Protection recommended during 1957 that the weekly maximum dose of 0.3 rem in any single week may be retained, for atomic energy workers, but that the total accumulated dose should not exceed an average of 5 rems per year past the age of 18 years. It may be remarked that the actual average exposure at installations of the U. S. Atomic Energy Commission and its contractors has been well below this suggested limit.* For the general population, it has been suggested that the total exposure, from all sources of radiation, including the natural background, should not exceed an *average* of 14 rems per individual from con-

ception to the age of 30 years, and one third that amount in each decade thereafter.

19.36. As far as sources of radiation within the body are concerned, an effort to avoid excessive exposure is made by placing a limit upon the rate of entry into the body. Since, in most instances, intake of the radioactive material occurs through the medium of air and water, *maximum permissible concentrations* have been recommended for a number of isotopes. These maximum concentrations in air and water are determined by the radioactive and biological half lives of the material, the radiosensitivity of the organ (if any) in which it tends to accumulate, and the energy and nature of the radiations.

19.37. Maximum safe average body contents of most radioisotopes are not known, since there is insufficient direct experience for establishing levels at which individual isotopes, except possibly radium (0.1 microcurie) and iodine-131 (0.3 microcurie), may be regarded as causing no detectable injury. For most radioelements which, like radium, accumulate in the skeleton, maximum permissible amounts in the body have been estimated, directly or indirectly, from comparative experimental studies with animals. Thus, for plutonium-239, the limit has been set at 0.04 microcurie for soluble compounds and 0.008 for insoluble sources, the former having a greater tendency to be eliminated. The maximum permissible body content of strontium-90 is believed to be 1 microcurie. For radioisotopes, which do not concentrate in bone, it is assumed that the body content should not exceed the lowest levels which will result in an average dose at some part of the body,

---

* During the ten year period 1947 through 1956, about 95 per cent of those employed received an average of less than 1 rem per year, and 99.4 per cent less than 5 rems.

other than the reproductive organs, of 0.3 rem per week. For the latter | organs, the absorbed dose must be lower than this amount.

RADIATION MONITORING

Monitoring of Personnel

19.38. A very important part of the work of the health physics group is to keep a check on the radiation exposure of individual personnel, and to measure the intensity of radiation in | able calibration they can consequently be made to give an indication of the number of roentgens to which they have been exposed. From this the corresponding exposure by an individual can be determined. The photographic

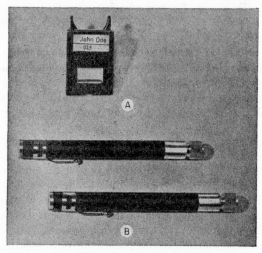

Fig. 19.1. Film badge (A) and ionization chambers (B) used for personnel monitoring.

various localities to which personnel have access. This procedure, generally known as *monitoring*, is divided into two broad categories, namely, personnel monitoring and area monitoring. In the latter may be included the checking of radiation intensities during the course of a process or operation.

19.39. The monitoring of personnel is both physical and biological. For the former, use is made of ionization chambers and of photographic film, both of which measure essentially the ionizing power of radiation. By suit- | film meter can be worn as a badge or on the wrist, or it may be in the form of a finger ring. The badge form (Fig. 19.1, A), which is most common, contains two pieces of film with different sensitivities, so as to measure different ranges of radiation. The films are wrapped in a thin opaque paper, to keep out light, and are placed in a frame, so that part of the film is covered with a thin cadmium shield, while the remainder is behind a "window." The beta radiations are absorbed by the cadmium, but the gamma rays can penetrate it and affect the photographic film. The cadmium plays a part in this connection by absorbing some of the gamma radiation of low energy, to which the film is particularly sensitive, thus making the response more uniform over the whole energy range. The film exposed at the "window" registers beta particles and, to some extent, soft, weakly penetrating gamma rays. From the blackening observed in the different parts of the film after development, the extent of exposure to the various radiations can be estimated.

19.40. Where there is a possibility of exposure to neutrons, an additional sensitive film, which can record proton tracks, is placed behind the beta-gamma film. Since cadmium has a high cross section for the absorption of slow neutrons (§ 11.98), only fast neutrons can penetrate the cadmium shield; these produce recoil protons which leave their tracks in the film. Both fast and slow neutrons pass through the "window," and in this region of the film, the slow neutrons give proton tracks as a result of the $N^{14}(n,p)C^{14}$ process, in addition to the proton-recoil tracks formed by the fast neutrons. The tracks are counted under a microscope after the film has been developed.

19.41. The film meters are usually examined at the end of each week, unless overexposure is suspected at any time. For daily monitoring, simple (electrostatic) ionization chambers (§ 6.17), shaped like a fountain pen and worn in the pocket (Fig. 19.1, B), are used. These devices are of two types. The common form of pocket chamber is merely an air condenser which is charged up to a known potential, usually 150 volts, before being issued. The entry of ionizing radiation, mainly gamma rays, causes the condenser to discharge, and the residual potential, observed on an electrometer at the end of the day, gives an approximate measure of the exposure of the individual. Air condensers lined with a boron compound are used in the same manner to estimate slow neutrons. Because of their occasional accidental discharge, pocket chambers are always carried in pairs. It should be mentioned that information concerning exposure to gamma rays and neutrons is important since these are more penetrating, and consequently less easily guarded against, than beta rays.

19.42. When performing an operation that may result in exposure to radiation, a pocket gamma-dosimeter is worn. This is also like a fountain pen in shape, but it is actually a combined (electrostatic) ionization chamber and a fiber electroscope, similar in principle to the Lauritsen electroscope (§ 6.18) but more compact. The fiber is charged with a battery, so that it indicates zero on a scale; the ionization produced by gamma radiation results in a partial discharge, and the fiber moves accordingly. By holding the dosimeter up to the light and looking through the eyepiece lens at one end, the image of the fiber can be seen against the built-in scale. For the detection of slow neutrons the dosimeter is lined internally with a boron compound. By means of these simple detectors the extent of exposure of the individual to gamma rays or to neutrons can be determined immediately.

19.43. The devices described above are all integrating instruments, since they measure the total quantity of the particular radiation absorbed in the course of a week, day or shorter time. For instantaneous measurements of radiation intensity, other detectors are used. For example, in handling radioactive materials the body or clothing of the worker may become contaminated. To check this possibility without delay, various types of Geiger-Müller counters are used. One such instrument counts and automatically records the beta and gamma emission from the two hands and the two feet separately during a period of 24 seconds. Doorways are surrounded by a set of G-M tubes, connected with an alarm circuit, so that there is an immediate indication of the passage of a person contaminated with a radioactive substance. A G-M tube, attached to a long handle, can then be used as a probe to find the location of the contaminant.

19.44. The uptake of active material, particularly the alpha-emitting plutonium and uranium and various beta and gamma emitters among the fission products, where this is likely to occur, is checked by the analysis of urine samples from the workers concerned. The radionuclides present are separated chemically and the amounts, which may be less than a billionth of a gram, are determined by counting alpha, beta or gamma activity, according to the circumstances. In some cases, the feces, sputum and perspiration are also examined for the presence of dangerous material.

19.45. If there is any reason to suspect a serious overexposure to radiation, then biological tests are necessary. Of these, the white cell count in the blood provides perhaps the best indication of possible radiation damage (§ 19.10). Excessive exposure to neutrons is sometimes apparent through the presence of radioactivity in the blood resulting from radionuclides formed by (n,γ) and (n,p) reactions with elements in the body.

19.46. Although they are not in general use for personnel monitoring, reference may be made here to two unusual types of instrument that have been designed to measure total radiation exposure doses under special conditions. One of these is the *phosphate glass dosimeter* for recording doses of from 10 to 600 r (or more). It is a simple, inexpensive and rugged device consisting of a special phosphate glass containing traces of a silver activator. After exposure to radiation, this glass emits a visible fluorescence when illuminated with ultraviolet light; the intensity of the fluorescence is a measure of the total radiation exposure dose. Since the change produced by ionizing radiation is fairly permanent, the instrument can be used to record the accumulated dose over a long period of time. It has been recommended for issuance in large numbers to the civilian and military population in an emergency. The phosphate glass dosimeter can also be used to measure exposures, in the range from 3000 to 2,000,000 roentgens, in connection with the sterilization and preservation of foods and drugs by radiation (§ 17.148).

19.47. The second type of dosimeter can be employed for most of the same purposes as the one just described. Its action is based on chemical reactions brought about by ionization radiation and so it is called a *chemical dosimeter*. There are several forms of this device, but many have the same essential constituents, namely, a chlorinated hydrocarbon, e.g., chloroform, some water and an indicator dye, sealed into a glass tube. As a result of the action of the radiation, hydrochloric acid is liberated from the chlorinated compound. This dissolves in the water and changes the color of the indicator. From the extent of the color change, the radiation exposure can be

estimated. Chemical and silver-acti-
vated phosphate glass dosimeters, like
photographic film badges, are calibrated by means of a standard radiation source, e.g., radium (primary
standard) or cobalt-60 (secondary
standard).

AREA AND OPERATION MONITORING

19.48. The monitoring or surveying
of working areas and of actual oper-

health physics surveyor is called upon
to make regular routine checks of all
areas where radioactive material is
likely to collect. The survey may also
detect faults in radiation shielding. In
the laboratory, where conditions are
changing from day to day, and where
spills or minor accidents are likely to
occur, the monitoring of table tops,
hoods, floors, walls and equipment is
of the utmost importance. Definite

FIG. 19.2.   Monitoring the removal of irradiated material from the Oak Ridge reactor,
for the production of isotopes.

ations is carried out with both fixed
and portable instruments; these are of
many types, such as electroscopes,
ionization chambers, or G-M tubes,
each being designed for a special purpose. Some are merely detecting instruments which show that a source of
radiation is present, but give only a
rough idea of its magnitude, whereas
others are measuring devices to indicate the actual radiation level. The

tolerance limits, based on experience,
have been set for the number of counts
per minute per square foot; any activity in excess of these limits is regarded as dangerous, and appropriate
steps must be taken to remove its
source.

19.49. One way in which radioactivity may be carried from place to
place is by dust particles, transmitted
through the air. Further, inhalation of

such air will lead to the presence of active material in the body. An important aspect of the work of the health physics surveyor is consequently the monitoring of the air inside buildings. For this purpose the air is drawn continuously through either an electrostatic precipitator or a filter to remove dust particles; the deposits are then examined for their radioactivity. The procedure is intended to simulate the separation of dust particles in the lungs as a result of inhaling the air.

19.50. In its widest aspects, area monitoring includes a check on the activity of the air, water and soil in the vicinity of establishments where work is being performed with radioactive materials. In virtually all cases the problem of the disposal of waste materials for which there is no further use must be considered, and in this connection it is necessary to make sure there is no contamination of surrounding areas. This aspect of radiation protection will be examined below.

19.51. When carrying out an operation in which large amounts of radioactivity are involved, the process should be continuously monitored so as to avoid overexposure of the operator. An interesting example of such monitoring is depicted in Fig. 19.2; this shows the method of removal of radioisotopes, produced by neutron irradiation in the Oak Ridge reactor, as described in § 17.9. The lead "coffin," which acts as a shield for gamma radiation, is wheeled up to the reactor and the graphite stringer, holding the aluminum cans containing the isotopes, is drawn into it with a long rod. The operator then removes the can from the stringer, through a hole in the "coffin," with the aid of a long-handled suction device, and transfers it to one of the lead shipping containers, standing on the skid. The whole process is monitored by the health physicist, shown holding an ionization-rate meter, for the detection of beta and gamma radiations, familiarly referred to as "Cutie Pie." The instrument on the low table at the left is known as a "monitron"; it automatically monitors the area and sounds an alarm if the radiation intensity exceeds the tolerance level.

RADIATION PROTECTION

Radiation Shielding

19.52. In order to continue operations with radioactive material day after day, as is done at the various installations and laboratories of the U. S. Atomic Energy Commission, and in many research institutions where studies with radioisotopes are proceeding, adequate precautions are taken to reduce exposure of personnel. The scientist and engineer cooperate with the health physicist in devising methods whereby particular processes can be carried out with a minimum of hazard.

19.53. The obvious way of avoiding radiation is to increase the distance between the operator and the source of the radiation or, better, by the employment of suitable absorbers, or shields, which either attenuate or absorb the radiations. In general, a combination of both is desired. Protective shielding should be used as far as possible for both the source of the radiation and the operating personnel. The nature of the protection depends largely on the material being handled. Rubber gloves, for example, are sufficient to absorb alpha particles, and most alpha emitters can be manipulated without difficulty, provided rigid precautions are taken to avoid inhalation. The work with such substances can be carried out in a well-ventilated space,* or a respirator should be worn. Gloves should be used, in any case, to prevent radioactive material of any kind from contact with the skin, and special protective clothing, which is shed when leaving the radioactive area, is advisable.

19.54. Among general precautions which must be taken are the following. Food should not be stored, prepared or eaten in places where radioactive substances are present, and there should be no smoking because of the danger of ingestion of active material from contaminated hands. The hands should be well washed, and both hands and shoes should be monitored for activity before leaving the work area. The finger nails should always be kept short, and special attention should be given to skin abrasions to prevent entry of radioactive material into the body.

19.55. The problem of shielding sources of radiation has been studied extensively, from both experimental and theoretical points of view†; it is, of course, a matter of the utmost importance in connection with the construction of nuclear reactors, as well as for work with radioisotopes. The methods used for shielding in the laboratory will be described later, while the procedures suitable for large-scale work will be considered here. As already indicated, protection from alpha particles is a relatively simple matter, and the same is largely true for beta radiation. The thickness of shielding for beta particles of a given energy decreases with increasing density of the material. The use of a heavy metal, which implies an element of high atomic number, is, however, not advisable, because the production of penetrating bremsstrahlung (or braking radiation) accompanying the deceleration of the beta particles in the absorber tends to increase with atomic number (§ 7.75). Actually, it is not necessary to use materials of high atomic weight for shielding from beta particles. Aluminum is satisfactory for many purposes and plastics, such as lucite, or even glass, can often be used.

19.56. On account of their considerable penetrating power, the absorption of neutrons and gamma rays is a much more difficult matter. Both of these radiations are extensively produced in nuclear reactors, the former being liberated in the fission process, whereas the latter are emitted by the fission products. It is the intense gamma activity of the latter which makes it necessary to handle spent fuel elements by remote control. As with beta rays, the best absorbers for gamma radiation are materials of high density. In this case, however, high atomic number is an advantage, and hence lead, which has both a high density and a high atomic number, has been accepted as one of the best materials for gamma shielding (§ 7.96). For nuclear reactors, in particular, and also for high-energy accelerators, where the gamma rays are accompanied by

---

* It has been stated that the reason why Marie and Pierre Curie suffered no serious injury as a result of their extraction of radium from pitchblende on a large scale, although they took no special precautions, was because of the natural ventilation in the dilapidated building in which they worked.

† A discussion of some of the factors which determine the absorption of different types of radiation in matter is given in Chapter VII.

neutrons, lead is not an altogether satisfactory shielding material, apart from its excessive cost.

19.57. Since the capture cross sections are, generally, larger for slow than for fast neutrons (§ 11.96), it is evident that the most effective neutron shielding can be achieved by first decreasing the speed of these particles, and then absorbing them in a suitable material. Slowing down of the neutrons of high energy, e.g., in excess of 1 Mev, is best achieved by taking advantage of the inelastic scattering with an element of fairly high mass number (§ 11.61). This will bring the neutron energy down to about 0.1 Mev when the familiar moderators, i.e., elements of low mass number, are most effective in slowing down neutrons. For this purpose, hydrogen, in the form of water, is particularly suitable. The hydrogen and other nuclei present also serve to capture slow neutrons in (n,γ) reactions. As a result, however, gamma radiation is emitted and this must be attenuated as far as possible.

19.58. Concrete has been widely used for reactor shielding, because it is also a convenient and cheap structural material. It contains a substantial amount of hydrogen, from the water used in its composition, as well as heavier elements, such as calcium and silicon, for slowing down and absorbing neutrons and attenuating gamma rays. About 8 feet of ordinary concrete is a satisfactory shield for most reactors, since the radiation which escapes does not exceed the maximum permissible dose for an 8-hour exposure. Instead of using ordinary concrete, reactor shields are generally constructed from special "heavy" concretes, incorporating an iron ore, such as limonite, and either steel punchings or the mineral barytes (barium sulfate). The elements of high mass number, i.e., iron and barium, slow down the very fast neutrons by inelastic scattering collisions, and also help greatly in the attenuation of the gamma radiations.

19.59. There is always a possibility, although a remote one, that an accident might lead to the disruption of a nuclear reactor and the consequent spread of fission products over a considerable area. Hence, reactors designed for central power supply purposes are either located underground (§ 15.79) or are surrounded by a large dome-shaped structure designed to contain any radioactive material that may escape from the core. These measures provide adequate protection for those living in localities surrounding nuclear power plants. As a further measure of protection, such plants are located at considerable distances from inhabited areas.

EFFLUENT CONTROL AND
WASTE DISPOSAL

19.60. The control of radioactive effluents from nuclear reactors and from plants where the spent fuel is processed, and the disposal of waste material from biological and chemical laboratories are important aspects of radiation protection. The problem of dealing with noxious waste products is not restricted to atomic energy installations; it is one which many large industries must deal with in their daily operations. But the disposal of radioactive material does represent a situation concerning which there has been virtually no past experience to act as a guide. Consequently, it is an area of health physics which is being given active attention. The danger associated with radioactive wastes is mainly due to the possibility that the soil or water may become contaminated, with the result that active material may ultimately find its way into food or drink consumed by human beings. It is this hazard that has to be borne in mind in the study of the treatment and control of radioactive effluents. As the nuclear power industry grows, so the amount of radioactive effluent to be treated will increase accordingly. Fortunately, research on the development of atomic energy and on the disposal of waste is being carried out simultaneously, so that progress in the latter will undoubtedly keep pace with the former.

19.61. By far the largest proportion of radioactive effluent material arises from nuclear reactors and the associated processing plants. The substances may be either in the gaseous, the liquid or the solid state, and the origin and disposal of these three types will be examined in turn. Gaseous radioactive effluent results from two causes: first, the air used for cooling reactors, and second, the gases liberated from, and in the treatment of, the fission products. The uranium-graphite reactors at Oak Ridge and at Brookhaven are both cooled by air. Due to the action of neutrons, this air is likely to contain the radionuclides C^{14}, N^{16}, O^{19} and A^{41}, arising from the reactions $N^{14}(n,p)C^{14}$, $N^{15}(n,\gamma)N^{16}$, $O^{18}(n,\gamma)O^{19}$ and $A^{40}(n,\gamma)A^{41}$, respectively. Of these, N^{16} and O^{19} present no hazard, since they have such short half lives, namely, 7.4 seconds and 29.4 seconds, respectively, and are formed in negligible amounts. The proportion of C^{14} is also small, and so the radioactive argon-41, with a half life of 110 minutes, is the chief source of danger. In addition there is a possibility that radioactive dust may be carried off in the air.

19.62. Consequently, after having traversed the reactor, to act as coolant, the air is passed through precipitators and filters, to remove suspended particles, and then is discharged through a tall stack. The one at Oak Ridge is 200 feet high, and that at Brookhaven has a height of 320 feet. At these high levels, the air containing small amounts of radio-argon rapidly mixes with large quantities of atmospheric air, thus greatly diluting the activity. In order to make sure there is no contamination, the air in the vicinity of the reactor building and at distances up to several miles from the stack is continuously monitored for radioactivity. At Brookhaven, the operation of the reactor is coordinated with an elaborate meteorological system, and it is shut down, partially or completely, whenever there are indications that the conditions may not be favorable for dispersal of the radioactive gases emerging from the stack.

19.63. When the spent fuel elements from a nuclear reactor are processed, they are first dissolved in nitric acid, and so radioactive gases are evolved. These include iodine vapor as well as the chemically inert krypton and xenon. The gases are diluted and carried away by large volumes of air from the ventilation system of the remotely controlled separation plants and are discharged to the atmosphere through high stacks. Monitoring of the area surrounding the plants at Hanford, Washington, indicated the desirability of removing solid particles and, if possible, the radioiodine. As a result, a simple but effective filter was designed and put into operation. It has proved very successful in reducing the activity of the gases coming from the separation plant. In any event, the chemical processing of spent fuel is stopped when the meteorological conditions show there is a possibility of the stack discharge gases being swept to the ground. If at any time it is decided that a further reduction in the radioactivity of the effluent gases is desirable, it can be achieved very simply by allowing a longer "cooling" period between removal of the spent fuel from the reactor and its transfer to the processing plant.

19.64. Liquid effluents are of several very different types. The simplest to deal with is the once-through cooling water, such as is used for the production reactors at the Hanford and Savannah River plants. The water acquires some activity due to the capture of neutrons by impurities, but this is kept at a minimum by purification of the water before it enters the reactor system. After passage through the reactor, the water is stored for some time to permit the radioactivity to decay to some extent before it is discharged at a controlled rate into a river. Because of the careful control, the river water, after the usual filtration treatment, has proved completely satisfactory for domestic use.

19.65. Essentially all power reactor designs, as described in Chapter XV, employ closed cooling systems. The coolant, whether it be water, sodium, a gas or an organic liquid, is used over and over again. The heat is transferred to water in a heat exchanger (or boiler), and this is also in a closed cycle. Even if some of this water or steam should escape, it would not represent a hazard since it is not radioactive. A possible exception might be in the case of a boiling water reactor (§ 15.82).

19.66. A more difficult type of liquid waste for disposal is that containing considerable amounts of fission products or other radioactive elements.

Two main procedures have been used: namely, (1) dilution and dispersal and (2) concentration and storage. The first method is more suited to liquids having a low level of activity. They are held for some time to permit much of the radioactivity to decay, and are then extensively diluted and dispersed in large volumes of water. Alternatively, if the soil has good ion-exchange properties (§ 13.78), the liquid waste may be run directly into pits dug in the ground. As the liquid percolates through the earth, the radioactive material is retained by the soil, whereas the residual liquid seeps away.

19.67. The treatment of liquids of moderate or high activity is more difficult. They are generally concentrated so as to reduce the volume, and then stored in a place where they do not constitute a hazard. One way of concentrating the liquid waste is to evaporate off excess water. This has proved to be very satisfactory, but it is expensive and so other procedures have been developed. Of these, the method described in § 15.113, whereby the radioactive material is concentrated in a special clay, appears to show promise. The concentrated waste, no matter how obtained, is either stored in underground tanks or it is buried directly in the ground in a suitable location.

19.68. Solid wastes are not encountered in large amounts; much of it is incidental material that has become contaminated with radioactive substances in the course of plant operation or experimental work. Sometimes metallic articles can be decontaminated chemically by means of acids or other reagents, otherwise they are buried in the ground in a protected area. Contaminated wooden buildings are washed, and then painted to hold in the radioactive particles, thus reducing the risks involved in dismantling. The boards, like other solid wastes, are then buried. The treatment of buildings liable to be contaminated is facilitated by painting the walls, floors and various objects with a film of plastic material. From time to time the film can be stripped off and buried, and a new film painted on. It would appear, at first sight, that contaminated wood, clothing, biological specimens and similar substances could be destroyed by burning. However, since the smoke is radioactive, special incinerators, which do not permit escape of smoke particles, must be used for this purpose.

RADIOCHEMICAL LABORATORIES

19.69. Since a great deal of chemical and biochemical work of various kinds is now being performed with radioactive materials, the question of the proper design of laboratories has become a matter of significance. In this connection there are two essential aspects which have to be kept in mind. The first is the necessity for preventing radioactive contamination of materials and equipment, which would vitiate the experimental results; and the second is the importance of avoiding access of active substances or of radiation to the body of the worker. Both of these considerations suggest the desirability of carrying out operations with radioactive materials in different laboratories, according to the degree of activity involved. The precautions which must be taken against the radiation hazard when dealing with quantities having an activity of a curie are very different from those necessary when the activity is only a millionth part of a curie, that is, a microcurie (§ 17.37). At the same time, the contamination, by a minute

quantity of material of curie activity, of an experiment being carried out at the microcurie level would be completely ruinous.

19.70. As far as the great majority of laboratory experiments are concerned, three levels of activity may be considered; these are first, activities below 1 microcurie; second, those between about 1 microcurie and 1 millicurie (one thousandth part of a curie); and third, those in the range from about 1 millicurie to 1 curie. It should be understood that the lower and upper limits mentioned in each case are approximate, and are intended as a rough indication only. Work involving materials with activities exceeding the curie level is performed in special concrete cells or cubicles, often referred to as "caves," with walls at least two feet thick.

19.71. A problem which radiochemical investigations of all activity levels have in common is that of preventing contamination of both equipment and personnel. The situation is, however, somewhat similar to that existing in bacteriological laboratories, and the proper techniques must accordingly be employed. But the procedures, which have been called *radiochemical asepsis*, must be learned and rigorously practiced at all times.

19.72. If the activity of the experimental material is below the microcurie level, the work can usually be done in an ordinary laboratory by taking reasonable precautions. This is the case with much isotopic tracer work with radionuclides which do not emit gamma radiation. The only special requirements are a place for storing and handling the main stock of the isotope, and, as in all radioactive studies, a well-shielded room for counting, where the background activity is kept as low as possible. In

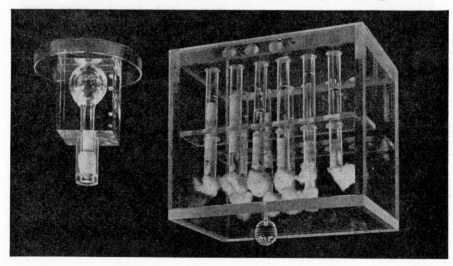

Fig. 19.3. Lucite shields for protection from beta radiation.

spite of the relatively feeble activity at the microcurie levels, precautions must be taken in handling the materials. Rubber gloves should be worn, and vessels containing radioactive solids and liquids should be manipulated with tongs.

19.73. For work in the intermediate range, roughly from 1 microcurie to 1 millicurie, a special "semi-hot" laboratory or, at least, one which has been suitably adapted, is recommended. An important feature of such a laboratory is a well-ventilated radiochemical

Fig. 19.4. Pantograph manipulator for pipette behind shield of lead bricks.

hood, with a stainless steel interior which can be cleaned with acid for removal of contamination. The working surface should also be of stainless steel. Alternatively, aluminum or other materials may be used to construct the hood, the interior being covered with a thin coat of plastic material which can be stripped off and repainted from time to time. The work

benches or desks should have stainless steel tops or stainless steel trays may be used on ordinary desk tops. Absorbent paper may be placed in the trays to facilitate cleaning up of spilled material.

19.74. At the intermediate activity level, which includes tracer experiments with appreciable amounts of beta emitters, especially if gamma radiations are present, proper shielding is essential to protect the operator.

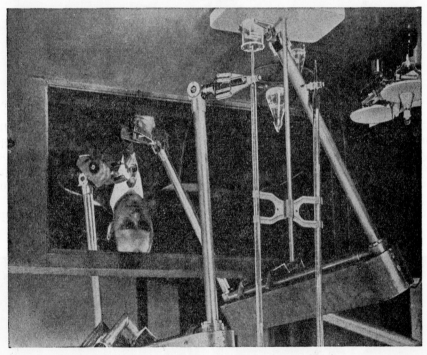

Fig. 19.5. Mechanical aid for performing delicate manipulations by remote control.

But for radionuclides which emit soft beta radiations of low energy, and no gamma rays, such as H^3 (tritium), C^{14}, S^{35} and Ca^{45}, a minimum distance of six inches from a glass vessel, achieved by means of tongs, combined with the use of heavy rubber gloves, provides sufficient protection in the activity range under consideration. Nevertheless, it should be remembered

that the activity over the top of an open beaker is greater than at the sides or below, because the glass absorbs much of the soft beta-radiation.

19.75. For other isotopes, two shielding techniques have been developed, the one to be used depending on the circumstances. In "close" shielding, each piece of equipment is shielded individually; it may be used with substances emitting soft gamma rays of low penetrating power. Trans-

tories, for experiments in which activities of one or more millicuries are involved, should be specially built for the purpose, with all surfaces, including floors and walls, of a non-absorbent washable material. Projections where dust particles can collect must be avoided. Virtually all the working space and the sinks should be of stainless steel under efficiently ven-

Fig. 19.6. Manipulation at a distance of radioisotope bottling device with the aid of a periscope.

tilated hoods. There should be adequate permanent shielding, of lead or concrete, built in underneath the table tops and behind the walls of hoods, and all work must be performed with proper barriers. Special care must, of course, be taken in the disposal of waste materials.

19.77. Because work with appreciable quantities of radioactive materials must be carried out on the

parent lucite shields, of about an inch in thickness, have been employed for this purpose (Fig. 19.3). For operations in which close shielding is not convenient, or where fairly hard gamma radiation is being emitted, "barrier" shielding is preferable. A sufficiently high barrier, usually made of interlocking lead blocks, is built around the material and equipment required for an experiment. Manipulation is carried out with long-handled tongs, or by means of various devices which have been developed for operating at a distance. A pantograph manipulator for filling and emptying pipettes is shown in Fig. 19.4; the operator views the instrument through a mirror seen at the back of the enclosure.

19.76. The so-called "hot" labora-

farther side of a high barrier, remote control becomes necessary. A variety of ingenious mechanical aids (Fig. 19.5) have been devised for making this possible. Where the equipment is not directly visible, periscopes and mirrors are frequently employed, but

Fig. 19.7. Glove box (or "dry box") for work with emitters of alpha or short-range beta particles.

the manipulation of apparatus at a distance, in this manner, obviously requires considerable practice (Fig. 19.6).

19.78. The highest activity range, where curie quantities are handled, is not commonly encountered except at a few atomic energy installations. The work is then performed, as stated earlier, in well-shielded "hot cells" or "caves." On account of the difficulties of manipulation, all operations are specially planned to be as simple as possible, so that they can be carried out by remote control. Experiments of this kind, and in fact many of the studies made in "hot" laboratories, are first carried out with inactive materials, so that a definite routine procedure is established before the haz-ardous substances are actually used.

19.79. It has been already mentioned that the chief danger when working with alpha emitters lies in the possibility of the active substance entering the human system. A few centimeters of air and the use of gloves is quite adequate to shield the experimenter from external alpha radiation. Small-scale operations with alpha-active radionuclides are consequently frequently performed in what is known as a "dry box" or, better, as

a "glove box" (Fig. 19.7). Various types have been designed, but in essence it is a closed box, with a sloping glass front, through which a current of air is drawn. A pair of rubber gloves are sealed in, so that the hands may be placed in them; operations can then be carried out inside the box with full visibility and without danger. Glove boxes are also often used for experimental work with emitters of soft, i.e., low energy and short range, beta particles.

19.80. The various procedures used for the monitoring of personnel and of operations, which were described in § 19.38 *et seq.*, are also adopted in all laboratories where appreciable quantities of radioactive materials are handled. In many instances the location and nature of the experiments are planned in advance, and even executed, in collaboration with health physicists and chemists.

19.81. In all laboratories using radioisotopes care must be taken in the disposal of waste material. It is not permissible simply to adopt the common chemical practice of washing wastes down the sink. Two general principles are recommended in the dis-

posal of radioactive wastes from tracer studies. First, the particular radioisotope should be mixed with a large amount of a stable isotope (or isotopes) of the same element in the same chemical form. In this way, the amount of active material likely to be taken up, by a plant or other living organism, is greatly diminished, since the various isotopes of a given element will be absorbed in the proportions present. Second, the waste solution should be very greatly diluted with water, so as to reduce the activity in a given volume before discharge to the sewer. By keeping below certain limits, radiophosphorus (P^{32}) and radioiodine (I^{131}) can be disposed of in this manner. Radioactive carbon (C^{14}) compounds can be burned, and the gases exhausted into the air, with due precautions to insure very thorough dilution. All radioactive wastes can be buried in the earth, at a minimum depth of five feet, in suitably restricted areas, provided the material is first mixed with a stable isotope of the same element, in the same chemical form. The activity of the material that may be buried each day is strictly limited.

GENETIC EFFECTS OF RADIATION

SPONTANEOUS MUTATIONS

19.82. According to the views generally accepted at the present time, the mechanism of heredity, which is basically similar in all sexually reproducing plants and animals, including man, is somewhat as follows. The microscopically visible chromosomes, present in dividing cells (§ 19.7), are believed to be differentiated along their length into thousands of submicroscopic units, called *genes*. Each gene is supposed to be associated with

a particular physical characteristic; in man, for example, among such characteristics would be hair color, eye color, body size, mental ability and so on. The chromosomes and genes exist in every cell in the body, but from the point of view of genetics (or heredity), it is only those in the germ cells, present in the reproductive organs, that are important.

19.83. Body cells normally contain a definite number of chromosomes consisting of two similar, but not identical, sets. For example, human body cells contain 46 chromosomes made up of two sets of 23 chromosomes. One of these sets is inherited from the mother, which contributes the egg cell, and the other set, equal in number but with somewhat different characteristics, comes from the sperm cell of the father. As the individual develops, following upon the fusion of the original egg and sperm cells, the chromosomes and genes, derived from the parents, are generally duplicated without change. In this way, all the characteristics of the offspring are derived from the genes of the parents.

19.84. In rare instances, however, a deviation from the normal behavior occurs and instead of the chromosomes duplicating themselves in every respect, there is a change in one or more of the genes; this change is called a *mutation*. A mutation is often apparent by the development of entirely new characteristics, not derived from the parents. In plants and animal breeding, such mutations are often referred to as "sports." If the mutation has occurred in a body cell (somatic mutation) some effect may be evident in the individual, but it will not be passed on to succeeding generations.* But if the mutation has taken place in a germ cell (genetic mutation), the new characteristic will probably appear in a later generation. The mutations which occur naturally, without any definitely assignable cause or human intervention, are called *spontaneous mutations*.

19.85. All genes have the property of being either dominant or recessive. If the gene is a dominant one, then the characteristic affected by that gene will appear in the offspring, even if it is contributed by the germ cell of only one of the parents. On the other hand,

a particular recessive gene must be present in the germ cells of both parents if the characteristic is to be apparent in the next generation. A recessive gene may consequently be latent for a number of generations, until the occasion arises for the union of sperm and egg cells, both of which contain the particular gene. As a general rule, gene mutations are recessive, but they are seldom completely recessive. Thus, some effect is observable in the next generation, even when the particular gene is inherited from only one parent.

19.86. Mutations are often differentiated in the respect that they are said to be beneficial or deleterious, although the exact classification may vary with the point of view. In the great majority of cases, mutations are deleterious to the plant or animal in which they occur, in the respect that they lead to decreased probability of survival. A very few of the changes accompanying mutations are undoubtedly beneficial, but their consequences become apparent only in the course of the slow process of biological evolution. Nevertheless, it is by the breeding and interbreeding of mutant strains that there have been obtained many fruits and vegetables which are useful to man.

MUTATIONS CAUSED BY RADIATIONS

19.88. In 1927, the important discovery was made by H. J. Muller in the United States that the rate of appearance of mutations in *Drosophila melanogaster*, the common fruit fly, could be increased by exposure to X-rays. Subsequently, mutations induced by radiations, including alpha and beta particles, gamma rays and neutrons, have been observed in other forms of life, both animal and vege-

* In plants such somatic mutations are perpetuated by vegetative propagation.

table. A considerable amount of work, especially from the biochemical standpoint, has been done on the influence of radiation on the red-colored bread mold known as *Neurospora crassa*, a simple form of plant life, which, for many reasons, is particularly suited to genetic studies. However, studies have also been made with various animal species, including mice, rats and rabbits. In general, the types of mutations induced by radiation are similar to those which occur spontaneously; essentially, the effect of radiation is to increase the probability of the occurrence of mutations.

19.89. The mechanism of the genetic effects of radiation is not yet understood, and three modes of action, which are not mutually exclusive, have been considered. In the first place, the radiation may produce toxic substances which affect the genes. It may be mentioned in this connection that certain chemicals, notably mustard gas and related compounds, cause mutations similar to those resulting from radiation exposure. The second possibility is that, due to ionization, chemical bonds may be broken in the genes, which are believed to be large, complex chemical molecules, similar to proteins, thus destroying them or changing their nature. A third suggestion is that the radiation may cause two or more breaks in the chromosome; the separate parts then tend to rejoin, as it is known they do, but as a result a short section, containing one or more genes, may be lost. In any case, there may be a rearrangement within the chromosome leading to genetic changes.

GENETIC EFFECTS OF RADIATION

19.90. Experiments with various types of animals have shown that the increased frequency of occurrence of gene mutations as a result of exposure to radiation is approximately proportional to the total dose received by the reproductive glands of the parents from the beginning of their development to the time of conception of the progeny. There is apparently no amount of radiation, however small, that does not cause some increase in the normal mutation frequency. In fact, it is probable that a certain proportion of the so-called spontaneous mutations may be due to the background radiation to which all living things are exposed (§ 19.29).

19.91. The dose rate of the radiation exposure and its duration have little effect on the increase in the mutation frequency. It is the total accumulated dose to the reproductive glands at the time of fusion of the egg and sperm cells that is the important quantity. It should be pointed out, however, that a large accumulated dose of radiation does not mean that the resulting mutations will be more harmful than for a smaller dose. With a large dose, the mutations will, in general, be the same as for a small dose, and they will also be similar to those occurring spontaneously, but the frequency of their occurrence will be increased.

19.92. The harmful effects of a deleterious mutation may be relatively minor, such as an increased susceptibility to disease or a decrease in life expectancy of a few months. On the other hand, they may be more serious, such as death in the embryonic stage or the inability to reproduce further generations. Thus, individuals bearing deleterious genes are handicapped relative to others, particularly in the respect that they have fewer progeny and die earlier, on the average. It is apparent, therefore, that such genes will be eventually eliminated **from**

the population. A gene that is very harmful will be eliminated rapidly, since few (if any) individuals carrying such genes will survive to the age of reproduction. On the other hand, a slightly deleterious gene may persist much longer and thereby do harm, although of a less severe character, to a larger number of individuals.

19.93. It has been estimated that the amount of radiation, in addition to that received from natural background sources, required to double the rate at which spontaneous mutations are already occurring in the human race, is an accumulated dose to the reproductive glands of probably between 30 and 80 roentgens, prior to conception, for each member of the population. A proportionately larger dose to a fraction of the population would have a somewhat similar effect on the frequency of mutations and their ultimate consequences. It is with the objective of minimizing the increase in the normal mutation rate that the recommendations concerning the maximum permissible total accumulated dose of radiation were made, as described in § 19.35.

19.94. The discussion so far has been concerned with deleterious mutations: what of the beneficial mutations? It is true that they are very rare, but they have nevertheless contributed to the evolutionary progress of the human race. It may be wondered, therefore, whether radiation exposure might not have some favorable effects due to the increase in the number of beneficial mutations. The general feeling, however, is that the present normal frequency of spontaneous mutations provides a sufficient degree of genetic variability for further evolution at a satisfactory rate. In other words, it is considered that the possible ultimate advantages to

the human race resulting from an increase in the beneficial mutations is greatly outweighed by the immediate drawbacks due to the more numerous deleterious mutations.

19.95. In the plant world, however, the situation is quite different. Plant breeders have long made use of the selection and breeding of mutant strains, produced spontaneously, to develop improved varieties of vegetables, cereals, fruits and flowers. Radiation has now provided a means for greatly increasing the mutation frequency, thereby increasing the probability of the occurrence of a desirable trait in a given plant. The fact that the great majority of the mutations which occur are undesirable is of no consequence to the plant breeder. These are simply rejected and further effort is concentrated on the few that appear to be favorable from one standpoint or another.

19.96. Considerable work is proceeding in various countries, notably Norway, Sweden, the United States and the U.S.S.R., for the purpose of developing improved varieties of useful plants by exposure of either the growing plant or the seed to radiation, e.g., to gamma rays from cobalt-60 or to neutrons in a reactor. Among the promising results achieved so far, the following may be mentioned: cereals which ripen earlier or give higher yields; peanuts which are superior in yield, better adapted to mechanical harvesting and are resistant to a serious leaf spot disease; a variety of oats resistant to stem rust and another, normally susceptible to Victoria blight, with a greatly increased resistance to this disease. In addition, several interesting somatic mutations, capable of vegetative propagation, have been produced in carnations and other flowers.

19.97. Perhaps the greatest interest of the production of mutations by radiations lies in the possibility of developing disease resistant varieties of agricultural plants. It has been estimated that, in the United States alone, plant diseases cause losses valued at about three billion dollars annually. It would thus appear to be appropriate to close this book with a quotation from Enrico Fermi, who contributed so much to the development of atomic physics: "I believe . . . that the conquest of atomic energy may be widely used to produce not destruction, but an age of plenty for the human race."

Name Index

Subject Index

Nucleus (*cont'd*):
  magnetic properties, 12.65–12.79
  properties, 4.83–4.86
  and radioactivity, 8.17
  radius, 4.15–4.21, 7.32, 12.57–12.64
  shielded, 12.98, 13.94
  spin quantum number, *see* Nuclear spin
  structure, *see* Nuclear structure
  transitions, *see* Nuclear transitions
Nuclide, definition, 8.49
  isotopic weights of, 8.60
  shielded, 12.98, 13.94
  stable, number of, 10.97
  "mirror," 7.82, 7.83, 12.101
Nuclon, 4.35

Oppenheimer-Phillips mechanism, 10.28, 10.-
  29
Optical model of nucleus, 11.116
Orbital-electron capture, 10.105–10.109
Oxygen isotopes, 8.61
  enriched, 8.111
  production, 17.19
  and temperature of ocean, 17.142, 17.143
  as tracers, 17.6, 17.96, 17.142, 17.143
  standard, atomic weight, 1.24, 1.32, 8.61
  and mass spectrum, 8.59, 8.60

Packing effect, 12.2
Packing fraction, 12.1–12.5
  curve, 12.2, 14.6, 14.9
  definition, 12.2
  and mass defect, 12.2
  and atomic energy, 14.6
Parasitic capture, 14.31, 14.35
Parity principle, 18.103–18.105
  overthrow, 18.106–18.111
Particle accelerators, 9.36–9.116
  betatron, 9.75–9.86
  cyclotron, 9.53–9.65
  electrostatic generator (Van de Graaff),
    9.39–9.44
  linear accelerator, 9.45–9.52, 9.113–9.116
  synchrocyclotron, 9.66–9.74
  synchrotron, alternating gradient, 9.105–
    9.112
    proton, 9.96–9.104
  voltage multiplier (Cockcroft-Walton),
    9.36–9.38
Pauli exclusion principle, 4.62–4.67, 4.70
  for nucleons, 12.111
Periodic law, 1.41
Periodic system, 1.40–1.49
  and group displacement law, 8.4–8.8
  groups, 1.46
  and orbital electrons, 4.68–4.70
  and radioelements, 8.1–8.8
Perpetual motion, 3.74
Phase stability, 9.71, 9.91
Phasotron, 9.72
Phosphor, *see* Scintillator
Phosphorescence, 2.92
Phosphorus, isotopes, in agriculture, 17.97–
  17.103
  in blood, 17.83

Phosphorus, isotopes (*cont'd*):
  in diagnosis, 17.88
  in leaves, 17.62
  production, 17.21
  specific activity, 17.38, 17.40
  in therapy, 17.89
  as tracers, 17.5, 17.64
Photodisintegration, 10.52–10.55, 11.19–11.21,
  13.17
Photoelectric effect, 2.48, 2.89, 6.45
  and gamma rays, 7.86–7.89, 7.98, 7.99
Photofission, 13.17
Photomultiplier tube, 6.45
Photon, 3.34–3.37
Photoneutron sources, 11.19–11.21, 11.87
Photonuclear reaction, *see* Photodisintegra-
  tion
Photosynthesis, and isotopes, 17.6, 17.92–
  17.96
Phototransmutation, *see* Photodisintegration
Piezoelectricity, 5.2, 5.3
Pile, 14.52; *see also* Reactor
Pinch effect, 14.109
Pions (or pi-mesons), *see* Mesons, pi
Planck's constant, 3.30
  quantum theory, 3.27–3.32
Plants, isotopic study, 17.92–17.106
Plasma, electrical, 14.94
Plutonium, 11.49, 14.23, 14.26, 14.63–14.77,
  16.24–16.39
  and actinide series, 16.65–16.71
  carrier free, 16.31, 16.39
  chemistry, 16.28, 16.30, 16.34–16.39
  discovery, 16.24
  isotopes, 16.24, 16.26, 16.27
  separation, 14.71, 14.75, 15.110, 16.25, 16.-
    28–16.33
Plutonium-239, and actinium series, 16.99
  and atomic bomb, 14.79, 14.80, 16.1
  breeding, 15.39–15.47
  fission, 13.18, 13.55, 13.69, 14.63, 16.26
    critical energy, 13.69
  in nature, 16.26
  odd-even character, 13.71, 14.63
  reactor fuel, 15.7, 15.11, 15.61, 15.107, 15.-
    108
Poles, electric, 2.11
Polonium, discovery, 5.5, 5.6
  isotopes, 8.6, 8.7, 8.14
Ponderator, 9.69, 9.92
Positive rays, 2.61–2.64, 2.106
  analysis, 8.26–8.32
  and isotopes, 8.33–8.39
Positive electron, *see* Positron
Positon, *see* Positron
Positron, 2.65–2.79
  in cosmic rays, 18.34, 18.35, 18.57, 18.61
  destruction, 2.76–2.79, 3.84–3.92
  discovery, 2.67
  emission in radioactive decay, 7.55, 7.56,
    10.81–10.83, 10.98, 10.100, 10.101, 10.-
    110–10.113
  formation, 2.72–2.75